Chapter 1: Problem Solving

MATH IN ▸ Criminal Investigation

In traditional cops-and-robbers movies, crime fighters use guns and fists to catch criminals, but in real life, more often than not it's brain power that brings the bad guys to justice. That's why the show CSI marked a revolution of sorts when it debuted in October of 2000: it featured scientists fighting crime, not tough guys. Solving a case is intimately tied to the process of problem solving: investigators are presented with a mystery and use whatever evidence they can find and their reasoning ability to reconstruct the crime. **Continue reading about Math in Criminal Investigation on page 3.**

Chapter 2: Sets

MATH IN ▸ Demographics

The world certainly has changed a lot in the last fifty years. If you could travel back to the middle of the twentieth century, you'd have an awful hard time finding anyone that would believe that one of the most famous, and richest, people in the world in the early twenty-first century would be a golfer that is part white, part African-American, and part Asian. Our society is becoming more and more diverse every year, to the point where even defining what we mean by "race" isn't so easy anymore. Sorting it all out to get any sort of meaningful picture of what we as Americans look like isn't easy, and the techniques of set theory are very useful tools in trying to do so. **Continue reading about Math in Demographics on page 41.**

Chapter 3: Logic

MATH IN ▸ The Art of Persuasion

Everywhere you turn in modern society, somebody is trying to convince you of something. "Vote for me!" "Buy my product!" "Lease a car from our dealership!" "Bailing out the auto industry is a bad idea!" "You should go out with me this weekend!" "Join our fraternity!" Logic is sometimes defined as correct thinking or correct reasoning. Some people refer to logic by a more casual name: common sense. Regardless of what you call it, the ability to think logically is crucial for everyone because our lives are inundated daily with advertisements, contracts, product and service warranties, political debates, and news commentaries, to name just a few. **Continue reading about Math in the Art of Persuasion on page 91.**

Chapter 4: Numeration Systems

MATH IN ▸ Retail Sales

If you're like most college students, having endured 10 to 12 years of math class as you grew up, you probably feel like you know an awful lot about numbers. That may well be true if you're talking about the base-ten number system that you started learning even before you went to school. But you may be surprised to learn that there are many other number systems that can be used. Some of them are historical artifacts that give us a glimpse into the developmental stages of mankind's study of mathematics. But others are used commonly today. In fact, you're using one every single time you buy an item from a store, even if you don't realize it. **Continue reading about Math in Retail Sales on page 147.**

Chapter 5: The Real Number System

MATH IN ▸ Government Spending

Most Americans have some vague idea that the government spends way more than they have, and that our nation is in debt. But very few people have any idea just how much money we're talking about. Maybe it's because ignorance is bliss, or maybe the numbers are just so staggering that not just anyone can appreciate their size. **Continue reading about Math in Government Spending on page 197.**

Chapter 6: Topics in Algebra

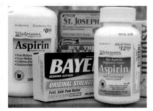

MATH IN ▷ Drug Administration

Have you ever looked at the dosage information on a bottle of aspirin and thought "It just doesn't seem reasonable to recommend the same dosage for all adults?" People come in all shapes and sizes, and the effect of a certain dosage is in large part dependent on the size of the individual. If a 105 pound woman and her 230 pound husband both take two aspirin the morning after their wedding reception, she is in effect getting more than twice as much medicine as he is. **Continue reading about Math in Drug Administration on page 277.**

Chapter 7: Additional Topics in Algebra

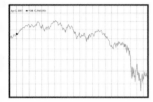

MATH IN ▷ The Stock Market

There was a time when the fluctuations of the stock market were exclusively of concern to the rich. Most people weren't directly invested in the market, and felt like it didn't impact their lives very much. But those days are long gone. Most people's retirement savings, at the very least, are invested in stocks and mutual funds. This means that value changes in the market are of more interest to more Americans than ever before, and the ability to monitor those changes is certainly a relevant skill. **Continue reading about Math in the Stock Market on page 347.**

Chapter 8: Consumer Mathematics

MATH IN ▷ Home Buying

Home buying shows have become very popular in the last couple of years. It's interesting to watch people looking for just the right home, and maybe more interesting to find out what homes are going for in other parts of the country. The down side as a viewer is that it can be pretty intimidating to find out just how much houses cost. Almost everyone wonders at some point "Will I ever be able to afford a home of my own?" **Continue reading about Math in Home Buying on page 419.**

Chapter 9: Measurement

MATH IN ▷ Travel

To measure something means to assign a number that represents its size. In fact, measurement might be the most common use of numbers in everyday life. Numbers are used to measure height, weight, distance, grades, weather, size of a home, capacity of bottles and cans, and much more. Even in our monetary system, we use numbers to measure sizes: little ones, like the cost of a candy bar, and big ones, like an annual salary. One obvious application of this skill comes into play when traveling outside the United States. Most countries use the metric system almost exclusively, meaning that to understand various bits of information, you need to be able to interpret measurements in an unfamiliar system. **Continue reading about Math in Travel on page 481.**

Chapter 10: Geometry

MATH IN ▷ Home Improvement

It probably won't surprise you to learn that one of the most common questions that math students ask is "How can I actually use this stuff?" Of course, how math is used in our world is the main theme of this book, and this chapter fits that framework especially well. The ideas presented are commonly used in everyday things like working around the home, so we'll present some actual projects that geometry was used for in the home of one of the authors. **Continue reading about Math in Home Improvement on page 511.**

Chapter 11: Probability and Counting Techniques

MATH IN ▷ Gambling

The fact that you're reading this sentence means that you're probably taking a math class right now. But maybe not...you could be an instructor evaluating the book, or maybe an editor looking for mistakes (unsuccessfully, we hope). Still, I would be willing to bet that you're taking a math class. The word "probably" indicates a certain likelihood of something happening, and that basic idea is the topic of this chapter. We call the study of the likelihood of events occurring probability. **Continue reading about Math in Gambling on page 573.**

Chapter 12: Statistics

MATH IN ▷ Sociology

Broadly defined, sociology is the study of human behavior within society. One important branch is criminology. This is not about investigating crimes, but rather studying patterns of criminal behavior and their effect on society. The main tool used by sociologists is statistics. This important area of math allows researchers to study patterns of behavior objectively by analyzing information gathered from a mathematical perspective, not a subjective one. **Continue reading about Math in Sociology on page 647.**

Chapter 13: Other Mathematical Systems

MATH IN ▷ Encryption

Cryptography is the study of hiding information using some sort of code. There was a time when codes were of interest mostly to military officers, spies, and grade school kids passing notes they didn't want the teacher to read. But that time passed very quickly with the advent of the computer age. According to some reports, more than half of all Americans made at least one purchase online in 2008. When sensitive financial information and passwords are being transmitted, encryption becomes of supreme importance. Without proper encryption, you could find your identity lost in the endless depths of cyberspace. **Continue reading about Math in Encryption on page 717.**

Chapter 14: Voting Methods

MATH IN ▷ College Football

Football and other sports have been used as examples dozens of times throughout this book because sports present an excellent example of a variety of ways that math gets used in our world. There are the obvious ways – keeping score, and adding up statistics like yards gained or home runs hit. But there are also many behind-the-scenes examples of the importance of math in sports. Allocation of salaries, ticket prices, devising a schedule that meets the needs of every team in a league, assigning officials to work games...these are just four of many such examples. **Continue reading about Math in College Football on page 743.**

Chapter 15: Graph Theory

MATH IN ▷ Road Trips

The road trip is a great American tradition. There's just something magical about the freedom of heading out to the open road and driving wherever you feel like. It usually takes about an hour for the magic to wear off, though. Then you just want to get to where you're headed as quickly as possible. The branch of mathematics known as graph theory was created to solve problems involving the most efficient way to travel between different locations. **Continue reading about Math in Road Trips on page 791.**

Registering for Your Course

To begin your Connect Hosted by ALEKS course experience, you'll have to register. The following is a step-by-step guide to help you get started.

Step

1

Go to **http://www.connectmath.com**. Click on **Sign up now!**

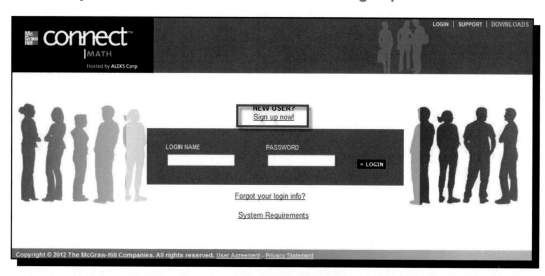

TIP:

Make sure you have your Connect Math **access code** as well as your **course code** before you register. Your course code will be provided to you by your instructor.

Step

2

Enter your course code

Students: Sign Up

To complete your registration, enter your 10-character course code below. You should have received this code from your instructor.

Course code: ☐☐☐☐☐ - ☐☐☐☐☐ what's this?

A course code has 10 alphanumeric characters *(sample: 98JH7-BV4D9)*. You should have received a course code from your instructor.

Please ask your instructor for the course code, and enter it into the fields to register with Connect Math.

» Continue

Step 3

Confirm Enrollment Information

You are about to register to use Connect Math in the following course. Please check the course details carefully. If the information is correct, click "Continue." If the information is incorrect, click "modify" to enter another course code.

Algebra

Course: Hendricks Beginning Algebra - 100
Book: Beginning Algebra DEMO, 1st Ed., Hendricks, Chow
Instructor: Prof. Math
School: McGraw-Hill Connect   (modify)

» Continue

Step 4

Enter your personal information, accept the Terms of Service, and you're done!

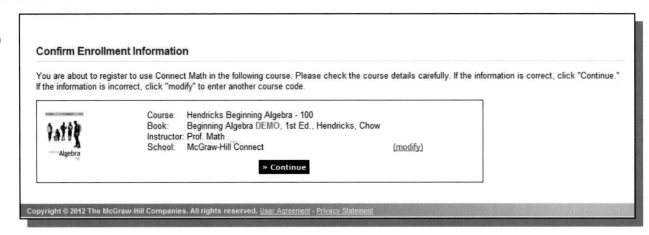

Enter Your Personal Information
First Name: *
Initial:
Last Name:

Enter Your E-mail Address
We will use this email to send your
E-mail:
                Example:

Choose a Password
You will use this password every tim
Password:
Confirm Password: *

(Optional) Enter Your Student ID

Review and Accept Connect Math Terms of Service

McGraw-Hill Connect Math User Agreement   ** IMPORTANT **   Print this document

End-User License for McGraw-Hill.com

All use   subject to the terms and conditions set forth be   eement to abide by the following terms and co

In the e   ore specific terms and conditions that apply to   specific terms and conditions of such other We

All inform   The McGraw-Hill Companies and its affiliates is owned by or licensed to The

☐ I have read and agree to the terms of the McGraw-Hill Connect Math User Agreement.

» Continue

Be sure to check this box before you Continue.

Registration Complete

Make sure to remember your login name and password. You will need them every time you log into Connect M

Your Login Name: **BFLAY2**

A copy of your login information will be sent to name@gmail.com

TIP

Write down your login name and password in a safe place.

» Continue

Your Connect Math Home Screen

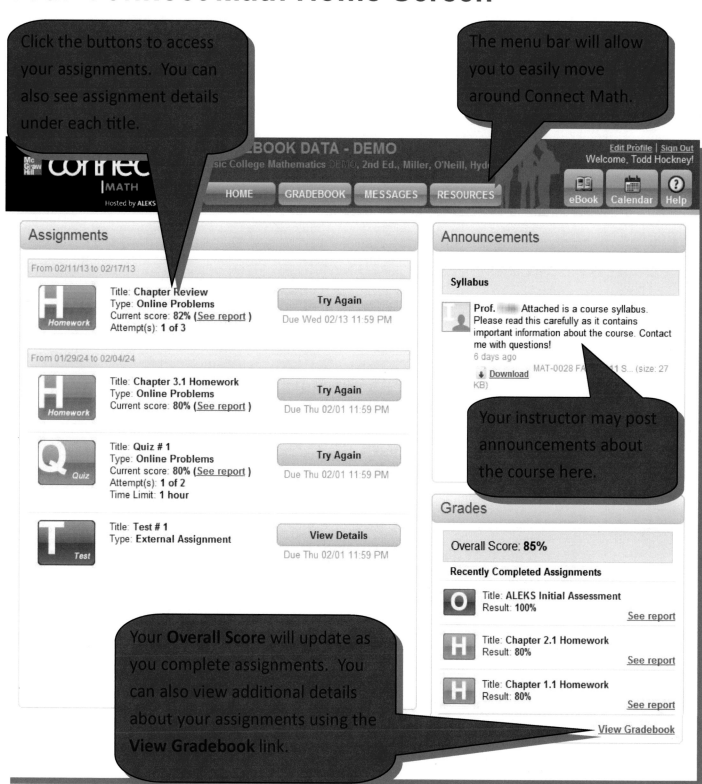

Click the buttons to access your assignments. You can also see assignment details under each title.

The menu bar will allow you to easily move around Connect Math.

Assignments

From 02/11/13 to 02/17/13

Title: **Chapter Review**
Type: **Online Problems**
Current score: **82%** (See report)
Attempt(s): **1 of 3**

Try Again
Due Wed 02/13 11:59 PM

From 01/29/24 to 02/04/24

Title: **Chapter 3.1 Homework**
Type: **Online Problems**
Current score: **80%** (See report)

Try Again
Due Thu 02/01 11:59 PM

Title: **Quiz # 1**
Type: **Online Problems**
Current score: **80%** (See report)
Attempt(s): **1 of 2**
Time Limit: **1 hour**

Try Again
Due Thu 02/01 11:59 PM

Title: **Test # 1**
Type: **External Assignment**

View Details
Due Thu 02/01 11:59 PM

Announcements

Syllabus

Prof. ▮▮▮ Attached is a course syllabus. Please read this carefully as it contains important information about the course. Contact me with questions!
6 days ago
MAT-0028 FA▮▮▮ ▮1 S... (size: 27 KB)
↓ Download

Your instructor may post announcements about the course here.

Grades

Overall Score: **85%**

Recently Completed Assignments

Title: **ALEKS Initial Assessment**
Result: **100%**
See report

Title: **Chapter 2.1 Homework**
Result: **80%**
See report

Title: **Chapter 1.1 Homework**
Result: **80%**
See report

View Gradebook

Your **Overall Score** will update as you complete assignments. You can also view additional details about your assignments using the **View Gradebook** link.

Taking An Assignment

The first time you take an assignment in Connect Math, you'll have access to the Tutorial, which walks you through how to enter answers. Once completed, you can continue with your assignment.

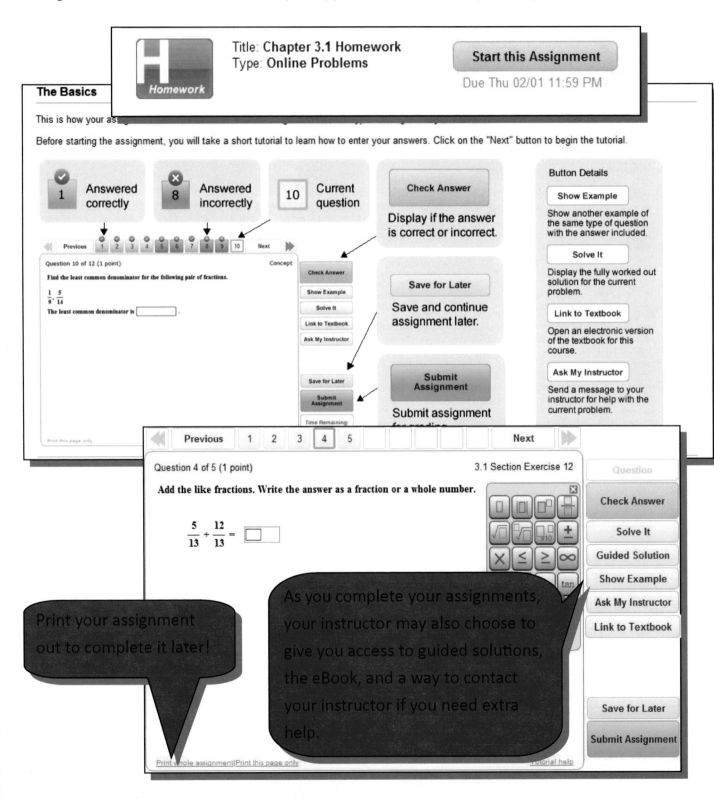

Accessing Additional Resources

Connect Math offers a variety of other tools that can help you master the material you're learning. If you visit the Resources menu, you have access to additional exercise sets and videos whenever you need them.

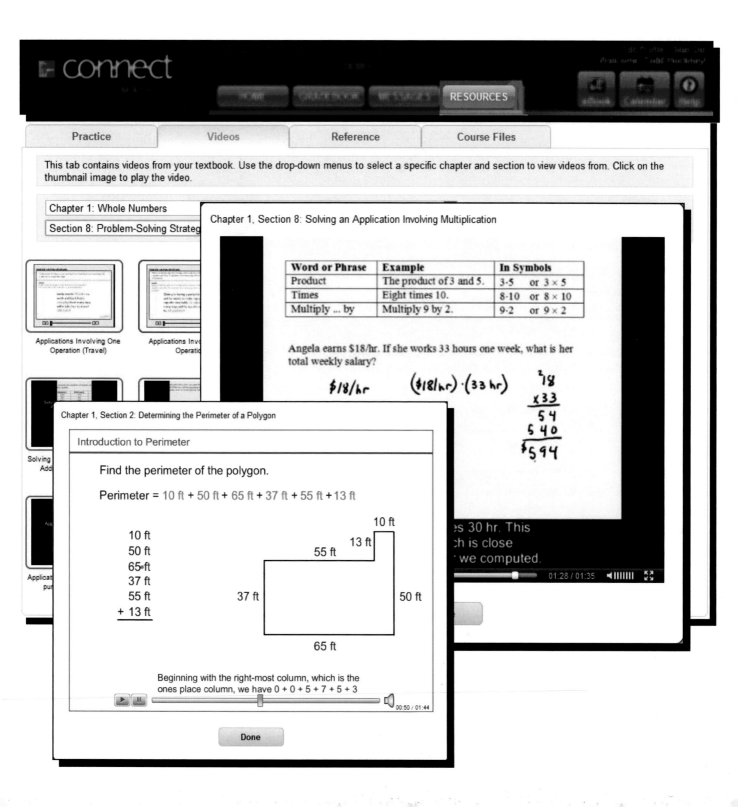

Using the

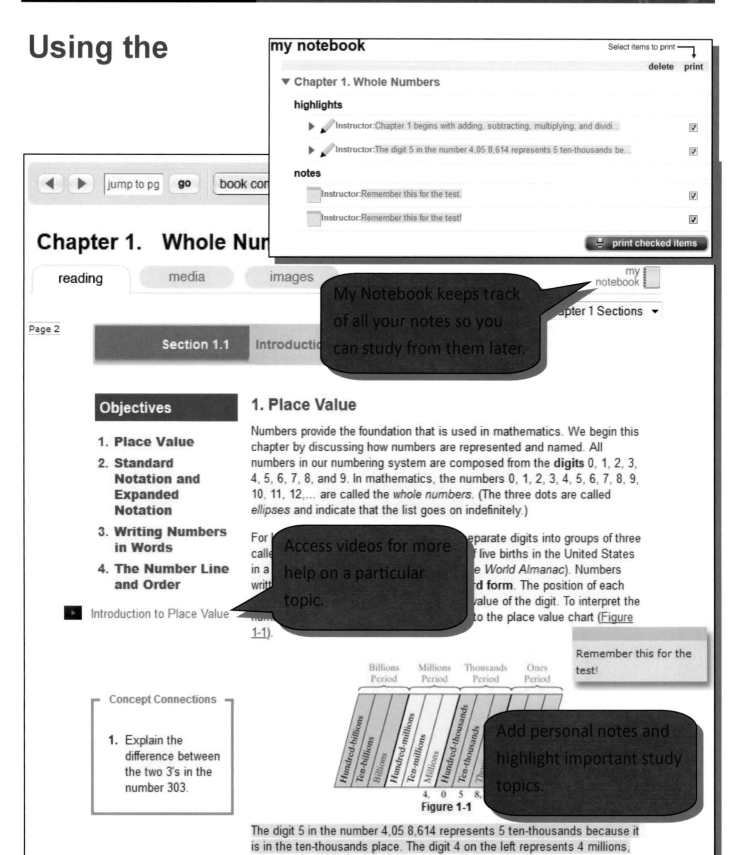

The Gradebook

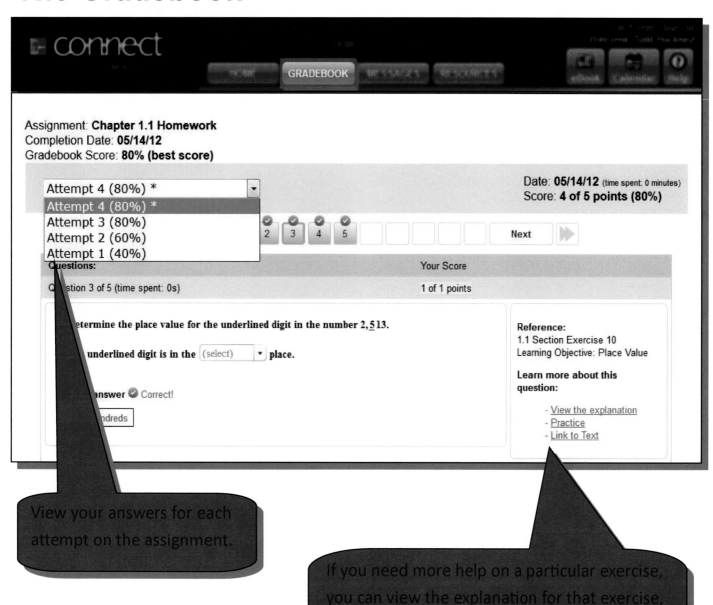

Assignment: **Chapter 1.1 Homework**
Completion Date: **05/14/12**
Gradebook Score: **80% (best score)**

Date: **05/14/12** (time spent: 0 minutes)
Score: **4 of 5 points (80%)**

Attempt 4 (80%) *
Attempt 4 (80%) *
Attempt 3 (80%)
Attempt 2 (60%)
Attempt 1 (40%)

2 3 4 5   Next

Questions: Your Score

Question 3 of 5 (time spent: 0s)   1 of 1 points

etermine the place value for the underlined digit in the number 2,513.

underlined digit is in the (select) ▼ place.

answer ✓ Correct!

ndreds

Reference:
1.1 Section Exercise 10
Learning Objective: Place Value

Learn more about this question:

- View the explanation
- Practice
- Link to Text

View your answers for each attempt on the assignment.

If you need more help on a particular exercise, you can view the explanation for that exercise, practice another version, and access the eBook after your assignment is submitted.

SECOND EDITION

MATH
in Our World

Mercer County College | MATH 108

Dave Sobecki
Associate Professor
Miami University Hamilton

Allan G. Bluman
Professor Emeritus
Community College of Allegheny County

Angela Schirck–Matthews
Professor
Broward College

Boston   Burr Ridge, IL   Dubuque, IA   New York   San Francisco   St. Louis
Bangkok   Bogotá   Caracas   Lisbon   London   Madrid
Mexico City   Milan   New Delhi   Seoul   Singapore   Sydney   Taipei   Toronto

Math in Our World, Media Update, Second Edition
Mercer County College
MATH 108

1 2 3 4 5 6 7 8 9 0   RJO RJO   14 13 12

ISBN-13: 978-0-07-767771-8
ISBN-10: 0-07-767771-4
Part of:
ISBN-13: 978-0-07-767772-5
ISBN-10: 0-07-767772-2

Learning Solutions Consultant: Jennifer Boyle
Production Editor: Mandy Maas
Printer/Binder: RR Donnelley - Johnson City

Brief Contents

About the Authors

Dave Sobecki

Dave Sobecki is an associate professor in the Department of Mathematics at Miami University in Hamilton, Ohio. He earned a B.A. in math education from Bowling Green State University before continuing on to earn an M.A. and a Ph.D. in mathematics from Bowling Green State University. He has written or coauthored five journal articles, eleven books, and five interactive CD-ROMs. Dave lives in Fairfield, Ohio, with his wife (Cat) and dogs (Macleod and Tessa).

His passions include Ohio State football, Cleveland Indians baseball, heavy metal music, travel, and home improvement projects.

Dedication: *To two of my biggest supporters: my wife Cat, and my friend Dawn.*

Allan G. Bluman

Allan G. Bluman is a professor emeritus at the Community College of Allegheny County, South Campus, near Pittsburgh, Pennsylvania. He has taught mathematics and statistics for over 35 years. He received an Apple for the Teacher award in recognition of his bringing excellence to the learning environment at South Campus. He has also taught statistics for Penn State University at the Greater Allegheny (McKeesport) Campus and at the Monroeville Center. He received his master's and doctor's degrees from the University of Pittsburgh.

He is the author of two other textbooks, *Elementary Statistics: A Step By Step Approach* and *Elementary Statistics: A Brief Version.* In addition, he is the author of four mathematics books in the McGraw-Hill DeMystified Series. They are *Pre-Algebra, Math Word Problems, Business Math,* and *Probability.*

He is married and has two sons and a granddaughter.

Dedication: *To Betty Bluman, Earl McPeek, and Dr. G. Bradley Seager, Jr.*

Angela Schirck-Matthews

Angela Schirck-Matthews is a Professor of Mathematics at Broward College in Davie, Florida, where she has been teaching mathematics since 1991. Before her employment at Broward College she taught undergraduate mathematics at the University of Miami in Coral Gables, Florida. She is also an alumna of both institutions; Angela earned an Associate of Arts degree in liberal arts at Broward College and went on to earn a Bachelor of Arts degree in mathematics at Florida Atlantic University in Boca Raton, Florida. After graduating from Florida Atlantic University, she continued her education at the University of Miami where she earned a Master of Science degree in mathematics and completed coursework toward a Ph.D. in mathematics.

Angela lives in Hollywood, Florida with her husband, three of her four children, and two dogs.

Dedication: *To my parents Joe and Karen, for their love and encouragement throughout my life.*

Letter from the Authors

Liberal arts math is a challenging course to teach because most of the time, the audience is very different from other college math classes. For most students the course is terminal, and in many cases represents the only math credits the student will take in college. Given this audience, it can often be a great challenge to motivate students and make them see the relevance of math, how math plays a role in our world, and how the thinking and problem-solving strategies that students will learn and practice can be used beyond the classroom.

The first step to gaining interest is to find a way to **engage** students. This is typically done using applications, but too often we rely on the old classics, the applications that we remember from our own education. This is where the two new coauthors come in (Dave and Angie): each is known for making math engaging to students, and together, they bring a fresh, modern approach to the second edition. To fully engage students in the 21st century, we need to think modern, emphasizing applications that show the relevance of math to today's students. We've made every attempt to make that the focus of this edition, from financing a car to figuring out a healthy daily calorie intake to understanding how overwhelming our national debt really is, and what that means to us as citizens. The pizza theme that is carried throughout the book is a constant reminder to students that math isn't a spectator sport, but something that plays an important role in their everyday lives.

No one has ever become stronger by watching someone else lift weights, and our students aren't going to be any better at thinking and problem-solving unless we encourage them to **practice** it on their own. *Math in Our World* includes a plethora of applications and real-world problems for students to hone their skills and give their brains a workout. The critical thinking skills they practice in using this text will serve them well in any future courses whether there is math involved or not. But more important, it will help them to become problem solvers and thinkers beyond the halls of academia.

Once we've drawn your students' attention and offered them plenty of practice, we turn to our ultimate goal in writing this text: helping your students to **succeed.** We're confident that this book offers a fantastic vehicle to drive your classes to higher pass rates because of the pedagogical elements, writing style, and interesting problem sets. Additionally, while no book can prevent the underpreparedness of students in a course like this, we've got you covered there as well with **Connect Math Hosted by Aleks Corporation.** You can read more about it on preface pages x through xiii.

Finally, to further emphasize clarity and consistency, we as an author team took it upon ourselves to produce the lecture videos, exercise videos, and solution manuals to accompany *Math in Our World,* allowing our voices to carry throughout these supplements, perfectly complementing the text. We hope that you and your students enjoy using *Math in Our World* as much as we enjoyed writing it and putting all the pieces together. Good luck, and please don't hesitate to contact your local McGraw-Hill representative to let us know what you think!

—*Dave, Al, and Angie*

Engage

Joint experiences in the classroom have helped each of the authors bring a unique perspective to the text, influencing the **writing style** significantly. Both practical and conversational, the writing functions as a tool to guide learning for students outside of the classroom. The goal is to draw in even the most hesitant students by relating to them through the casual, spoken language they regularly use with friends. By doing so, students gain both a firm initial understanding of the basic concepts fundamental to the curriculum and also a greater degree of retention of the long-term implications of those concepts.

CHAPTER **1**

Problem Solving

MATH IN Criminal Investigation

In traditional cops-and-robbers movies, crime fighters use guns and fists to catch criminals, but in real life, often it's brain power that brings the bad guys to justice. That's why the TV show *CSI* marked a revolution of sorts when it debuted in October 2000: it featured scientists fighting crime, not tough guys. Solving a case is intimately tied to the process of problem solving: investigators are presented with a mystery, and they use whatever evidence they can find and their reasoning ability to reconstruct the crime. Hopefully, this will lead them to a suspect.

Of course, this isn't limited to just crime fighting. Students in math classes often ask, "When am I going to use what I learn?" The best answer to that question is, "Every day!" Math classes are not only about facts and formulas: they're also about exercising your mind, training your brain to think logically, and learning effective strategies for solv-

to be useful tools that you can apply in the rest of your education. But more importantly, they can be applied just as well to situations outside the classroom.

And this brings us back to our friends from *CSI*. The logic and reasoning that they use to identify suspects and prove their guilt are largely based on problem-solving skills we'll study in this chapter. By the time you've finished the chapter, you should be able to evaluate the situations below, all based on episodes of *CSI*. In each case, you should identify the type of reasoning that was used and decide whether the conclusion would stand up as proof in a court of law.

- After a violent crime, the investigators identify a recently paroled suspect living in the area who had previously committed three very similar crimes.
- A homeless man is found dead from exposure after being roughed up. His wrists look like he had been

MATH IN Criminal Investigation REVISITED

1. The suspect was identified by specific incidents in the past, which makes this inductive reasoning that would not hold up in court without further evidence.

2. Fingerprints positively identify the officer as having had contact with the victim. This is deductive reasoning and would be useful in court.

3. Like fingerprints, DNA can positively show that the suspect had physical contact with the victim. This evidence, based on deductive reasoning, would hurt the suspect badly in court.

4. While this is compelling evidence, it's based on assuming that those five drawings indicate the artist is the killer. While unlikely, it could be a coincidence based on five drawings, so this is inductive reasoning. It might impress a jury to some extent, but wouldn't be sufficient for a conviction.

Review Exercises

Section 1-1

For Exercises 1–4, make reasonable conjectures for the next three numbers or letters in the sequence.

1. 3 4 6 7 9 10 12 13 15 16 ___ ___ ___
2. 2 7 4 9 6 11 8 13 ___ ___ ___

For Exercises 5 and 6, make a reasonable conjecture and draw the next figure.

5.    ____

Chapter Openers directly engage student interest by immediately tying mathematical concepts to each of their everyday lives. These vignettes introduce concepts by referencing popular topics familiar to a wide variety of students— travel, demographics, the economy, television, and even college football. By taking slower steps to reach the critical topics of a chapter, students are able to more fully grasp how math really does relate to their own world, further solidifying the connections imperative to retention of information.

Used to clarify concepts and emphasize particularly important points, **Math Notes** provide suggestions for students to keep in mind as they progress through the chapter.

"Gives helpful hints that need to be reinforced."
—*Greg Wisloski, Indiana University of Pennsylvania*

"Very useful...looks like they often anticipate students' questions."
—*Robert Koca, Community College of Baltimore County, Essex*

"I like how they get important details to the student without getting too wordy. I think students would pay attention to them because they are so brief."
—*Mark Ellis, Central Piedmont Community College*

Math Note

We often use the word *nearest* to describe the place value to round to. Instead of saying, "Round to the hundreds place," we might say, "Round to the nearest hundred."

Sidelights contain carefully chosen material highlighting relevant interdisciplinary connections within math to encourage both curiosity and motivation in students who have a wide variety of interests. These include biographic vignettes about famous mathematicians as well as other interesting facts that emphasize the importance of math in areas like weather, photography, music, and health.

Sidelight **AN ARBITRARY DISCUSSION**

In common usage, the word *arbitrary* is often misinterpreted as a synonym for *random*. When reaching into a bag of potato chips, you make a random selection, and some people would also call this an arbitrary selection. But in math, the word *arbitrary* means something very different. When randomly selecting that chip, you have still chosen a specific chip—it is probably not representative of every chip in the bag. Some chips will be bigger, and others smaller. Still others may have more salt, some less.

When we use *arbitrary* in math, we're referring to a non-specific item that is able to represent *all* such items. In the series of calculations we looked at above, we could never

be sure that the result will always be 3 [...] numbers. Why? Because we'd have to try [...] which is of course impossible. You have [...] than spend the rest of your life testing nu[...] The value of performing the calculation [...] ber *x* is that this one calculation proves [...] *every* number you choose. It is absolutely [...] of mathematics to understand that cho[...] bers can almost never *prove* a result, be[...] every number. Instead, we'll rely on usin[...] and deductive reasoning.

"They are valuable to explain certain concepts from a practical or a historical view. Faculty could use these as "jumping off" points for projects and/or group work."
—*Judith Wood, Central Florida Community College*

"They are well written, beautifully illustrated, and relate historical figures and their mathematical genius and discoveries to the topic covered in the text. They are most informative on so many events and disciplines."
—*Corinna M. Goehring, Jackson State Community College*

"The variety of real-world applications makes the discrete much more concrete for the students."
—*Kristin Chatas, Washtenaw Community College*

"Excellent, interesting, current."
—*Vesna Kilibarda, Indiana University Northwest*

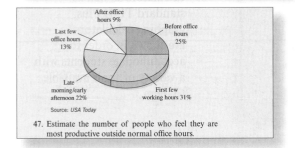

34. Estimate the total cost of the following items for your dorm room:
    Loft bed $159.95
    Beanbag chair $49.95
    Storage cubes $29.95
    Lava lamp $19.95
35. Estimate the time it would take you in a charity bike tour to ride 86 miles at a rate of 11 miles per hour.
36. If a person earns $48,300.00 per year, estimate how

After office hours 9%
Before office hours 25%
Last few office hours 13%
Late morning/early afternoon 22%
First few working hours 31%
Source: *USA Today*

47. Estimate the number of people who feel they are most productive outside normal office hours.

Highly relevant real-world **Application Exercises and Examples** drawn from the experiences and research of the author team further emphasize the importance that *Math in Our World* places upon students' ability to form a distinct connection with the mathematical content. This helps students relate mathematical concepts presented in a section and the real life relevance of something familiar to them, increasing both student interest and motivation—key factors affecting their comprehension. The new edition brings many brand new and updated application exercises to students in each chapter, ranging in topics from MP3 player usage, college degree majors, elections, relevant business decisions, and scenarios involving popular statistics.

An **Index of Applications** is located immediately after the Detailed Table of Contents and is organized by discipline to help identify applications relevant to specific fields. Additional exercises that have been added to this Media Update are highlighted in this index.

5 *Your students want an interactive eBook with rich functionality integrated into the product.*

Hosted by ALEKS Corp.

Integrated Media-Rich eBook

▶ A Web-optimized eBook is seamlessly integrated within ConnectPlus Math Hosted by ALEKS Corp for ease of use.

▶ Students can access videos, images, and other media in context within each chapter or subject area to enhance their learning experience.

▶ Students can highlight, take notes, or even access shared instructor highlights/notes to learn the course material.

▶ The integrated eBook provides students with a cost-saving alternative to traditional textbooks.

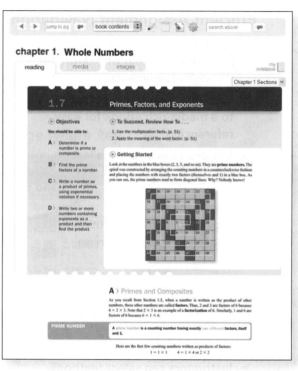

6 *You want a flexible gradebook that is easy to use.*

Flexible Instructor Gradebook

▶ Based on instructor feedback, Connect Math Hosted by ALEKS Corp's straightforward design creates an intuitive, visually pleasing grade management environment.

▶ Assignment types are color-coded for easy viewing.

▶ The gradebook allows instructors the flexibility to import and export additional grades.

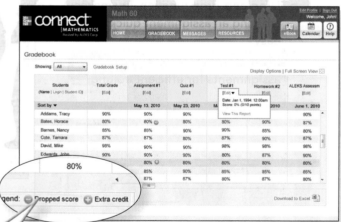

Instructors have the ability to drop grades as well as assign extra credit.

Built by Math Educators
for Math Educators

 7 **You want algorithmic content that was developed by math faculty to ensure the content is pedagogically sound and accurate.**

Digital Content Development Story

The development of McGraw-Hill's Connect Math Hosted by ALEKS Corp. content involved collaboration between McGraw-Hill, experienced instructors, and ALEKS, a company known for its high-quality digital content. The result of this process, outlined below, is accurate content created with your students in mind. It is available in a simple-to-use interface with all the functionality tools needed to manage your course.

1. McGraw-Hill selected experienced instructors to work as Digital Contributors.
2. The Digital Contributors selected the textbook exercises to be included in the algorithmic content to ensure appropriate coverage of the textbook content.
3. The Digital Contributors created detailed, stepped-out solutions for use in the Guided Solution and Show Me features.
4. The Digital Contributors provided detailed instructions for authoring the algorithm specific to each exercise to maintain the original intent and integrity of each unique exercise.
5. Each algorithm was reviewed by the Contributor, went through a detailed quality control process by ALEKS Corporation, and was copyedited prior to being posted live.

Connect Math Hosted by ALEKS Corp.
Built by Math Educators for Math Educators

Lead Digital Contributors

Stephen Toner
Victory Valley College

Tim Chappell
Metropolitan Community College, Penn Valley

Amy Naughten

Digital Contributors

Vanessa Coffelt, *Blinn College*
Darlene Diaz, *Santiago Canyon College*
Donna Gerken, *Miami-Dade College*
Kimberly Graham
Nancy Ikeda, *Fullerton College*
Vickie Flanders, *Baton Rouge Community College*
Nic LaHue, *Metropolitan Community College, Penn Valley*

Michael Lanstrum, *Cuyahoga Community College*
Jackie Miller, *The Ohio State University*
Anne Marie Mosher, *St. Louis Community College, Florissant Valley*
Reva Narasimhan, *Kean University*
Christy Peterson, *College of DuPage*
David Ray, *University of Tennessee, Martin*

Catherine Sausville, *George Mason University*
Kristin Stoley, *Blinn College*
Paul Vroman, *St. Louis Community College, Florissant Valley*
Michelle Whitmer, *Lansing Community College*

Supplements

Instructor Supplements
- **Computerized Test Bank Online:** Utilizing Brownstone Diploma® algorithm-based testing software, this supplement enables users to create customized exams quickly.
- **Instructor Solutions Manual:** Written by author Angela Schirck-Matthews, the *Instructor Solutions Manual* provides comprehensive, worked-out solutions to all exercises in the text. The methods used to solve the problems in the manual are the same as those used to solve the examples in the textbook.
- **PowerPoint Slides:** These slides closely follow the textbook, and are completely editable.

Student Supplements
- **Student Solutions Manual:** Written by author Angela Schirck-Matthews, the *Student Solutions Manual* provides comprehensive, worked-out solutions to all of the odd-numbered chapter exercises. The steps shown in the solutions match the style of the worked examples found in the text.
- **Lecture Videos:** Engaging lectures by author Dave Sobecki introduce concepts, definitions, theorems, formulas, and problem solving procedures to help students better comprehend key topics.
- **Exercise Videos:** Presented by author Angela Schirck-Matthews, these videos work through selected exercises, following the solution methodology found in the text.

McGraw Hill Tegrity campus

- Tegrity Campus is a service that makes class time available all the time by automatically capturing every lecture in a searchable format for students to review when they study and complete assignments. With a simple one-click start and stop process, you capture all computer screens and corresponding audio. Students replay any part of any class with easy-to-use browser-based viewing on a PC or Mac.
- Educators know that the more students can see, hear, and experience class resources, the better they learn. With Tegrity Campus, students quickly recall key moments by using Tegrity Campus's unique search feature. This search helps students efficiently find what they need, when they need it across an entire semester of class recordings. Help turn all your students' study time into learning moments immediately supported by your lecture.
- To learn more about Tegrity watch a 2 minute Flash demo at **http://tegritycampus.mhhe.com.**

ALEKS® (Assessment and LEarning in Knowledge Spaces) is a dynamic online learning system for mathematics education, available over the Web 24/7. ALEKS assesses students, accurately determines their knowledge, and then guides them to the material that they are most ready to learn.

With a variety of reports, Textbook Integration Plus, quizzes, and homework assignment capabilities, ALEKS offers flexibility and ease of use for instructors.

- ALEKS uses artificial intelligence to determine exactly what each student knows and is ready to learn. ALEKS remediates student gaps and provides highly efficient learning and improved learning outcomes
- ALEKS is a comprehensive curriculum that aligns with syllabi or specified textbooks. Used in conjunction with McGraw-Hill texts, students also receive links to text-specific videos, multimedia tutorials, and textbook pages.
- ALEKS offers a dynamic classroom management system that enables instructors to monitor and direct student progress toward mastery of course objectives.

ALEKS Prep/Remediation:
- Helps instructors meet the challenge of remediating unequally prepared or improperly placed students.
- Assesses students on their prerequisite knowledge needed for the course they are entering (for example, calculus students are tested on precalculus knowledge) and prescribes unique and efficient learning paths specific to their strengths and weaknesses.
- Students can address prerequisite knowledge gaps outside of class, freeing the instructor to use class time pursuing course outcomes.

Electronic Textbook: CourseSmart is a new way for faculty to find and review e-textbooks. It's also a great option for students who are interested in accessing their course materials digitally and saving money. CourseSmart offers thousands of the most commonly adopted textbooks across hundreds of courses from a wide variety of higher education publishers. It is the only place for faculty to review and compare the full text of a textbook online, providing immediate access without the environmental impact of requesting a print exam copy. At CourseSmart, students can save up to 50 percent off the cost of a print book, reduce their impact on the environment, and gain access to powerful Web tools for learning including full text search, notes and highlighting, and email tools for sharing notes between classmates. To learn more, visit **www.CourseSmart.com.**

Create: Craft your teaching resources to match the way you teach! With McGraw-Hill Create, **www.mcgrawhillcreate.com**, you can easily rearrange chapters, combine material from other content sources, and quickly upload content you have written—like your course syllabus or teaching notes. Find the content you need in Create by searching through thousands of leading McGraw-Hill textbooks. Arrange your book to fit your teaching style. Create even allows you to personalize your book's appearance by selecting the cover and adding your name, school, and course information. Order a Create book and you'll receive a complimentary print review copy in 3–5 business days or a complimentary electronic review copy (eComp) via email in about one hour.

Updated Content

CHAPTER 2 Sets

- Coverage is greatly increased throughout the chapter, including new sub-sections on cardinality of sets (Section 2-1), set subtraction and Cartesian product (Section 2-2), DeMorgan's laws and cardinality of unions (Section 2-3), and countable and uncountable sets (Section 2-5).
- Eight new applications have been added to Section 2-1, establishing a total of thirty-four questions based on current events and relevant data. Additionally, thirty-six new application exercises have been added to Sections 2-3 and 2-4.
- Two new sidelights on infinite sets in Section 2-5 have been added to increase the interdisciplinary connections students can make to enhance their understanding of key concepts.

CHAPTER 3 Logic

- The coverage of truth tables has been standardized by using the method of building new columns for parts of compound statements as the main presentation. To accommodate a variety of teaching styles, the method of writing truth values underneath connectives is still presented as an alternative method.
- An application of truth tables has been added as a worked example in Section 3-2.
- Content updates include the addition of DeMorgan's laws to Section 3-3 and circular reasoning among common fallacies in Section 3-4.
- A total of thirty-eight new application exercises have been added to Sections 3-2 and 3-3 and the applications in Section 3-4 have been updated to reflect current student interests.

CHAPTER 4 Numeration Systems

- Coverage of tally systems and multiplicative grouping systems have been added and the Chinese system has been expanded from a Sidelight to full coverage in Section 4-1.
- Tools and Algorithms in Arithmetic, located in Section 4-2, is completely new to the second edition.

CHAPTER 8 Consumer Mathematics

- Formerly Chapter 9, it has undergone significant changes to content coverage, including new sub-sections on the banker's rule and discounted loans (Section 8-2), a new subsection on fixed installment loans and APR (Section 8-4), and an entirely new section on stocks and bonds (Section 8-6).
- Organizationally, the discussion of interest has been split into two sections, one on simple interest and one on compound interest.
- The coverage of annuities in Section 8-3 has been expanded, and a section formerly focused on markup and markdown has been replaced with a more thorough coverage of percent increase and decrease, including an example on deceptive use of percents in advertising.
- Updates to the discussion of home ownership now reflect current interest rates and trends.

CHAPTER 11 Probability and Counting Techniques

- The entire chapter has been completely reorganized and rewritten to include a new section on the binomial theorem. This includes shifting counting techniques to be presented prior to probability and the addition of permutations when some objects are alike.
- Dozens of new application exercises are found throughout the chapter, including comparisons of expected value for common games of chance and real world applications of probability and counting.

CHAPTER 12 Statistics

- Nearly all worked examples and exercises featuring statistics have been replaced with problems featuring newer, more relevant data.
- A table is now included in Section 12-3 to compare the strengths and weaknesses of different measures of average.
- Coverage of the empirical rule can now be found in the discussion of the normal distribution and the discussion of finding area under the normal curve has been streamlined.
- The presentation of correlation is now based on an interesting real-world example of a correlation between MySpace usage and illiteracy and helpful information regarding the use of technology to find correlation coefficients and regression lines has been added.

CHAPTER 13 Other Mathematical Systems

- Formerly Chapter 6, coverage of mathematical systems has been moved to Section 13-1 so that clock and modular arithmetic can be taught in the context of mathematical systems.
- Mathematical systems are now introduced in terms of the familiar example of making turns at intersections and new application exercises in Section 13-1 include the pull chain on a ceiling fan and mixing paint colors.
- Presentation of clock arithmetic now uses the standard clock with numbers from 1 through 12, and also includes clocks with other numbers of hours.
- Congruences in modular arithmetic have been revised so that now all use the $\equiv$ symbol.

Acknowledgements

McGraw-Hill's 360° Development Process is an ongoing, market-oriented approach to building accurate and innovative print and digital products. It is dedicated to continual large-scale and incremental improvement driven by multiple customer feedback loops and checkpoints. This process is initiated during the early planning stages of our new products, intensifies during the development and production stages, and then begins again upon publication, in anticipation of the next edition.

A key principle in the development of any mathematics text is its ability to adapt to teaching specifications in a universal way. The only way to do so is by contacting those universal voices—and learning from their suggestions. We are confident that our book has the most current content the industry has to offer, thus pushing our desire for accuracy to the highest standard possible. In order to accomplish this, we have moved through an arduous road to production. Extensive and open-minded advice is critical in the production of a superior text.

We engaged dozens of instructors and students to provide us with guidance during the development of the second edition. By investing in this extensive endeavor, McGraw-Hill delivers to you a product suite that has been created, refined, tested, and validated to be a successful tool in your course.

The McGraw-Hill mathematics team and the authors wish to thank the following instructors who participated in postpublication reviews of the first edition, the proposed second edition table of contents, and both first and second drafts of the second edition manuscript to give feedback on reworked narrative, design changes, pedagogical enhancements, and organizational changes. This feedback was summarized by the book team and used to guide the direction of the final text.

Gerald Angelichio, *Herkimer County Community College*
Anne Antonippillai, *University of Wisconsin–Stout*
Hamid Attarzadeh, *Jefferson Community and Technical College*
Jon Becker, *Indiana University-Northwest-Gary*
Andrew Beiderman, *Community College of Baltimore County Essex*
Laverne Blagmon-Earl, *University of District of Columbia*
Mike Bosch, *Iowa Lakes Community College*
Caroline Boulis, *Lee University*
Mark Brenneman, *Mesa Community College*
Sam Buckner, *North Greenville University*
Brian Burrell, *University of Massachusetts–Amherst*
Gerald Burton, *Virginia State University*
Fred Butler, *York College of Pennsylvania*

David Capaldi, *Johnson & Wales University*
Blayne Carroll, *Lee University*
Gail Carter, *St. Petersburg College–Tarpon Springs*
Florence Chambers, *Southern Maine Community College*
Kristin Chatas, *Washtenaw Community College*
Sandy Cohen, *Saint Petersburg College*
Lynn Craig, *Baton Rouge Community College*
Karen Crossin, *George Mason University*
Cheryl Davids, *Central Carolina Tech College*
Mark Ellis, *Central Piedmont Community College*
Dan Endres, *University of Central Oklahoma*
Scott Fallstrom, *University of Oregon*
Shurron Farmer, *University of District of Columbia*
Nicki Feldman, *Pulaski Technical College*
Scott Garten, *Northwest Missouri State University*

Mahmood Ghamsary, *California State University, Fullerton*
Carrie Goehring, *Jackson State Community College*
John Grant, *Towson University*
Bo Green, *Abilene Christian University*
Sheryl Griffith, *Iowa Central Community College*
Renu Gupta, *Louisiana State University–Alexandria*
Kim Hagens, *Louisiana State University*
Quin Hearn, *Brevard Community College–Cocoa*
Thomas Hoffman, *Coastal Carolina University*
Lori Holdren, *Lake City Community College*
Robert Jajcay, *Indiana State University, Terre Haute*
Maryann Justinger, *Erie Community College South Campus–Orchard Park*
Joseph Kazimir, *East Los Angeles College*
David Keller, *Kirkwood Community College*
Betsy Kiedaisch, *College of Dupage*
Vesna Kilibarda, *Indiana University Northwest*
Bob Koca, *Community College Of Baltimore County, Essex*
Bhaskara Kopparty, *Indiana State University–Terre Haute*
Steve Kristoff, *Ivy Tech Community College of Indiana*
Pamela Krompak, *Owens Community College*
Valerie LaFrance, *Saint Petersburg College*
Marcia Lambert, *Pitt Community College*
Eveline Lapierre, *Johnson & Wales University*
John Lattanzio, *Indiana University of Pennsylvania*
Edith Lester, *Volunteer State Community College*
Antonio Magliaro, *Quinnipiac University*

Barbara Manley, *Jackson State Community College*
Carrie McCammon, *Ivy Tech Community College of Indiana*
Cornelius Nelan, *Quinnipiac University*
Bernard Omolo, *University of South Carolina Upstate*
Eugenia Peterson, *Richard J Daley College*
Becky Pohle, *Ivy Tech Community College of Indiana*
Elaine Previte, *Bristol Community College*
Carolyn Reed, *Austin Community College*
Natalie Rivera, *Estrella Mountain Community College*
Lisa Rombes, *Washtenaw Community College*
Fary Sami, *Harford Community College*
Nancy Schendel, *Iowa Lakes Community College, Estherville*
Mike Skowronski, *University of Wisconsin, Oshkosh*
Zeph Smith, *Salt Lake Community College*
Laura Stapleton, *Marshall University*
Janet Teeguarden, *Ivy Tech Community College of Indiana*
William Thralls, *Johnson & Wales University, North Miami*
David Troidl, *Erie Community College*
John Ward, *Jefferson Community and Technical College*
Susan Warner, *Friends University*
John Weglarz, *Kirkwood Community College*
Ronald White, *Norfolk State University*
Greg Wisloski, *Indiana University of Pennsylvania*
Judith Wood, *Central Florida Community College*

The authors would like to thank the many people who have helped bring the second edition of *Math in Our World* to life. First and foremost we acknowledge the comments and suggestions we received from all reviewers of the manuscript. Their thoughtful insights allowed us to understand how we can better help their students learn and be engaged by math, and guided us through this substantial revision. We think the result is a truly student-friendly text. Additionally, we thank Cindy Trimble and George Watson whose invaluable contributions have helped us to ensure that we present the most accurate information possible, and Jennifer Siegel of Broward College for providing many application exercises with style and flair. Special thanks to Professor Karen Crossin from George Mason University for her helpful input on the additional exercise sets found in this media update. Thank you also to Michael Lanstrum from Cuyahoga Community College for compiling a list of suggestions from himself, his students, and his colleagues as they used the second edition of *Math in Our World*. These are reflected throughout this media update.

Finally, at McGraw-Hill Higher Education, we thank John Osgood, Sponsoring Editor; Christina Lane, Developmental Editor; Kevin Ernzen, Marketing Manager; Peggy Selle, Lead Project Manager; Tara McDermott, Designer; Amber Bettcher, Digital Product Manager; and Sandy Schnee, Senior Media Project Manager. Their expertise helped transform this work from raw manuscript to a finished product we're very proud of.

Detailed Table of Contents

Index of Applications

MATH
in Our World

CHAPTER **2**

Sets

Outline

MATH IN ▶ Demographics

The world certainly has changed a lot in the last 50 years. If you could travel back to the middle of the 20th century, you'd have an awful hard time finding anyone who would believe that one of the most famous, and richest, people in the world in the early 21st century would be a golfer who is part white, part African-American, *and* part Asian. Our society is becoming more and more diverse every year, to the point where even defining what we mean by *race* isn't so easy anymore. The most common racial groups referred to in population statistics are white, black, Asian, and Hispanic, but many people fall into more than one category (including the President of the United States!). But it's even more confusing than that: *Hispanic* isn't really a race, but rather an ethnic group, and many Hispanics also report themselves as either white or black.

Sorting it all out to get any sort of meaningful picture of what we as Americans look like isn't easy, and the techniques of set theory are very useful tools in trying to do so. In this chapter, we'll define what we mean by sets, and we'll study sets and how they can be used to organize information in an increasingly complex world. The concept of sets has been used extensively since people began studying mathematics, but it wasn't until the late 1800s that the theory of sets was studied as a specific branch of math. One of the major tools that we will use to study sets—the Venn diagram—was introduced in an 1880 paper by a man named John Venn. These diagrams allow us to picture complicated relationships between sets of objects, like people of certain races.

Because race and ethnicity are self-reported in a variety of different ways, it's very difficult to find detailed data on the breakdown of races, but there are some reasonable estimates out there. The following estimates were cobbled together from a number of different sources. In a group of 1,000 randomly selected Americans, 777 would self-report as white, 139 as black, and 149 as Hispanic. In addition, 19 would self-report as black and white, 18 as black and Hispanic, and 85 as white and Hispanic. Finally, 7 would self-report as all three. Based on these estimates, after completing this chapter, you should be able to answer the following questions:

1. How many of the original 1,000 report as white only, black only, and Hispanic only?
2. How many report as Hispanic and black, but not white?
3. How many report as either Hispanic or black?
4. How many report as none of white, black, or Hispanic?

For answers, see Math in Demographics Revisited on page 87

Section 2-1 The Nature of Sets

LEARNING OBJECTIVES

☐ 1. Define set.

☐ 2. Write sets in three different ways.

☐ 3. Classify sets as finite or infinite.

☐ 4. Define the empty set.

☐ 5. Find the cardinality of a set.

☐ 6. Decide if two sets are equal or equivalent.

☑ 1. Define set.

Groups of people, categories of items in stores, laws that apply to traffic—our world is divided into groups of things, or sets. So studying sets from a mathematical standpoint is a good opportunity to study how math is used in our world.

Basic Concepts

We will begin with a basic definition of sets.

> A **set** is a well-defined collection of objects.

By *well-defined* we mean that given any object, we can definitely decide whether it is or is not in the set. For example, the set "letters of the English alphabet" is well-defined since it consists of the 26 symbols we use to make up our alphabet, and no other objects. The set "tall people in your class" is not well-defined because who exactly belongs to that set is open to interpretation.

Each object in a set is called an **element** or a **member** of the set. One method of designating a set is called the **roster method,** in which elements are listed between braces, with commas between the elements. The order in which we list elements isn't important: $\{2, 5, 7\}$ and $\{5, 2, 7\}$ are the same set. Often, we will name sets by using a capital letter.

Laws that specify who can vote in a specific election determine a well-defined set of people. There are many other laws that might affect certain sets, like the set of businesses in a certain industry. These laws need to clearly define the set the law applies to—if that set were not well-defined, it would be almost impossible to enforce the law.

EXAMPLE 1   Listing the Elements in a Set

Math Note

The commas make it clear that it is the words, not the letters, that are the elements of the set.

Write the set of months of the year that begin with the letter M.

SOLUTION

The months that begin with M are March and May. So, the answer can be written in set notation as

$$M = \{\text{March, May}\}$$

Each element in the set is separated by a comma.

▼ Try This One 1

Write the set of the Great Lakes.

In math, the set of *counting numbers* or **natural numbers** is defined as $N = \{1, 2, 3, 4, \ldots\}$. (When we are designating sets, the three dots, or *ellipsis,* mean that the list of elements continues indefinitely in the same pattern.)

| EXAMPLE 2 | **Writing Sets Using the Roster Method** |

Use the roster method to do the following:

(a) Write the set of natural numbers less than 6.
(b) Write the set of natural numbers greater than 4.

SOLUTION

(a) $\{1, 2, 3, 4, 5\}$
(b) $\{5, 6, 7, 8, \ldots\}$

> **Math Note**
>
> You can list an element of a set more than once if it means a lot to you, but it's common to choose not to list repeats. For example, the set of letters in the word *letters* is written as $\{l, e, t, r, s\}$.

▼ **Try This One 2**

Write each set, using the roster method.

(a) The set of even natural numbers from 80 to 90.
(b) The set of odd natural numbers greater than 10.

The symbol $\in$ is used to show that an object is a member or element of a set. For example, let set $A = \{2, 3, 5, 7, 11\}$. Since 2 is a member of set A, it can be written as

$$2 \in \{2, 3, 5, 7, 11\} \quad \text{or} \quad 2 \in A$$

Likewise,

$$5 \in \{2, 3, 5, 7, 11\} \quad \text{or} \quad 5 \in A$$

When an object is not a member of a set, the symbol $\notin$ is used. Because 4 is not an element of set A, this fact is written as

$$4 \notin \{2, 3, 5, 7, 11\} \quad \text{or} \quad 4 \notin A$$

The 2008 U.S. Olympic team is a set of athletes. Swimmer Michael Phelps is an element of that set.

| EXAMPLE 3 | **Understanding Set Notation** |

Decide whether each statement is true or false.

(a) Oregon $\in A$, where A is the set of states west of the Mississippi River.
(b) $27 \in \{1, 5, 9, 13, 17, \ldots\}$
(c) $z \notin \{v, w, x, y, z\}$

SOLUTION

(a) Oregon is west of the Mississippi, so Oregon is an element of A. The statement is true.
(b) The pattern shows that each element is 4 more than the previous element. So the next three elements are 21, 25, and 29; this shows that 27 is not in the set. The statement is false.
(c) The letter z is an element of the set, so the statement is false.

> **Math Note**
>
> Be sure to use correct symbols when you show membership in a set. For example, the notation $\{6\} \in \{2, 4, 6\}$ is incorrect since the set $\{6\}$ is not a member of this set: the number 6 is.

▼ Try This One 3

Decide whether each statement is true or false.

(a) July $\in A$, where A is the set of months between Memorial Day and Labor Day.
(b) $21 \in \{2, 5, 8, 11, \ldots\}$
(c) map $\notin \{m, a, p\}$

There are three common ways to designate sets:

1. The *list* or *roster* method.

2. The *descriptive* method.

3. *Set-builder* notation.

We already know a lot about using the list or roster method; the elements of the set are listed in braces and are separated by commas, as in Examples 1 through 3.

The **descriptive method** uses a short statement to describe the set.

EXAMPLE 4   Describing a Set in Words

Use the descriptive method to describe the set E containing $2, 4, 6, 8, \ldots$.

SOLUTION

The elements in the set are called the even natural numbers. The set E is the set of even natural numbers.

▼ Try This One 4

Use the descriptive method to describe the set A containing $-3, -2, -1, 0, 1, 2, 3$.

Math Note

When you hear *variable*, you might automatically think *letter*, like x or y. But you should think about what the word *variable* really means: something that can change, or vary. A variable is just a symbol that represents some number or object that can change.

The third method of designating a set is **set-builder notation**, and this method uses *variables*.

A **variable** is a symbol (usually a letter) that can represent different elements of a set.

Set-builder notation uses a variable, braces, and a vertical bar | that is read as "such that." For example, the set $\{1, 2, 3, 4, 5, 6\}$ can be written in set-builder notation as $\{x \mid x \in N \text{ and } x < 7\}$. It is read as "the set of elements x such that x is a natural number and x is less than 7." We can use any letter or symbol for the variable, but it's common to use x.

EXAMPLE 5   Writing a Set Using Set-Builder Notation

Use set-builder notation to designate each set, then write how your answer would be read aloud.

(a) The set R contains the elements 2, 4, and 6.
(b) The set W contains the elements red, yellow, and blue.

SOLUTION

(a) $R = \{x \mid x \in E$ and $x < 7\}$, the set of all x such that x is an even natural number and x is less than 7.

(b) $W = \{x \mid x$ is a primary color$\}$, the set of all x such that x is a primary color.

▼ Try This One 5

Use set-builder notation to designate each set; then write how your answer would be read aloud.

(a) The set K contains the elements $10, 12, 14, 16, 18$.

(b) The set W contains the elements Democratic and Republican.

EXAMPLE 6   **Using Different Set Notations**

Designate the set S with elements $32, 33, 34, 35, \ldots$ using

(a) The roster method.
(b) The descriptive method.
(c) Set-builder notation.

SOLUTION

(a) $\{32, 33, 34, 35, \ldots\}$
(b) The set S is the set of natural numbers greater than 31.
(c) $\{x \mid x \in N$ and $x > 31\}$

▼ Try This One 6

Designate the set with elements $11, 13, 15, 17, \ldots$ using

(a) The roster method.
(b) The descriptive method.
(c) Set-builder notation.

If a set contains many elements, we can again use an ellipsis to represent the missing elements. For example, the set $\{1, 2, 3, \ldots, 99, 100\}$ includes all the natural numbers from 1 to 100. Likewise, the set $\{a, b, c, \ldots, x, y, z\}$ includes all the letters of the alphabet.

EXAMPLE 7   **Writing a Set Using an Ellipsis**

Using the roster method, write the set containing all even natural numbers between 99 and 201.

SOLUTION

$\{100, 102, 104, \ldots, 198, 200\}$

▼ **Try This One 7**

2. Write sets in three different ways.

Using the roster method, write the set of odd natural numbers between 50 and 500.

Finite and Infinite Sets

Sets can be classified as *finite* or *infinite*.

If a set has no elements or a specific natural number of elements, then it is called a **finite set.** A set that is not a finite set is called an **infinite set.**

The set {p, q, r, s} is called an finite set since it has four members: p, q, r, and s. The set {10, 20, 30, . . .} is called an infinite set since it has an unlimited number of elements: the natural numbers that are multiples of 10.

EXAMPLE 8   **Classifying Sets as Finite or Infinite**

Classify each set as finite or infinite.

(a) $\{x \mid x \in N \text{ and } x < 100\}$
(b) Set R is the set of letters used to make Roman numerals.
(c) {100, 102, 104, 106, . . .}
(d) Set M is the set of people in your immediate family.
(e) Set S is the set of songs that can be written.

SOLUTION

(a) The set is finite since there are 99 natural numbers that are less than 100.
(b) The set is finite since the letters used are C, D, I, L, M, V, and X.
(c) The set is infinite since it consists of an unlimited number of elements.
(d) The set is finite since there is a specific number of people in your immediate family.
(e) The set is infinite because an unlimited number of songs can be written.

▼ **Try This One 8**

3. Classify sets as finite or infinite.

Classify each set as finite or infinite.

(a) Set P is the set of numbers that are multiples of 6.
(b) $\{x \mid x \text{ is a member of the U.S. Senate}\}$
(c) {3, 6, 9, . . . , 24}

There are some situations in which it is necessary to define a set with no elements. For example, the set of female Presidents of the United States would contain no people, so it would have no elements.

A set with no elements is called an *empty set* or **null set.** The symbols used to represent the null set are { } or ∅.

EXAMPLE 9 Identifying Empty Sets

Which of the following sets are empty?

(a) The set of woolly mammoth fossils in museums
(b) $\{x \mid x$ is a living woolly mammoth$\}$
(c) $\{\varnothing\}$
(d) $\{x \mid x$ is a natural number between 1 and 2$\}$

SOLUTION

(a) There is certainly at least one woolly mammoth fossil in a museum somewhere, so the set is not empty.
(b) Woolly mammoths have been extinct for almost 8,000 years, so this set is most definitely empty.
(c) Be careful! Each instance of { } and $\varnothing$ represents the empty set, but $\{\varnothing\}$ is a set with one element: $\varnothing$.
(d) This set is empty because there are no natural numbers between 1 and 2.

▼ Try This One 9

Which of the following sets are empty sets?

(a) $\{x \mid x$ is a natural number divisible by 7$\}$
(b) $\{x \mid x$ is a human being living on Mars$\}$
(c) $\{+, -, \times, \div\}$
(d) The set Z consists of the living people on earth who are over 200 years old.

CAUTION   Don't write the empty set as $\{\varnothing\}$. This is the set *containing* the empty set.

☑ 4. Define the empty set.

Cardinal Number of a Set

The number of elements in a set is called the *cardinal number* of a set. For example, the set $R = \{2, 4, 6, 8, 10\}$ has a cardinal number of 5 since it has 5 elements. This could also be stated by saying the **cardinality** of set R is 5. Formally defined,

> The **cardinal number** of a finite set is the number of elements in the set. For a set A the symbol for the cardinality is $n(A)$, which is read as "n of A."

EXAMPLE 10 Finding the Cardinality of a Set

Find the cardinal number of each set.

(a) $A = \{5, 10, 15, 20, 25, 30\}$ (c) $C = \{16\}$
(b) $B = \{10, 12, 14, \ldots, 28, 30\}$ (d) $\varnothing$

SOLUTION

(a) $n(A) = 6$ since set A has 6 elements
(b) $n(B) = 11$ since set B has 11 elements
(c) $n(C) = 1$ since set C has 1 element
(d) $n(\varnothing) = 0$ since there are no elements in an empty set

☑ 5. Find the cardinality of a set.

▼ Try This One 10

Find the cardinal number of each set.

(a) $A = \{z, y, x, w, v\}$ (c) $C = \{Chevrolet\}$
(b) $B = \{1, 3, 5, 7, \ldots, 27, 29\}$

Math Note

All equal sets are equivalent since both sets will have the same number of members, but not all equivalent sets are equal. For example, the sets {x, y, z} and {10, 20, 30} have three members, but in this case, the members of the sets are not identical. The two sets are equivalent but not equal.

Equal and Equivalent Sets

In set theory, it is important to understand the concepts of *equal* sets and *equivalent* sets.

> Two sets A and B are **equal** (written $A = B$) if they have exactly the same members or elements. Two finite sets A and B are said to be **equivalent** (written $A \cong B$) if they have the same number of elements: that is, $n(A) = n(B)$.

For example, the two sets {a, b, c} and {c, b, a} are equal since they have exactly the same members, a, b, and c. Also the set {4, 5, 6} is equal to the set {4, 4, 5, 6} since 4 need not be written twice in the second set. The set $C = \{x, y, z\}$ is equivalent to the set $D = \{10, 20, 30\}$ (i.e., $C \cong D$) since both sets have three elements, but the sets are not equal.

EXAMPLE 11   Deciding If Sets Are Equal or Equivalent

State whether each pair of sets is equal, equivalent, or neither.

(a) {p, q, r, s}; {a, b, c, d}
(b) {8, 10, 12}; {12, 8, 10}
(c) {213}; {2, 1, 3}
(d) {1, 2, 10, 20}; {2, 1, 20, 11}
(e) {even natural numbers less than 10}; {2, 4, 6, 8}

SOLUTION

(a) Equivalent
(b) Equal and equivalent
(c) Neither
(d) Equivalent
(e) Equal and equivalent

Two sets of basketball teams on the court have a one-to-one correspondence. (Assuming each has five healthy players!)

▼ Try This One 11

State whether each pair of sets is equal, equivalent, or neither.

(a) {d, o, g}; {c, a, t}
(b) {run}; {r, u, n}
(c) {t, o, p}; {p, o, t}
(d) {10, 20, 30}; {1, 3, 5}

The elements of two equivalent sets can be paired in such a way that they are said to have a *one-to-one correspondence* between them.

Two sets have a **one-to-one correspondence** of elements if each element in the first set can be paired with exactly one element of the second set and each element of the second set can be paired with exactly one element of the first set.

EXAMPLE 12 | **Putting Sets in One-to-One Correspondence**

Show that (a) the sets {8, 16, 24, 32} and {s, t, u, v} have a one-to-one correspondence and (b) the sets {x, y, z} and {5, 10} do not have a one-to-one correspondence.

SOLUTION

(a) We need to demonstrate that each element of one set can be paired with one and only one element of the second set. One possible way to show a one-to-one correspondence is this:

$$\{8, \quad 16, \quad 24, \quad 32\}$$
$$\updownarrow \quad \updownarrow \quad \updownarrow \quad \updownarrow$$
$$\{s, \quad t, \quad u, \quad v\}$$

(b) The elements of the sets {x, y, z} and {5, 10} can't be put in one-to-one correspondence. No matter how we try, there will be an element in the first set that doesn't correspond to any element in the second set.

▼ **Try This One 12**

Show that the sets {North, South, East, West} and {sun, rain, snow, sleet} have a one-to-one correspondence.

Using one-to-one correspondence, we can decide if two sets are equivalent without actually counting the elements. This can come in handy for large sets, and *really* handy for infinite sets!

Correspondence and Equivalent Sets

Two sets are

- Equivalent if you can put their elements in one-to-one correspondence.

- Not equivalent if you cannot put their elements in one-to-one correspondence.

☑ 6. Decide if two sets are equal or equivalent.

In this section, we defined sets and some other basic terms. In Section 2-2, subsets and set operations will be explained.

Answers to Try This One

1 {Ontario, Erie, Huron, Michigan, Superior}

2 (a) {80, 82, 84, 86, 88, 90}
    (b) {11, 13, 15, 17, . . .}

3 (a) True   (b) False   (c) True

4 The set of integers from −3 to 3

5 (a) $K = \{x | x \in E, x > 9, \text{ and } x < 19\}$, the set of all x such that x is an even natural number, x is greater than 9, and x is less than 19.

(b) $W = \{x | x \text{ is a major American political party}\}$, the set of all x such that x is a major American political party.

6 (a) $\{11, 13, 15, 17, \ldots\}$

(b) The set of odd natural numbers greater than 10

(c) $\{x | x \in N, x \text{ is odd, and } x > 10\}$

7 $\{51, 53, 55, \ldots, 497, 499\}$

8 (a) Infinite   (b) Finite   (c) Finite

9 (b) and (d)

10 (a) 5   (b) 15   (c) 1

11 (a) Equivalent   (c) Equal and equivalent

(b) Neither   (d) Equivalent

12

North	South	East	West
↕	↕	↕	↕
Sun	Rain	Snow	Sleet

EXERCISE SET 2-1

Writing Exercises

1. Explain what a set is.
2. List three ways to write sets.
3. What is the difference between equal and equivalent sets?
4. Explain the difference between a finite and an infinite set.
5. What is meant by "one-to-one correspondence between two sets"?
6. Define the empty set and give two examples of an empty set.

Computational Exercises

For Exercises 7–20, write each set, using roster notation. Do not include repeats.

7. S is the set of letters in the word *stress*.
8. A is the set of letters in the word *Alabama*.
9. P is the set of natural numbers between 50 and 60.
10. R is the set of even natural numbers between 10 and 40.
11. Q is the set of odd natural numbers less than 15.
12. M is the set of even natural numbers less than 8.
13. $G = \{x | x \in N \text{ and } x > 10\}$
14. B is the set of natural numbers greater than 100.
15. Y is the set of natural numbers between 2,000 and 3,000.
16. $Z = \{x | x \in N \text{ and } 500 < x < 6,000\}$
17. W is the set of days in the week.
18. C is the set of colors in a U.S. flag.
19. D is the set of suits in a deck of cards.
20. F is the set of face cards in a deck of cards.

For Exercises 21–28, write each set, using the descriptive method.

21. $\{2, 4, 6, 8, \ldots\}$
22. $\{1, 3, 5, 7, \ldots\}$
23. $\{9, 18, 27, 36\}$
24. $\{5, 10, 15, 20\}$
25. $\{m, a, r, y\}$
26. $\{t, h, o, m, a, s\}$
27. $\{100, 101, 102, \ldots, 199\}$
28. $\{21, 22, 23, \ldots, 29, 30\}$

For Exercises 29–34, write each set, using set-builder notation.

29. $\{10, 20, 30, 40, \ldots\}$
30. $\{55, 65, 75, 85\}$
31. X is the set of natural numbers greater than 20.
32. Z is the set of even natural numbers less than 12.
33. $\{1, 3, 5, 7, 9\}$
34. $\{18, 21, 24, 27, 30\}$

For Exercises 35–40, list the elements in each set.

35. H is the set of natural numbers less than 0.
36. $\{x | x \in N \text{ and } 70 < x < 80\}$
37. $\{7, 14, 21, \ldots, 63\}$
38. $\{5, 12, 19, \ldots, 40\}$
39. $\{x | x \text{ is an even natural number between 100 and 120}\}$
40. $\{x | x \text{ is an odd natural number between 90 and 100}\}$

For Exercises 41–48, state whether each collection is well-defined or not well-defined.

41. J is the set of seasons in the year.
42. $\{x \mid x \in N\}$
43. $\{x \mid x$ is an excellent instructor$\}$
44. $\{10, 15, 20\}$
45. $\{1, 2, 3, \ldots, 100\}$
46. $\{x \mid x$ is a good professional golfer$\}$
47. $\{100, \ldots\}$
48. W is the set of days of the week.

For Exercises 49–54, state whether each is true or false.

Let $A = \{$Saturday, Sunday$\}$
  $B = \{1, 2, 3, 4, 5\}$
  $C = \{$p, q, r, s, t$\}$

49. $3 \in B$
50. $a \in C$
51. Wednesday $\notin A$
52. $7 \notin B$
53. $r \in C$
54. $q \in B$

For Exercises 55–62, state whether each set is infinite or finite.

55. $\{x \mid x \in N$ and x is even$\}$
56. $\{1, 2, 3, \ldots, 999, 1,000\}$
57. K is the set of letters of the English alphabet.
58. $\{x \mid x \in$ years in which the past Presidents of the United States were born$\}$
59. $\{3, 6, 9, 12, \ldots\}$
60. $\varnothing$
61. $\{x \mid x$ is a current television program$\}$
62. $\{x \mid x$ is a fraction$\}$

For Exercises 63–70, state whether each pair of sets is equal, equivalent, or neither.

63. $\{6, 12, 18, 20\}$ and $\{20, 12, 6, 18\}$
64. $\{$p, q, r, s, t$\}$ and $\{5, 3, 4, 2, 1\}$
65. $\{2, 3, 7, 8\}$ and $\{1, 4, 5\}$
66. $\{2, 4, 6, 8\}$ and $\{2, 4, 6, 8, \ldots\}$
67. $\{1, 2, 3, \ldots, 99, 100\}$ and $\{1,001, 1,002, 1,003, \ldots, 1,100\}$
68. $\{$s, t, o, p$\}$ and $\{$p, o, t, s$\}$
69. $\{x \mid x$ is a three-digit number$\}$ and $\{1, 2, 3, \ldots, 100\}$
70. $\{$January, June, July$\}$ and $\{x \mid x$ is a month that begins with J$\}$

For Exercises 71–74, show that each pair of sets is equivalent by using a one-to-one correspondence.

71. $\{10, 20, 30, 40\}$ and $\{40, 10, 20, 30\}$
72. $\{$w, x, y, z$\}$ and $\{1, 2, 3, 4\}$
73. $\{1, 2, 3, \ldots, 25, 26\}$ and $\{$a, b, c, $\ldots$, x, y, z$\}$
74. $\{x \mid x$ is an odd natural number less than 11$\}$ and $\{x \mid x$ is an even natural number less than 12$\}$

For Exercises 75–82, find the cardinal number for each set.

75. $A = \{18, 24, 32, 63, 48\}$
76. $B = \{1, 3, 5, 7, \ldots, 37\}$
77. $C = \{x \mid x$ is a day of the week$\}$
78. $D = \{x \mid x$ is a month of the year$\}$
79. $E = \{$three$\}$
80. $F = \{$t, h, r, e, e$\}$
81. $G = \{x \mid x \in N$ and x is negative$\}$
82. $H = \varnothing$

For Exercises 83–90, determine whether each statement is true or false.

83. $\{1, 3, 5\} = \{3, 1, 5\}$
84. $\{2, 4, 6\} \neq \{1, 3, 5\}$
85. All equal sets are equivalent.
86. No equivalent sets are equal.
87. $\varnothing = \{\varnothing\}$
88. $\{2, 6, 10, 12\} = \{2, 6, 10\}$
89. $n(\{\varnothing\}) = 0$
90. $E = \{2, 4, 6, 8, \ldots\}$ is a finite set

Real-World Applications

91. The table below shows the top 10 states in number of immigrants in 2006.

State	Number of Immigrants	% of Total Immigrants to United States
California	264,677	20.9
New York	180,165	14.2
Florida	155,996	12.3
Texas	89,037	7.0
New Jersey	65,934	5.2
Illinois	52,459	4.1
Virginia	38,488	3.0
Massachusetts	35,560	2.8
Georgia	32,202	2.5
Maryland	30,204	2.4

Source: *The World Almanac and Book of Facts*, 2008.

(a) List the set of states with more than 100,000 immigrants.
(b) List the set of states in the top 10 with fewer than 50,000 immigrants.
(c) List $\{x \mid x$ is a state with at least 5% of the immigrant total$\}$.
(d) List $\{x \mid x$ is a state with between 3% and 9% of the immigrant total$\}$.

92. There is a relatively young workforce in the U.S. information technology industry. The percentage of people by age group working at Internet service providers (ISPs), Web search portals, and data processing companies in 2006 is shown in the table on the next page.

Age Group	Percentage Working at ISPs, Web Search Portals, and Data Processing Companies
16–19	1.1
20–24	10.1
25–34	26.8
35–44	31.8
45–54	19.6
55–64	7.8
65 and older	2.2

Source: http://www.bls.gov/oco/cg/cgs055.htm

(a) List the set of age groups of those whose percentages are over 18%. What can you conclude?

(b) List the set of age groups of those whose percentages are less than 10%. What can you conclude?

(c) List the set of percentages of those who are between 20 and 44 years old.

(d) Find $\{x \mid x$ is the age group with the largest percentage in the industry$\}$.

(e) Find $\{x \mid x$ is the percentage in the industry for those between ages 45 and 64$\}$.

(f) Find $\{x \mid x$ is the percentage in the industry for those under age 16$\}$.

93. Excessive alcohol consumption by those aged 18–24 affects nearly all U.S. college students, whether they choose to drink or not. The consequences of excessive drinking are listed below.

Consequence	Average Number of College Students Aged 18–24 Affected per Year
Death	1,700
Injury	599,000
Assault	696,000
Sexual abuse	97,000
Unsafe sex	500,000
Health problems	150,000
Drunk driving	2,100,000

Source: http://www.collegedrinkingprevention.gov/StatsSummaries/snapshot.aspx

(a) List the set of the three consequences with the most students affected by excessive alcohol consumption.

(b) List the set of consequences that affect between 100,000 and 600,000 college students each year.

(c) Find the set $\{x \mid x$ is a consequence of which over a half million students are affected$\}$.

(d) Find the set $\{x \mid x$ is the average number of college students affected by sexual abuse, death, or health problems$\}$.

(e) Find a set of three elements that do not belong in the set $\{x \mid x$ is a consequence of excessive drinking to college students ages 18–24$\}$.

94. The number of bachelor's degrees awarded by degree-granting institutions in the United States in different years is shown below.

Major	1991	1998	2005
Business	249,200	232,100	311,600
Social sciences	125,100	125,000	156,900
Education	110,800	105,800	105,500
Psychology	58,700	74,100	85,600
Health professions	59,900	86,800	80,700
Engineering	79,800	78,700	78,600
Communications	51,700	49,400	72,700
Computers	25,200	27,800	54,100
Physical sciences	16,300	19,400	18,900
Mathematics	14,400	11,800	14,400
Philosophy	7,400	8,400	11,600

Source: http://nces.ed.gov/programs/coe/2007/section5/table.asp?tableID=739

(a) List the set of majors that increased in popularity every year listed.

(b) List the set of majors that did not increase in popularity from 1998 to 2005.

(c) List the set of majors that had between 50,000 and 110,000 degrees awarded in 1998.

(d) Find the set $\{x \mid x$ increased in popularity between 1991 and 1998$\}$.

(e) Find the set $\{x \mid x$ is a major that starts with the letter M, P, or E$\}$.

(f) To find the percent increase P between an original amount O and a new amount N, use the following formula: $P = (N - O)/O$. Calculate the percent increase for any major that saw an increase in degrees awarded between 1998 and 2005. List the set of majors that increased at least 30%.

95. Identity theft is the fastest-growing crime in the United States, and college students aged 18–24 are the most affected. Of the 675,000 identity theft complaints in 2005 to the Federal Trade Commission, 29% were made by college students in this age group. The following charts show types of identity theft fraud reported in 2005 and the percentage of victims by age.

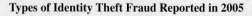

Types of Identity Theft Fraud Reported in 2005

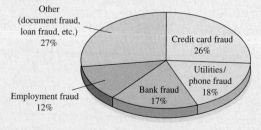

Percentage of Victims by Age

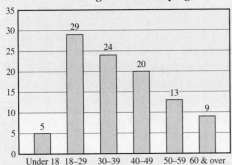

(a) List the set of the two types of identity fraud with the lowest percentage of reported crimes.

(b) List the set of age groups that are above 18%.

(c) List the set of identity fraud types that have more than 17% of reported crimes.

(d) Find the set $\{x|x$ is a percentage of those 40 and over who are victims of identity fraud$\}$.

(e) Find the set $\{x|x$ is a type of fraud that has between 10% and 20% of reported crimes$\}$.

96. Many people are now using MP3 players on their cell phones rather than a separate MP3 player to listen to music. The chart below shows age groups for those who have phones with MP3 players, those who listened to music using an MP3 player on a phone in the last 12 months, and those who downloaded music to an MP3 on their phone in the last 12 months.

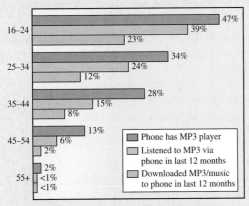

Source: http://www.cellular-news.com/story/20124.php

(a) List the set of age groups of those in which at least 20% listened to an MP3 via cell phone in the last year.

(b) List the set of age groups of those in which less than 10% downloaded music to their phones in the last year.

(c) Find the set $\{x|x$ is an age group in which at least 30% had a phone with an MP3 player$\}$.

(d) Find the set $\{x|x$ is a percentage for those aged 35–44 who have a phone with an MP3 player and listened to MP3 via phone in the last 12 months$\}$.

97. The rising cost of medical care has become one of the biggest burdens on working families in the last 10 years. The graph below represents the average prescription drug price in dollars for the years 2000 to 2006.

Average Prescription Drug Price ($)

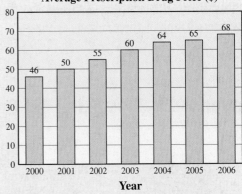

(a) Find the set of years when the average prescription drug price was less than $60.

(b) Find the set of years when the average prescription drug price was between $50 and $68.

(c) Find $\{x|x$ is a year in which the average prescription drug price was greater than $50\}$.

(d) Find $\{x|x$ is a year in which the average prescription drug price was more than $60\}$.

98. Housing prices have been in the news a lot in recent years, as the boom that began in 2004 has given way to the bust just a few years later. The graph below displays the median housing prices for all houses sold in the United States between 2003 and 2008.

Median Home Prices in the United States

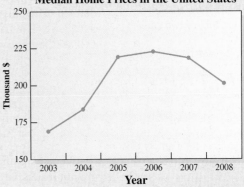

(a) List the set of years in which the median price was above $200,000.

(b) List the set of years in which the median price was between $175,000 and $200,000.

(c) Find $\{x|x$ is a year in which the median price increased from the year before$\}$.

(d) Find $\{x|x$ is a year in which the median price decreased from the year before$\}$.

Critical Thinking

99. If $A \cong B$ and $A \cong C$, is $B \cong C$? Explain your answer.
100. Is $\{0\}$ equivalent to $\varnothing$? Explain your answer.
101. The set of people who attend college is not well-defined. How could you alter the definition to make this set well-defined?
102. The set of students in your math class has many subsets. Think of three subsets of this set.

103. Think of two sets of popular songs that are equivalent. Think of a third set of popular songs that is not equivalent to either of the first two sets.
104. Think of two sets of four elements each that have a one-to-one correspondence.

Section 2-2 Subsets and Set Operations

When we classify things in the real world, sets often have relationships with one another. For example, you are a member of both the set of college students and the set of students taking a college math course. You could be in the set of sophomores or the set of juniors, but not in both. You might be in the set of students living off campus and the set of students who walk to class. In this section, we'll be studying relationships between sets.

To begin, we need to consider a new concept called a *universal set.*

A **universal set,** symbolized by U, is the set of all potential elements under consideration for a specific situation.

LEARNING OBJECTIVES

☐ 1. Define the complement of a set.

☐ 2. Find all subsets of a set.

☐ 3. Use subset notation.

☐ 4. Find the number of subsets for a set.

☐ 5. Find intersections, unions, and differences of sets.

☐ 6. Find the Cartesian product of two sets.

In the examples above, a reasonable choice of U would be the set of all college students, since all the elements under consideration are college students. Once we define a universal set in a given setting, we are restricted to considering only elements from that set. If $U = \{1, 2, 3, 4, 5, 6, 7, 8\}$, then the only elements we can use to define other sets in this setting are the integers from 1 to 8.

In the remainder of this chapter, we'll use a clever method for visualizing sets and their relationships called a *Venn diagram* (so named because it was developed by a man named John Venn in the 1800s). Figure 2-1 shows an example.

You can get a lot of information from this simple diagram. A set called A is being defined. The universal set from which elements of A can be chosen is $U = \{1, 2, 3, 4, 5, 6, 7, 8\}$. The set A is $\{2, 4, 6, 8\}$, and the elements not in A are $\{1, 3, 5, 7\}$. We will call the elements in U that are not in A the *complement* of A, and denote it A'.

Math Note

The complement of the universal set is the empty set: $U' = \varnothing$. The complement of the empty set is the universal set: $\varnothing' = U$.

The **complement** of a set A, symbolized A', is the set of elements contained in the universal set that are *not* in A. Using set-builder notation, the complement of A is $A' = \{x \mid x \in U \text{ and } x \notin A\}$.

In a Venn diagram, the complement of a set A is all the things inside the rectangle that are not inside the circle representing set A. This is shown in Figure 2-2.

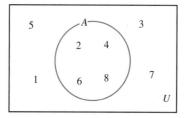

Figure 2-1

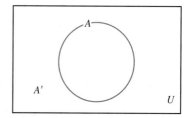

Figure 2-2

EXAMPLE 1   Finding the Complement of a Set

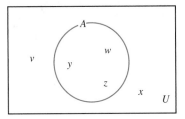

Figure 2-3

Let $U = \{$v, w, x, y, z$\}$ and $A = \{$w, y, z$\}$. Find A' and draw a Venn diagram that illustrates these sets.

SOLUTION

Using the list of elements in U, we just have to cross out the ones that are also in A. The elements left over are in A'.

$$U = \{\text{v, }\cancel{\text{w}}\text{, x, }\cancel{\text{y}}\text{, }\cancel{\text{z}}\}\qquad A' = \{\text{v, x}\}$$

The Venn diagram is shown in Figure 2-3.

▼ **Try This One 1**

☑ 1. Define the complement of a set.

Let $U = \{$10, 20, 30, 40, 50, 60, 70, 80, 90$\}$ and $A = \{$10, 30, 50$\}$. Find A' and draw a Venn diagram that illustrates these sets.

Subsets

At the beginning of the section, we pointed out that you're in both the set of college students and the set of students taking a college math course. Notice that everyone in the second set is automatically in the first one. We could say that the set of students taking a college math course is contained in the set of all college students. When one set is contained in a second set, we call the smaller set a *subset* of the larger one.

> If every element of a set A is also an element of a set B, then A is called a **subset** of B. The symbol $\subseteq$ is used to designate a subset; in this case, we write $A \subseteq B$.

There are many subsets of this set of spring breakers: the subset of female students, the subset of sophomores, the subset of students who had their fake I.D. confiscated by the police, and so on.

An alternate definition is that A is a subset of B if there are no elements in A that are not also in B.

Here are a couple of observations about subsets.

- Every set is a subset of itself. Every element of a set A is of course an element of set A, so $A \subseteq A$.

- The empty set is a subset of every set. The empty set has no elements, so for any set A, you can't find an element of $\varnothing$ that is not also in A.

If we start with the set $\{$x, y, z$\}$, let's look at how many subsets we can form:

Number of Elements in Subset	Subsets with That Number of Elements	
3	$\{$x, y, z$\}$	(One subset)
2	$\{$x, y$\}$, $\{$x, z$\}$, $\{$y, z$\}$	(Three subsets)
1	$\{$x$\}$, $\{$y$\}$, $\{$z$\}$	(Three subsets)
0	$\varnothing$	(One subset)

So for a set with three elements, we can form eight subsets.

EXAMPLE 2   **Finding All Subsets of a Set**

Find all subsets of $A = \{American\ Idol,\ Survivor\}$.

SOLUTION
The subsets are

> $\{American\ Idol,\ Survivor\}$
> $\{American\ Idol\}$
> $\{Survivor\}$
> $\varnothing$

Note that a set with 2 elements has 4 subsets.

▼ Try This One 2

Find all subsets of $B = \{Verizon,\ Nextel,\ AT\&T\}$.

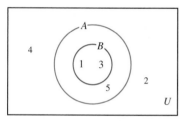

Figure 2-4 $B \subset A$

To indicate that a set is not a subset of another set, the symbol $\not\subseteq$ is used. For example, $\{1, 3\} \not\subseteq \{0, 3, 5, 7\}$ since $1 \notin \{0, 3, 5, 7\}$.

Of the four subsets in Example 2, only one is equal to the original set. We will call the remaining three *proper subsets* of A. The Venn diagram for a proper subset is shown in Figure 2-4. In this case, $U = \{1, 2, 3, 4, 5\}$, $A = \{1, 3, 5\}$, and $B = \{1, 3\}$.

> If a set A is a subset of a set B and is not equal to B, then we call A a **proper subset** of B, and write $A \subset B$.

EXAMPLE 3   **Finding Proper Subsets of a Set**

Find all proper subsets of $\{x, y, z\}$.

SOLUTION
> $\{x, y\}$ $\{x, z\}$ $\{y, z\}$
> $\{x\}$ $\{y\}$ $\{z\}$
> $\varnothing$

▼ Try This One 3

Find all proper subsets of $\{\blacklozenge, \heartsuit, \spadesuit, \clubsuit\}$.

☑ 2. Find all subsets of a set.

The symbol $\not\subset$ is used to indicate that the set is not a proper subset. For example, $\{1, 3\} \subset \{1, 3, 5\}$, but $\{1, 3, 5\} \not\subset \{1, 3, 5\}$.

EXAMPLE 4   **Understanding Subset Notation**

State whether each statement is true or false.

(a) $\{1, 3, 5\} \subseteq \{1, 3, 5, 7\}$ (b) $\{a, b\} \subset \{a, b\}$

(c) $\{x \mid x \in N \text{ and } x > 10\} \subset N$
(d) $\{2, 10\} \nsubseteq \{2, 4, 6, 8, 10\}$
(e) $\{r, s, t\} \nsubseteq \{t, s, r\}$
(f) $\{\text{Lake Erie, Lake Huron}\} \subset$ The set of Great Lakes

SOLUTION

(a) All of 1, 3, and 5 are in the second set, so $\{1, 3, 5\}$ is a subset of $\{1, 3, 5, 7\}$. The statement is true.
(b) Even though $\{a, b\}$ is a subset of $\{a, b\}$, it is not a proper subset, so the statement is false.
(c) Every element in the first set is a natural number, but not all natural numbers are in the set, so that set is a proper subset of the natural numbers. The statement is true.
(d) Both 2 and 10 are elements of the second set, so $\{2, 10\}$ is a subset, and the statement is false.
(e) The two sets are identical, so $\{r, s, t\}$ is not a proper subset of $\{t, s, r\}$. The statement is true.
(f) Lake Erie and Lake Huron are both Great Lakes, so the statement is true.

▼ Try This One 4

State whether each statement is true or false.

(a) $\{8\} \subseteq \{x \mid x \text{ is an even natural number}\}$
(b) $\{6\} \subseteq \{1, 3, 5, 7, \ldots\}$
(c) $\{2, 3\} \subseteq \{x \mid x \in N\}$
(d) $\{a, b, c\} \subset \{\text{letters of the alphabet}\}$
(e) $\varnothing \in \{x, y, z\}$

EXAMPLE 5 Understanding Subset Notation

State whether each statement is true or false.

(a) $\varnothing \subset \{5, 10, 15\}$
(b) $\{u, v, w, x\} \subseteq \{x, w, u\}$
(c) $\{0\} \subseteq \varnothing$
(d) $\varnothing \subset \varnothing$

SOLUTION

(a) True: the empty set is a proper subset of every set except itself.
(b) False: v is an element of $\{u, v, w, x\}$ but not $\{x, w, u\}$.
(c) The set on the left has one element, 0. The empty set has no elements, so the statement is false.
(d) The empty set is a subset of itself (as well as every other set), but not a proper subset of itself. The statement is false.

▼ Try This One 5

State whether each statement is true or false.

(a) $\varnothing \subseteq \{\text{red, yellow, blue}\}$
(b) $\varnothing \subseteq \varnothing$
(c) $\{100, 200, 300, 400\} \subset \{200, 300, 400\}$
(d) $\{\varnothing\} \subseteq \varnothing$

☑ 3. Use subset notation.

A set with one element has two subsets—itself and the empty set. We have seen that if a set has two elements, there are four subsets, and if a set has three elements, there are eight subsets. This is an excellent opportunity to use the inductive reasoning that we practiced in Chapter 1!

Number of elements	0	1	2	3
Number of subsets	1	2	4	8

Based on this pattern, it's reasonable to conjecture that a set with 4 elements will have 16 subsets, a set with 5 elements will have 32 subsets, and so forth. (Notice that the number of subsets in each case is 2 raised to the number of elements.) It turns out that this is always the case. We also know that the number of proper subsets of a set is always 1 less than the total number of subsets, since only the set itself is excluded when forming proper subsets. We conclude:

The Number of Subsets for a Finite Set

If a finite set has n elements, then the set has 2^n subsets and $2^n - 1$ proper subsets.

EXAMPLE 6   Finding the Number of Subsets of a Set

Find the number of subsets and proper subsets of the set $\{1, 3, 5, 7, 9, 11\}$.

SOLUTION

The set has $n = 6$ elements, so there are 2^n, or $2^6 = 64$, subsets. Of these, $2^n - 1$, or 63, are proper.

▼ Try This One 6

☑ 4. Find the number of subsets for a set.

Find the number of subsets and proper subsets of the set $\{$OSU, USC, KSU, MSU, UND, PSU, UT, FSU$\}$.

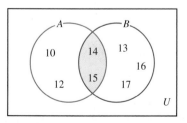

The advertisement is looking for people in the *intersection* of three sets of potential employees.

Figure 2-5 $A \cap B = \{14, 15\}$

Intersection and Union of Sets

At the beginning of the section, we pointed out that you might be in both the set of students living off campus and the set of students who walk to class. We will identify objects that are common to two or more sets by using the term *intersection*.

> The **intersection** of two sets A and B, symbolized by $A \cap B$, is the set of all elements that are in both sets. In set-builder notation, $A \cap B = \{x \mid x \in A \text{ and } x \in B\}$.

For example, if $A = \{10, 12, 14, 15\}$ and $B = \{13, 14, 15, 16, 17\}$, then the intersection $A \cap B = \{14, 15\}$, since 14 and 15 are the elements that are common to both sets. The Venn diagram for $A \cap B$ is shown in Figure 2-5. Notice that the elements of A are placed inside the circle for set A, and the elements of B are inside the circle for set B. The elements in the intersection are placed into the portion where the circles overlap: $A \cap B$ is the shaded portion.

Intersection is an example of a **set operation**—a rule for combining two or more sets to form a new set. The intersection of three or more sets consists of the set of elements that are in every single set. Note that the word *and* is sometimes used to indicate intersection; $A \cap B$ is the set of elements in A and B.

EXAMPLE 7 **Finding Intersections**

If $A = \{5, 10, 15, 20, 25\}$, $B = \{0, 10, 20, 30, 40\}$, and $C = \{30, 50, 70, 90\}$, find

(a) $A \cap B$ (b) $B \cap C$ (c) $A \cap C$

SOLUTION

(a) The elements 10 and 20 are in both sets A and B, so $A \cap B = \{10, 20\}$.
(b) The only member of both sets B and C is 30, so $B \cap C = \{30\}$.
(c) There are no elements common to sets A and C, so $A \cap C = \varnothing$.

▼ **Try This One 7**

If $A = \{$Cleveland, Indianapolis, Chicago, Des Moines, Detroit$\}$, $B = \{$New York, Los Angeles, Chicago, Detroit$\}$, and $C = \{$Seattle, Los Angeles, San Diego$\}$, find $A \cap B$, $B \cap C$, and $A \cap C$.

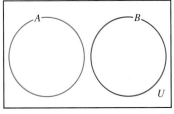

Figure 2-6 $A \cap B = \varnothing$

When the intersection of two sets is the empty set, the sets are said to be *disjoint*. For example, the set of students who stop attending class midway through a term and the set of students earning A's are disjoint, because you can't be a member of both sets. The Venn diagram for a pair of disjoint sets A and B is shown in Figure 2-6. If the sets have no elements in common, the circles representing them don't overlap at all.

Another way of combining sets to form a new set is called *union*.

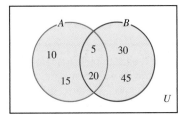

Figure 2-7 $A \cup B$

The **union** of two sets A and B, symbolized by $A \cup B$, is the set of all elements that are in either set A or set B (or both). In set-builder notation,

$$A \cup B = \{x \mid x \in A \quad \text{or} \quad x \in B\}$$

For example, if $A = \{5, 10, 15, 20\}$ and $B = \{5, 20, 30, 45\}$, then the union $A \cup B = \{5, 10, 15, 20, 30, 45\}$. Even though 5 and 20 are in both sets, we list them only once in the union. The Venn diagram for $A \cup B$ is shown in Figure 2-7. The set $A \cup B$ is the shaded area consisting of all elements in either set.

EXAMPLE 8 **Finding Unions**

If $A = \{0, 1, 2, 3, 4, 5\}$, $B = \{2, 4, 6, 8, 10\}$, and $C = \{1, 3, 5, 7\}$, find each.

(a) $A \cup B$ (b) $A \cup C$ (c) $B \cup C$

SOLUTION

To find a union, just make a list of all the elements in either set without writing repeats.

(a) $A \cup B = \{0, 1, 2, 3, 4, 5, 6, 8, 10\}$
(b) $A \cup C = \{0, 1, 2, 3, 4, 5, 7\}$
(c) $B \cup C = \{1, 2, 3, 4, 5, 6, 7, 8, 10\}$

▼ Try This One 8

If $A = \{a, b, c, d, e\}$, $B = \{a, c, e, g, i\}$, and $C = \{b, d, f, h, j\}$, find $A \cup B$, $A \cup C$, and $B \cup C$.

What about operations involving more than two sets? Just like with operations involving numbers, we use parentheses to indicate an order of operations. This is illustrated in Example 9.

EXAMPLE 9   **Performing Set Operations**

Let $A = \{l, m, n, o, p\}$, $B = \{o, p, q, r\}$, and $C = \{r, s, t, u\}$. Find each.

(a) $(A \cup B) \cap C$ (b) $A \cap (B \cup C)$ (c) $(A \cap B) \cup C$

SOLUTION

(a) First find $A \cup B$: $A \cup B = \{l, m, n, o, p, q, r\}$. Then intersect this set with set C; the only common element is r, so $(A \cup B) \cap C = \{r\}$.
(b) First find $B \cup C$: $B \cup C = \{o, p, q, r, s, t, u\}$. Then intersect this set with set A to get $\{o, p\}$.
(c) First find $A \cap B$: $A \cap B = \{o, p\}$. Then find the union of this set with set C to get $\{o, p, r, s, t, u\}$.

▼ Try This One 9

If $A = \{2, 3, 4, 5, 6, 7\}$, $B = \{7, 8, 9, 10\}$, and $C = \{0, 5, 10, 15, 20\}$, find $A \cup (B \cap C)$, $(A \cap B) \cup C$, and $A \cap (B \cup C)$.

CAUTION

When combining union and intersection with complements, we'll have to be extra careful. Pay particular attention to the parentheses and to whether the complement symbol is inside or outside the parentheses.

EXAMPLE 10   **Performing Set Operations**

If $U = \{10, 20, 30, 40, 50, 60, 70, 80\}$, $A = \{10, 30, 50, 70\}$, $B = \{40, 50, 60, 70\}$, and $C = \{20, 40, 60\}$, find each.

(a) $A' \cap C'$ (b) $(A \cap B)' \cap C$ (c) $B' \cup (A \cap C')$

SOLUTION

(a) First, write A' and C': $A' = \{20, 40, 60, 80\}$ and $C' = \{10, 30, 50, 70, 80\}$. Now note that 80 is the only element common to both: $A' \cap C' = \{80\}$.
(b) The parentheses tell us that we should find $A \cap B$ first: $A \cap B = \{50, 70\}$. Next we find the complement: $(A \cap B)' = \{10, 20, 30, 40, 60, 80\}$. Finally, we find the intersection of this set and C: $(A \cap B)' \cap C = \{20, 40, 60\}$.
(c) First, find $A \cap C'$: $C' = \{10, 30, 50, 70, 80\}$, and all but 80 are also in A, so $A \cap C' = \{10, 30, 50, 70\}$. Next note that $B' = \{10, 20, 30, 80\}$. Now form the union: $B' \cup (A \cap C') = \{10, 20, 30, 50, 70, 80\}$.

▼ Try This One 10

Let $U = \{1, 2, 3, 4, 5, 6, 7, 8\}$, $A = \{1, 3, 5, 7\}$, $B = \{2, 4, 6, 8\}$, and $C = \{2, 3, 5, 7\}$. Find each.

(a) C' (b) $(A \cup B)'$ (c) $A' \cap C'$ (d) $(A \cup B) \cap C'$

The union and intersection of sets are commonly used in real life—it's just that you might not have thought of it in those terms. For example, the intersection of the set of U.S. citizens older than 17 and the set of U.S. citizens who are not convicted felons makes up the set of those eligible to vote. The union of the set of your mom's parents and your dad's parents forms the set of your grandparents.

Set Subtraction

The third set operation we'll study is called the *difference* of sets. We also call it *set subtraction* and use a minus sign to represent it.

> The **difference** of set A and set B is the set of elements in set A that are *not* in set B. In set-builder notation, $A - B = \{x \mid x \in A \text{ and } x \notin B\}$.

EXAMPLE 11 Finding the Difference of Two Sets

Math Note

Sometimes operations can be written in terms of other operations. For example, $3 - 5$ is also $3 + (-5)$. Can you think of a way to write $A - B$ using intersection and complement? Drawing a Venn diagram might help.

Let $U = \{2, 4, 6, 8, 10, 12\}$, $A = \{4, 6, 8, 10\}$, $B = \{2, 6, 12\}$, $C = \{8, 10\}$

Find each.

(a) $A - B$ (b) $A - C$ (c) $B - C$

SOLUTION

(a) Start with the elements in set A and take out the elements in set B that are also in set A. In this case, only 6 is removed, and $A - B = \{4, 8, 10\}$.
(b) Start with the elements in set A and remove the elements in set C that are also in set A. In this case, 8 and 10 are removed, and $A - C = \{4, 6\}$.
(c) Start with the elements in set B and take out the elements in set C that are also in set B. In this case, none of the elements in B are also in C. So $B - C = \{2, 6, 12\}$.

▼ Try This One 11

Let $L = \{p, q, r, s, t, u, v, w\}$, $M = \{p, s, t, u, y, z\}$, and $N = \{u, v, w, z\}$. Find

(a) $L - M$ (b) $L - N$ (c) $M - N$

☑ 5. Find intersections, unions, and differences of sets.

Cartesian Products

The fourth set operation we'll study is called the *Cartesian product* or *cross product*. To define it, we need to first define an *ordered pair*. An ordered pair is a pair of numbers or objects that are associated by writing them together in a set of parentheses, like (3, 5). In this ordered pair, 3 is called the *first component* and 5 is called the *second component*.

As indicated by the term *ordered pair,* the order in which numbers are written is important: (3, 5) is not the same ordered pair as (5, 3).

Math Note

The Cartesian product $A \times B$ is usually read aloud as "A cross B."

> The **Cartesian product** (denoted $A \times B$) of two sets A and B is formed by writing all possible ordered pairs in which the first component is an element of A and the second component is an element of B. Using set-builder notation, $A \times B = \{(x, y) \mid x \in A \text{ and } y \in B\}$.

EXAMPLE 12 Finding Cartesian Products

Math Note

It's important to note that the Cartesian product of two sets is also a set, so it should be enclosed within braces.

If $A = \{1, 3, 5\}$ and $B = \{2, 4\}$, find $A \times B$ and $B \times A$.

SOLUTION

To form $A \times B$, first form ordered pairs with first component 1: (1, 2) and (1, 4). Then form pairs with first component 3: (3, 2) and (3, 4). Finally, use 5 as the first component: (5, 2) and (5, 4). $A \times B = \{(1, 2), (1, 4), (3, 2), (3, 4), (5, 2), (5, 4)\}$. For $B \times A$, form all possible ordered pairs with first components from B and second components from A: $B \times A = \{(2, 1), (2, 3), (2, 5), (4, 1), (4, 3), (4, 5)\}$.

▼ Try This One 12

☑ 6. Find the Cartesian product of two sets.

If $R = \{c, d, e\}$ and $S = \{g, h\}$, find $R \times S$, $S \times R$, and $S \times S$.

CAUTION

Even though we use a multiplication sign for Cartesian product, it has nothing to do with multiplying elements!

In this section, we defined subsets, Venn diagrams, and four basic operations for combining sets: intersection, union, subtraction, and Cartesian product. In the next section, we'll examine how Venn diagrams can be used to study set operations in greater depth.

Answers to Try This One

1 $A' = \{20, 40, 60, 70, 80, 90\}$

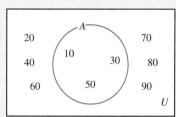

2   {Verizon, Nextel, AT&T}, {Verizon, Nextel}, {Verizon, AT&T}, {Nextel, AT&T}, {Verizon}, {Nextel}, {AT&T}, ∅

3 $\{\blacklozenge, \heartsuit, \spadesuit\}$, $\{\blacklozenge, \heartsuit, \clubsuit\}$, $\{\blacklozenge, \spadesuit, \clubsuit\}$, $\{\heartsuit, \spadesuit, \clubsuit\}$, $\{\blacklozenge, \heartsuit\}$, $\{\blacklozenge, \spadesuit\}$, $\{\blacklozenge, \clubsuit\}$, $\{\heartsuit, \spadesuit\}$, $\{\heartsuit, \clubsuit\}$, $\{\spadesuit, \clubsuit\}$, $\{\blacklozenge\}$, $\{\heartsuit\}$, $\{\spadesuit\}$, $\{\clubsuit\}$, ∅

4   (a) True   (c) True   (e) False
       (b) False   (d) True

5   (a) True   (b) True   (c) False   (d) False

6   Subsets: $2^8 = 256$; proper subsets: 255

7 $A \cap B = \{\text{Chicago, Detroit}\}$;
       $B \cap C = \{\text{Los Angeles}\}$; $A \cap C = \emptyset$

8 $A \cup B = \{a, b, c, d, e, g, i\}$;
$A \cup C = \{a, b, c, d, e, f, h, j\}$;
$B \cup C = \{a, b, c, d, e, f, g, h, i, j\}$

9 $A \cup (B \cap C) = \{2, 3, 4, 5, 6, 7, 10\}$
$(A \cap B) \cup C = \{0, 5, 7, 10, 15, 20\}$
$A \cap (B \cup C) = \{5, 7\}$

10   (a) $\{1, 4, 6, 8\}$ (c) $\{4, 6, 8\}$
(b) $\varnothing$ (d) $\{1, 4, 6, 8\}$

11   (a) $\{q, r, v, w\}$ (b) $\{p, q, r, s, t\}$ (c) $\{p, s, t, y\}$

12 $R \times S = \{(c, g), (c, h), (d, g), (d, h), (e, g), (e, h)\}$
$S \times R = \{(g, c), (g, d), (g, e), (h, c), (h, d), (h, e)\}$
$S \times S = \{(g, g), (g, h), (h, g), (h, h)\}$

EXERCISE SET 2-2

Writing Exercises

1. What is a subset?
2. Explain the difference between a subset and a proper subset.
3. Explain the difference between a subset and an element of a set.
4. Explain why the empty set is a subset, but not a proper subset, of itself.
5. Explain the difference between the union and intersection of two sets.
6. When are two sets said to be disjoint?
7. What is a universal set?
8. What is the complement of a set?
9. Write an example from real life that represents the union of sets and explain why it represents union.
10. Write an example from real life that represents the difference of sets and explain why it represents difference.

Computational Exercises

For Exercises 11–14, let $U = \{2, 3, 5, 7, 11, 13, 17, 19\}$, $A = \{5, 7, 11, 13\}$, $B = \{2\}$, $C = \{13, 17, 19\}$, *and* $D = \{2, 3, 5\}$. *Find each set.*

11. A'
12. B'
13. C'
14. D'

For Exercises 15–22, find all subsets of each set.

15. $\{r, s, t\}$
16. $\{2, 5, 7\}$
17. $\{1, 3\}$
18. $\{p, q\}$
19. $\{\ \}$
20. $\varnothing$
21. $\{5, 12, 13, 14\}$
22. $\{m, o, r, e\}$

For Exercises 23–28, find all proper subsets of each set.

23. $\{1, 10, 20\}$
24. $\{March, April, May\}$
25. $\{6\}$
26. $\{t\}$
27. $\varnothing$
28. $\{\ \}$

For Exercises 29–38, state whether each is true or false.

29. $\{3\} \subseteq \{1, 3, 5\}$
30. $\{a, b, c\} \subset \{c, b, a\}$
31. $\{1, 2, 3\} \subseteq \{123\}$
32. $\varnothing \subset \varnothing$
33. $\varnothing \in \{\ \}$
34. $\{Mars, Venus, Sun\} \subset \{planets\ in\ our\ solar\ system\}$
35. $\{3\} \in \{1, 3, 5, 7, \dots\}$
36. $\{x \mid x \in N\ and\ x > 10\} \subseteq \{x \mid x \in N\ and\ x \geq 10\}$
37. $\varnothing \subset \{a, b, c\}$
38. $\varnothing \in \{r, s, t, u\}$

For Exercises 39–44, find the number of subsets and proper subsets each set has. Do not list the subsets.

39. $\{25, 50, 75\}$
40. $\{1, 2, 3, 4, 5, 6, 7, 8, 9, 10\}$
41. $\varnothing$
42. $\{0\}$
43. $\{x, y\}$
44. $\{a, b, c, d, e\}$

For Exercises 45–54, use the Venn diagram and find the elements in each set.

45. U
46. A
47. B
48. $A \cap B$
49. $A \cup B$
50. A'
51. B'
52. $(A \cup B)'$
53. $(A \cap B)'$
54. $A \cap B'$

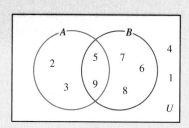

For Exercises 55–64, let

$U = \{10, 20, 30, 40, 50, 60, 70, 80, 90, 100\}$
$A = \{10, 30, 50, 70, 90\}$
$B = \{20, 40, 60, 80, 100\}$
$C = \{30, 40, 50, 60\}$

Find each set.

55. $A \cup C$	60. $(A \cap B) \cap C$
56. $A \cap B$	61. $(A \cup B)' \cap C$
57. A'	62. $A \cap B'$
58. $(A \cap B) \cup C$	63. $(B \cup C) \cap A'$
59. $A' \cap (B \cup C)$	64. $(A' \cup B)' \cup C'$

For Exercises 65–74, let

$U = \{a, b, c, d, e, f, g, h\}$
$P = \{b, d, f, g\}$
$Q = \{a, b, c, d\}$
$R = \{e, f, g\}$

Find each set.

65. $P \cap Q$	70. $P \cup (Q \cap R)$
66. $Q \cup R$	71. $(Q \cup P)' \cap R$
67. P'	72. $P \cap (Q \cap R)$
68. Q'	73. $(P \cup Q) \cap (P \cup R)$
69. $R' \cap P'$	74. $Q' \cup R'$

For Exercises 75–84, let

$U = \{1, 2, 3, 4, 5, 6, 7, 8, 9, 10, 11, 12\}$
$W = \{2, 4, 6, 8, 10, 12\}$
$X = \{1, 3, 5, 7, 9, 11\}$
$Y = \{1, 2, 3, 4, 5, 6\}$
$Z = \{2, 5, 6, 8, 10, 11, 12\}$

Find each set.

75. $W \cap Y$	80. $(Y \cup Z)'$
76. $X \cup Z$	81. $(X \cup Y) \cap Z$
77. $W \cup X$	82. $(Z \cap Y) \cup W$
78. $(X \cap Y) \cap Z$	83. $W' \cap X'$
79. $W \cap X$	84. $(Z \cup X)' \cap Y$

For Exercises 85–88, let

$U = \{1, 2, 3, \ldots\}$
$A = \{3, 6, 9, 12, \ldots\}$
$B = \{9, 18, 27, 36, \ldots\}$
$C = \{2, 4, 6, 8, \ldots\}$

Find each set.

85. $A \cap B$	87. $A \cap (B \cup C')$
86. $A' \cap C$	88. $A \cup B$

For Exercises 89–94, let

$U = \{20, 40, 60, 80, 100, 110\}$
$A = \{20, 60, 100, 110\}$
$B = \{60, 80, 100\}$
$C = \{80, 100, 110\}$

Find each set.

89. $A - B$	91. $B - C$	93. $C \cap B'$
90. $A - C$	92. $B - A$	94. $A \cap C'$

For Exercises 95–100, let

$U = \{p, q, r, s, t, u, v, w\}$
$A = \{p, q, r, s, t\}$
$B = \{r, s, t, u, v\}$
$C = \{p, r, t, v\}$

Find each set.

95. $C - B$	97. $B - C$	99. $B \cap C'$
96. $A - C$	98. $B - A$	100. $C \cap A'$

For Exercises 101–104, let

$A = \{9, 12, 18\}$
$B = \{1, 2, 3\}$

Find each set.

101. $A \times B$ 102. $B \times A$ 103. $A \times A$ 104. $B \times B$

For Exercises 105–108, let

$A = \{1, 2, 4, 8\}$
$B = \{1, 3\}$

Find each set.

105. $A \times B$ 106. $B \times A$ 107. $B \times B$ 108. $A \times A$

Real-World Applications

109. A student can have a cell phone, a laptop, and an iPod while hanging out on campus between classes. List all the sets of different communication options a student can select, considering all, some, or none of these technologies.

110. If a person is dealt five cards and has a chance of discarding any number including 0, how many choices will the person have?

111. A college freshman can choose one, some, or all of the following classes for her first semester: an English class, a math class, a foreign language class, a science class, a philosophy class, a physical education class, and a history class. How many different possibilities does she have for her new schedule?

112. Since the student union is being remodeled, there is a limited choice of foods and drinks a student can buy for a snack between classes. Students can choose none, some, or all of these items: pizza, fries, big soft pretzels, Coke, Diet Coke, and Hawaiian Punch. How many different selections can be made?

113. Suzie is buying a new laptop for school and can select none, some, or all of the following choices

of peripherals: a laser mouse, a DVD burner, a Web cam, or a jump drive. How many different selections of peripherals are possible for her laptop?

114. To integrate aerobics into her exercise program, Claire can select one, some, or all of these machines: treadmill, cycle, and stair stepper. List all possibilities for her aerobics selection.

Critical Thinking

115. Can you find two sets whose union and intersection are the same set?

116. Write a short paragraph listing five things you admire about your role model and five things you like about yourself. Find the union of the two sets. Find the intersection of the two sets.

117. Select two medications and find a resource on the Internet that lists the possible side effects of each. Find the intersection of the sets.

118. Select two possible careers you may pursue and write the job responsibilities you would have with each one. What responsibilities do the jobs have in common? If you could combine these careers somehow, what would your new job responsibilities be?

Section 2-3 Using Venn Diagrams to Study Set Operations

The world we live in is a pretty complicated place. Everywhere you look, there are interactions between sets of people, businesses, products, objects—we could go on, but you probably get the picture. The more complicated these interactions are, the more challenging it can be to sort them out. One good way to get a handle on a complicated situation is to diagram it. When we are dealing with sets, Venn diagrams will be our tool of choice.

In this section, we'll develop a method for drawing Venn diagrams that will help us to illustrate set operations. We'll start with diagrams involving interactions between two sets, as in Figure 2-8. Notice that there are four distinct regions in a Venn diagram illustrating two sets A and B. Let's label these regions with Roman numerals to designate that they represent regions and not elements in the sets.

The procedure that we will use to illustrate set statements, found in the box below, is demonstrated in Examples 1 and 2.

LEARNING OBJECTIVES

☐ 1. Illustrate set statements involving two sets with Venn diagrams.

☐ 2. Illustrate set statements involving three sets with Venn diagrams.

☐ 3. Use DeMorgan's laws.

☐ 4. Use Venn diagrams to decide if two sets are equal.

☐ 5. Use the formula for the cardinality of a union.

Illustrating a Set Statement with a Venn Diagram

Step 1 Draw a diagram for the sets, with Roman numerals in each region.

Step 2 Using the Roman numerals, list the regions for each set.

Step 3 Find the set of numerals that correspond to the set given in the set statement.

Step 4 Shade the area corresponding to the set of numerals found in step 3.

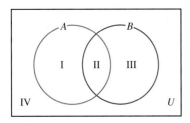

Region I represents the elements in set A that are not in set B.
Region II represents the elements in both sets A and B.
Region III represents the elements in set B that are not in set A.
Region IV represents the elements in the universal set that are in neither set A nor set B.

Figure 2-8

EXAMPLE 1   Drawing a Venn Diagram

Draw a Venn diagram to illustrate the set $(A \cup B)'$.

SOLUTION

Step 1 Draw the diagram and label each area.

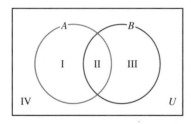

Step 2 From the diagram, list the regions that make up each set.

$U = \{\text{I, II, III, IV}\}$
$A = \{\text{I, II}\}$
$B = \{\text{II, III}\}$

Step 3 Using the sets in step 2, find $(A \cup B)'$.

First, all of I, II, and III are in either A or B, so $A \cup B = \{\text{I, II, II}\}$. The complement is $(A \cup B)' = \{\text{IV}\}$.

Step 4 Shade region IV to illustrate $(A \cup B)'$.

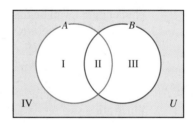

▼ Try This One 1

Draw a Venn diagram to illustrate the set $A' \cap B$.

EXAMPLE 2   Drawing a Venn Diagram

Draw a Venn diagram to illustrate the set $A \cap B'$.

SOLUTION

Step 1 Draw the diagram and label each area. This will be the same diagram as in Step 1 of Example 1.

Step 2 From the diagram, list the regions that make up each set.

$U = \{\text{I, II, III, IV}\}$
$A = \{\text{I, II}\}$
$B = \{\text{II, III}\}$

Step 3 Using the sets in step 2, find $A \cap B'$.

First, regions I and IV are outside of set B. Of these two regions, I is also in set A, so $A \cap B' = \{I\}$.

Step 4 Shade region I to illustrate $A \cap B'$.

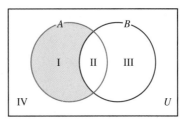

▼ Try This One 2

Draw a Venn diagram to illustrate the set $A' \cup B$.

☑ 1. Illustrate set statements involving two sets with Venn diagrams.

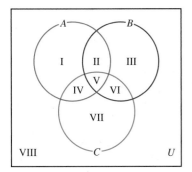

Figure 2-9

A similar procedure can be used to illustrate set statements involving three or more sets. The Venn diagram for three sets is shown in Figure 2-9.

Region I represents the elements in set A but not in set B or set C.
Region II represents the elements in set A and set B but not in set C.
Region III represents the elements in set B but not in set A or set C.
Region IV represents the elements in sets A and C but not in set B.
Region V represents the elements in sets A, B, and C.
Region VI represents the elements in sets B and C but not in set A.
Region VII represents the elements in set C but not in set A or set B.
Region VIII represents the elements in the universal set U, but not in set A, B, or C.

We can use the same four-step procedure (see page 65) to illustrate operations involving three sets. The process is demonstrated in Example 3.

EXAMPLE 3 Drawing a Venn Diagram with Three Sets

Draw a Venn diagram to illustrate the set $A \cap (B \cap C)'$.

SOLUTION

Step 1 Draw and label the diagram as in Figure 2-9.

Step 2 From the diagram, list the regions that make up each set.

$U = \{I, II, III, IV, V, VI, VII, VIII\}$
$A = \{I, II, IV, V\}$
$B = \{II, III, V, VI\}$
$C = \{IV, V, VI, VII\}$

Step 3 Using the sets in step 2, find $A \cap (B \cap C)'$.

First, find $B \cap C$: $B \cap C = \{V, VI\}$. The complement is $(B \cap C)' = \{I, II, III, IV, VII, VIII\}$. Regions I, II, and IV are also part of A, so $A \cap (B \cap C)' = \{I, II, IV\}$.

Step 4 Shade regions I, II, and IV to illustrate $A \cap (B \cap C)'$.

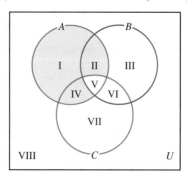

▼ Try This One 3

☑ 2. Illustrate set statements involving three sets with Venn diagrams.

Draw a Venn diagram to illustrate the set $(A \cap B') \cup C$.

De Morgan's Laws

There are two very well-known formulas that are useful in simplifying some set operations. They're named in honor of a 19th-century mathematician named Augustus De Morgan.

First, we'll write the formulas and illustrate each with an example. Then we'll see how Venn diagrams can be used to prove the formulas.

De Morgan's Laws

For any two sets A and B,

$(A \cup B)' = A' \cap B'$

$(A \cap B)' = A' \cup B'$

The first law states that the complement of the union of two sets will always be equal to the intersection of the complements of each set.

EXAMPLE 4   Using De Morgan's Laws

If $U = \{a, b, c, d, e, f, g, h\}$, $A = \{a, c, e, g\}$, and $B = \{b, c, d, e\}$, find $(A \cup B)'$ and $A' \cap B'$.

SOLUTION

$$A \cup B = \{a, b, c, d, e, g\} \qquad \text{and} \qquad (A \cup B)' = \{f, h\}$$

$$A' = \{b, d, f, h\} \qquad B' = \{a, f, g, h\} \qquad \text{and} \qquad A' \cap B' = \{f, h\}$$

Notice that $(A \cup B)'$ and $A' \cap B'$ are equal, illustrating the first of De Morgan's laws.

▼ Try This One 4

If $U = \{15, 30, 45, 60, 75, 90, 105\}$, $A = \{30, 60, 90\}$, and $B = \{15, 45, 75, 90\}$, find $(A \cup B)'$ and $A' \cap B'$.

Sidelight **NOW AND VENN**

Venn diagrams are generally credited to the British math- ematician John Venn, who introduced them in an 1880 paper as they are used today. That makes it sound like a pretty old concept, but the general idea can be traced back much further. The great mathematician Leonhard Euler used similar diagrams in the 1700s, and other figures like them can be traced as far back as the 1200s!

The second law states that the complement of the intersection of two sets will equal the union of the complements of the sets.

EXAMPLE 5   **Using De Morgan's Laws**

If $U = \{10, 11, 12, 13, 14, 15, 16\}$, $A = \{10, 11, 12, 13\}$, and $B = \{12, 13, 14, 15\}$, find $(A \cap B)'$ and $A' \cup B'$.

SOLUTION

$$A \cap B = \{12, 13\} \quad \text{and} \quad (A \cap B)' = \{10, 11, 14, 15, 16\}$$
$$A' = \{14, 15, 16\} \quad B' = \{10, 11, 16\}; \quad A' \cup B' = \{10, 11, 14, 15, 16\}$$

Notice that $(A \cap B)'$ and $A' \cup B'$ are equal, illustrating the second of De Morgan's laws.

☑ 3. Use De Morgan's laws.

▼ **Try This One 5**

If $U = \{$ABC, NBC, CBS, Fox, USA, TBS, TNT, MTV$\}$, $A = \{$NBC, Fox, USA, TBS$\}$, and $B = \{$ABC, NBC, CBS, Fox$\}$, find $(A \cap B)'$ and $A' \cup B'$.

Venn diagrams can be used to show the equality of two set statements. To do this, we draw a Venn diagram for the set statement on each side of the equation. If the same regions are shaded, then the equation is true. The next example shows how to verify the first of De Morgan's laws by using Venn diagrams. We'll leave the second for you to try.

EXAMPLE 6   **Using a Venn Diagram to Show Equality of Sets**

Use Venn diagrams to show that $(A \cup B)' = A' \cap B'$.

SOLUTION

Start by drawing the Venn diagram for $(A \cup B)'$.

Step 1 Draw the figure (as shown in Step 4).

Step 2 Set U contains regions I, II, III, and IV. Set A contains regions I and II, and B contains regions II and III.

Step 3 $A \cup B = \{$I, II, II$\}$, so $(A \cup B)' = \{$IV$\}$.

Step 4 Shade region IV to illustrate $(A \cup B)'$.

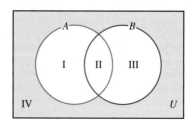

Next draw the Venn diagram for $A' \cap B'$. Steps 1 and 2 are the same as above.

Step 3 $A' = \{III, IV\}$ and $B' = \{I, IV\}$, so $A' \cap B' = \{IV\}$.

Step 4 Shade region IV to illustrate $A' \cap B'$.

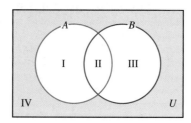

Since the diagrams for each side are identical, we use deductive reasoning to conclude that $(A \cup B)' = A' \cap B'$.

▼ Try This One 6

Use Venn diagrams to show that $(A \cap B)' = A' \cup B'$.

Here's an example using three sets.

EXAMPLE 7   Using Venn Diagrams to Decide If Two Sets Are Equal

Determine if the two sets are equal by using Venn diagrams: $(A \cup B) \cap C$ and $(A \cap C) \cup (B \cap C)$.

SOLUTION

The set $A \cup B$ consists of regions I through VI. Of these, IV, V, and VI are also in C, so $(A \cup B) \cap C$ consists of regions IV, V, and VI.

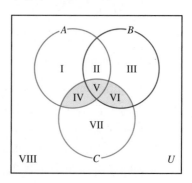

The set $A \cap C$ consists of regions IV and V, and the set $B \cap C$ consists of regions V and VI. Their union is regions IV, V, and VI.

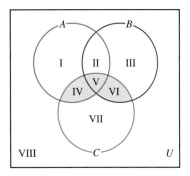

Since the shaded areas are the same, the two sets are equal.

☑ 4. Use Venn diagrams to decide if two sets are equal.

▼ Try This One 7

Determine if the two sets are equal by using Venn diagrams: $B \cup (A \cap C)$ and $(A \cup B) \cap (B \cup C)$.

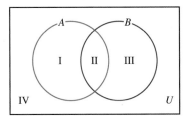

Figure 2-10

The Cardinal Number of a Union

For two sets A and B, how many elements would you guess are in $A \cup B$? Many students guess the number of elements in A plus the number of elements in B, and those students are incorrect when they do. This is an area that Venn diagrams can help us with.

As we can see in Figure 2-10, if we start with the number of elements in A, we're counting all the members in regions I and II. When we add the number of elements in B, we're counting all the members in regions II and III. Do you see the issue? The elements in region II get counted twice. We can fix that by subtracting the number of elements in region II. Since region II represents $A \cap B$, we get the following useful formula:

Math Note

In words, the formula to the right says that to find the number of elements in the union of A and B, you add the number of elements in A and B and then subtract the number of elements in the intersection of A and B.

The Cardinality of a Union

If $n(A)$ represents the cardinal number of set A, then for any two finite sets A and B, $n(A \cup B) = n(A) + n(B) - n(A \cap B)$.

Next, we'll see how this formula can be used in an applied situation.

EXAMPLE 8   Using the Formula for Cardinality of a Union

In a survey of 100 randomly selected freshmen walking across campus, it turns out that 42 are taking a math class, 51 are taking an English class, and 12 are taking both. How many students are taking either a math class or an English class?

SOLUTION

If we call the set of students taking a math class A and the set of students taking an English class B, we're asked to find $n(A \cup B)$. We're told that $n(A) = 42$, $n(B) = 51$, and $n(A \cap B) = 12$. So

$$n(A \cup B) = n(A) + n(B) - n(A \cap B) = 42 + 51 - 12 = 81$$

5. Use the formula for the cardinality of a union.

▼ Try This One 8

A telephone poll of 200 registered Democrats during the 2008 primary season found that 94 supported Barack Obama, 85 supported Hillary Clinton, and 20 supported both. How many supported either Obama or Clinton?

In this section, we saw how Venn diagrams can be used to illustrate sets, prove equality of two sets, and solve problems. We'll explore the problem-solving aspect of Venn diagrams further in Section 2-4.

Answers to Try This One

1
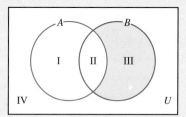

2
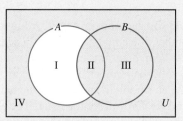

3
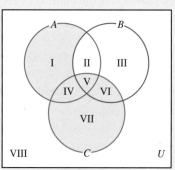

4   Both are {105}.

5   Both are {ABC, CBS, USA, TBS, TNT, MTV}.

6   Both diagrams are
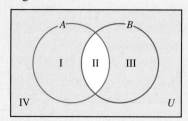

7   Both diagrams are
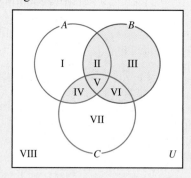

8   159

EXERCISE SET 2-3

Writing Exercises

1. Explain in your own words how to draw a Venn diagram representing the set $A \cup B$.
2. Explain in your own words how to draw a Venn diagram representing the set $A \cap B$.
3. Describe in your own words what De Morgan's laws say.
4. Describe in your own words how to find the cardinal number of the union of two sets.

Computational Exercises

For Exercises 5–28, draw a Venn diagram and shade the sections representing each set.

5. $A \cup B'$
6. $(A \cup B)'$
7. $A' \cup B'$
8. $A' \cup B$
9. $A' \cap B'$
10. $A \cap B'$
11. $A \cup (B \cap C)$
12. $A \cap (B \cup C)$
13. $(A \cup B) \cup (A \cap C)$
14. $(A \cup B) \cap C$
15. $(A \cup B) \cap (A \cup C)$
16. $(A \cap B) \cup C$
17. $(A \cap B)' \cup C$
18. $(A \cup B) \cup C'$
19. $A \cap (B \cup C)'$
20. $A' \cap (B' \cup C')$
21. $(A' \cup B') \cap C$
22. $A \cap (B \cap C)'$
23. $(A \cup B)' \cap (A \cup C)$
24. $(B \cup C) \cup C'$
25. $A' \cap (B' \cap C')$
26. $(A \cup B)' \cap C'$
27. $A' \cap (B \cup C)'$
28. $(A \cup B) \cap (A \cap C)$

For Exercises 29–36, determine whether the two sets are equal by using Venn diagrams.

29. $(A \cap B)'$ and $A' \cup B'$
30. $(A \cup B)'$ and $A' \cup B'$
31. $(A \cup B) \cup C$ and $A \cup (B \cup C)$
32. $A \cap (B \cup C)$ and $(A \cap B) \cup (A \cap C)$
33. $A' \cup (B \cap C')$ and $(A' \cup B) \cap C'$
34. $(A \cap B) \cup C'$ and $(A \cap B) \cup (B \cap C')$
35. $(A \cap B)' \cup C$ and $(A' \cup B') \cap C$
36. $(A' \cup B') \cup C$ and $(A \cap B)' \cap C'$

For Exercises 37–46, use the following Venn diagram to find the cardinality of each set.

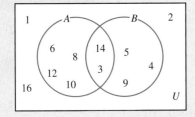

37. $n(A)$
38. $n(B)$
39. $n(A \cap B)$
40. $n(A \cup B)$
41. $n(A')$
42. $n(B')$

43. $n(A' \cap B')$
44. $n(A' \cup B')$
45. $n(A - B)$
46. $n(B - A)$

For Exercises 47–56, use the following information. Note that A and B are subsets of the universal set U.

$$U = \{x \mid x \text{ is a natural number} < 13\}$$
$$A = \{x \mid x \text{ is an odd natural number}\}$$
$$B = \{x \mid x \text{ is a prime number}\}$$

(*Hint:* The prime numbers less than 13 are 2, 3, 5, 7, and 11.) *Find each.*

47. $n(A)$
48. $n(B)$
49. $n(A \cap B)$
50. $n(A \cup B)$
51. $n(A \cap B')$
52. $n(A' \cup B)$
53. $n(A')$
54. $n(B')$
55. $n(A - B)$
56. $n(B' - A)$

In Exercises 57–60, A = {people who drive an SUV} and B = {people who drive a hybrid vehicle}. Draw a Venn diagram of the following, and write a sentence describing what the set represents.

57. $A \cup B$ 59. A'
58. $A \cap B$ 60. $(A \cap B)'$

In Exercises 61–64, O = {students in online courses}, B = {students in blended courses}, and T = {students in traditional courses}. Draw a Venn diagram of the following, and write a sentence describing what the set represents.

61. $O \cap (T \cup B)$
62. $B \cup (O \cap T)$
63. $B \cap O \cap T$
64. $(B \cup O) \cap (T \cup O)$

In Exercises 65–68, D = {students voting Democrat}, R = {students voting Republican}, and I = {students voting Independent}. Draw a Venn diagram of the following, and write a sentence describing what the set represents.

65. $D' \cup R$ 67. $(D \cup R) \cap I'$
66. $D' \cap I'$ 68. $I - (D \cup R)$

In Exercises 69–72, G = {people who regularly use Google}, Y = {people who regularly use Yahoo!}, and M = {people who regularly use MSN Live}. Draw a Venn diagram of the following, and write a sentence describing what the set represents.

69. $G - Y$
70. $G - (Y \cap M)$
71. $G' \cap Y' \cap M'$
72. $(Y \cap M) \cup (Y \cap G)$

The table and Venn diagram below are to be used for Exercises 73–78. The table shows the four baseball teams that made the playoffs in the American League from 2005 to 2007. For each exercise, write the region(s) of the Venn diagram that would include the team listed.

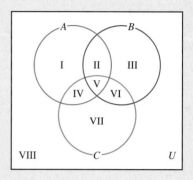

Year	2005	2006	2007
Teams	Boston Red Sox	Detroit Tigers	Boston Red Sox
	Chicago White Sox	Minnesota Twins	Cleveland Indians
	Los Angeles Angels	New York Yankees	Los Angeles Angels
	New York Yankees	Oakland A's	New York Yankees

Note: set A represents 2005 playoff teams, set B represents 2006 playoff teams, and set C represents 2007 playoff teams.

73. Boston Red Sox
74. Los Angeles Angels
75. Cleveland Indians

76. Minnesota Twins
77. New York Yankees
78. Oakland A's

Critical Thinking

79. For two finite sets A and B, is $n(A - B)$ equal to $n(A) - n(B)$? If not, can you find a formula for $n(A - B)$?

80. Can you find a formula for $n(A \cap B)$ in terms of only $n(A)$ and $n(B)$? Why or why not? See if you can find a formula for $n(A \cap B)$ using any sets you like.

81. Make a conjecture about another form for the set $(A \cup B \cup C)'$ based on the first of De Morgan's laws. Check out your conjecture by using a Venn diagram.

82. Make a conjecture about another form for the set $(A \cap B \cap C)'$ based on the second of De Morgan's laws. Check out your conjecture by using a Venn diagram.

Section 2-4 Using Sets to Solve Problems

LEARNING OBJECTIVE

☐ 1. Solve problems by using Venn diagrams.

We live in the information age—every time you turn around, somebody somewhere is trying to gather information about you, your opinions, and (most commonly) your spending habits. Surveys are conducted by the thousands every day, and every person, pet, pastime, and product are classified. Some of the things we've learned about sets can be very helpful in interpreting information from surveys and classifications, and that will be the focus of this section.

When things are classified into two distinct sets, we can use a two-set Venn diagram to interpret the information. This is illustrated in Example 1.

EXAMPLE 1   Solving a Problem by Using a Venn Diagram

In 2008, there were 36 states that had some form of casino gambling in the state, 42 states that sold lottery tickets of some kind, and 34 states that had both casinos and lotteries. Draw a Venn diagram to represent the survey results, and find how many states have only casino gambling, how many states have only lotteries, and how many states have neither.

SOLUTION

Step 1 Draw a Venn diagram with circles for casino gambling and lotteries, labeling the regions as usual.

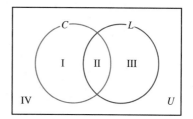

Step 2 Thirty-four states have both, so put 34 in the intersection of C and L, which is region II.

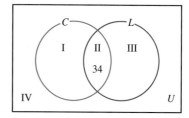

Step 3 Since 36 states have casino gambling and 34 have both, there must be 2 that have only casino gambling. Put 2 in region I. Since 42 states have lotteries and 34 have both, there are 8 that have only lotteries. Put 8 in region III.

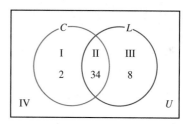

Step 4 Now 44 states are accounted for, so there must be 6 left to put in region IV.

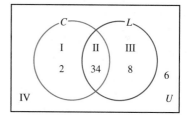

Now we can answer the questions easily. There are only two states that have casino gambling but no lottery (Nevada and Wyoming, in case you're wondering). There are eight states that have lotteries but no casino gambling (region III), and just six states that have neither (region IV).

▼ Try This One 1

In an average year, Columbus, Ohio, has 163 days with some rain, 63 days with some snow, and 24 days with both. Draw a Venn diagram to represent these averages, and find how many days have only rain, only snow, and neither.

We can use the results of Example 1 to write a general procedure for using a Venn diagram to interpret information that can be divided into two sets.

Using Venn Diagrams with Two Sets

Step 1   Find the number of elements that are common to both sets and write that number in region II.

Step 2   Find the number of elements that are in set *A* and not set *B* by subtracting the number in region II from the total number of elements in *A*. Then write that number in region I. Repeat for the elements in *B* but not in region II, and write in region III.

Step 3   Find the number of elements in *U* that are not in either *A* or *B*, and write it in region IV.

Step 4   Use the diagram to answer specific questions about the situation.

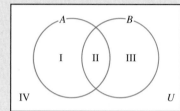

Many news websites include daily surveys, like this one from cnn.com.

One of the most useful applications of Venn diagrams is for studying the results of surveys. Whether they are for business-related research or just to satisfy curiosity, surveys seem to be everywhere these days, especially online. Example 2 analyzes the results of a survey on tattoos and body piercings.

EXAMPLE 2   Solving a Problem by Using a Venn Diagram

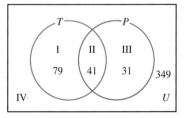

In a survey published in the *Journal of the American Academy of Dermatologists*, 500 people were polled by random telephone dialing. Of these, 120 reported having a tattoo, 72 reported having a body piercing, and 41 had both. Draw a Venn diagram to represent these results, and find out how many respondents have only tattoos, only body piercings, and neither.

SOLUTION

In this example, we'll insert just one diagram at the end, and we will refer to it as we go.

Step 1   Place the number of respondents with both tattoos and body piercings (41) in region II.

Step 2   There are 120 people with tattoos and 41 with both, so there are $120 - 41$, or 79, people with only tattoos. This goes in region I. By the same logic, there are $72 - 41$, or 31, people with only piercings. This goes in region III.

Step 3   We now have $41 + 79 + 31 = 151$ of the 500 people accounted for, so $500 - 151 = 349$ goes in region IV.

Step 4   There are 79 people with only tattoos, 31 with only piercings, and 349 with neither.

▼ Try This One 2

According to an online survey on Howstuffworks.com, 12,595 people gave their thoughts on Coke versus Pepsi. Of these, 7,642 drink Coke, 5,619 drink Pepsi, and 1,856 drink both. Draw a Venn diagram to represent these results, and find out how many respondents drink only Coke, only Pepsi, and neither.

Sidelight **HOW MUCH IS YOUR OPINION WORTH?**

Sidelight **HOW MUCH IS YOUR OPINION WORTH?**

Communication in our society is becoming cheaper, easier, and more effective all the time. In the age of cell phones and Internet communication, businesses are finding it simpler than ever to contact people for their opinions, and more and more people are finding out that companies are willing to pay to hear what they have to say. There are literally hundreds of companies in the United States today whose main function is to gather opinions on everything from political candidates to potato chips. In fact, over $6 *billion* is spent on market research in the United States each year. Maybe you'll think twice the next time somebody asks you for your opinion for free.

When a classification problem or a survey consists of three sets, a similar procedure is followed, using a Venn diagram with three sets. We just have more work to do since there are now eight regions instead of four.

EXAMPLE 3   **Solving a Problem by Using a Venn Diagram**

A survey of 300 first-year students at a large midwestern university was conducted to aid in scheduling for the following year. Responses indicated that 194 were taking a math class, 210 were taking an English class, and 170 were taking a speech course. In addition, 142 were taking both math and English, 111 were taking both English and speech, 91 were taking both math and speech, and 45 were taking all three. Draw a Venn diagram to represent these survey results, and find the number of students taking

(a) Only English.
(b) Math and speech but not English.
(c) Math or English.
(d) None of these three subjects.

SOLUTION

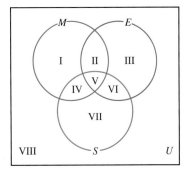

Step 1 The only region we know for sure from the given information is region V—the number of students taking all three classes. So we begin by putting 45 in region V.

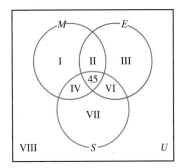

Step 2 There are 142 students taking both math and English, but we must subtract the number in all three classes to find the number in region II: $142 - 45 = 97$. In the same way, we get $91 - 45 = 46$ in region IV (both math and speech) and $111 - 45 = 66$ in region VI (both English and speech).

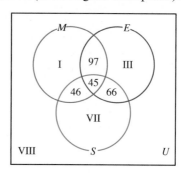

Step 3 Now we can find the number of elements in regions I, III, and VII. There are 194 students in math classes, but $97 + 45 + 46 = 188$ are already accounted for in the diagram, so that leaves 6 in region I. Of the 210 students in English classes, $97 + 45 + 66 = 208$ are already accounted for, leaving just 2 in region III. There are 170 students in speech classes, with $46 + 45 + 66 = 157$ already accounted for. This leaves 13 in region VII.

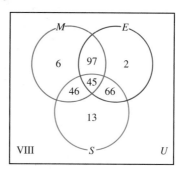

Step 4 Adding up all the numbers in the diagram so far, we get 275. That leaves 25 in region VIII.

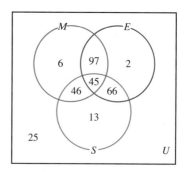

Step 5 Now that we have the diagram completed, we turn our attention to the questions.

(a) Students taking only English are represented by region III—there are only 2.
(b) Math and speech but not English is region IV, so there are 46 students.
(c) Students taking math or English are represented by all but regions VII and VIII. So there are only 38 students not taking either math or English, and $300 - 38 = 262$ who are.
(d) There are 25 students outside of the regions for all of math, English, and speech.

Math Note

Notice that in filling in the Venn diagram in Example 3, we started with the number of elements in the innermost region and worked our way outward.

▼ **Try This One 3**

An online music service surveyed 500 customers and found that 270 listen to hip-hop music, 320 listen to rock, and 160 listen to country. In addition, 140 listen to both rock and hip-hop, 120 listen to rock and country, and 80 listen to hip-hop and country. Finally, 50 listen to all three. Draw a Venn diagram to represent the results of the survey and find the number of customers who

(a) Listen to only hip-hop.
(b) Listen to rock and country but not hip-hop.
(c) Don't listen to any of these three types of music.
(d) Don't listen to country music.

1. Solve problems by using Venn diagrams.

We can use the results of Example 3 to write a general procedure for using a Venn diagram to interpret information that can be divided into three sets.

Using Venn Diagrams with Three Sets

Step 1   Put the number of elements common to all three sets in region V.

Step 2   Find the number of elements in $A \cap B$, $A \cap C$, and $B \cap C$. Subtract the number of elements in all three, and place these numbers in regions II, IV, and VI.

Step 3   Subtract the number of elements you now have inside each large set from the total number you were given for each set: these will be the numbers you put in regions I, III, and VII.

Step 4   Add all the numbers inside the circles and subtract that from the total number of elements in U to get the number in region VIII.

Step 5   Use the completed diagram to answer specific questions.

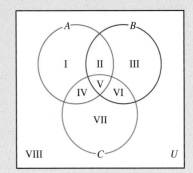

We've come a pretty long way from simply defining what sets and elements are! In this section, we've seen that Venn diagrams can be effectively used to sort out some pretty complicated real-world situations. And the better you are at interpreting information, the better equipped you'll be to survive and thrive in the information age.

Answers to Try This One

1   Only rain: 139; only snow: 39; neither: 163 (assuming it's not leap year!)

2   Only Coke: 5,786; only Pepsi: 3,763; neither: 1,190

3   (a) 100   (b) 70
        (c) 40   (d) 340

EXERCISE SET 2-4

Real-World Applications

1. In a survey of 40 students, 20 use myspace.com, 25 use facebook.com, and 7 use both myspace.com and facebook.com.

   (a) How many use myspace.com only?
   (b) How many use facebook.com only?
   (c) How many use neither myspace.com nor facebook.com?

2. In a class of 25 students, 18 were mathematics majors, 12 were computer science majors, and 7 were dual majors in mathematics and computer science.

   (a) How many students were majoring in mathematics only?
   (b) How many students were not majoring in computer science?
   (c) How many students were not mathematics or computer science majors?

3. There were 16 recycling bins in the student union. Eight of them contained only paper, five contained only plastic, and three contained paper and plastic.

   (a) How many contained only paper?
   (b) How many contained only plastic?
   (c) How many contained neither paper nor plastic?

4. In the cafeteria, 25 students were seated at tables. Fifteen were enrolled in psychology, nine were enrolled in physics, and four were enrolled in both psychology and physics.

   (a) How many students were enrolled in psychology only?
   (b) How many students were not enrolled in physics?
   (c) How many students were enrolled in at least one of these courses?

5. The financial aid department at a college surveyed 70 students, asking if they receive any type of financial aid. The results of the survey are summarized in the table below.

Financial Aid	Number of Students
Scholarships	16
Student loans	24
Private grants	20
Scholarships and loans	9
Loans and grants	11
Scholarships and grants	7
Scholarships, loans, and grants	2

   (a) How many students got only scholarships?
   (b) How many got loans and private grants but not scholarships?
   (c) How many didn't get any of these types of financial aid?

6. The manager of a campus gym is planning the schedule of fitness classes for a new school year, and will decide how often to hold certain classes based on the interests of students. She polls 47 students at various times of day, asking what type of classes they'd be interested in attending. The results are summarized in the table below.

Type of Class	Students Interested
Yoga	17
Pilates	13
Spinning	12
Yoga and pilates	9
Pilates and spinning	3
Yoga and spinning	5
All three	2

   (a) How many students are interested in yoga or spinning, but not pilates?
   (b) How many are interested in exactly two of the three classes?
   (c) How many are interested in yoga but not pilates?

7. One semester in a chemistry class, 14 students failed due to poor attendance, 23 failed due to not studying, 15 failed because they did not turn in assignments, 9 failed because of poor attendance and not studying, 8 failed because of not studying and not turning in assignments, 5 failed because of poor attendance and not turning in assignments, and 2 failed because of all three of these reasons.

   (a) How many failed for exactly two of the three reasons?
   (b) How many failed because of poor attendance and not studying but not because of not turning in assignments?
   (c) How many failed because of exactly one of the three reasons?
   (d) How many failed because of poor attendance and not turning in assignments but not because of not studying?

8. Last Super Bowl weekend, there were 109 pizzas ordered for the sophomore dorm. That weekend

32 customers ordered their pizza with just pepperoni, 40 ordered their pizza with just sausage, 18 ordered theirs with just onions, 13 ordered theirs with pepperoni and sausage, 10 ordered theirs with sausage and onions, 9 ordered theirs with pepperoni and onions, and 7 ordered theirs with all three items.

(a) How many customers ordered their pizza with pepperoni or sausage (or both)?

(b) How many customers ordered their pizza with sausage or onions (or both)?

(c) How many customers ordered a pizza without pepperoni, sausage, or onions?

9. There were 70 students in line at the campus bookstore to sell back their textbooks after finals: 19 had history books to return, 21 had business books to return, and 19 had math books to return. Nine were selling back both history and business books, eight were selling back both business and math books, five were selling back history and math books, and three were selling back history, business, and math books.

(a) How many students were selling back at most two of these three types of books?

(b) How many students were selling back history and math books but not business books?

(c) How many were selling back neither history nor math books?

10. A survey of 96 students on campus showed that 29 read the *Campus Observer* student newspaper that morning, 24 read the news via the Internet that morning, and 20 read the local city paper that morning. Eight read the *Campus Observer* and the Internet news that morning, while four read the Internet news and the local paper, seven read the *Campus Observer* and the local city paper, and one person read the *Campus Observer,* the Internet news, and the local paper.

(a) How many read the Internet news or local paper but not both?

(b) How many read the Internet news and the local paper but not the *Campus Observer?*

(c) How many read the Internet news or the *Campus Observer* or both?

11. Sixty-one students in an art class were surveyed about their musical tastes. Of those asked, 20 liked alternative, 26 liked hip-hop, 20 liked techno, 9 liked alternative and hip-hop, 15 liked hip-hop and techno, 6 liked alternative and techno, and 3 liked all three types of music.

(a) How many liked none of these three types?

(b) How many liked exactly three of these types?

(c) How many liked exactly one of these types?

12. In a survey of 200 college students, 128 watched at least one reality show on television each week, 131 watched at least one video on MTV each week, 114 watched a national news show on CNN each week, 75 watched a reality show and a video, 59 watched a video and a news show, 81 watched a reality show and a news show, and 33 watched a reality show, a video, and a news show each week.

(a) How many watched exactly two of these?

(b) How many watched only one of these?

(c) How many did not watch a reality show?

13. In a survey of 121 students, 39 belonged to a club on campus, 51 regularly attended a campus sporting event, and 26 belonged to a professional organization. Furthermore, 25 regularly attended campus sporting events and belonged to a campus club, 14 belonged to a professional organization and attended campus sporting events, 18 belonged to a professional organization and a campus club, and 10 were involved in all three.

(a) How many students did exactly one of these?

(b) How many students regularly attended a sporting event, but did not belong to a professional organization?

(c) How many students did not regularly attend a campus sporting event or belong to a professional organization?

14. Out of 20 students taking a midterm exam, 15 answered the first of two bonus questions, 13 answered the second bonus question, and 2 answered neither bonus question. How many students answered both bonus questions?

15. In a group of 34 people waiting in line at the local java house, 18 wanted to order a cappuccino, 20 wanted to order a latte, and 2 wanted to order neither of these drinks. How many wanted to order both a cappuccino and a latte?

16. An entertainment magazine conducted an online poll of 230 college students who watch late-night TV, asking what shows they watch regularly. There were 119 who watch David Letterman, 101 who watch Conan O'Brien, and 75 who watch Jimmy Fallon. In addition, 69 watch Letterman and O'Brien, 48 watch Letterman and Fallon, 38 watch Fallon and O'Brien, and 28 watch all three.

(a) How many don't watch any of these three shows?

(b) How many watch only one of the three shows?

(c) How many watch exactly two of the three shows?

Critical Thinking

17. A researcher was hired to examine the drinking habits of energy drink consumers. Explain why he was fired when he published the results below, from a survey of 40 such consumers:

    23 said they drink Red Bull.
    18 said they drink Monster.
    19 said they drink G2.
    12 said they drink Red Bull and Monster.
    6 said they drink Monster and G2.
    7 said they drink Red Bull and G2.
    2 said they drink all three (not at the same time, hopefully).
    2 said they don't drink any of the three brands.

18. The marketing research firm of OUWant12 designed and sent three spam advertisements to 40 e-mail accounts. The first one was an ad for hair removal cream, the second was an ad for Botox treatments, and the third was an ad for a new all lima bean diet. Explain why, when the following results occurred, the sponsors discontinued their services.

    23 recipients deleted the ad for hair removal cream without looking at it.
    18 recipients deleted the ad for Botox treatments.
    19 recipients deleted the ad for the all lima bean diet.
    12 recipients deleted the ads for hair removal cream and Botox treatments.
    6 recipients deleted the ads for Botox treatments and the all lima bean diet.
    7 recipients deleted the ads for the hair removal cream and the all lima bean diet.
    2 recipients deleted all three ads.

Section 2-5 Infinite Sets

LEARNING OBJECTIVES

❏ 1. Formally define infinite sets.

❏ 2. Show that a set is infinite.

❏ 3. Find a general term of an infinite set.

❏ 4. Define countable and uncountable sets.

The night sky may look infinite, but have you ever thought about what that really means?

Infinity is a concept that's tremendously difficult for us human beings to wrap our minds around. Because our thoughts are shaped by experiences in a physical world with finite dimensions, things that are infinitely large always seem just out of our grasp. Whether you're a believer in the Big Bang theory or creationism, you probably think that one or the other must be true because the alternative is too far beyond our experience: that time didn't have a beginning at all, but extends infinitely far in each direction. Some philosophers feel that human beings are fundamentally incapable of grasping the concept of something infinitely large at all!

The study of infinity and infinite sets from a mathematical standpoint is a relatively young one compared to the history of math in general. For at least a couple of thousand years, the nature of infinity so confounded the greatest human minds that they chose to not deal with it at all. And yet in working with a set as simple as the natural numbers, we deal with infinite sets in math all the time. It's an interesting paradox.

A Definition of Infinite Sets

Recall from Section 2-1 that a set is considered to be finite if the number of elements is either zero or a natural number. Otherwise, it is considered to be an infinite set. For example, the set $\{10, 20, 30, 40\}$ is finite because the number of elements (four) is a natural number. But the set $\{10, 20, 30, 40, \ldots\}$ is infinite because the number of elements is unlimited, and therefore not a natural number.

You might recognize an infinite set when you see one, but it's not necessarily easy to make a precise definition of what it means for a set to be infinite (other than the obvious definition, "not finite"). The German mathematician Georg Cantor, widely regarded as the father of set theory, is famous for his 19th-century study of infinite sets. (Sadly his work was not highly regarded in his lifetime, and he died in a mental institution.) Cantor's simple and elegant definition of an infinite set is as follows:

A set is **infinite** if it can be placed into a one-to-one correspondence with a proper subset of itself.

☑ 1. Formally define infinite sets.

First, notice that a finite set definitely does not meet the condition in this definition: if a set has some finite number of elements, let's say 10, then any proper subset has at most 9 elements, and an attempt at one-to-one correspondence will always leave out at least one member.

The trickier thing is to understand how an infinite set can meet this definition. We'll illustrate with an infinite set we know well, the set of natural numbers $\{1, 2, 3, 4, \ldots\}$. The set of even natural numbers $\{2, 4, 6, 8, \ldots\}$ is of course a proper subset: every even number is also a natural number, but there are natural numbers that are not even numbers. Now we demonstrate the clever way to put these two sets in one-to-one correspondence: match each natural number with its double.

$$1 \leftrightarrow 2, \quad 2 \leftrightarrow 4, \quad 3 \leftrightarrow 6, \quad 4 \leftrightarrow 8, \ldots$$

In general, we can define our correspondence as matching any n from the set of natural numbers with a corresponding even number $2n$. This is a one-to-one correspondence because every natural number has a match (its double), and every even number has a match (its half). So we've put the natural numbers into one-to-one correspondence with a proper subset, and they are an infinite set.

Let's try another example.

EXAMPLE 1　　Showing That a Set Is Infinite

Show that the set $\{5, 10, 15, 20, 25, \ldots\}$ is an infinite set.

SOLUTION

A simple way to put this set in correspondence with a proper subset of itself is to match every element n with its double $2n$:

$$\{5, \ 10, \ 15, \ 20, \ 25, \ldots\}$$
$$\updownarrow \ \updownarrow \ \updownarrow \ \updownarrow \ \updownarrow$$
$$\{10, 20, 30, 40, 50, \ldots\}$$

The second set, $\{10, 20, 30, 40, 50, \ldots\}$ is a proper subset of the first, and the two are in one-to-one correspondence, so $\{5, 10, 15, 20, 25, \ldots\}$ is an infinite set.

▼ Try This One 1

☑ 2. Show that a set is infinite.

Show that the set $\{-1, -2, -3, -4, -5, \ldots\}$ is an infinite set.

A General Term of an Infinite Set

One consequence of the way we showed that the set of natural numbers is infinite is that we can find a generic formula for the set of even numbers: $2n$, where n is the set $\{1, 2, 3, 4, \ldots\}$. We will call $2n$ in this case a **general term** of the set of even numbers. Notice that we said "a general term," not "the general term." There are other general terms we could write for this set: $2n - 6$, where n is the set $\{4, 5, 6, 7, \ldots\}$, is another possibility. But in most cases the simplest general term is the one where the first listed number is obtained from substituting in 1 for n, and that's the one we'll typically find.

Sidelight THE INFINITE HOTEL

Suppose a hotel in some far-off galaxy was so immense that it actually had infinitely many rooms, numbered 1, 2, 3, 4, ... There's a big convention of creepy alien creatures in town, so every room is filled. A weary traveler drags into the lobby and asks for a room, and when he's informed that the hotel is full, he protests that the hotel can most definitely accommodate him. Do you agree? Can they find a room for him without kicking someone out?

People tend to be split on this question about half and half: half think they can't accommodate him because all the rooms are full, and half think they can because there are infinitely many rooms. In fact, the traveler is correct—it just takes inconveniencing every other guest! If the manager asks every guest to move into the room whose number is 1 higher than his or her current room, everyone that was originally in a room still has one, and our traveler can rest his weary body in room 1.

This clever little mind exercise is a consequence of the fact that the natural numbers form an infinite set—they can be put in one-to-one correspondence with a proper subset of themselves by corresponding any n with $n + 1$.

EXAMPLE 2   Finding a General Term for an Infinite Set

Find a general term for the set $\{4, 7, 10, 13, 16, \ldots\}$.

SOLUTION

We should always begin by trying to recognize a pattern in the numbers of the set. In this case, the pattern is that the numbers increase by 3. When this is the case, $3n$ is a good choice, because as n increases by 1, $3n$ increases by 3. But simply using $3n$ will give us the set $\{3, 6, 9, 12, \ldots\}$, which is not quite what we want. We remedy that by adding 1 to our general term, to get $3n + 1$. (We encourage you to check that answer by substituting in $1, 2, 3, \ldots$ for n to see that it generates the set $\{4, 7, 10, 13, 16, \ldots\}$.)

> ### *Math Note*
>
> Finding a general term for a set is not always easy. In some cases, it can be very difficult or even impossible. You may need to do some trial and error before finding a formula that works.

☑ 3. Find a general term of an infinite set.

▼ Try This One 2

Find a general term for the set $\{2, 8, 14, 20, 26, \ldots\}$.

Different Kinds of Infinity?

Quick, which set is bigger, the set of natural numbers or the set of real numbers? You probably answered the set of real numbers. But both sets are infinitely large, so aren't they the same size? Cantor attacked this problem in the late 1800s. He defined a set to be **countable** if it is finite or can be placed into one-to-one correspondence with the natural numbers and an infinite set to be **uncountable** if it cannot. He used the symbol $\aleph_0$, pronounced aleph-null or aleph-naught (aleph is the first letter of the Hebrew alphabet), to represent the cardinality of a countable set.

☑ 4. Define countable and uncountable sets.

One of Cantor's greatest achievements was to show that the set of real numbers is not countable. So in this case, your intuition was correct: there *are* more real numbers than natural numbers. But the study of infinite sets is a strange and interesting one, with unexpected results at nearly every turn. For example, it can be shown that the cardinality of the set of numbers between 0 and 1 is the same as the cardinality of the entire set of real numbers! If you're interested in learning about a *really* unusual infinite set, do an Internet search for "Cantor set."

Answers to Try This One

1 Can be done in many ways: one choice is to correspond -1 with -2, -2 with -4, and in general $-n$ with $-2n$.

2 $6n - 4$

EXERCISE SET 2-5

Writing Exercises

1. Define an infinite set, both in your own words and by using Cantor's definition.
2. What is meant by a general term for an infinite set?
3. What does it mean for a set to be countable?
4. Explain how you can tell that the set of natural numbers and the set of even numbers have the same cardinality.

Computational Exercises

For Exercises 5–20, find a general term for the set.

5. $\{7, 14, 21, 28, 35, \ldots\}$
6. $\{1, 8, 27, 64, 125, \ldots\}$
7. $\{4, 16, 64, 256, 1{,}024, \ldots\}$
8. $\{1, 4, 9, 16, 25, \ldots\}$
9. $\{-3, -6, -9, -12, -15, \ldots\}$
10. $\{22, 44, 66, 88, 110, \ldots\}$
11. $\left\{\frac{1}{2}, \frac{1}{3}, \frac{1}{4}, \frac{1}{5}, \frac{1}{6}, \ldots\right\}$
12. $\left\{\frac{1}{3}, \frac{2}{3}, \frac{3}{3}, \frac{4}{3}, \frac{5}{3}, \ldots\right\}$
13. $\{2, 6, 10, 14, 18, \ldots\}$
14. $\{1, 4, 7, 10, 13, \ldots\}$
15. $\left\{\frac{2}{3}, \frac{3}{4}, \frac{4}{5}, \frac{5}{6}, \frac{6}{7}, \ldots\right\}$
16. $\left\{\frac{1}{1}, \frac{1}{4}, \frac{1}{9}, \frac{1}{16}, \frac{1}{25}, \ldots\right\}$
17. $\{100, 200, 300, 400, 500, \ldots\}$
18. $\{50, 100, 150, 200, 250, \ldots\}$
19. $\{-4, -7, -10, -13, -16, \ldots\}$
20. $\{-3, -5, -7, -9, -11, \ldots\}$

For Exercises 21–30, show each set is an infinite set.

21. $\{3, 6, 9, 12, 15, \ldots\}$
22. $\{10, 15, 20, 25, 30, \ldots\}$
23. $\{9, 18, 27, 36, 45, \ldots\}$
24. $\{4, 10, 16, 22, 28, \ldots\}$
25. $\{2, 5, 8, 11, 14, \ldots\}$
26. $\{20, 24, 28, 32, 36, \ldots\}$
27. $\{10, 100, 1{,}000, 10{,}000, \ldots\}$
28. $\{100, 200, 300, 400, 500, \ldots\}$
29. $\left\{\frac{5}{1}, \frac{5}{2}, \frac{5}{3}, \frac{5}{4}, \frac{5}{5}, \ldots\right\}$
30. $\left\{\frac{1}{2}, \frac{1}{4}, \frac{1}{8}, \frac{1}{16}, \ldots\right\}$

Critical Thinking

31. Recall that $\aleph_0$ is the cardinality of the natural numbers (and any other countable set). What do you think $\aleph_0 + 1$ should be? What about $\aleph_0 + \aleph_0$?
32. Can you think of a one-to-one correspondence that will show that the set of integers is countable? (The set of integers consists of the natural numbers, their negatives, and zero.)
33. The set of rational numbers is the set of all possible fractions that have integer numerators and denominators. Intuitively, do you think there are more rational numbers than natural numbers? Why? Do you think that the set of rational numbers is countable?
34. Can you think of any set of tangible objects that is infinite? Why or why not?

CHAPTER **2** **Summary**

Section	Important Terms	Important Ideas
2-1	Set Roster method Element Well-defined Natural numbers Descriptive method Set-builder notation Variable Finite set Infinite set Cardinal number Null set Equal sets Equivalent sets One-to-one correspondence	**A set** is a well-defined collection of objects. Each object is called an element or member of the set. We use three ways to identify sets. They are the roster method, the descriptive method, and set-builder notation. Sets can be finite or infinite. A finite set contains a specific number of elements, while an infinite set contains an unlimited number of elements. If a set has no elements, it is called an empty set or a null set. Two sets are equal if they have the same elements, and two finite sets are equivalent if they have the same number of elements. Two sets are said to have a one-to-one correspondence if it is possible to pair the elements of one set with the elements of the other set in such a way that for each element in the first set there exists one and only one element in the second set, and for each element in the second set there exists one and only one element of the first set.
2-2	Universal set Complement Subset Proper subset Intersection Union Subtraction Cartesian product	**The universal** set is the set of all elements used for a specific problem or situation. The complement of a specific set is a set that consists of all elements in the universal set that are not in the specific set. If every element of one set is also an element of another set, then the first set is said to be a subset of the second set. A subset A of a set B is a proper subset if A is not equal to B. The union of two sets is a set containing all elements of one set or the other set, while the intersection of two sets is a set that contains the elements that both sets have in common. The difference of set A and set B, denoted $A - B$, is the set of elements in set A but not in set B. The Cartesian product of two sets A and B is $A \times B = \{(x, y) \mid x \in A \text{ and } y \in B\}$.
2-3	Venn diagram	**A mathematician** named John Venn devised a way to represent sets pictorially. His method uses overlapping circles to represent the sets. De Morgan's laws for two sets A and B are $(A \cup B)' = A' \cap B'$ and $(A \cap B)' = A' \cup B'$. For any two finite sets A and B, $n(A \cup B) = n(A) + n(B) - n(A \cap B)$.
2-4		**Venn diagrams** can be used to solve real-world problems involving surveys and classifications.
2-5	Infinite set Countable set Uncountable set General term	**An infinite** set can be placed in a one-to-one correspondence with a proper subset of itself. A set is called countable if it is finite or if there is a one-to-one correspondence between the set and the set of natural numbers. A set is called uncountable if it is not countable.

MATH IN ▶ Demographics REVISITED

The Venn diagram shown to the right is based on the given demographic estimates:

1. White only: 680; black only: 109; Hispanic only: 53

2. Hispanic and black, but not white: 11

3. Hispanic or black: 270

4. None of white, black, or Hispanic: 50

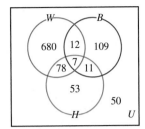

Review Exercises

Section 2-1

For Exercises 1–8, write each set in roster notation.

1. The set D is the set of even numbers between 50 and 60.
2. The set F is the set of odd numbers between 3 and 40.
3. The set L is the set of letters in the word *letter*.
4. The set A is the set of letters in the word *Arkansas*.
5. The set B is $\{x \mid x \in N \text{ and } x > 500\}$.
6. The set C is the set of natural numbers between 5 and 12.
7. The set M is the set of months in the year that begin with the letter P.
8. The set G is the set of days in the week that end with the letter e.

For Exercises 9–12, write each set by using set-builder notation.

9. $\{18, 20, 22, 24\}$
10. $\{5, 10, 15, 20\}$
11. $\{101, 103, 105, 107, \ldots\}$
12. $\{8, 16, 24, \ldots 72\}$

For Exercises 13–18, state whether the set is finite or infinite.

13. $\{x \mid x \in N \text{ and } x \geq 9\}$
14. $\{4, 8, 12, 16, \ldots\}$
15. $\{x, y, z\}$
16. $\{3, 7, 9, 12\}$
17. $\varnothing$
18. {people who have naturally red hair}

Section 2-2

For Exercises 19–22, decide if the statement is true or false.

19. $\{80, 100, 120, \ldots\} \subseteq \{40, 80, 120, \ldots\}$
20. $\{6\} \subset \{6, 12, 18\}$
21. $\{5, 6, 7\} \subseteq \{5, 7\}$

22. $\{a, b, c\} \subset \{a, b, c\}$
23. Find all subsets of $\{r, s, t\}$.
24. Find all subsets of $\{m, n, o\}$.
25. How many subsets and proper subsets does the set $\{p, q, r, s, t\}$ have?
26. How many subsets and proper subsets does the set $\{a, e, i, o, u, y\}$ have?

For Exercises 27–38, let $U = \{p, q, r, s, t, u, v, w, x, y, z\}$, $A = \{p, r, t, u, v\}$, $B = \{t, u, v, x, y\}$, and $C = \{s, w, z\}$. Find each.

27. $A \cap B$
28. $B \cup C$
29. $(A \cap B) \cap C$
30. B'
31. $A - B$
32. $B - A$
33. $(A \cup B)' \cap C$
34. $B' \cap C'$
35. $(B \cup C) \cap A'$
36. $(A \cup B) \cap C'$
37. $(B' \cap C') \cup A'$
38. $(A' \cap B) \cup C$

For Exercises 39–42, let $M = \{s, t, u\}$ and $N = \{v, w, x\}$. Find each set.

39. $M \times N$
40. $N \times M$
41. $M \times M$
42. $N \times N$

Section 2-3

For Exercises 43–48, use the Venn diagram below. Describe the region or regions provided in each problem, using set operations on A and B. There may be more than one right answer.

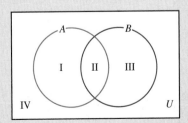

43. Region I
44. Region II
45. Region III
46. Region IV
47. Regions I and III
48. Regions I and IV

For Exercises 49–52, draw a Venn diagram and shade the appropriate area for each.

49. $A' \cap B$
50. $(A \cup B)'$
51. $(A' \cap B') \cup C$
52. $A \cap (B \cup C)'$
53. If $n(A) = 15$, $n(B) = 9$, and $n(A \cap B) = 4$, find $n(A \cup B)$.
54. If $n(A) = 24$, $n(B) = 20$, and $n(A \cap B) = 14$, find $n(A \cup B)$.

The table and Venn diagram below are to be used for Exercises 55–58. The table shows the top five states in terms of number of violent crimes per 100,000 citizens in each year from 2004 to 2006. For each exercise, write the region of the Venn diagram that would include the state listed.

Year	2004	2005	2006
State	1. South Carolina	1. South Carolina	1. South Carolina
	2. Florida	2. Tennessee	2. Tennessee
	3. Maryland	3. Florida	3. Nevada
	4. Tennessee	4. Maryland	4. Florida
	5. New Mexico	5. New Mexico	5. Louisiana

Source: swivel.com

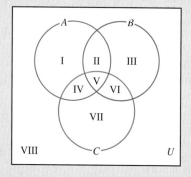

Note: Set *A* represents 2004, set *B* represents 2005, and set *C* represents 2006.

55. Florida
56. Louisiana
57. New Mexico
58. Nevada

Section 2-4

59. In a recent survey of 25 students, 10 had used a chat room that day, 5 posted a new blog that day, and 2 students used a chat room and posted a new blog that day.

    (a) How many did not use a chat room or post a blog that day?
    (b) How many only posted a new blog that day?

60. In a group of 24 students asked what they did last Saturday night, 9 tailgated after the big game, 18 went to a rave, and 3 tailgated and went to a rave.

    (a) How many only went to a rave?
    (b) How many did not go to a rave?

61. Fifty-three callers to the campus radio station were asked what they usually listened to while driving to school. Of those asked, 22 listened to a local radio station, 18 listened to satellite radio, 33 listened to MP3 players, 8 listened to a local radio station and satellite radio, 13 listened to satellite radio and MP3 players, 11 listened to a local radio station and an MP3 player, and 6 listened to all three.

    (a) How many listened to only satellite radio?
    (b) How many listened to local radio stations and MP3 players but not satellite radio?
    (c) How many listened to none of these?

62. Of the last 41 customers at the student bookstore, 15 paid in cash, 16 used a debit card, 20 used a financial aid voucher, 4 used cash and a debit card, 8 used a debit card and a financial aid voucher, 8 used cash and a financial aid voucher, and 1 used all three.

    (a) How many used none of these payment types?
    (b) How many only used a debit card?
    (c) How many used cash and a financial aid voucher but not a debit card?

Section 2-5

63. Find a general term for the set $\{-5, -7, -9, -11, -13, \ldots\}$
64. Show that the set $\{12, 24, 36, 48, 60, \ldots\}$ is an infinite set.

Chapter Test

For Exercises 1–8, write each set in roster notation.

1. The set *P* is the set of even natural numbers between 90 and 100.
2. The set *J* is the set of odd natural numbers between 40 and 50.
3. The set *K* is the set of letters in the word *envelope*.
4. The set *W* is the set of letters in the word *Washington*.
5. $X = \{x \mid x \in N \text{ and } x < 80\}$
6. $Y = \{x \mid x \in N \text{ and } 16 < x < 25\}$
7. The set *J* is the set of months of the year that begin with the letter J.
8. The set *L* is the set of days of the week that end in the letter a.

For Exercises 9–12, write each set using set-builder notation.

9. {12, 14, 16, 18}   11. {201, 203, 205, 207,…}
10. {30, 35, 40, 45}   12. {4, 8, 16,…128}

For Exercises 13–17, state whether the set is finite or infinite.

13. {15, 16, 17, 18,…}
14. {$x \mid x \in N$ and x is a multiple of 6}
15. {a, b, c}
16. {4, 7, 8, 10}
17. The set V is the set of people with three eyes.
18. Find all subsets of {d, e, f}.
19. Find all subsets of {p, q, r}.
20. How many subsets and proper subsets does the set {a, b, c, d, e} have?

For Exercises 21–30, let U = {a, b, c, d, e, f, g, h, i, j, k}, A = {a, b, d, e, f}, B = {a, g, i, j, k}, and C = {e, h, j}. Find each.

21. $A \cap B$
22. $B \cup C$
23. B'
24. $(A \cup B)'$
25. $(A \cap B)' \cup C'$
26. $A - B$
27. $B - C$
28. $(A - B) - C$
29. $A - C$
30. Draw and shade a Venn diagram for the area representing $A - B$.

For Exercises 31–34, let A = {@, !, α} and B = {π, #}. Find each set.

31. $A \times B$ 33. $B \times B$
32. $B \times A$ 34. $A \times A$

For Exercises 35–37, draw a Venn diagram for each set.

35. $A' \cap B$
36. $(A \cap B)'$
37. $(A' \cup B') \cap C'$
38. If $n(A) = 1{,}500$, $n(B) = 1{,}150$, and $n(A \cap B) = 350$, find $n(A \cup B)$.
39. At a special graduation ceremony of 24 honors students, 8 used a digital camera, 9 used a camera in their cell phones, and 4 used both digital cameras and cell phone cameras.

    (a) How many did not use either of these?
    (b) How many used a digital camera only?

40. Find a general term for the set {15, 30, 45, 60, 75,…}.
41. Show that the set {1, −1, 2, −2, 3, −3,…} is an infinite set.

For Exercises 42–53, state whether each is true or false.

42. {a, b, c} is equal to {x, y, z}.
43. {1, 2, 3, 4} is equivalent to {p, q, r, s}.
44. {4, 8, 12, 16,…} $\subseteq$ {2, 4, 6, 8,…}
45. {15} $\subset$ {3, 6, 9, 12,…}
46. 4 $\in$ {even natural numbers}
47. 9 $\notin$ {2, 4, 5, 6, 10}
48. {a, e, i, o, u, y} $\subseteq$ {a, e, i, o, u}
49. {12} $\in$ {12, 24, 36,…}
50. For any set, $\varnothing' = U$.
51. 0 $\in \varnothing$
52. For any set, $A \cap \varnothing = U$.
53. For any set, $A \cup B = B \cup A$.

Projects

1. Have the students in your class fill out this questionnaire:

   A. Gender: Male _____   Female _____
   B. Age: Under 21 _____   21 or older _____
   C. Work: Yes _____   No _____

   Draw a Venn diagram, and from the information answer these questions:

   (a) How many students are female?
   (b) How many students are under 21?
   (c) How many students work?
   (d) How many students are under 21 and work?
   (e) How many students are males and do not work?
   (f) How many students are 21 or older and work?
   (g) How many students are female, work, and are under 21?

2. Select five of these set properties. Explain why they are true for all sets. Then illustrate, using Venn diagrams.

   (a) $(A')' = A$
   (b) $\varnothing' = U$ and $U' = \varnothing$
   (c) $A \cup \varnothing = A$ and $A \cap \varnothing = \varnothing$
   (d) $A \cup U = U$ and $A \cap U = A$
   (e) $A \cup A' = U$ and $A \cap A' = \varnothing$
   (f) $A \cup A = A$ and $A \cap A = A$
   (g) $A \cup B = B \cup A$ and $A \cap B = B \cap A$
   (h) $(A \cup B) \cup C = A \cup (B \cup C)$ and $(A \cap B) \cap C = A \cap (B \cap C)$
   (i) $A \cup (B \cap C) = (A \cup B) \cap (A \cup C)$ and $A \cap (B \cup C) = (A \cap B) \cup (A \cap C)$
   (j) $(A \cup B)' = A' \cap B'$ and $(A \cap B)' = A' \cup B'$

CHAPTER **3**

Logic

Outline

MATH IN ▶ The Art of Persuasion

Everywhere you turn in modern society, somebody is trying to convince you of something. "Vote for me!" "Buy my product!" "Lease a car from our dealership!" "Bailing out the auto industry is a bad idea!" "You should go out with me this weekend!" "Join our fraternity!" Logic is sometimes defined as correct thinking or correct reasoning. Some people refer to logic by a more casual name: *common sense*. Regardless of what you call it, the ability to think logically is crucial for all of us because our lives are inundated daily with advertisements, contracts, product and service warranties, political debates, and news commentaries, to name just a few. People often have problems processing these things because of misinterpretation, misunderstanding, and faulty logic.

You can look up the truth or falseness of a fact on the Internet, but that won't help you in analyzing whether a certain claim is logically valid. The term *common sense* is misleading, because evaluating logical arguments can be a challenging and involved process. This chapter introduces the basic concepts of formal symbolic logic and shows how to determine whether arguments are valid or invalid by using truth tables. One of our biggest goals will be to examine the form of an argument and determine if its conclusion follows logically from the statements in the argument.

To that end, we've written some claims below. Your job is to determine which of the arguments is valid, meaning that a conclusion can be logically drawn from a set of statements. The skills you learn in this chapter will help you to do so.

- Where there's smoke, there's fire.
- Having a lot of money makes people happy. My neighbor is a really happy guy, so he must have a lot of money.
- Every team in the SEC is good enough to play in a bowl game. Florida State is not in the SEC, so they're not good enough to play in a bowl game.
- Scripture is the word of God. I know this because it says so in the Bible.
- If Iraq has weapons of mass destruction, we should go to war. It turns out that they don't have them, so we should not go to war.
- It will be a snowy day in Hawaii before Tampa Bay makes it to the World Series. Tampa Bay played in the 2008 World Series, so it must have snowed in Hawaii.

For answers, see Math in the Art of Persuasion Revisited on Page 141

Section 3-1 Statements and Quantifiers

LEARNING OBJECTIVES

☐ 1. Define and identify statements.

☐ 2. Define the logical connectives.

☐ 3. Write the negation of a statement.

☐ 4. Write statements symbolically.

As the world gets more complex and we are bombarded with more and more information, it becomes more important than ever to be able to make sensible, objective evaluations of that information. One of the most effective tricks that advertisers, politicians, and con artists use is to encourage emotions to enter into these evaluations. They use carefully selected words and images that are designed to keep you from making decisions objectively. The field of **symbolic logic** was designed exactly for this reason. Symbolic logic uses letters to represent statements and special symbols to represent words like *and, or,* and *not*. Use of this symbolic notation in place of the statements themselves allows us to analytically evaluate the validity of the logic behind an argument without letting bias and emotion cloud our judgment. And these unbiased evaluations are the main goal of this chapter.

Statements

In the English language there are many types of sentences, including factual statements, commands, opinions, questions, and exclamations. In the objective study of logic, we will use only factual statements.

> A **statement** is a declarative sentence that can be objectively determined to be true or false, but not both.

For example, sentences like

> It is raining.
> The United States has sent a space probe to Mars.
> $2 + 2 = 4$
> $10 - 5 = 4$

are statements because they are either true or false and you don't use an opinion to determine this.

Whether a sentence is true or false doesn't matter in determining if it is a statement. Notice in the above example the last statement "$10 - 5 = 4$" is false, but it's still a statement.

The following sentences, however, are not statements:

> Give me onion rings with my order.
> What operating system are you running?
> Sweet!
> The guy sitting next to me is kind of goofy.

The first is not a statement because it is a command. The second is not a statement because it is a question. The third is not a statement because it is an exclamation, and the fourth is not a statement because the word *goofy* is subjective; that is, it requires an opinion.

EXAMPLE 1 **Recognizing Statements**

Decide which of the following are statements and which are not.

(a) Most scientists agree that global warming is a threat to the environment.
(b) Is that your laptop?
(c) Man, that hurts!
(d) $8 - 2 = 6$
(e) This book is about database management.
(f) Everybody should watch reality shows.

SOLUTION

Parts (a), (d), and (e) are statements because they can be judged as true or false in a nonsubjective manner.
Part (b) is not a statement because it is a question.
Part (c) is not a statement because it is an exclamation.
Part (f) is not a statement because it requires an opinion.

☑ 1. Define and identify statements.

▼ Try This One 1

Decide which of the following are statements and which are not.

(a) Cool!
(b) $12 - 8 = 5$
(c) Ryan Seacrest is the host of *American Idol*.
(d) Cat can send text messages with her cell phone.
(e) When does the party start?
(f) History is interesting.

Simple and Compound Statements

Statements can be classified as *simple* or *compound*. A **simple statement** contains only one idea. Each of these statements is an example of a simple statement.

These cargo pants are khaki.

My dorm room has three beds in it.

Daytona Beach is in Florida.

A statement such as "I will take chemistry this semester, and I will get an A" is called a **compound statement** since it consists of two simple statements.

Compound statements are formed by joining two simple statements with what is called a *connective*.

The basic **connectives** are *and, or, if . . . then,* and *if and only if.*

Each of the connectives has a formal name: *and* is called a **conjunction,** *or* is called a **disjunction,** *if . . . then* is called a **conditional,** and *if and only if* is called a **biconditional.** Here are some examples of compound statements using connectives.

John studied for 5 hours, and he got an A.   (conjunction)

Luisa will run in a mini triathlon or she will play in the campus tennis tournament.   (disjunction)

If I get 80% of the questions on the LSAT right, then I will get into law school. (conditional)

We will win the game if and only if we score more points than the other team. (biconditional)

Math Note

In standard usage, the word *then* is often omitted from a conditional statement; instead of "If it snows, then I will go skiing," you'd probably just say, "If it snows, I'll go skiing."

EXAMPLE 2　Classifying Statements as Simple or Compound

Math Note

Technically, we've given the names *conjunction*, *disjunction*, *conditional*, and *biconditional* to the connectives, but from now on, we'll refer to whole statements using these connectives by those names. For example, we would call the compound statement in Example 2d a disjunction.

☑ 2. Define the logical connectives.

Classify each statement as simple or compound. If it is compound, state the name of the connective used.

(a) Our school colors are red and white.
(b) If you register for WiFi service, you will get 3 days of free access.
(c) Tomorrow is the last day to register for classes.
(d) I will buy a hybrid or I will buy a motorcycle.

SOLUTION

(a) Don't let use of the word *and* fool you! This is a simple statement.
(b) This if … then statement is compound and uses a conditional connective.
(c) This is a simple statement.
(d) This is a compound statement, using a disjunction.

▼ Try This One 2

Classify each statement as simple or compound. If it is compound, state the name of the connective used.

(a) The jacket is trendy and it is practical.
(b) This is an informative website on STDs.
(c) If it does not rain, then I will go windsurfing.
(d) I will buy a flash drive or I will buy a zip drive.
(e) Yesterday was the deadline to withdraw from a class.

Sidelight　A BRIEF HISTORY OF LOGIC

The basic concepts of logic can be attributed to Aristotle, who lived in the fourth century BCE. He used words, sentences, and deduction to prove arguments using techniques we will study in this chapter. In addition, in 300 BCE, Euclid formalized geometry using deductive proofs. Both subjects were considered to be the "inevitable truths" of the universe revealed to rational people.

In the 19th century, people began to reject the idea of inevitable truths and realized that a deductive system like Euclidean geometry is only true based on the original assumptions. When the original assumptions are changed, a new deductive system can be created. This is why there are different types of geometry. (See Section 10-7 on non-Euclidean geometry.)

Eventually, several people developed the use of symbols rather than words and sentences in logic. One such person was George Boole (1815–1864). Boole created the symbols used in this chapter and developed the theory of symbolic logic. He also used symbolic logic in mathematics. His manuscript, entitled "An Investigation into the Laws of Thought, on Which Are Founded the Mathematical Theories of Logic and Probabilities," was published when he was 39 in 1854.

Boole was a friend of Augustus De Morgan, who formulated De Morgan's laws, which we studied in Chapter 2. Much earlier, Leonhard Euler (1707–1783) used circles to represent logical statements and proofs. The idea was refined into Venn diagrams by John Venn (1834–1923).

Quantified Statements

Math Note

We'll worry later about determining whether statements involving quantifiers and connectives are true or false. For now, focus on learning and understanding the terms.

Quantified statements involve terms such as *all, each, every, no, none, some, there exists,* and *at least one*. The first five (*all, each, every, no, none*) are called *universal quantifiers* because they either include or exclude every element of the universal set. The latter three (*some, there exists, at least one*) are called *existential quantifiers* because they show the existence of something, but do not include the entire universal set. Here are some examples of quantified statements:

Every student taking Math for Liberal Arts this semester will pass.

Some people who are Miami Hurricane fans are also Miami Dolphin fans.

There is at least one professor in this school who does not have brown eyes.

No Marlin fan is also a Yankee fan.

The first and the fourth statements use universal quantifiers, and the second and third use existential quantifiers. Note that the statements using existential quantifiers are not "all inclusive" (or all exclusive) as the other two are.

Negation

The *negation* of a statement is a corresponding statement with the opposite truth value. For example, for the statement "My dorm room is blue," the negation is "My dorm room is not blue." It's important to note that the truth values of these two are completely opposite: one is true, and the other is false—period. You can't negate "My dorm room is blue" by saying "My dorm room is yellow," because it's completely possible that *both* statements are false. To make sure that you have a correct negation, check that if one of the statements is true, the other must be false, and vice versa. The typical way to negate a simple statement is by adding the word *not,* as in these examples:

Statement	**Negation**
Auburn will win Saturday.	Auburn will not win Saturday.
I took a shower today.	I did not take a shower today.
My car is clean.	My car is not clean.

You have to be especially careful when negating quantified statements. Consider the example statement "All dogs are fuzzy." It's not quite right to say that the negation is "All dogs are not fuzzy," because if some dogs are fuzzy and others aren't, then both statements are false. All we need for the statement "All dogs are fuzzy" to be false is to find at least one dog that is not fuzzy, so the negation of the statement "All dogs are fuzzy" is "Some dogs are not fuzzy." (In this setting, we define the word *some* to mean *at least one*.)

We can summarize the negation of quantified statements as follows:

Math Note

The words *each, every,* and *all* mean the same thing, so what we say about *all* in this section applies to the others as well. Likewise, *some, there exists,* and *at least one* are considered to be the same and are treated that way as well.

Statement Contains...	**Negation**
All do	Some do not, or not all do
Some do	None do, or all do not
Some do not	All do
None do	Some do

EXAMPLE 3 **Writing Negations**

Write the negation of each of the following quantified statements.

(a) Every student taking Math for Liberal Arts this semester will pass.
(b) Some people who are Miami Hurricane fans are also Miami Dolphin fans.
(c) There is at least one professor in this school who does not have brown eyes.
(d) No Marlin fan is also a Yankee fan.

SOLUTION

(a) Some student taking Math for Liberal Arts this semester will not pass (or, not every student taking Math for Liberal Arts this semester will pass).
(b) No people who are Miami Hurricane fans are also Miami Dolphin fans.
(c) All professors in this school have brown eyes.
(d) Some Marlin fan is also a Yankee fan.

CAUTION

Be especially careful when negating statements. Remember that the negation of "Every student will pass" is *not* "Every student will fail".

☑ 3. Write the negation of a statement.

▼ Try This One 3

Write the negation of each of the following quantified statements.

(a) All cell phones have cameras.
(b) No woman can win the lottery.
(c) Some professors have Ph.Ds.
(d) Some students in this class will not pass.

Symbolic Notation

> **Math Note**
>
> For three of the four connectives in Table 3-1, the order of the simple statements doesn't matter: for example, $p \wedge q$ and $q \wedge p$ represent the same compound statement. The same is true for the connectives $\vee$ (disjunction) and $\leftrightarrow$ (biconditional). The one exception is the conditional ($\rightarrow$), where order is crucial.

Recall that one of our goals in this section is to write statements in symbolic form to help us evaluate logical arguments objectively. Now we'll introduce the symbols and methods that will be used. The symbols for the connectives *and, or, if . . . then,* and *if and only if* are shown in Table 3-1.

Simple statements in logic are usually denoted with lowercase letters like p, q, and r. For example, we could use p to represent the statement "I get paid Friday" and q to represent the statement "I will go out this weekend." Then the conditional statement "If I get paid Friday, then I will go out this weekend" can be written in symbols as $p \rightarrow q$.

The symbol ~ (tilde) represents a negation. If p still represents "I get paid Friday," then $\sim p$ represents "I do not get paid Friday."

We often use parentheses in logical statements when more than one connective is involved in order to specify an order. (We'll deal with this in greater detail in the next section.) For example, there is a difference between the compound statements $\sim p \wedge q$ and $\sim(p \wedge q)$. The statement $\sim p \wedge q$ means to negate the statement p first, then use the negation of p in conjunction with the statement q. For example, if p is the statement "Fido is a dog" and q is the statement "Pumpkin is a cat," then $\sim p \wedge q$ reads, "Fido is not a dog and Pumpkin is a cat." The statement $\sim p \wedge q$ could also be written as $(\sim p) \wedge q$.

TABLE 3-1   Symbols for the Connectives

Connective	Symbol	Name
and	$\wedge$	Conjunction
or	$\vee$	Disjunction
if . . . then	$\rightarrow$	Conditional
if and only if	$\leftrightarrow$	Biconditional

The statement $\sim(p \wedge q)$ means to negate the conjunction of the statement p and the statement q. Using the same statements for p and q as before, the statement $\sim(p \wedge q)$ is written, "It is not the case that Fido is a dog and Pumpkin is a cat."

The same reasoning applies when the negation is used with other connectives. For example, $\sim p \to q$ means $(\sim p) \to q$.

Example 4 illustrates in greater detail how to write statements symbolically.

EXAMPLE 4   Writing Statements Symbolically

Let p represent the statement "It is cloudy" and q represent the statement "I will go to the beach." Write each statement in symbols.

(a) I will not go to the beach.
(b) It is cloudy, and I will go to the beach.
(c) If it is cloudy, then I will not go to the beach.
(d) I will go to the beach if and only if it is not cloudy.

SOLUTION

(a) This is the negation of statement q, which we write as $\sim q$.
(b) This is the conjunction of p and q, written as $p \wedge q$.
(c) This is the conditional of p and the negation of q: $p \to \sim q$.
(d) This is the biconditional of q and not p: $q \leftrightarrow \sim p$.

▼ Try This One 4

Let p represent the statement "I will buy a Coke" and q represent the statement "I will buy some popcorn." Write each statement in symbols.

(a) I will buy a Coke, and I will buy some popcorn.
(b) I will not buy a Coke.
(c) If I buy some popcorn, then I will buy a Coke.
(d) I will not buy a Coke, and I will buy some popcorn.

You probably noticed that some of the compound statements we've written sound a little awkward. It isn't always necessary to repeat the subject and verb in a compound statement using *and* or *or*. For example, the statement "It is cold, and it is snowing" can be written "It is cold and snowing." The statement "I will go to a movie, or I will go to a play" can be written "I will go to a movie or a play." Also the words *but* and *although* can be used in place of *and*. For example, the statement "I will not buy a television set, and I will buy a CD player" can also be written as "I will not buy a television set, but I will buy a CD player."

Statements written in symbols can also be written in words, as shown in Example 5.

EXAMPLE 5   Translating Statements from Symbols to Words

Write each statement in words. Let p = "My dog is a golden retriever" and q = "My dog is fuzzy."

(a) $\sim p$ (b) $p \vee q$ (c) $\sim p \to q$ (d) $q \leftrightarrow p$ (e) $q \wedge p$

If this is your dog (which it's not, because it's mine), statement (e) describes it pretty well.

SOLUTION

(a) My dog is not a golden retriever.
(b) My dog is a golden retriever or my dog is fuzzy.
(c) If my dog is not a golden retriever, then my dog is fuzzy.
(d) My dog is fuzzy if and only if my dog is a golden retriever.
(e) My dog is fuzzy, and my dog is a golden retriever.

▼ Try This One 5

Write each statement in words. Let $p =$ "My friend is a football player" and $q =$ "My friend is smart."

(a) $\sim p$ (b) $p \lor q$ (c) $\sim p \to q$ (d) $p \leftrightarrow q$ (e) $p \land q$

In this section, we defined the basic terms of symbolic logic and practiced writing statements using symbols. These skills will be crucial in our objective study of logical arguments, so we're off to a good start.

☑ 4. Write statements symbolically.

Answers to Try This One

1 (b), (c), and (d) are statements.

2 (a) (conjunction), (c) (conditional), and (d) (disjunction) are compound; (b) and (e) are simple.

3 (a) Some cell phones don't have cameras.
(b) Some women can win the lottery.
(c) No professors have Ph.Ds.
(d) All students in this class will pass.

4 (a) $p \land q$ (b) $\sim p$ (c) $q \to p$ (d) $\sim p \land q$

5 (a) My friend is not a football player.
(b) My friend is a football player or my friend is smart.
(c) If my friend is not a football player, then my friend is smart.
(d) My friend is smart if and only if my friend is a football player.
(e) My friend is a football player and my friend is smart.

EXERCISE SET 3-1

Writing Exercises

1. Define the term *statement* in your own words.
2. Explain the difference between a simple and a compound statement.
3. Describe the terms and symbols used for the four connectives.

4. Explain why the negation of "All spring breaks are fun" is not "All spring breaks are not fun."

Real-World Applications

For Exercises 5–14, state whether the sentence is a statement or not.

5. Please do not use your cell phone in class.
6. $5 + 9 = 14$
7. $9 - 3 = 2$
8. Nicki is a student in vet school.
9. Who will win the student government presidency?
10. Neither Sam nor Mary arrives to the exam on time.
11. You should carry a cell phone with you.
12. Bill Gates is the creator of Microsoft.
13. Go with the flow.
14. Math is not hard.

For Exercises 15–24, decide if each statement is simple or compound.

15. He goes to parties and hangs out at the coffee shop.
16. Sara got her hair highlighted.
17. Raj will buy an iMac or a Dell computer.
18. Euchre is fun if and only if you win.
19. February is when Valentine's Day occurs.
20. Diane is a chemistry major.
21. If you win the Megabucks multistate lottery, then you will be rich.
22. He listened to his iPod and he typed a paper.
23. $8 + 9 = 12$
24. Malcolm and Alisha will both miss the spring break trip.

For Exercises 25–32, identify each statement as a conjunction, disjunction, conditional, or biconditional.

25. Bob and Tom like stand-up comedians.
26. Either he passes the test, or he fails the course.
27. A number is even if and only if it is divisible by 2.
28. Her nails are long, and they have rhinestones on them.
29. I will go to the big game, or I will go to the library.
30. If a number is divisible by 3, then it is an odd number.
31. A triangle is equiangular if and only if three angles are congruent.
32. If your battery is dead, then you need to charge your phone overnight.

For Exercises 33–38, write the negation of the statement.

33. The sky is blue.
34. It is not true that your computer has a virus.
35. The dorm room is not large.
36. The class is not full.
37. It is not true that you will fail this class.
38. He has large biceps.

For Exercises 39–50, identify the quantifier in the statement as either universal or existential.

39. All fish swim in water.
40. Everyone who passes algebra has studied.
41. Some people who live in glass houses throw stones.
42. There is at least one person in this class who won't pass.
43. Every happy dog wags its tail.
44. No men can join a sorority.
45. There exists a four-leaf clover.
46. Each person who participated in the study will get $100.
47. No one with green eyes wears glasses.
48. Everyone in the class was bored by the professor's lecture.
49. At least one of my friends has an iPhone.
50. No one here gets out alive.

For Exercises 51–62, write the negation of the statements in Exercises 39–50.

For Exercises 63–72, write each statement in symbols. Let p = "Sara is a political science major" and let q = "Jane is a quantum physics major."

63. Sara is a political science major, and Jane is a quantum physics major.
64. Sara is not a political science major.
65. If Jane is not a quantum physics major, then Sara is a political science major.
66. It is not true that Jane is a quantum physics major or Sara is a political science major.
67. It is false that Jane is a quantum physics major.
68. It is not true that Sara is a political science major.
69. Jane is a quantum physics major, or Sara is not a political science major.
70. Jane is not a quantum physics major, or Sara is a political science major.
71. Jane is a quantum physics major if and only if Sara is a political science major.
72. If Sara is a political science major, then Jane is a quantum physics major.

For Exercises 73–82, write each statement in symbols. Let p = "My dad is cool" and q = "My mom is cool." Let nerdy mean not cool.

73. My mom is not cool.
74. Both my dad and my mom are nerdy.
75. If my mom is cool, then my dad is cool.
76. It is not true that my dad is cool.
77. Either my mom is nerdy, or my dad is cool.
78. It is not true that my mom is nerdy and my dad is cool.
79. My mom is cool if and only if my dad is cool.
80. Neither my mom nor my dad is cool.
81. If my mom is nerdy, then my dad is cool.
82. My dad is nerdy if and only if my mom is not cool.

For Exercises 83–92, write each statement in words. Let p = *"The plane is on time." Let* q = *"The sky is clear."*

83. $p \wedge q$
84. $\sim p \vee q$
85. $q \rightarrow p$
86. $q \rightarrow \sim p$
87. $\sim p \wedge \sim q$

88. $q \leftrightarrow p$
89. $p \vee \sim q$
90. $\sim p \leftrightarrow \sim q$
91. $q \rightarrow (p \vee \sim p)$
92. $(p \rightarrow q) \vee \sim p$

For Exercises 93–102, write each statement in words. Let p = *"Mark lives on campus." Let* q = *"Trudy lives off campus."*

93. $\sim q$
94. $p \rightarrow q$
95. $p \vee \sim q$
96. $q \leftrightarrow p$
97. $\sim p \rightarrow \sim q$

98. $\sim p$
99. $p \vee q$
100. $(\sim p \vee q) \vee \sim q$
101. $q \vee p$
102. $(p \vee q) \rightarrow \sim(\sim q)$

Critical Thinking

103. Explain why the sentence "All rules have exceptions" is not a statement.

104. Explain why the sentence "This statement is false" is not a statement.

Section 3-2 Truth Tables

LEARNING OBJECTIVES

☐ 1. Construct truth tables for negation, disjunction, and conjunction.

☐ 2. Construct truth tables for the conditional and biconditional.

☐ 3. Construct truth tables for compound statements.

☐ 4. Identify the hierarchy of logical connectives.

☐ 5. Construct truth tables by using an alternative method.

"You can't believe everything you hear." Chances are you were taught this when you were younger, and it's pretty good advice. In an ideal world, everyone would tell the truth all the time, but in the real world, it is extremely important to be able to separate fact from fiction. When someone is trying to convince you of some point of view, the ability to logically evaluate the validity of an argument can be the difference between being informed and being deceived—and maybe between you keeping and you being separated from your hard-earned money!

This section is all about deciding when a compound statement is or is not true, based not on the situation itself, but simply on the structure of the statement and the truth of the underlying components. We learned about logical connectives in Section 3-1. In this section, we'll analyze these connectives using *truth tables*. A **truth table** is a diagram in table form that is used to show when a compound statement is true or false based on the truth values of the simple statements that make up the compound statement. This will allow us to analyze arguments objectively.

Negation

According to our definition of *statement,* a statement is either true or false, but never both. Consider the simple statement p = "Today is Tuesday." If it is in fact Tuesday, then p is true, and its negation ($\sim p$) "Today is not Tuesday" is false. If it's not Tuesday, then p is false and $\sim p$ is true. The truth table for the negation of p looks like this.

p	$\sim p$
T	F
F	T

There are two possible conditions for the statement p—true or false—and the table tells us that in each case, the negation $\sim p$ has the opposite truth value.

Conjunction

If we have a compound statement with two component statements p and q, there are four possible combinations of truth values for these two statements:

Possibilities	Symbolic value of each

	p	q
1. p and q are both true.	T	T
2. p is true and q is false.	T	F
3. p is false and q is true.	F	T
4. p and q are both false.	F	F

So when setting up a truth table for a compound statement with two component statements, we'll need a row for each of the four possibilities.

Now we're ready to analyze conjunctions. Recall that a conjunction is a compound statement involving the word *and*. Suppose a friend who's prone to exaggeration tells you, "I bought a new computer and a new iPod." This compound statement can be symbolically represented by $p \wedge q$, where $p =$ "I bought a new computer" and $q =$ "I bought a new iPod." When would this conjunctive statement be true? If your friend actually had made both purchases, then of course the statement "I bought a new computer and a new iPod" would be true. In terms of a truth table, that tells us that if p and q are both true, then the conjunction $p \wedge q$ is true as well, as shown below.

p	q	$p \wedge q$
T	T	T

On the other hand, suppose your friend bought only a new computer or only a new iPod, or maybe neither of those things. Then the statement "I bought a new computer and a new iPod" would be false. In other words, if either or both of p and q are false, then the compound statement $p \wedge q$ is false as well. With this information, we complete the truth table for a basic conjunction:

	p	q	$p \wedge q$
Bought computer and iPod	T	T	T
Bought computer, not iPod	T	F	F
Bought iPod, not computer	F	T	F
Bought neither	F	F	F

Truth Values for a Conjunction

The conjunction $p \wedge q$ is true only when both p and q are true.

Disjunction

Next, we'll look at truth tables for *or* statements. Suppose your friend from the previous example made the statement, "I bought a new computer *or* a new iPod" (as opposed to *and*). If your friend actually did buy one or the other, then this statement would be true. And if he or she bought neither, then the statement would be false. So a partial truth table looks like this:

	p	q	$p \vee q$
Bought computer and iPod	T	T	
Bought computer, not iPod	T	F	T
Bought iPod, not computer	F	T	T
Bought neither	F	F	F

Sidelight   **Logical Gates and Computer Design**

Logic is used in electrical engineering in designing circuits, which are the heart of computers. The truth tables for *and*, *or*, and *not* are used for computer gates. These gates determine whether electricity flows through a circuit. When a switch is closed, the current has an uninterrupted path and will flow through the circuit. This is designated by a 1. When a switch is open, the path at the current is broken, and it will not flow. This is designated by a 0. The logical gates are illustrated here—notice that they correspond exactly with our truth tables.

This simple little structure is responsible for the operation of almost every computer in the world—at least until quantum computers become a reality. If you're interested, do a Google search for *quantum computer* to read about the future of computing.

But what if the person actually bought both items? You might lean toward the statement "I bought a new computer or a new iPod" being false. Believe it or not, it depends on what we mean by the word *or*. There are two interpretations of that word, known as the *inclusive or* and the *exclusive or*. The inclusive or has the possibility of both statements being true; but the exclusive or does not allow for this, that is, exactly one of the two simple statements must be true. In English when we use the word *or*, we typically think of the exclusive or. If I were to say, "I will go to work or I will go to the beach," you would assume I am doing one or the other, but not both. In logic we generally use the inclusive or. When the inclusive or is used, the statement "I will go to work or I will go to the beach" would be true if I went to both work and the beach. For the remainder of this chapter we will assume the symbol $\lor$ represents the inclusive or and will drop *inclusive* and just say *or*.

The completed truth table for the disjunction is

		p	q	$p \lor q$
Bought computer and iPod		T	T	T
Bought computer, not iPod		T	F	T
Bought iPod, not computer		F	T	T
Bought neither		F	F	F

Truth Values for a Disjunction

✅ 1. Construct truth tables for negation, disjunction, and conjunction.

The disjunction $p \lor q$ is true when either p or q or both are true. It is false only when both p and q are false.

Conditional Statement

A conditional statement, which is sometimes called an *implication*, consists of two simple statements using the connective if...then. For example, the statement "If I bought a ticket, then I can go to the concert" is a conditional statement. The first component, in this case "I bought a ticket," is called the *antecedent*. The second component, in this case "I can go to the concert," is called the *consequent*.

Conditional statements are used commonly in every area of math, including logic. You might remember statements from high school algebra like "If two lines are parallel, then they have the same slope." Remember that we represent the conditional statement "If p, then q" by using the symbol $p \rightarrow q$.

To illustrate the truth table for the conditional statement, think about the following simple example: "If it is raining, then I will take an umbrella." We'll use p to represent "It is raining" and q to represent "I will take an umbrella," then the conditional statement is $p \rightarrow q$. We'll break the truth table down into four cases.

Case 1: It is raining and I do take an umbrella (p and q are both true). Since I am doing what I said I would do in case of rain, the conditional statement is true. So the first line in the truth table is

Raining, take umbrella

p	q	$p \rightarrow q$
T	T	T

Case 2: It is raining and I do not take an umbrella (p is true and q is false). Since I am not doing what I said I would do in case of rain, I'm a liar and the conditional statement is false. So the second line in the truth table is

Raining, do not take umbrella

p	q	$p \rightarrow q$
T	T	T
T	F	F

Case 3: It is not raining and I do take an umbrella (p is false and q is true). This requires some thought. I never said in the original statement what I would do if it were not raining, so there's no reason to regard my original statement as false. Based on the information given, we consider the original statement to be true, and the third line of the truth table is

Not raining, take umbrella

p	q	$p \rightarrow q$
T	T	T
T	F	F
F	T	T

Case 4: It is not raining, and I do not take my umbrella (p and q are both false). This is essentially the same as case 3—I never said what I would do if it did not rain, so there's no reason to regard my statement as false based on what we know. So we consider the original statement to be true, and the last line of the truth table is

Not raining, do not take umbrella

p	q	$p \rightarrow q$
T	T	T
T	F	F
F	T	T
F	F	T

For cases 3 and 4, it might help to think of it this way: unless we have definite proof that a statement is false, we will consider it to be true.

Truth Values for a Conditional Statement

The conditional statement $p \rightarrow q$ is false only when the antecedent p is true and the consequent q is false.

Biconditional Statement

A biconditional statement is really two statements in a way; it's the conjunction of two conditional statements. For example, the statement "I will stay in and study Friday if and only if I don't have any money" is the same as "If I don't have any money, then I will stay in and study Friday *and* if I stay in and study Friday, then I don't have any money." In symbols, we can write either $p \leftrightarrow q$ or $(p \to q) \wedge (q \to p)$. Since the biconditional is a conjunction, for it to be true, both of the statements $p \to q$ and $q \to p$ must be true. We will once again look at cases to build the truth table.

Case 1: Both p and q are true. Then both $p \to q$ and $q \to p$ are true, and the conjunction $(p \to q) \wedge (q \to p)$, which is also $p \leftrightarrow q$, is true as well.

p	q	$p \leftrightarrow q$
T	T	T

Case 2: p is true and q is false. In this case, the implication $p \to q$ is false, so it doesn't even matter whether $q \to p$ is true or false—the conjunction has to be false.

p	q	$p \leftrightarrow q$
T	T	T
T	F	F

Case 3: p is false and q is true. This is case 2 in reverse. The implication $q \to p$ is false, so the conjunction must be as well.

p	q	$p \leftrightarrow q$
T	T	T
T	F	F
F	T	F

Case 4: p is false and q is false. According to the truth table for a conditional statement, both $p \to q$ and $q \to p$ are true in this case, so the conjunction is as well. This completes the truth table.

p	q	$p \leftrightarrow q$
T	T	T
T	F	F
F	T	F
F	F	T

A technician who designs an automated irrigation system needs to decide whether the system should turn on *if* the water in the soil falls below a certain level or *if and only if* the water in the soil falls below a certain level. In the first instance, other inputs could also turn on the system.

☑ 2. Construct truth tables for the conditional and biconditional.

Truth Values for a Biconditional Statement

The biconditional statement $p \leftrightarrow q$ is true when p and q have the same truth value and is false when they have opposite truth values.

Table 3-2 on the next page provides a summary of the truth tables for the basic compound statements and the negation. The last thing you should do is to try and memorize these tables! If you understand how we built them, you can rebuild them on your own when you need them.

Truth Tables for Compound Statements

Once we know truth values for the basic connectives, we can use truth tables to find the truth values for any logical statement. The key to the procedure is to take it step

TABLE 3-2	**Truth Tables for the Connectives and Negation**

Conjunction "and"

p	q	$p \wedge q$
T	T	T
T	F	F
F	T	F
F	F	F

Disjunction "or"

p	q	$p \vee q$
T	T	T
T	F	T
F	T	T
F	F	F

Conditional "if ... then"

p	q	$p \rightarrow q$
T	T	T
T	F	F
F	T	T
F	F	T

Biconditional "if and only if"

p	q	$p \leftrightarrow q$
T	T	T
T	F	F
F	T	F
F	F	T

Negation "not"

p	$\sim p$
T	F
F	T

by step, so that in every case, you're deciding on truth values based on one of the truth tables in Table 3-2.

EXAMPLE 1	**Constructing a Truth Table**

"My leg isn't better, or I'm taking a break" is an example of a statement that can be written as $\sim p \vee q$.

Construct a truth table for the statement $\sim p \vee q$.

SOLUTION

Step 1 Set up a table as shown.

p	q
T	T
T	F
F	T
F	F

The order in which you list the Ts and Fs doesn't matter as long as you cover all the possible combinations. For consistency in this book, we'll always use the order TTFF for p and TFTF for q when these are the only two letters in the logical statement.

Step 2 Find the truth values for $\sim p$ by negating the values for p, and put them into a new column, column 3, marked $\sim p$.

p	q	$\sim p$
T	T	F
T	F	F
F	T	T
F	F	T
②	③	

Truth values for $\sim p$ are opposite those for p.

Step 3 Find the truth values for the disjunction $\sim p \vee q$. Use the T and F values for $\sim p$ and q in columns 2 and 3, and use the disjunction truth table from earlier in the section.

p	q	$\sim p$	$\sim p \vee q$
T	T	F	T
T	F	F	F
F	T	T	T
F	F	T	T
			④

The disjunction is true unless $\sim p$ and q are both false.

The truth values for the statement $\sim p \vee q$ are found in column 4. The statement is true unless p is true and q is false.

▼ Try This One 1

Construct a truth table for the statement $p \vee \sim q$.

When a statement contains parentheses, we find the truth values for the statements in parentheses first, as shown in Example 2. This is similar to the order of operations used in arithmetic and algebra.

EXAMPLE 2   Constructing a Truth Table

Construct a truth table for the statement $\sim(p \rightarrow \sim q)$.

SOLUTION

Step 1 Set up the table as shown.

p	q
T	T
T	F
F	T
F	F

Step 2 Find the truth values for $\sim q$ by negating the values for q, and put them into a new column.

"It is not true that if it rains, then we can't go out" is an example of a statement that can be written as $\sim(p \rightarrow \sim q)$.

p	q	$\sim q$
T	T	F
T	F	T
F	T	F
F	F	T
①		③

Truth values for $\sim q$ are opposite those for q.

Step 3 Find the truth values for the implication $p \rightarrow \sim q$, using the values in columns 1 and 3 and the implication truth table from earlier in the section.

p	q	$\sim q$	$p \rightarrow \sim q$
T	T	F	F
T	F	T	T
F	T	F	T
F	F	T	T
			④

The conditional is true unless p is true and ~q is false.

Step 4 Find the truth values for the negation $\sim(p \rightarrow \sim q)$ by negating the values for $p \rightarrow \sim q$ in column 4.

p	q	$\sim q$	$p \rightarrow \sim q$	$\sim(p \rightarrow \sim q)$
T	T	F	F	T
T	F	T	T	F
F	T	F	T	F
F	F	T	T	F
			④	⑤

The negation has opposite values from column 4.

The truth values for $\sim(p \rightarrow \sim q)$ are in column 5. The statement is true only when p and q are both true.

▼ Try This One 2

Construct a truth table for the statement $p \leftrightarrow (\sim p \wedge q)$.

We can also construct truth tables for compound statements that involve three or more components. For a compound statement with three simple statements p, q, and r, there are eight possible combinations of Ts and Fs to consider. The truth table is set up as shown in step 1 of Example 3.

EXAMPLE 3   Constructing a Truth Table with Three Components

Construct a truth table for the statement $p \vee (q \rightarrow r)$.

SOLUTION

Step 1 Set up the table as shown.

p	q	r
T	T	T
T	T	F
T	F	T
T	F	F
F	T	T
F	T	F
F	F	T
F	F	F
②	③	

"I'll do my math assignment, or if I think of a good topic, then I'll start my English essay" is an example of a statement that can be written as $p \vee (q \rightarrow r)$.

Again, the order of the Ts and Fs doesn't matter as long as all the possible combinations are listed. Whenever there are three letters in the statement, we'll use the order shown in Step 1 for consistency.

Step 2 Find the truth value for the statement in parentheses, $q \rightarrow r$. Use the values in columns 2 and 3 and the conditional truth table from earlier in the section. Put those values in a new column.

p	q	r	$q \rightarrow r$
T	T	T	T
T	T	F	F
T	F	T	T
T	F	F	T
F	T	T	T
F	T	F	F
F	F	T	T
F	F	F	T

The conditional is true unless q is true and r is false.

① ④

Step 3 Find the truth values for the disjunction $p \vee (q \rightarrow r)$, using the values for p from column 1 and those for $q \rightarrow r$ from column 4. Use the truth table for disjunction from earlier in the section, and put the results in a new column.

p	q	r	$q \rightarrow r$	$p \vee (q \rightarrow r)$
T	T	T	T	T
T	T	F	F	T
T	F	T	T	T
T	F	F	T	T
F	T	T	T	T
F	T	F	F	F
F	F	T	T	T
F	F	F	T	T

The disjunction is true unless both p and q → r are false.

⑤

The truth values for the statement $p \vee (q \rightarrow r)$ are found in column 5. The statement is true unless p and r are false while q is true.

▼ Try This One 3

Construct a truth table for the statement $(p \wedge q) \vee \sim r$.

☑ 3. Construct truth tables for compound statements.

In the method we've demonstrated for constructing truth tables, we begin by setting up a table with all possible combinations of Ts and Fs for the component letters from the statement. Then we build new columns, one at a time, by writing truth values for parts of the compound statement, using the basic truth tables we built earlier in the section.

We have seen that when we construct truth tables, we find truth values for statements inside parentheses first. To avoid having to always use parentheses, a hierarchy of connectives has been agreed upon by those who study logic.

1. Biconditional $\leftrightarrow$
2. Conditional $\rightarrow$
3. Conjunction $\wedge$, disjunction $\vee$
4. Negation $\sim$

Math Note

When parentheses are used to emphasize order, the statement $p \vee q \rightarrow r$ is written as $(p \vee q) \rightarrow r$. The statement $p \leftrightarrow q \wedge r$ is written as $p \leftrightarrow (q \vee r)$.

When we find the truth value for a compound statement without parentheses, we find *the truth value of a lower-order connective first*. For example, $p \vee q \rightarrow r$ is a conditional statement since the conditional ($\rightarrow$) is of a higher order than the disjunction ($\vee$). If you were constructing a truth table for the statement, you would find the truth value for $\vee$ first. The statement $p \leftrightarrow q \wedge r$ is a biconditional statement since the biconditional ($\leftrightarrow$) is of a higher order than the order of the conjunction ($\wedge$). When constructing a truth table for the statement, the truth value for the conjunction ($\wedge$) would be found first. The conjunction and disjunction are of the same order; the statement $p \wedge q \vee r$ cannot be identified unless parentheses are used. In this case, $(p \wedge q) \vee r$ is a disjunction and $p \wedge (q \vee r)$ is a conjunction.

EXAMPLE 4   **Using the Hierarchy of Connectives**

For each, identify the type of statement using the hierarchy of connectives, and rewrite by using parentheses to indicate order.

(a) $\sim p \vee \sim q$ (b) $p \rightarrow \sim q \wedge r$ (c) $p \vee q \leftrightarrow q \vee r$ (d) $p \rightarrow q \leftrightarrow r$

SOLUTION

(a) The $\vee$ is higher than the $\sim$; the statement is a disjunction and looks like $(\sim p) \vee (\sim q)$ with parentheses.
(b) The $\rightarrow$ is higher than the $\wedge$ or $\sim$; the statement is a conditional and looks like $p \rightarrow (\sim q \wedge r)$ with parentheses.
(c) The $\leftrightarrow$ is higher than $\vee$; the statement is a biconditional and looks like $(p \vee q) \leftrightarrow (q \vee r)$ with parentheses.
(d) The $\leftrightarrow$ is higher than the $\rightarrow$; the statement is a biconditional and looks like $(p \rightarrow q) \leftrightarrow r$ with parentheses.

☑ 4. Identify the hierarchy of logical connectives.

▼ Try This One 4

For each, identify the type of statement using the hierarchy of connectives, and rewrite by using parentheses to indicate order.

(a) $\sim p \vee q$ (c) $p \vee q \leftrightarrow \sim p \vee \sim q$ (e) $p \leftrightarrow q \rightarrow r$
(b) $p \vee \sim q \rightarrow r$ (d) $p \wedge \sim q$

EXAMPLE 5   **An Application of Truth Tables**

Use the truth value of each simple statement to determine the truth value of the compound statement.

p: O. J. Simpson was convicted in California in 1995.
q: O. J. Simpson was convicted in Nevada in 2008.
r: O. J. Simpson gets sent to prison.

Statement: $(p \vee q) \rightarrow r$

SOLUTION

In probably the most publicized trial of recent times, Simpson was acquitted of murder in California in 1995, so statement p is false. In 2008, however, Simpson was convicted of robbery and kidnapping in Nevada, so statement q is true. Statement r is also true, as Simpson was sentenced in December 2008.

Now we'll analyze the compound statement. First, the disjunction $p \vee q$ is true when either p or q is true, so in this case, $p \vee q$ is true. Finally, the implication $(p \vee q) \rightarrow r$ is true when both r and $p \vee q$ are true, which is the case here. So the compound statement $(p \vee q) \rightarrow r$ is true.

▼ Try This One 5

Using the simple statements in Example 5, find the truth value of the compound statement $(\sim p \wedge \sim q) \rightarrow r$.

An Alternative Method for Constructing Truth Tables

In the next two examples, we will illustrate a second method for constructing truth tables so that you can make a comparison. The problems are the same as Examples 2 and 3.

EXAMPLE 6   Constructing a Truth Table by Using an Alternative Method

Construct a truth table for $\sim(p \rightarrow \sim q)$.

SOLUTION

Step 1 Set up the table as shown.

p	q	$\sim(p \rightarrow \sim q)$
T	T	
T	F	
F	T	
F	F	

Step 2 Write the truth values for p and q underneath the respective letters in the statement as shown, and label the columns as 1 and 2.

p	q	$\sim(p \rightarrow \sim q)$
T	T	T T
T	F	T F
F	T	F T
F	F	F F
		① ②

Step 3 Find the negation of q since it is inside the parentheses, and place the truth values in column 3. Draw a line through the truth values in column 2 since they will not be used again.

p	q	$\sim(p$	$\rightarrow$	$\sim$	$q)$
T	T	T		F	T
T	F	T		T	F
F	T	F		F	T
F	F	F		T	F
		①		③	②

"It is not true that if it rains, then we can't go out," is an example of a statement that can be written as $\sim(p \rightarrow \sim q)$.

Step 4 Find the truth values for the conditional ($\rightarrow$) by using the T and F values in columns 1 and 3 and the conditional truth table from earlier in the section.

Place these values in column 4 and draw a line through the T and F values in columns 1 and 3, as shown.

p	q	$\sim($	p	$\rightarrow$	$\sim$	$q)$
T	T		T	F	F	T
T	F		T	T	T	F
F	T		F	T	F	T
F	F		F	T	T	F
			①	④	③	②

The conditional is true unless p is true and $\sim q$ is false.

Step 5 Find the negations of the truth values in column 4 (since the negation sign is outside the parentheses).

p	q	$\sim$	$(p$	$\rightarrow$	$\sim$	$q)$
T	T	T	T	F	F	T
T	F	F	T	T	T	F
F	T	F	F	T	F	T
F	F	F	F	T	T	F
		⑤	①	④	③	②

The negation has values opposite those in column 4.

The truth value of $\sim(p \rightarrow \sim q)$ is found in column 5. Fortunately, these are the same values we found in Example 2.

Math Note

It isn't necessary to label the columns with numbers or to draw a line through the truth values in the columns when they are no longer needed; however, these two strategies can help reduce errors.

▼ Try This One 6

Construct a truth table for the statement $p \leftrightarrow (\sim p \wedge q)$, using the alternative method.

EXAMPLE 7 **Constructing a Truth Table by Using an Alternative Method**

Construct a truth table for the statement $p \vee (q \rightarrow r)$.

SOLUTION

Step 1 Set up the table as shown.

p	q	r	$p \vee (q \rightarrow r)$
T	T	T	
T	T	F	
T	F	T	
T	F	F	
F	T	T	
F	T	F	
F	F	T	
F	F	F	

Step 2 Recopy the values of p, q, and r under their respective letters in the statement as shown.

p	q	r	$p \vee (q \rightarrow r)$		
T	T	T	T	T	T
T	T	F	T	T	F
T	F	T	T	F	T
T	F	F	T	F	F
F	T	T	F	T	T
F	T	F	F	T	F
F	F	T	F	F	T
F	F	F	F	F	F

① ② ③

Step 3 Using the truth values in columns 2 and 3 and the truth table for the conditional ($\rightarrow$), find the values inside the parentheses for the conditional and place them in column 4.

p	q	r	p $\vee$	$(q$	$\rightarrow$	$r)$
T	T	T	T	T	T	T
T	T	F	T	T	F	F
T	F	T	T	F	T	T
T	F	F	T	F	T	F
F	T	T	F	T	T	T
F	T	F	F	T	F	F
F	F	T	F	F	T	T
F	F	F	F	F	T	F

①   ② ④ ③

The conditional is true unless q is true and r is false.

Step 4 Complete the truth table, using the truth values in columns 1 and 4 and the table for the disjunction ($\vee$), as shown.

p	q	r	p	$\vee$	$(q$	$\rightarrow$	$r)$
T	T	T	T	T	T	T	T
T	T	F	T	T	T	F	F
T	F	T	T	T	F	T	T
T	F	F	T	T	F	T	F
F	T	T	F	T	T	T	T
F	T	F	F	F	T	F	F
F	F	T	F	T	F	T	T
F	F	F	F	T	F	T	F

① ⑤ ② ④ ③

The disjunction is true unless p and q → r are both false.

The truth value for $p \vee (q \rightarrow r)$ is found in column 5. These are the same values we found in Example 3.

▼ **Try This One 7**

Construct a truth table for the statement $(p \wedge q) \vee \sim r$ using the alternative method.

☑ 5. Construct truth tables by using an alternative method.

The best approach to learning truth tables is to try each of the two methods and see which one is more comfortable for you. In any case, we have seen that truth tables are an effective way to organize truth values for statements, allowing us to determine the truth values of some very complicated statements in a systematic way.

Answers to Try This One

1

p	q	$\sim q$	$p \vee \sim q$
T	T	F	T
T	F	T	T
F	T	F	F
F	F	T	T

2

p	q	$\sim p$	$\sim p \wedge q$	$p \leftrightarrow (\sim p \wedge q)$
T	T	F	F	F
T	F	F	F	F
F	T	T	T	F
F	F	T	F	T

3

p	q	r	$p \wedge q$	$\sim r$	$(p \wedge q) \vee \sim r$
T	T	T	T	F	T
T	T	F	T	T	T
T	F	T	F	F	F
T	F	F	F	T	T
F	T	T	F	F	F
F	T	F	F	T	T
F	F	T	F	F	F
F	F	F	F	T	T

4 (a) Disjunction; $(\sim p) \vee q$
(b) Conditional; $(p \vee \sim q) \rightarrow r$
(c) Biconditional; $(p \vee q) \leftrightarrow (\sim p \vee \sim q)$
(d) Conjunction; $p \wedge (\sim q)$
(e) Biconditional; $p \leftrightarrow (q \rightarrow r)$

5 True

6

p	q	p	$\leftrightarrow$	$(\sim$	p	$\wedge$	$q)$
T	T	T	F	F	T	F	T
T	F	T	F	F	T	F	F
F	T	F	F	T	F	T	T
F	F	F	T	T	F	F	F
		①	⑤	③	①	④	②

7

p	q	r	$(p$	$\wedge$	$q)$	$\vee$	$\sim$	r
T	T	T	T	T	T	T	F	T
T	T	F	T	T	T	T	T	F
T	F	T	T	F	F	F	F	T
T	F	F	T	F	F	T	T	F
F	T	T	F	F	T	F	F	T
F	T	F	F	F	T	T	T	F
F	F	T	F	F	F	F	F	T
F	F	F	F	F	F	T	T	F
			①	④	②	⑥	⑤	③

EXERCISE SET 3-2

Writing Exercises

1. Explain the purpose of a truth table.
2. Explain the difference between the inclusive and exclusive disjunctions.
3. Explain the difference between the conditional and biconditional statements.
4. Describe the hierarchy for the basic connectives.

Computational Exercises

For Exercises 5–34, construct a truth table for each.

5. $\sim(p \lor q)$

6. $q \rightarrow p$

7. $\sim p \land q$

8. $\sim q \rightarrow \sim p$

9. $\sim p \leftrightarrow q$

10. $(p \lor q) \rightarrow \sim p$

11. $\sim(p \land q) \rightarrow p$

12. $(p \lor q) \land (q \land p)$

13. $(\sim q \land p) \rightarrow \sim p$

14. $q \land \sim p$

15. $(p \land q) \leftrightarrow (q \lor \sim p)$

16. $p \rightarrow (q \lor \sim p)$

17. $(p \land q) \lor p$

18. $(q \rightarrow p) \lor \sim r$

19. $(r \land q) \lor (p \land q)$

20. $(r \rightarrow q) \lor (p \rightarrow r)$

21. $\sim(p \lor q) \rightarrow \sim(p \land r)$

22. $(\sim p \lor \sim q) \rightarrow \sim r$

23. $(\sim p \lor q) \land r$

24. $p \land (q \lor \sim r)$

25. $(p \land q) \leftrightarrow (\sim r \lor q)$

26. $\sim(p \land r) \rightarrow (q \land r)$

27. $r \rightarrow \sim(p \lor q)$

28. $(p \lor q) \lor (\sim p \lor \sim r)$

29. $p \rightarrow (\sim q \land \sim r)$

30. $(q \lor \sim r) \leftrightarrow (p \land \sim q)$

31. $\sim(q \rightarrow p) \land r$

32. $q \rightarrow (p \land r)$

33. $(r \lor q) \land (r \land p)$

34. $(p \land q) \leftrightarrow \sim r$

Real-World Applications

For Exercises 35–40, use the truth value of each simple statement to determine the truth value of the compound statement. Use the Internet if you need help determining the truth value of a simple statement.

35. *p*: Japan bombs Pearl Harbor.
    q: The United States stays out of World War II.
    Statement: $p \rightarrow q$

36. *p*: Barack Obama wins the Democratic nomination in 2008.
    q: Mitt Romney wins the Republican nomination in 2008.
    Statement: $p \land q$

37. *p*: NASA sends a manned spacecraft to the Moon.
    q: NASA sends a manned spacecraft to Mars.
    Statement: $p \lor q$

38. *p*: Michael Phelps wins eight gold medals.
    q: Michael Phelps gets a large endorsement deal.
    Statement: $p \rightarrow q$

39. *p*: Apple builds a portable MP3 player.
    q: Apple stops making computers.
    r: Microsoft releases the Vista operating system.
    Statement: $(p \lor q) \land r$

40. *p*: Hurricane Katrina hits New Orleans.
    q: New Orleans Superdome is damaged.
    r: New Orleans Saints play home games in 2005 in Baton Rouge.
    Statement: $(p \land q) \rightarrow r$

Exercises 41–46 are based on the compound statement below.

A new weight loss supplement claims that if you take the product daily and cut your calorie intake by 10%, you will lose at least 10 pounds in the next 4 months.

41. This compound statement is made up of three simple statements. Identify them and assign a letter to each.

42. Write the compound statement in symbolic form, using conjunctions and the conditional.

43. Construct a truth table for the compound statement you wrote in Exercise 42.

44. If you take this product daily and don't cut your calorie intake by 10%, and then don't lose 10 pounds, is the claim made by the advertiser true or false?

45. If you take the product daily, don't cut your calorie intake by 10%, and do lose 10 pounds, is the claim true or false?

46. If you don't take the product daily, cut your calorie intake by 10%, and do lose 10 pounds, is the claim true or false?

Exercises 47–52 are based on the compound statement below.

The owner of a professional baseball team publishes an open letter to fans after another losing season. He claims that if attendance for the following season is over 2 million, then he will add $20 million to the payroll and the team will make the playoffs the following year.

47. This compound statement is made up of three simple statements. Identify them and assign a letter to each.

48. Write the compound statement in symbolic form, using conjunction and the conditional.

49. Construct a truth table for the compound statement you wrote in Exercise 48.

50. If attendance goes over 2 million the next year and the owner raises payroll by $20 million, but the team fails to make the playoffs, is the owner's claim true or false?

51. If attendance is less than 2 million but the owner still raises the payroll by $20 million and the team makes the playoffs, is the owner's claim true or false?

52. If attendance is over 2 million, the owner doesn't raise the payroll, but the team still makes the playoffs, is the owner's claim true or false?

Critical Thinking

53. Using the hierarchy for connectives, write the statement $p \rightarrow q \lor r$ by using parentheses to indicate the proper order. Then construct truth tables for $(p \rightarrow q) \lor r$ and $p \rightarrow (q \lor r)$. Are the resulting truth values the same? Are you surprised? Why or why not?

54. The hierarchy of connectives doesn't distinguish between conjunctions and disjunctions. Does that matter? Construct truth tables for $(p \lor q) \land r$ and $p \lor (q \land r)$ to help you decide.

55. In 2003, New York City Council was considering banning indoor smoking in bars and restaurants. Opponents of the ban claimed that it would have a negligible effect on indoor pollution, but a huge negative effect on the economic success of these businesses. Eventually, the ban was enacted, and a 2004 study by the city department of health found that there was a sixfold decrease in indoor air pollution in bars and restaurants, but jobs, liquor licenses, and tax revenues all increased. Assign truth values to all the premises of the opponents' claim; then write the claim as a compound statement and determine its validity.

Section 3-3 Types of Statements

LEARNING OBJECTIVES

❏ 1. Classify a statement as a tautology, a self-contradiction, or neither.

❏ 2. Identify logically equivalent statements.

❏ 3. Write negations of compound statements.

❏ 4. Write the converse, inverse, and contrapositive of a statement.

It's no secret that weight loss has become big business in the United States. It seems like almost every week, a new company pops into existence with the latest miracle pill to turn you into a supermodel.

A typical advertisement will say something like "Use of our product may result in significant weight loss." That sounds great, but think about what that statement really means. If use of the product "may" result in significant weight loss, then it also may not result in weight loss at all! The statement could be translated as "You will lose weight or you will not lose weight." Of course, this statement is always true. In this section, we will study statements of this type.

Tautologies and Self-Contradictions

In our study of truth tables in Section 3-2, we saw that most compound statements are true in some cases and false in others. What we have not done is think about whether that's true for *every* compound statement. Some simple examples should be enough to convince you that this is most definitely not the case.

Consider the simple statement "I'm going to Cancun for spring break this year." Its negation is "I'm not going to Cancun for spring break this year." Now think about these two compound statements:

> "I'm going to Cancun for spring break this year, or I'm not going to Cancun for spring break this year."

> "I'm going to Cancun for spring break this year, and I'm not going to Cancun for spring break this year."

Hopefully, it's pretty clear to you that the first statement is always true, while the second statement is always false (whether you go to Cancun or not). The first is an example of a *tautology,* while the second is an example of a *self-contradiction.*

When a compound statement is always true, it is called a **tautology.**
When a compound statement is always false, it is called a **self-contradiction.**

> **CAUTION** Don't make the mistake of thinking that every statement is either a tautology or a self-contradiction. We've seen many examples of statements that are sometimes true and other times false.

The sample statements above are simple enough that it's easy to tell that they are always true or always false based on common sense. But for more complicated statements, we'll need to construct a truth table to decide if a statement is a tautology, a self-contradiction, or neither.

EXAMPLE 1   Using a Truth Table to Classify a Statement

Let p = "I am going to a concert" and q = "I will wear black." Translate each statement in Example 1 into a word statement using this choice of p and q. Can you predict which statements are tautologies, self-contradictions, or neither?

Determine if each statement is a tautology, a self-contradiction, or neither.

(a) $(p \wedge q) \rightarrow p$ (b) $(p \wedge q) \wedge (\sim p \wedge \sim q)$ (c) $(p \vee q) \rightarrow q$

SOLUTION

(a) The truth table for statement (a) is

p	q	$p \wedge q$	$(p \wedge q) \rightarrow p$
T	T	T	T
T	F	F	T
F	T	F	T
F	F	F	T

Since the truth table value consists of all Ts, the statement is always true, that is, a tautology.

(b) The truth table for statement (b) is

p	q	$\sim p$	$\sim q$	$p \wedge q$	$\sim p \wedge \sim q$	$(p \wedge q) \wedge (\sim p \wedge \sim q)$
T	T	F	F	T	F	F
T	F	F	T	F	F	F
F	T	T	F	F	F	F
F	F	T	T	F	T	F

Since the truth value consists of all Fs, the statement is always false, that is, a self-contradiction.

(c) The truth table for statement (c) is

p	q	$p \vee q$	$(p \vee q) \rightarrow q$
T	T	T	T
T	F	T	F
F	T	T	T
F	F	F	T

Since the statement can be true in some cases and false in others, it is neither a tautology nor a self-contradiction.

☑ 1. Classify a statement as a tautology, a self-contradiction, or neither.

▼ Try This One 1

Determine if each statement is a tautology, a self-contradiction, or neither.

(a) $(p \vee q) \wedge (\sim p \rightarrow q)$ (b) $(p \wedge \sim q) \wedge \sim p$ (c) $(p \rightarrow q) \vee \sim q$

Logically Equivalent Statements

Next, consider the two logical statements $p \rightarrow q$ and $\sim p \vee q$. The truth table for the two statements is

p	q	$\sim p$	$p \rightarrow q$	$\sim p \vee q$
T	T	F	T	T
T	F	F	F	F
F	T	T	T	T
F	F	T	T	T

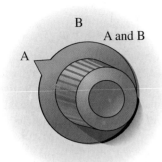

The statements "If the red dial is set to A, then use only speaker A" and "The red dial is not set to speaker A, or only speaker A is used" can be modeled with the logic statements $p \rightarrow q$ and $\sim p \vee q$.

Notice that the truth values for both statements are *identical,* that is, TFTT. When this occurs, the statements are said to be *logically equivalent;* that is, both compositions of the same simple statements have the same meaning. For example, the statement "If it snows, I will go skiing" is logically equivalent to saying "It is not snowing or I will go skiing." Formally defined,

Two compound statements are **logically equivalent** if and only if they have the same truth table values. The symbol for logically equivalent statements is $\equiv$.

EXAMPLE 2 Identifying Logically Equivalent Statements

Determine if the two statements $p \rightarrow q$ and $\sim q \rightarrow \sim p$ are logically equivalent.

SOLUTION

The truth table for the statements is

p	q	$\sim p$	$\sim q$	$p \rightarrow q$	$\sim q \rightarrow \sim p$
T	T	F	F	T	T
T	F	F	T	F	F
F	T	T	F	T	T
F	F	T	T	T	T

Since both statements have the same truth values, they are logically equivalent.

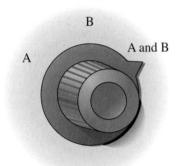

In the red dial example, $\sim q \rightarrow \sim p$ would be "If speaker A is not the only one used, then the red dial is not set to A."

☑ 2. Identify logically equivalent statements.

▼ Try This One 2

Determine which two statements are logically equivalent.

(a) $\sim(p \wedge \sim q)$ (b) $\sim p \wedge q$ (c) $\sim p \vee q$

De Morgan's laws for logic give us an example of equivalent statements.

De Morgan's Laws for Logic

For any statements p and q,

$$\sim(p \vee q) \equiv \sim p \wedge \sim q \quad \text{and} \quad \sim(p \wedge q) \equiv \sim p \vee \sim q$$

Notice the similarities between De Morgan's laws for sets and De Morgan's laws for logic. De Morgan's laws can be proved by constructing truth tables; the proofs will be left to you in the exercises.

De Morgan's laws are most often used to write the negation of conjunctions and disjunctions. For example, the negation of the statement "I will go to work or I will go to the beach" is "I will not go to work and I will not go to the beach." Notice that when you negate a conjunction, it becomes a disjunction; and when you negate a disjunction, it becomes a conjunction—that is, the *and* becomes an *or,* and the *or* becomes an *and.*

EXAMPLE 3   Using De Morgan's Laws to Write Negations

Write the negations of the following statements, using De Morgan's laws.

(a) Studying is necessary and I am a hard worker.
(b) It is not easy or I am lazy.
(c) I will pass this test or I will drop this class.
(d) She is angry or she's my friend, and she is cool.

SOLUTION

(a) Studying is not necessary or I am not a hard worker.
(b) It is easy and I am not lazy.
(c) I will not pass this test and I will not drop this class.
(d) She is not angry and she is not my friend, or she is not cool.

▼ Try This One 3

Write the negations of the following statements, using De Morgan's laws.

(a) I will study for this class or I will fail.
(b) I will go to the dance club and the restaurant.
(c) It is not silly or I have no sense of humor.
(d) The movie is a comedy or a thriller, and it is awesome.

Earlier in this section, we saw that the two statements $p \rightarrow q$ and $\sim p \vee q$ are logically equivalent. Now that we know De Morgan's laws, we can use this fact to find the negation of the conditional statement $p \rightarrow q$.

$$\sim(p \rightarrow q) \equiv \sim(\sim p \vee q)$$
$$\equiv \sim(\sim p) \wedge \sim q \qquad \text{Note: } \sim(\sim p) \equiv p$$
$$\equiv p \wedge \sim q$$

This can be checked by using a truth table as shown.

p	q	$\sim q$	$p \rightarrow q$	$\sim(p \rightarrow q)$	$p \wedge \sim q$
T	T	F	T	F	F
T	F	T	F	T	T
F	T	F	T	F	F
F	F	T	T	F	F

So the negation of $p \rightarrow q$ is $p \wedge \sim q$.

For example, if you say, "It is false that if it is sunny, then I will go swimming," this is equivalent to the statement "It's sunny and I will not go swimming."

EXAMPLE 4   Writing the Negation of a Conditional Statement

Write the negation of the statement "If I have a computer, then I will use the Internet."

SOLUTION

Let $p =$ "I have a computer" and $q =$ "I will use the Internet." The statement $p \rightarrow q$ can be negated as $p \wedge {\sim}q$. This translates to "I have a computer and I will not use the Internet."

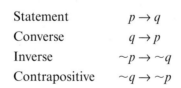

▼ Try This One 4

☑ 3. Write negations of compound statements.

Write the negation of the statement "If the video is popular, then it can be found on YouTube."

Table 3-3 summarizes the negations of the basic compound statements.

TABLE 3-3   Negation of Compound Statements

Statement	Negation	Equivalent Negation
$p \wedge q$	${\sim}(p \wedge q)$	${\sim}p \vee {\sim}q$
$p \vee q$	${\sim}(p \vee q)$	${\sim}p \wedge {\sim}q$
$p \rightarrow q$	${\sim}(p \rightarrow q)$	$p \wedge {\sim}q$

Variations of the Conditional Statement

From the conditional statement $p \rightarrow q$, three other related statements can be formed: the **converse,** the **inverse,** and the **contrapositive.** They are shown here symbolically.

Statement	$p \rightarrow q$
Converse	$q \rightarrow p$
Inverse	${\sim}p \rightarrow {\sim}q$
Contrapositive	${\sim}q \rightarrow {\sim}p$

Using the statement "If Tessa is a chocolate Lab, then Tessa is brown" as our original conditional statement, we find the related statements are as follows:

Converse: If Tessa is brown, then Tessa is a chocolate Lab.

Inverse: If Tessa is not a chocolate Lab, then Tessa is not brown.

Contrapositive: If Tessa is not brown, then Tessa is not a chocolate Lab.

Based on the photo, we can see that the original statement is true, but of the three related statements, only the contrapositive is also true. This is an important observation—one that we'll elaborate on shortly.

EXAMPLE 5 Writing the Converse, Inverse, and Contrapositive

Write the converse, the inverse, and the contrapositive for the statement "If you earned a bachelor's degree, then you got a high-paying job."

SOLUTION

It's helpful to write the original implication in symbols: $p \rightarrow q$, where p = "You earned a bachelor's degree" and q = "You got a high-paying job."

Converse: $q \rightarrow p$. "If you got a high-paying job, then you earned a bachelor's degree."

Inverse: $\sim p \rightarrow \sim q$. "If you did not earn a bachelor's degree, then you did not get a high-paying job."

Contrapositive: $\sim q \rightarrow \sim p$. "If you did not get a high-paying job, then you did not earn a bachelor's degree."

▼ Try This One 5

Write the converse, the inverse, and the contrapositive for the statement "If you do well in math classes, then you are intelligent."

Math Note

Many people using logic in real life assume that if a statement is true, the converse is automatically true. Consider the following statement: "If a person earns more than $200,000 per year, that person can buy a Corvette." The converse is stated as "If a person can buy a Corvette, then that person earns more than $200,000 per year." This may be far from the truth since a person may have to make very large payments, live in a tent, or work three jobs in order to afford the expensive car.

The relationships between the variations of the conditional statements can be determined by looking at the truth tables for each of the statements.

p	q	$p \rightarrow q$	$q \rightarrow p$	$\sim p \rightarrow \sim q$	$\sim q \rightarrow \sim p$
T	T	T	T	T	T
T	F	F	T	T	F
F	T	T	F	F	T
F	F	T	T	T	T

Since the original statement ($p \rightarrow q$) and the contrapositive statement ($\sim q \rightarrow \sim p$) have the same truth values, they are equivalent. Also note that the converse ($q \rightarrow p$) and the inverse ($\sim p \rightarrow \sim q$) have the same truth values, so they are equivalent as well. Finally, notice that the original statement is not equivalent to the converse or the inverse since the truth values of the converse and inverse differ from those of the original statement.

Since the conditional statement $p \rightarrow q$ is used so often in logic as well as mathematics, a more detailed analysis is helpful. Recall that the conditional statement $p \rightarrow q$ is also called an *implication* and consists of two simple statements; the first is the *antecedent p* and the second is the *consequent q*. For example, the statement "If I jump into the pool, then I will get wet" consists of the antecedent p, "I jump into the pool," and the consequent q, "I will get wet," connected by the if . . . then connective.

The conditional can also be stated in these other ways:

p implies *q*

q if *p*

p only if *q*

p is sufficient for *q*

q is necessary for *p*

All *p* are *q*

In four of these six forms, the antecedent comes first, but for "*q* if *p*" and "*q* is necessary for *p*," the consequent comes first. So identifying the antecedent and consequent is important.

For example, think about the statement "If you drink and drive, you get arrested." Writing it in the different possible forms, we get:

Drinking and driving implies you get arrested.

You get arrested if you drink and drive.

You drink and drive only if you get arrested.

Drinking and driving is sufficient for getting arrested.

Getting arrested is necessary for drinking and driving.

All those who drink and drive get arrested.

Of course, these all say the same thing. To illustrate the importance of getting the antecedent and consequent in the correct order, consider the "*q* if *p*" form, in this case "You get arrested if you drink and drive." If we don't start with the consequent, we get "You drink and drive if you get arrested." This is completely false—there are any number of things you could get arrested for other than drinking and driving.

EXAMPLE 6 **Writing Variations of a Conditional Statement**

Write each statement in symbols. Let p = "A person is over 6′ 6′′" and q = "A person is tall."

(a) If a person is over 6′6′′, then the person is tall.
(b) Being tall is necessary for being over 6′6′′.
(c) A person is over 6′6′′ only if the person is tall.
(d) Being 6′6′′ is sufficient for being tall.
(e) A person is tall if the person is over 6′6′′.

SOLUTION

(a) If p, then q; $p \rightarrow q$
(b) q is necessary for p; $p \rightarrow q$
(c) p only if q; $p \rightarrow q$
(d) p is sufficient for q; $p \rightarrow q$
(e) q if p; $p \rightarrow q$

Actually, these statements all say the same thing!

✓ 4. Write the converse, inverse, and contrapositive of a statement.

▼ Try This One 6

Write each statement in symbols. Let p = "A student comes to class every day" and q = "A student gets a good grade."

(a) A student gets a good grade if a student comes to class every day.
(b) Coming to class every day is necessary for getting a good grade.
(c) A student gets a good grade only if a student comes to class every day.
(d) Coming to class every day is sufficient for getting a good grade.

In this section, we saw that some statements are always true (tautologies) and others are always false (self-contradictions). We also defined what it means for two statements to be logically equivalent—they have the same truth values. Now we're ready to analyze logical arguments to determine if they're legitimate or not.

Answers to Try This One

1 (a) Neither   (b) Self-contradiction
       (c) Tautology

2 (a) and (c)

3 (a) I will not study for this class and I will not fail.
       (b) I will not go to the dance club or the
            restaurant.
       (c) It is silly and I have a sense of humor.
       (d) The movie is not a comedy and it is not a
            thriller, or it is not awesome.

4 The video is popular and it cannot be found on
       YouTube.

5 Converse: If you are intelligent, then you do well
       in math classes.
            Inverse: If you do not do well in math classes,
       then you are not intelligent.
            Contrapositive: If you are not intelligent, then
       you do not do well in math classes.

6 (a) $p \rightarrow q$ (b) $q \rightarrow p$ (c) $q \rightarrow p$ (d) $p \rightarrow q$

EXERCISE SET 3-3

Writing Exercises

1. Explain the difference between a tautology and a self-contradiction.
2. Is every statement either a tautology or a self-contradiction? Why or why not?
3. Describe how to find the converse, inverse, and contrapositive of a conditional statement.
4. How can you decide if two statements are logically equivalent?
5. How can you decide if one statement is the negation of another?
6. Is a statement always logically equivalent to its converse? Explain.

Computational Exercises

For Exercises 7–16, determine which statements are tautologies, self-contradictions, or neither.

7. $(p \vee q) \vee (\sim p \wedge \sim q)$
8. $(p \rightarrow q) \wedge (p \vee q)$
9. $(p \wedge q) \wedge (\sim p \vee \sim q)$
10. $\sim p \vee (p \rightarrow q)$
11. $(p \leftrightarrow q) \vee \sim (q \leftrightarrow p)$
12. $(p \wedge q) \leftrightarrow (p \rightarrow \sim q)$
13. $(p \vee q) \wedge (\sim p \vee \sim q)$
14. $(p \wedge q) \vee (p \vee q)$
15. $(p \leftrightarrow q) \wedge (\sim p \leftrightarrow \sim q)$
16. $(p \rightarrow q) \wedge (\sim p \vee q)$

For Exercises 17–26, determine if the two statements are logically equivalent statements, negations, or neither.

17. $\sim q \rightarrow p$; $\sim p \rightarrow q$
18. $p \wedge q$; $\sim q \vee \sim p$
19. $\sim (p \vee q)$; $p \rightarrow \sim q$
20. $\sim (p \rightarrow q)$; $\sim p \wedge q$
21. $q \rightarrow p$; $\sim (p \rightarrow q)$
22. $p \vee (\sim q \wedge r)$; $(p \wedge \sim q) \vee (p \wedge r)$
23. $\sim (p \vee q)$; $\sim (\sim p \wedge \sim q)$
24. $(p \vee q) \rightarrow r$; $\sim r \rightarrow \sim (p \vee q)$
25. $(p \wedge q) \vee r$; $p \wedge (q \vee r)$
26. $p \leftrightarrow \sim q$; $(p \wedge \sim q) \vee (\sim p \wedge q)$

For Exercises 27–32, write the converse, inverse, and contrapositive of each.

27. $p \rightarrow q$
28. $\sim p \rightarrow \sim q$
29. $\sim q \rightarrow p$
30. $\sim p \rightarrow q$
31. $p \rightarrow \sim q$
32. $q \rightarrow p$

Real-World Applications

In Exercises 33–42, use De Morgan's laws to write the negation of the statement.

33. The concert is long or it is fun.
34. The soda is sweet or it is not carbonated.
35. It is not cold and I am soaked.
36. I will walk in the Race for the Cure walkathon and I will be tired.
37. I will go to the beach and I will not get sunburned.
38. The coffee is a latte or an espresso.
39. The student is a girl or the professor is not a man.
40. I will go to college and I will get a degree.
41. It is right or it is wrong.
42. Our school colors are not blue or they are not green.

For Exercises 43–49, let p = "I need to talk to my friend" and q = "I will send her a text message." Write each of the following in symbols (see Example 6).

43. If I need to talk to my friend, I will send her a text message.
44. If I will not send her a text message, I do not need to talk to my friend.
45. Sending a text message is necessary for needing to talk to my friend.
46. I will send her a text message if I need to talk to my friend.
47. Needing to talk to my friend is sufficient for sending her a text message.

48. I need to talk to my friend only if I will send her a text message.

49. I do not need to talk to my friend only if I will not send her a text message.

50. Are any of the statements in Exercises 43–49 logically equivalent?

For Exercises 51–56, write the converse, inverse, and contrapositive of the conditional statement.

51. If he graduated with a Bachelor's degree in Management Information Systems, then he will get a good job.

52. If she does not earn $5,000 this summer as a barista at the coffeehouse, then she cannot buy the green Ford Focus.

53. If the *American Idol* finale is today, then I will host a party in my dorm room.

54. If my cell phone will not charge, then I will replace the battery.

55. I will go to Nassau for spring break if I lose 10 pounds by March 1.

56. The politician will go to jail if he gets caught taking kickbacks.

Critical Thinking

57. In this section, we wrote the negation of $p \rightarrow q$ by using a disjunction. See if you can write the negation of $p \rightarrow q$ by using a conjunction.

58. Try to write the negation of the biconditional $p \leftrightarrow q$ by using only conjunctions, disjunctions, and negations.

59. Can you think of a true conditional statement about someone you know so that the converse is true as well? How about so that the converse is false?

60. Can you think of a true conditional statement about someone you know so that the inverse is true as well? How about so that the inverse is false?

61. Prove the first of De Morgan's laws by using truth tables:

$$\sim(p \vee q) \equiv \sim p \wedge \sim q$$

62. Prove the second of De Morgan's laws by using truth tables:

$$\sim(p \wedge q) \equiv \sim p \vee \sim q$$

Section 3-4 Logical Arguments

LEARNING OBJECTIVES

☐ 1. Define *valid argument* and *fallacy*.

☐ 2. Use truth tables to determine the validity of an argument.

☐ 3. Identify common argument forms.

☐ 4. Determine the validity of arguments by using common argument forms.

Common sense is a funny thing in our society: we all think we have it, and we also think that most other people don't. This thing that we call common sense is really the ability to think logically, to evaluate an argument or situation and decide what is and is not reasonable. It doesn't take a lot of imagination to picture how valuable it is to be able to think logically. We're pretty well protected by parents for our first few years of life, but after that the main tool we have to guide us through the perils of life is our brain. The more effectively that brain can analyze and evaluate information, the more successful we're likely to be. The work we've done in building the basics of symbolic logic in the first three sections of this chapter has prepared us for the real point: analyzing logical arguments objectively. That's the topic of this important section.

Valid Arguments and Fallacies

A logical argument is made up of two parts: a premise or premises and a conclusion based on those premises. We will call an argument **valid** if assuming the premises are true guarantees that the conclusion is true as well. An argument that is not valid is called **invalid** or a **fallacy.**

Let's look at an example.

Premise 1:	All students in this class will pass.
Premise 2:	Rachel is a student in this class.
Conclusion:	Rachel will pass this class.

We can easily tell that if the two premises are true, then the conclusion is true, so this is an example of a valid argument.

Many students find it troubling that an argument can be considered valid even if the conclusion is clearly false. But arguing in favor of something that you don't necessarily believe to be true isn't a new idea by any means—lawyers do it all the time, and it's commonly practiced in the area of formal debate, a style of intellectual competition that has its roots in ancient times.

In formal debate (also known as forensics), speakers are given a topic and asked to argue one side of a related issue. Judges determine which speakers make the most effective arguments and declare the winners accordingly. One of the most interesting aspects is that in many cases, the contestants don't know which side of the issue they will be arguing until right before the competition begins. While that aspect is intended to test the debater's flexibility and preparation, a major consequence is that opinion, and sometimes truth, is taken out of the mix, and contestants and judges must focus on the validity of arguments.

A variety of organizations sponsor national competitions in formal debate for colleges. The largest is an annual

championship organized by the National Forensics Association. Students from well over 100 schools participate in a wide variety of categories. The 2008 team champions were Tennessee State University, Kansas State University, California State Long Beach, and Western Kentucky University.

It's very important at this point to understand the difference between a true statement and a conclusion to a valid argument. A statement that is known to be false can still be a valid conclusion if it follows logically from the given premises. For example, consider this argument:

> Los Angeles is in California or Mexico.
> Los Angeles is not in California.
> Therefore, Los Angeles is in Mexico.

☑ 1. Define *valid argument* and *fallacy*.

This is a valid argument: if the two premises are true, then the conclusion, "Los Angeles is in Mexico," must be true as well. We know, however, that Los Angeles isn't actually in Mexico. That's the tricky part. In determining whether an argument is valid, *we will always assume that the premises are true*. In this case, we're assuming that the premise "Los Angeles is not in California" is true, even though in fact it is not. We will discuss this aspect of logical arguments in greater depth later in this section.

Truth Table Method

One method for determining the validity of an argument is by using truth tables. We will use the following procedure.

Procedure for Determining the Validity of Arguments

Step 1 Write the argument in symbols.

Step 2 Write the argument as a conditional statement; use a conjunction between the premises and the implication ($\Rightarrow$) for the conclusion. (*Note:* The $\Rightarrow$ is the same as $\rightarrow$ but will be used to designate an argument.)

Step 3 Set up and construct a truth table as follows:

Symbols | Premise ∧ Premise ⇒ Conclusion

Step 4 If all truth values under ⇒ are Ts (i.e., a tautology), then the argument is valid; otherwise, it is invalid.

EXAMPLE 1 Determining the Validity of an Argument

Determine if the following argument is valid or invalid.

If a figure has three sides, then it is a triangle.
This figure is not a triangle.
Therefore, this figure does not have three sides.

SOLUTION

Step 1 *Write the argument in symbols.* Let p = "The figure has three sides," and let q = "The figure is a triangle."

Translated into symbols:

$p \rightarrow q$ (Premise)

$\sim q$ (Premise)

$\therefore \sim p$ (Conclusion)

A line is used to separate the premises from the conclusion and the three triangular dots $\therefore$ mean "therefore."

Step 2 *Write the argument as an implication* by connecting the premises with a conjunction and implying the conclusion as shown.

Premise 1		Premise 2		Conclusion
$(p \rightarrow q)$	$\wedge$	$\sim q$	$\Rightarrow$	$\sim p$

Step 3 *Construct a truth table* as shown.

p	q	$\sim p$	$\sim q$	$p \rightarrow q$	$(p \rightarrow q) \wedge \sim q$	$[(p \rightarrow q) \wedge \sim q] \Rightarrow \sim p$
T	T	F	F	T	F	T
T	F	F	T	F	F	T
F	T	T	F	T	F	T
F	F	T	T	T	T	T

Step 4 *Determine the validity of the argument.* Since all the values under the ⇒ are true, the argument is valid.

▼ Try This One 1

Determine if the argument is valid or invalid.

I will run for student government or I will join the athletic boosters.
I did not join the athletic boosters.
Therefore, I will run for student government.

EXAMPLE 2   Determining the Validity of an Argument

Determine the validity of the following argument. "If a professor is rich, then he will buy an expensive automobile. The professor bought an expensive automobile. Therefore, the professor is rich."

SOLUTION

Step 1 *Write the argument in symbols.* Let p = "The professor is rich," and let q = "The professor buys an expensive automobile."

$$p \rightarrow q$$
$$\underline{q\qquad\quad}$$
$$\therefore p$$

Step 2 *Write the argument as an implication.*

$$(p \rightarrow q) \wedge q \Rightarrow p$$

Step 3 *Construct a truth table* for the argument.

p	q	$p \rightarrow q$	$(p \rightarrow q) \wedge q$	$[(p \rightarrow q) \wedge q] \Rightarrow p$
T	T	T	T	T
T	F	F	F	T
F	T	T	T	F
F	F	T	F	T

Step 4 *Determine the validity of the argument.* This argument is invalid since it is not a tautology. (Remember, when the values are not all Ts, the argument is invalid.) In this case, it cannot be concluded that the professor is rich.

▼ Try This One 2

Determine the validity of the following argument. "If John blows off work to go to the playoff game, he will lose his job. John lost his job. Therefore, John blew off work and went to the playoff game."

CAUTION

Remember that in symbolic logic, whether or not the conclusion is true is not important. The main concern is whether the conclusion follows from the premises.

Consider the following two arguments.

1. Either $2 + 2 \neq 4$ or $2 + 2 = 5$

$$\underline{2 + 2 = 4\qquad\qquad}$$
$$\therefore 2 + 2 = 5$$

2. If $2 + 2 \neq 5$, then I passed the math quiz.

$$\underline{\text{I did not pass the quiz.}}$$
$$\therefore 2 + 2 \neq 5$$

The truth tables on the next page show that the first argument is valid even though the conclusion is false, and the second argument is invalid even though the conclusion is true!

Let p be the statement "$2 + 2 = 4$" and q be the statement "$2 + 2 = 5$." Then the first argument is written as

$$(\sim p \vee q)$$
$$\underline{p}$$
$$\therefore q$$

Truth table for argument 1

p	q	$\sim p$	$\sim p \vee q$	$(\sim p \vee q) \wedge p$	$[(\sim p \vee q) \wedge p]$ $\Rightarrow q$
T	T	F	T	T	T
T	F	F	F	F	T
F	T	T	T	F	T
F	F	T	T	F	T

Let p be the statement "$2 + 2 \neq 5$" and q be the statement "I passed the math quiz." The second argument is written as

$$p \rightarrow q$$
$$\underline{\sim q}$$
$$\therefore p$$

Truth table for argument 2

p	q	$\sim q$	$p \rightarrow q$	$(p \rightarrow q) \wedge \sim q$	$[(p \rightarrow q) \wedge \sim q]$ $\Rightarrow p$
T	T	F	T	F	T
T	F	T	F	F	T
F	T	F	T	F	T
F	F	T	T	T	F

The validity of arguments that have three variables can also be determined by truth tables, as shown in Example 3.

EXAMPLE 3   Determining the Validity of an Argument

Determine the validity of the following argument.

$$p \rightarrow r$$
$$q \wedge r$$
$$\underline{p}$$
$$\therefore \sim q \rightarrow p$$

SOLUTION

Step 1 *Write the argument in symbols.* This has been done already.

Step 2 *Write the argument as an implication.* Make a conjunction of all three premises and imply the conclusion:

$$(p \rightarrow r) \wedge (q \wedge r) \wedge p \Rightarrow (\sim q \rightarrow p)$$

Step 3 *Construct a truth table.* When there are three premises, we will begin by finding the truth values for each premise and then work the conjunction from left to right as shown.

p	q	r	$\sim q$	$p \rightarrow r$	$q \wedge r$	$\sim q \rightarrow p$	$(p \rightarrow r) \wedge (q \wedge r) \wedge p$	$[(p \rightarrow r) \wedge (q \wedge r) \wedge p]$ $\Rightarrow (\sim q \rightarrow p)$
T	T	T	F	T	T	T	T	T
T	T	F	F	F	F	T	F	T
T	F	T	T	T	F	T	F	T
T	F	F	T	F	F	T	F	T
F	T	T	F	T	T	T	F	T
F	T	F	F	T	F	T	F	T
F	F	T	T	T	F	F	F	T
F	F	F	T	T	F	F	F	T

Since the truth value for $\Rightarrow$ is all Ts, the argument is valid.

2. Use truth tables to determine the validity of an argument.

▼ Try This One 3

Determine whether the following argument is valid or invalid.

$$p \lor q$$
$$\underline{p \lor \sim r}$$
$$\therefore q$$

Common Valid Argument Forms

We have seen that truth tables can be used to test an argument for validity. But some argument forms are common enough that they are recognized by special names. When an argument fits one of these forms, we can decide if it is valid or not just by knowing the general form, rather than constructing a truth table.

We'll start with a description of some commonly used valid arguments.

1. *Law of detachment* (also known by Latin name *modus ponens*):

$$p \to q$$
$$\underline{p}$$
$$\therefore q$$

Example:

If our team wins Saturday, then they go to a bowl game.
Our team won Saturday.

Therefore, our team goes to a bowl game.

2. *Law of contraposition* (Latin name *modus tollens*):

$$p \to q$$
$$\underline{\sim q}$$
$$\therefore \sim p$$

Example:

If I try hard, I'll get an A.
I didn't get an A.

Therefore, I didn't try hard.

3. *Law of syllogism,* also known as *law of transitivity:*

$$p \to q$$
$$\underline{q \to r}$$
$$\therefore p \to r$$

Example:

If I make an illegal U-turn, I'll get a ticket.
If I get a ticket, I'll get points on my driving record.

Therefore, if I make an illegal U-turn, I'll get points on my driving record.

4. *Law of disjunctive syllogism:*

$$p \lor q$$
$$\underline{\sim p}$$
$$\therefore q$$

Example:

You're either brilliant or insane.

You're not brilliant.

Therefore, you're insane.

Common Fallacies

> **Math Note**
>
> It's more common to mistakenly think that an invalid argument is valid rather than the other way around, so you should pay special attention to the common fallacies listed.

Next, we will list some commonly used arguments that are invalid.

1. *Fallacy of the converse:*

$$p \to q$$
$$q$$
$$\therefore p$$

Example:

If it's Friday, then I will go to happy hour.

I am at happy hour.

Therefore, it is Friday.

This is not valid! You can go to happy hour other days, too.

2. *Fallacy of the inverse:*

$$p \to q$$
$$\sim p$$
$$\therefore \sim q$$

Example:

If I exercise every day, then I will lose weight.

I don't exercise every day.

Therefore, I won't lose weight.

This is also not valid. You could still lose weight without exercising *every* day.

3. *Fallacy of the inclusive or:*

$$p \lor q$$
$$p$$
$$\therefore \sim q$$

Example:

I'm going to take chemistry or physics.

I'm taking chemistry.

Therefore, I'm not taking physics.

Remember, we've agreed that by *or* we mean *one or the other, or both*. So you could be taking both classes.

You will be asked to prove that some of these are invalid by using truth tables in the exercises.

Many times the premises can be diagrammed in several ways. If there is even one way in which the diagram contradicts the conclusion, the argument is *invalid* since the conclusion does not necessarily follow from the premises.

Examples 1, 2, and 3 show how to determine the validity of an argument by using Euler circles.

EXAMPLE 1   **Using Euler Circles to Determine the Validity of an Argument**

Use Euler circles to determine whether the argument is valid.

All cats have four legs.

Some cats are black.
_____

Therefore, some four-legged animals are black.

SOLUTION

The first premise, "All cats have four legs," is the universal affirmative; the set of cats diagrammed as a subset of four-legged animals is shown.

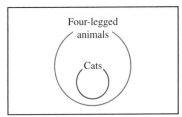

The second premise, "Some cats are black," is the particular affirmative and is shown by placing an ✕ in the intersection of the cats' circle and the black animals' circle. The diagram for this premise is drawn on the diagram of the first premise and can be done in two ways, as shown.

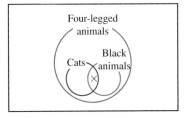 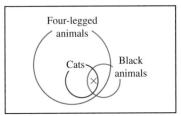

The conclusion is that some four-legged animals are black, so the diagram for the conclusion must have an ✕ in the four-legged animals' circle and in the black animals' circle. Notice that both of the diagrams corresponding to the premises do have an ✕ in both circles, so the conclusion matches the premises and the argument is valid. Since there is no other way to diagram the premises, the conclusion is shown to be true without a doubt.

▼ Try This One 1

Use Euler circles to determine whether the argument is valid.

All college students buy textbooks.

Some book dealers buy textbooks.
_____

Therefore, some college students are book dealers.

It isn't necessary to use actual subjects such as cats, four-legged animals, etc. in syllogisms. Arguments can use letters to represent the various sets, as shown in Example 2.

EXAMPLE 2   Using Euler Circles to Determine the Validity of an Argument

Use Euler circles to determine whether the argument is valid or invalid.

Some A is not B.
All C is B.
———————
∴ Some A is C.

SOLUTION

The first premise, "Some A is not B," is diagrammed as shown.

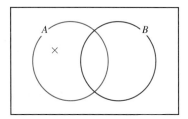

The second premise, "All C is B," is diagrammed by placing circle C inside circle B. This can be done in several ways, as shown.

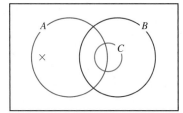   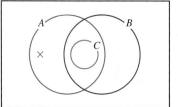

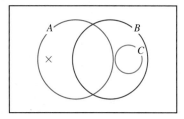

The third diagram shows that the argument is invalid. It matches both premises, but there are no members of A that are also in C, so it contradicts the conclusion "Some A is C."

▼ Try This One 2

Use Euler circles to determine whether the argument is valid.

Some A is B.
Some A is not C.
———————
∴ Some B is not C.

Let's try one more specific example.

EXAMPLE 3   Using Euler Circles to Determine the Validity of an Argument

Use Euler circles to determine whether the argument is valid.

> No criminal is admirable.
> Some athletes are not criminals.
> ∴ Some admirable people are athletes.

SOLUTION

Diagram the first premise, "No criminal is admirable."

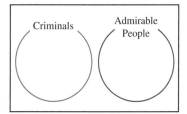

We can add the second premise, "Some athletes are not criminals," in at least two different ways:

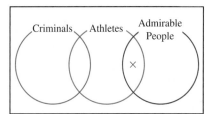 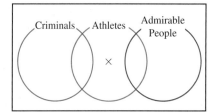

In the first diagram, the conclusion appears to be valid: some athletes are admirable. But the second diagram doesn't support that conclusion, so the argument is invalid.

☑ 2. Use Euler circles to determine the validity of an argument.

▼ Try This One 3

Use Euler circles to determine whether the argument is valid.

All dogs bark.
No animals that bark are cats.
∴ No dogs are cats.

We have now seen that for syllogisms that involve the quantifiers *all, some,* or *none,* Euler circles are an efficient way to determine the validity of the argument. We diagram both premises on the same figure, and if all possible diagrams display the conclusion, then the conclusion must be valid.

Answers to Try This One

1 Invalid

2 Invalid

3 Valid

Section	Important Terms	Important Ideas
3-1	Statement Simple statement Compound statement Connective Conjunction Disjunction Conditional Biconditional Negation	**Formal** symbolic logic uses statements. A statement is a sentence that can be determined to be true or false but not both. A simple statement contains only one idea. A compound statement is formed by joining two or more simple statements with connectives. The four basic connectives are the conjunction (which uses the word *and* and the symbol ∧), the disjunction (which uses the word *or* and the symbol ∨), the conditional (which uses the words *if...then* and the symbol →), and the biconditional (which uses the words *if and only if* and the symbol ↔). The symbol for negation is ∼. Statements are usually written using logical symbols and letters of the alphabet to represent simple statements.
3-2	Truth table	**A truth** table can be used to determine when a compound statement is true or false. A truth table can be constructed for any logical statement.
3-3	Tautology Self-contradiction Logically equivalent statements Converse Inverse Contrapositive De Morgan's laws	**A statement** that is always true is called a tautology. A statement that is always false is called a self-contradiction. Two statements that have the same truth values are said to be logically equivalent. De Morgan's laws are used to find the negation of a conjunction or disjunction. From the conditional statement, three other statements can be made: the converse, the inverse, and the contrapositive.
3-4	Argument Premise Conclusion	**Truth** tables can be used to determine the validity of an argument. An argument consists of two or more statements called premises and a statement called the conclusion. An argument is valid if when the premises are true, the conclusion is true. Otherwise, the argument is invalid.
3-5	Syllogism Euler circles Universal affirmative Universal negative Particular affirmative Particular negative	**A mathematician** named Leonhard Euler developed a method using circles to determine the validity of an argument that is particularly effective for syllogisms involving quantifiers. This method uses four types of statements: (1) the universal affirmative, (2) the universal negative, (3) the particular affirmative, and (4) the particular negative. Euler circles are similar to Venn diagrams.

MATH IN ▸ **The Art of Persuasion REVISITED**

All the arguments on the list are logically invalid except the last one. Even though the claim made by the last argument is false—it did not snow in Hawaii in 2008—this is so because the first premise is false. Remember, the validity of an argument is based on whether it follows from the premises, not on its actual truth.

The first is invalid because there are sources of smoke other than fire. The second is invalid because it's possible to be happy for some reason other than having lots of money. The third is invalid because the initial statement says nothing about teams not in the SEC. The fourth is invalid because it is circular reasoning (see Sidelight in Section 3-4). The fifth is invalid because the first statement doesn't say that weapons of mass destruction are the *only* reason to go to war.

Review Exercises

Section 3-1

For Exercises 1–5, decide whether the sentence is a statement.

1. Let's go with the flow.
2. My duvet cover is indigo.
3. The girls at this school are smart.
4. Ignorance is always a choice.
5. Are we there yet?

For Exercises 6–10, decide whether each statement is simple or compound.

6. Andre is interesting and caring.
7. The monitor is blinking.
8. If it is not raining, I will go kiteboarding.
9. The book is stimulating or informative.
10. There is a silver lining behind every cloud.

For Exercises 11–20, write the negation of the statement.

11. It is scary.
12. The cell phone is out of juice.
13. The Popsicle is green.
14. No people who live in glass houses throw stones.
15. Some failing students can learn new study methods.
16. Everyone will pass the test on logic.
17. There is a printer that has no ink.
18. None of these links are broken.
19. At least one of the contestants will be voted off the island.
20. All SUVs are gas guzzlers.

For Exercises 21–25, classify the statement as a conjunction, disjunction, conditional, or biconditional.

21. In the department store the air is scented and stuffy.
22. If you dream it, you can achieve it.
23. I will go to the 7-Eleven or to the IHOP.
24. It is dangerous if and only if there is ice on the sidewalk.
25. I will slip if I walk on the icy sidewalk.

For Exercises 26–35, let p = "It is ambitious" and let q = "It is worthwhile." Write each statement in symbols.

26. It is ambitious and worthwhile.
27. If it is worthwhile, then it is ambitious.
28. It is worthwhile if and only if it is ambitious.
29. It is worthwhile and not ambitious.
30. If it is not ambitious, then it is not worthwhile.
31. It is not true that it is worthwhile and ambitious.
32. It is not true that if it is ambitious, then it is worthwhile.
33. It is not worthwhile if and only if it is not ambitious.
34. It is not true that it is not worthwhile.
35. It is neither ambitious nor worthwhile.

For Exercises 36–40, let p = "It is cool." Let q = "It is cloudy." Write each statement in words.

36. $p \vee \sim q$
37. $q \to p$
38. $p \leftrightarrow q$
39. $(p \vee q) \to p$
40. $\sim(\sim p \vee q)$

Section 3-2

For Exercises 41–48, construct a truth table for each statement.

41. $p \leftrightarrow \sim q$
42. $\sim p \to (\sim q \vee p)$
43. $(p \to q) \wedge \sim q$
44. $\sim p \vee (\sim q \to p)$
45. $\sim q \leftrightarrow (p \to q)$
46. $(p \to \sim q) \vee r$
47. $(p \vee \sim q) \wedge r$
48. $r \to (\sim p \vee q)$

For Exercises 49–52, use the truth value of each simple statement to determine the truth value of the compound statement.

49. p: January is the first month of the year.
    q: It snows in January in every state.
    Statement: $p \to q$

50. p: Gas prices reached record highs in 2008.
    q: Automobile manufacturers started marketing more fuel efficient cars in 2008.
    Statement: $p \wedge q$

51. p: Barack Obama was a Presidential candidate in 2008.
    q: Lindsay Lohan was a Presidential candidate in 2008.
    r: Obama won the Democratic nomination in 2008.
    Statement: $(p \vee q) \to r$

52. p: Attending college costs thousands of dollars.
    q: Lack of education does not lead to lower salaries.
    r: The average college graduate will make back more than they paid for school.
    Statement: $(p \wedge \sim q) \leftrightarrow r$

Section 3-3

For Exercises 53–57, determine if the statement is a tautology, self-contradiction, or neither.

53. $p \to (p \vee q)$
54. $(p \to q) \to (p \vee q)$
55. $(p \wedge \sim q) \leftrightarrow (q \wedge \sim p)$
56. $q \to (p \vee \sim p)$
57. $(\sim q \vee p) \wedge q$

For Exercises 58–60, determine whether the two statements are logically equivalent.

58. $\sim(p \to q); \sim p \wedge \sim q$
59. $\sim p \vee \sim q; \sim(p \leftrightarrow q)$
60. $(\sim p \wedge q) \vee r; (\sim p \vee r) \wedge (q \vee r)$

MATH IN ▸ Retail Sales

If you're like most college students, having endured 10 to 12 years of math class as you grew up, you probably feel like you know an awful lot about numbers. That may well be true if you're talking about the base 10 number system that you started learning even before you went to school. But you may be surprised to learn that there are many other number systems that can be used. Some of them are historical artifacts that give us a glimpse into the developmental stages of mankind's study of mathematics. But others are used commonly today. In fact, you're using one every single time you buy an item from a store, even if you don't realize it.

At first, it seems odd to many students to study different types of numbers, especially ancient number systems that are no longer in common use. But just as studying other languages gives you a deeper appreciation for the nuances of language itself, the study of other number systems provides deeper insight into the one we commonly use. The history of human thought is intimately tied to the development of language and mathematics, so studying early number systems gives us an interesting look at our species' intellectual past.

The first systems we will study use symbols to represent numbers that are completely different from the ones you're accustomed to. But we'll also study different systems that use familiar numerals like 0 and 1. One system is of particular interest in the modern world: the binary system, which uses only 0 and 1 as its digits.

The binary system is the mathematical driving force behind most of the world's computers, and is the system we had in mind when we referred to buying items. Unless you just got here from Mars, you're familiar with the UPC bar codes that tell the register at a store how much an item costs. What is the bar code really telling the register? A binary number that identifies every product for sale. The register is then programmed with the appropriate price for that item.

In Section 4-3, when we learn about the binary system, a Sidelight will help you to decode the familiar UPC codes. If all goes well, and you have a keen eye, you can use what you learn to find what products the bar codes below come from. When you know the 10-digit number that each represents, you can look that number up on the Internet to find that each code is from a product that most college students are very familiar with.

For answers, see Math in Retail Sales Revisited on page 193

Section 4-1 Early and Modern Numeration Systems

LEARNING OBJECTIVES

☐ 1. Define a numeration system.

☐ 2. Work with numbers in the Egyptian system.

☐ 3. Work with numbers in the Chinese system.

☐ 4. Identify place values in the Hindu-Arabic system.

☐ 5. Write Hindu-Arabic numbers in expanded notation.

☐ 6. Work with numbers in the Babylonian system.

☐ 7. Work with Roman numerals.

☑ 1. Define a numeration system.

Are the words "number" and "numeral" synonymous? Most people answer yes to that question, but the answer is actually no. A **number** is a *concept,* or an idea, used to represent some quantity. A **numeral,** on the other hand, is a *symbol* used to represent a number. For example, there's only one concept of the number "five," but there are many different numerals (symbols) that can be used to represent the number five; 5, V, cinco, and ||||| are just a few.

Just as there are a wide variety of languages that developed in various parts of the world, there are a wide variety of systems for representing numbers that developed at different times and in different places. In this section we will study a few of them.

> A **numeration system** consists of a set of symbols (numerals) to represent numbers, and a set of rules for combining those symbols.

We will examine four basic types of numeration systems: tally, simple grouping, multiplicative grouping, and positional.

Tally Systems

A tally system is the simplest kind of numeration system, and almost certainly the oldest. In a tally system there is only one symbol needed and a number is represented by repeating that symbol. For example, an ancient cave dweller might have drawn three stick-figure children on the wall of his cave to indicate that he had three children living there.

In modern times, tally systems are still used as a crude method of counting items. Most often, they are used to keep track of the number of occurrences of some event. For example, umpires in baseball often keep track of the runs scored by each team by making a mark for each run as it scores.

The most common symbol used in tally systems is |, which we call a stroke. Tallies are usually grouped by fives, with the fifth stroke crossing the first four, as in ||||.

EXAMPLE 1   Using a Tally System

An amateur golfer gets the opportunity to play with Tiger Woods, and, starstruck, his game completely falls apart. On the very first hole, it takes him six shots to reach the green, then three more to hole out. Use a tally system to represent his total number of shots on that hole.

SOLUTION

The total number of shots is nine, which we tally up as |||| ||||.

▼ Try This One 1

During the unfortunate experience in Example 1, 10 people watched from the tee and 8 more watched from around the green. Use a tally system to represent the total number of people who watched.

The most obvious disadvantage to tally systems is that they make it tremendously cumbersome to represent large numbers. That's where grouping systems have an advantage.

Simple Grouping Systems

In a simple grouping system there are symbols that represent select numbers. Often, these numbers are powers of 10. To write a number in a simple grouping system, repeat the symbol representing the appropriate value(s) until the desired quantity is reached. For example, suppose in a simple grouping system the symbol Δ represents the quantity "ten" and the symbol Γ represents the quantity "one." Then to write the numeral representing the quantity "fifty-three" in this system we would use five Δ's and three Γ's as follows: ΔΔΔΔΔΓΓΓ.

The Egyptian Numeration System

One of the earliest formal numeration systems was developed by the Egyptians sometime prior to 3000 BCE. It used a system of hieroglyphics using pictures to represent numbers. These symbols are shown in Figure 4-1.

Symbol	Number	Description	Symbol	Number	Description
|	1	Vertical staff	⌒	10,000	Pointing finger
∩	10	Heel bone	⋈	100,000	Burbot fish (or tadpole)
⑨	100	Scroll	⚛	1,000,000	Astonished person
⨎	1,000	Lotus flower			

Figure 4-1

Sidelight MAYAN MATHEMATICS

The Mayans lived in Southeastern Mexico and the Central American countries of Guatemala, Honduras, and El Salvador. Their civilization lasted from 2000 BCE until 1700 CE, although some archaeological finds date it to earlier times. They built many temples, most on the Yucatan peninsula, similar to the pyramids of Egypt. They had a highly developed civilization that contained the elements of religion, trade, government, mathematics, and astronomy. They developed an advanced form of writing consisting of symbols similar to Egyptian hieroglyphics. They made paper from fig tree bark and wrote books that contained astronomical tables and religious ceremonies. They had two calendars. One consisted of 260 days and was used for religious purposes. The other consisted of 365 days and was based on the orbit of the earth about the sun. This calendar divided the year into 18 months with 20 days in each month and 5 days were added at the end of the year.

Their mathematical symbols consisted of three symbols. A dot represented a one. A horizontal line represented a five, and the symbol ⟳ was used for a zero. (This was one of the first cultures to have a specific symbol for zero.)

It is interesting to examine how these symbols were used to create numbers. For example, the number 3 was written as • • •. The number 12 was written ⚌•. The numbers were written vertically, except for the ones. Using the two symbols • and —, the Mayans could write all the numbers up through 19. However, once the number 20 was reached, a space would be needed between the digits. For example, the number

$$\begin{array}{c} \bullet\ \bullet \\ \bullet\ \bullet\ \bullet\ \bullet \end{array}$$

represents 14 ones plus 7 twenties or $14 \times 1 + 7 \times 20 = 154$.

The next place value after 20 is 360, which is 18×20. This value was used because the calendar had $360 + 5$ days. The numeral

⚏••••	Three hundred sixties
⚌	Twenties
••••	Ones

represents $9 \times 1 + 10 \times 20 + 13 \times 360 = 4,889$.

The next higher place value is 18×20^2 or 7,200. The symbol for zero was used to indicate that there were no digits in a place value position of a number. For example, the number

$$\begin{array}{c} \bullet\ \bullet\ \bullet \\ \equiv \\ \bigcirc \\ \bullet \end{array}$$

means $11 \times 1 + 0 \times 20 + 18 \times 360 = 6,491$. The Mayan system combines elements of two types studied in this section: grouping and positional systems.

The Egyptian system is a simple grouping system: the value of any numeral is determined by counting up the number of each symbol and multiplying the number of occurrences by the corresponding value from Figure 4-1. Then the numbers for each symbol are added, as we see in Example 2.

EXAMPLE 2   **Using the Egyptian Numeration System**

Find the numerical value of each Egyptian numeral.

(a) ∩∩∩∩|||

(b) ⋖⋖⋖⫟𝇋𝇋𝇋𝇋𝟡𝟡∩∩|||||

(c) 𝕐𝇋𝇋𝇋⨍⨍𝟡∩|||

SOLUTION

(a) The number has 4 heel bones (or 4 tens) and 3 vertical staffs (or 3 ones); this equals $4 \times 10 + 3 \times 1$ or 43.

(b) The number consists of 3 one hundred thousands, 3 ten thousands, 2 hundreds, 3 tens, and 6 ones; it equals $3 \times 100{,}000 + 3 \times 10{,}000 + 2 \times 100 + 3 \times 10 + 6 \times 1 = 300{,}000 + 30{,}000 + 200 + 30 + 6 = 330{,}236$.

(c) The number consists of 1 million, 2 ten thousands, 2 thousands, 1 hundred, 1 ten, and 3 ones; the number is $1{,}000{,}000 + 20{,}000 + 2{,}000 + 100 + 10 + 3 = 1{,}022{,}113$.

▼ Try This One 2

Find the numerical value of each Egyptian numeral.

(a) 𝟡𝟡𝟡𝟡∩∩∩∩|||||

(b) ⨍𝟡𝟡∩|

(c) 𝕐⋖⨍⨍∩∩∩∩|

In order to write numbers using hieroglyphic symbols, simple groupings of ones, tens, hundreds, etc. are used. For example, 28 is equal to $10 + 10 + 8$ and is equal to

EXAMPLE 3   **Writing Numbers in Egyptian Notation**

Write each number as an Egyptian numeral.

(a) 42   (b) 137   (c) 5,283   (d) 3,200,419

SOLUTION

(a) Forty-two can be written as $4 \times 10 + 2 \times 1$, so it consists of four tens and two ones. We would write it using four of the tens symbol (the heel bone) and two of the ones symbol (the vertical staff).

(b) Since 137 consists of 1 hundred, 3 tens, and 7 ones, it is written as

ꝅ∩∩∩|||||||

(c) Since 5,283 consists of 5 thousands, 2 hundreds, 8 tens, and 3 ones, it is written as

𓆼𓆼𓆼𓆼𓆼ꝅꝅ∩∩∩∩∩∩∩∩|||

(d) Since 3,200,419 consists of 3 millions, 2 hundred thousands, 4 one hundreds, 1 ten, and 9 ones, it is written as

𓁨𓁨𓁨𓆐𓆐ꝅꝅꝅꝅ∩|||||||||

▼ Try This One 3

Write each number as an Egyptian numeral.

(a) 43   (b) 627   (c) 3,286

Addition and subtraction can be performed by grouping symbols, as shown in Examples 4 and 5.

EXAMPLE 4   **Adding in the Egyptian System**

Find the sum of ꝅꝅ∩∩∩∩∩∩|||||| + ꝅ∩∩∩∩∩∩∩|||||.

SOLUTION

The answer is found by taking the total number of each symbol and converting the appropriate symbols. The total number of symbols is

ꝅꝅꝅ $\underbrace{∩∩∩∩∩∩∩∩∩∩}_{ꝅ}$ ∩∩ $\underbrace{|||||||||||}_{∩}$

For each 10 heel bones, replace them with a scroll and for each 10 vertical staffs, replace them with a heel bone. The final answer is

ꝅꝅꝅꝅ∩∩∩|

Math Note

One of the objectives of this section is to expand your numerical ability by performing calculations using numerical systems other than our own. So in problems like Examples 4 and 5, you should be using these systems in your solution. But don't forget that you can check your answer by converting the original problem into our system, performing the calculation, and seeing if it matches your result.

▼ Try This One 4

Perform the addition in Egyptian notation.

ꝅꝅ∩∩∩∩∩|||||||||| + ꝅꝅꝅꝅ∩∩∩||||

EXAMPLE 5   Subtracting in the Egyptian System

Subtract

SOLUTION

In this case, we're going to have to do some rewriting before we subtract since there are more heel bones and vertical staffs in the number being subtracted. In the top number, we can convert one heel bone (10) into 10 vertical staffs, and one scroll (100) into 10 heel bones. Once this is done, the number of symbols can be subtracted as shown below, with the answer on the bottom line. You might find it helpful to cross out matching symbols in both lines.

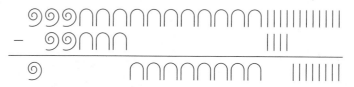

▼ Try This One 5

Perform the subtraction in Egyptian notation.

𓆼𓆼𓆼𓆼∩∩𓏮𓏮 − 𓆼𓆼𓆼𓆼𓆼∩∩∩∩𓏮𓏮𓏮

☑ 2. Work with numbers in the Egyptian system.

Multiplicative Grouping Systems

In a multiplicative grouping system, there is a symbol for each value 1 through 9 (the multipliers), and also for select other numbers (usually powers of 10 or some other common base). To write a number in a multiplicative grouping system, a multiplier is followed by the symbol representing the value of the appropriate power of 10.

For example, to write the number 53 in a multiplicative grouping system there would be two "groups" of two. The first group would consist of the multiplier representing the number five, followed by the symbol for ten ($5 \times 10 = 50$); the second group would be the multiplier representing the number three, followed by the symbol for one ($3 \times 1 = 3$). (*Note:* the symbol for one is sometimes omitted in a multiplicative system.)

EXAMPLE 6   Using a Multiplicative Grouping System

Suppose the symbols used in a multiplicative grouping system are as follows:

one	α	six	θ
two	β	seven	γ
three	χ	eight	η
four	δ	nine	ι
five	ε	ten	φ

Write the symbols that would be used to represent the number 45.

Symbol	Value
零 or ◯	0
一	1
二	2
三	3
四	4
五	5
六	6
七	7
八	8
九	9
十	10
百	100
千	1,000

Figure 4-2

SOLUTION

Forty-five consists of four 10s and five 1s. To represent four 10s, we write δφ (the multiplier 4 times the base value 10). To represent five 1s, we write εα (the multiplier 5 times the base value 1), or we could simply write ε. So the number 45 is written δφ εα, or δφ ε.

▼ **Try This One 6**

Using the symbols in Example 6, write the symbols that would be used to represent the number 96.

The traditional Chinese numeration system is an example of a multiplicative grouping system.

The Chinese Numeration System

The symbols used for the Chinese numeration system are shown in Figure 4-2. Because Chinese is written vertically rather than horizontally, their numbers are also represented vertically. Fifty-three would be written:

五   five
十   tens
     and
三   three ones

EXAMPLE 7   **Using the Chinese Numeration System**

Find the value of each Chinese numeral.

(a) 六
百
五
十
四

(b) 三
千
七
百
二
十
六

(c) 五
千
六
十
五

SOLUTION

Reading from the top down, we can calculate each value as below. Remember that in each group of symbols, the multiplier comes first, followed by the power of 10.

(a) 六 ⎫
    百 ⎭ $6 \times 100 = 600$
            +
    五 ⎫
    十 ⎭ $5 \times 10 = 50$
            +
    四 } 4   = 4
           654

(b) 三 ⎫
    千 ⎭ $3 \times 1,000 = 3,000$
            +
    七 ⎫
    百 ⎭ $7 \times 100 = 700$
            +
    二 ⎫
    十 ⎭ $2 \times 10 = 20$
            +
    六 } 6   = 6
         3,726

(c) 五 ⎫
    千 ⎭ $5 \times 1,000 = 5,000$
            +
    六 ⎫
    十 ⎭ $6 \times 10 = 60$
            +
    五 } 5   = 5
         5,065

▼ Try This One 7

Find the value of each Chinese numeral.

(a) 四
百
二
十
七

(b) 六
千
七
十
五

(c) 二
十
六

EXAMPLE 8   Writing Numbers in the Chinese Numeration System

Write each number as a Chinese numeral.

(a) 65   (b) 183   (c) 8,749

SOLUTION

(a) 六
十 } 6×10
五 } 5

(b) 一
百 } 1×100
八
十 } 8×10
三 } 3

(c) 八
千 } $8 \times 1{,}000$
七
百 } 7×100
四
十 } 4×10
九 } 9

▼ Try This One 8

☑ 3. Work with numbers in the Chinese system.

Write each number as a Chinese numeral.

(a) 45   (b) 256   (c) 6,321

Positional Systems

In a **positional system** no multiplier is needed. The value of the symbol is understood by its position in the number. To represent a number in a positional system you simply put the numeral in an appropriate place in the number, and its value is determined by its location.

The Hindu-Arabic Numeration System

Many of the numeration systems we study in this chapter rely heavily on exponents, so a clear understanding of exponents is important.

For any number b and natural number n, we define the **exponential expression** b^n as

$$b^n = b \cdot b \cdot b \cdots b$$

where b appears as a factor n times. The number b is called the **base,** and n is called the **exponent.** We also define $b^1 = b$ for any base b, and $b^0 = 1$ for any nonzero base b.

The numeration system we use today is called the Hindu-Arabic system. (See the sidelight on page 159 for some perspective on this name.) It uses 10 symbols called **digits:** 0, 1, 2, 3, 4, 5, 6, 7, 8, and 9.

The Hindu-Arabic system is a positional system since the position of each digit indicates a specific value. The place value of each number is given as

billion	hundred million	ten million	million	hundred thousand	ten thousand	thousand	hundred	ten	one
10^9	10^8	10^7	10^6	10^5	10^4	10^3	10^2	10^1	1

The number 82,653 means there are 8 ten thousands, 2 thousands, 6 hundreds, 5 tens, and 3 ones. We say that the place value of the 6 in this numeral is hundreds.

EXAMPLE 9 Finding Place Values

In the number 153,946, what is the place value of each digit?

(a) 9   (b) 3   (c) 5   (d) 1   (e) 6

SOLUTION

(a) hundreds
(b) thousands
(c) ten thousands
(d) hundred thousands
(e) ones

☑ 4. Identify place values in the Hindu-Arabic system.

▼ Try This One 9

According to the U.S. Census Bureau, there were 8,724,560 people in New Jersey in 2006. What are the place values of the digits 5, 6, 7, and 8?

To clarify the place values, Hindu-Arabic numbers are sometimes written in **expanded notation.** An example, using the numeral 32,569, is shown below.

$$32,569 = 30,000 \quad + 2,000 \quad + 500 \quad + 60 \quad + 9$$
$$= 3 \times 10,000 + 2 \times 1,000 + 5 \times 100 + 6 \times 10 + 9$$
$$= 3 \times 10^4 \quad + 2 \times 10^3 \quad + 5 \times 10^2 + 6 \times 10^1 + 9$$

Since all of the place values in the Hindu-Arabic system correspond to powers of 10, the system is known as a **base 10 system.** We will study base number systems in depth in Section 4-3.

EXAMPLE 10   Writing a Base 10 Number in Expanded Notation

Write 9,034,761 in expanded notation.

SOLUTION

9,034,761 can be written as

$$9{,}000{,}000 + 30{,}000 + 4{,}000 + 700 + 60 + 1$$
$$= 9 \times 1{,}000{,}000 + 3 \times 10{,}000 + 4 \times 1{,}000 + 7 \times 100 + 6 \times 10 + 1$$
$$= 9 \times 10^6 + 3 \times 10^4 + 4 \times 10^3 + 7 \times 10^2 + 6 \times 10^1 + 1.$$

▼ Try This One 10

☑ 5. Write Hindu-Arabic numbers in expanded notation.

Write each number in expanded notation.

(a) 573   (b) 86,471   (c) 2,201,567

So far, we have studied four types of numeration systems, but they are not the only ones that exist. The ancient Babylonian system is sort of a cross between a multiplier system and a positional system. The Roman numeration system, which is still in use today, is basically a grouping system with a twist—the use of subtraction. We'll conclude this section by studying these two systems. But remember that there are many other numeration systems that we haven't discussed.

The Babylonian Numeration System

The Babylonians had a numerical system consisting of two symbols. They are ◀ and ❕. (These wedge-shaped symbols are known as "cuneiform.") The ◀ represents the number of 10s, and ❕ represents the number of 1s.

EXAMPLE 11   Using the Babylonian Numeration System

What number does ◀◀◀❕❕❕❕❕❕ represent?

SOLUTION

Since there are 3 tens and 6 ones, the number represents 36.

▼ Try This One 11

What number does  represent?

You might think it would be cumbersome to write large numbers in this system; however, the Babylonian system was also positional. Numbers from 1 to 59 were written using the two symbols shown in Example 11, but after the number 60, a space was left between the groups of numbers. For example, the number 2,538 was written as

and means that there are 42 sixties and 18 ones. The space separates the 60s from the ones. The value is found as follows:

$$42 \times 60 = 2,520$$
$$+\ 18 \times\ \ 1 = \ \ \ \ \ 18$$
$$\overline{2,538}$$

When there are three groupings of numbers, the symbols to the left of the first space represent the number of 3,600s (note that $3,600 = 60 \times 60$). The next group of symbols represents the number of 60s, and the final group represents the number of 1s.

A Babylonian clay tablet with numeric symbols.

EXAMPLE 12 Using the Babylonian Numeration System

Write the numbers represented.

(a) ⟨⟨⟨⟨⟨⟨❘❘ ⟨⟨⟨❘❘❘❘

(b) ⟨❘❘ ⟨⟨⟨⟨⟨⟨❘ ⟨⟨❘❘❘

SOLUTION

(a) There are 52 sixties and 34 ones; so the number represents

$$52 \times 60 = 3,120$$
$$+\ 34 \times\ 1 = \ \ \ \ 34$$
$$\overline{3,154}$$

(b) There are twelve 3,600s, fifty-one 60s, and twenty-three 1s. The numeral represents

$$12 \times 3,600 = 43,200$$
$$51 \times\ \ \ \ \ 60 = \ \ 3,060$$
$$23 \times\ \ \ \ \ \ \ 1 = \ \ \ \ \ \ 23$$
$$\overline{46,283}$$

▼ Try This One 12

Write the number represented.

(a) 𒌋𒌋𒁹𒁹 𒌋𒌋𒌋𒌋𒌋𒁹𒁹𒁹𒁹𒁹 (b) 𒌋𒁹 𒌋𒌋𒁹 𒌋𒁹𒁹𒁹

EXAMPLE 13 Writing a Number in the Babylonian System

Write 5,217 using the Babylonian numeration system.

SOLUTION

Since the number is greater than 3,600, it must be divided by 3,600 to see how many 3,600s are contained in the number.

$$5{,}217 \div 3{,}600 = 1 \text{ remainder } 1{,}617$$

The remainder, 1,617, is then divided by 60 to see how many 60s are in 1,617.

$$1{,}617 \div 60 = 26 \text{ remainder } 57$$

So, the number 5,217 consists of

$1 \times 3{,}600 =$	3,600	𒁹
$26 \times 60 =$	1,560	𒌋𒌋𒁹𒁹𒁹𒁹𒁹𒁹
$57 \times 1 =$	57	𒌋𒌋𒌋𒌋𒌋𒁹𒁹𒁹𒁹𒁹𒁹𒁹
Total $=$	5,217	

It can be written as

𒁹 𒌋𒌋𒁹𒁹𒁹𒁹𒁹𒁹 𒌋𒌋𒌋𒌋𒌋𒁹𒁹𒁹𒁹𒁹𒁹𒁹

Math Note

The Babylonians didn't have a symbol for zero. This complicated their writings. For example, how is the number 7,200 distinguished from the number 72?

▼ Try This One 13

☑ 6. Work with numbers in the Babylonian system.

Write each number using the Babylonian numeration system.

(a) 42 (b) 384 (c) 4,278

The Roman Numeration System

The Romans used letters to represent their numbers. They are

Symbol	Number
I	1
V	5
X	10
L	50
C	100
D	500
M	1,000

The Roman system is similar to a simple grouping system, but to save space, the Romans also used the concept of subtraction. For example, 8 is written as VIII, but 9 is written as IX, meaning that 1 is subtracted from 10 to get 9. There are three rules for writing numbers in Roman numerals:

1. When a letter is repeated in sequence, its numerical value is added. For example, XXX represents 10 + 10 + 10, or 30.

2. When smaller-value letters follow larger-value letters, the numerical values of each are added. For example, LXVI represents 50 + 10 + 5 + 1, or 66.

3. When a smaller-value letter precedes a larger-value letter, the smaller value is subtracted from the larger value. For example, IV represents 5 − 1, or 4, and XC represents 100 − 10, or 90.

In addition, I can only precede V or X, X can only precede L or C, and C can only precede D or M. Then 4 is written as IV, 9 is written as IX, 40 is written as XL, 90 is written XC, 400 is written as CD, and 900 is written as CM.

Example 14 shows how to convert Roman numerals to Hindu-Arabic numerals.

EXAMPLE 14 Using Roman Numerals

Roman numerals are still in use today. For example, many clocks and watches contain Roman numerals. Can you think of other places Roman numerals are still used?

Find the value of each Roman numeral.

(a) LXVIII (b) XCIV (c) MCML (d) CCCXLVI (e) DCCCLV

SOLUTION

(a) L = 50, X = 10, V = 5, and III = 3; so LXVIII = 68.
(b) XC = 90 and IV = 4; so XCIV = 94.
(c) M = 1,000, CM = 900, L = 50; so MCML = 1,950.
(d) CCC = 300, XL = 40, V = 5, and I = 1; so CCCXLVI = 346.
(e) D = 500, CCC = 300, L = 50, V = 5; so DCCCLV = 855.

▼ Try This One 14

Convert each Roman numeral to a Hindu-Arabic numeral.

(a) XXXIX (b) MCLXIV (c) CCCXXXIII

Sidelight ROMAN AND HINDU-ARABIC NUMERALS

The Romans spread their system of numerals throughout the world as they conquered their enemies. The system was well entrenched in Europe until the 1500s, when our present system, called the Hindu-Arabic system, became widely accepted.

The present system is thought to have been invented by the Hindus before 200 BCE. It was spread throughout Europe by the Arabs, who traded with the Europeans and traveled throughout the Mediterranean region. It is interesting to note that for about 400 years, the mathematicians of early Europe were divided into two groups—those favoring the use of the Roman system and those favoring the use of the Hindu-Arabic system. The Hindu-Arabic system eventually won out, although Roman numerals are still widely used today.

Numbers can be written using Roman numerals as shown in Example 15.

EXAMPLE 15 Writing Numbers Using Roman Numerals

Math Note

For larger numbers, the Romans placed a bar over their symbols. The bar means to multiply the numerical value of the number under the bar by 1,000. For example, $\overline{VII}$ means $7 \times 1,000$ or 7,000, and $\overline{XL}$ means 40,000.

☑ 7. Work with Roman numerals.

Write each number using Roman numerals.

(a) 19   (b) 238   (c) 1,999   (d) 840   (e) 72

SOLUTION

(a) 19 is written as 10 + 9 or XIX.
(b) 238 is written as 200 + 30 + 8 or CCXXXVIII.
(c) 1,999 is written as 1,000 + 900 + 90 + 9 or MCMXCIX.
(d) 840 is written as 500 + 300 + 40 or DCCCXL.
(e) 72 is written as 50 + 20 + 2 or LXXII.

▼ Try This One 15

Write each number using Roman numerals.

(a) 67   (b) 192   (c) 202   (d) 960

Remember that the value of studying other number systems is that it allows us to develop a deeper understanding of the symbols we use to represent numbers, even if we always use our own system to represent numbers and perform calculations.

Answers to Try This One

1

2 (a) 456;
   (b) 1,211;
   (c) 1,102,041

3 (a) ∩∩∩∩|||
   (b) 𝟡𝟡𝟡𝟡𝟡𝟡∩∩|||||||
   (c) ⨍⨍⨍𝟡𝟡∩∩∩∩∩∩∩|||||

4 𝟡𝟡𝟡𝟡𝟡𝟡𝟡∩||

5 𝟡𝟡𝟡𝟡𝟡𝟡𝟡∩∩∩∩∩|||||||||

6 ιφ θ

7 (a) 427
   (b) 6,075
   (c) 26

8 (a) 四十五   (b) 二百五十六   (c) 六千三百二十

9 5: hundreds; 6: tens; 7: hundred thousands; 8: millions

10 (a) $5 \times 10^2 + 7 \times 10^1 + 3$
   (b) $8 \times 10^4 + 6 \times 10^3 + 4 \times 10^2 + 7 \times 10^1 + 1$
   (c) $2 \times 10^6 + 2 \times 10^5 + 1 \times 10^3 + 5 \times 10^2 + 6 \times 10^1 + 7$

11 52

12 (a) 1,375;   (b) 40,873

13 (a) ⟨⟨⟨⟨▼▼
   (b) ▼▼▼▼▼▼ ⟨⟨▼▼▼▼
   (c) ▼ ⟨▼ ⟨▼▼▼▼▼▼▼▼

14 (a) 39; (b) 1,164; (c) 333

15 (a) LXVII; (b) CXCII; (c) CCII; (d) CMLX

EXERCISE SET 4-1

Writing Exercises

1. Describe the difference between a number and a numeral.
2. Briefly describe how a grouping system works.
3. Briefly describe how a multiplicative grouping system works.
4. Describe what place values are and what they represent in the Hindu-Arabic numeration system.
5. Both the Roman and Egyptian systems use symbols to represent certain numbers. Explain how they differ (aside from the fact that they use different symbols).
6. Describe how to write a number in the Hindu-Arabic system in expanded notation.

Computational Exercises

For Exercises 7–16, write each number using Hindu-Arabic numerals.

7. ∩∩∩|||||
8. ⟟⟟⟟⟟∩∩∩||
9. ⟋⟋⟋⟟∩∩|||||
10. ⊲⟟⊲⟟∩∩∩||
11. ⟋⟋⟋⟟∩∩∩∩∩|||
12. ⚲⟟⟟∩
13. ⟋⟋⟟⟟⟟∩||||
14. ⚲⚲⊲⟟⊲
15. ⚲⊲⟋ℇℇ∩
16. ℇℇ∩∩∩∩|||||||||

For Exercises 17–26, write each number using Egyptian numerals.

17. 7   21. 168   25. 1,256
18. 18   22. 365   26. 8,261
19. 37   23. 801
20. 52   24. 955

For Exercises 27–32, perform the indicated operations. Write your answers as Egyptian numerals.

27. ∩∩∩∩∩||| + ∩∩∩∩∩|||

28. ⟟⟟∩∩|| + ⟟∩∩∩||
29. ⊲⟟⊲⟋⟋|| + ⊲⟟⟋⟋⟋∩∩∩|||
30. ∩∩∩|| − ∩|||||
31. ⟋⟋⟟⟟|||| − ⟋⟟⟟⟟||||
32. ⚲⊲⟋ℇ∩∩||||− ⊲⟋ℇℇ∩∩∩|||||

For Exercises 33–38, write each number using Hindu-Arabic numerals.

33. 一百八十九
34. 三千四百七
35. 五十二九千八百三十四
36. (as above)
37. 七百一十三八十九
38. (as above)

For Exercises 39–44, write each number using Chinese numerals.

39. 89   41. 284   43. 2,356
40. 567   42. 9,857   44. 21

For Exercises 45–50, use the number 3,421,578 and find the place value of the given digit.

45. 5
46. 1
47. 2
48. 3
49. 8
50. 4

For Exercises 51–60, write each number in expanded notation.

51. 86
52. 325
53. 1,812
54. 32,714
55. 6,002
56. 29,300
57. 162,873
58. 200,321,416
59. 17,531,801
60. 1,326,419

For Exercises 61–70, write each number using Hindu-Arabic numerals.

61. ❮❙❙
62. ❮❮❮❙❙❙❙
63. ❮❮❮❮❮❮❙
64. ❮❮❮❙❙❙❙❙
65. ❮❙   ❮❮❮❙   ❮❙
66. ❮❮❙❙   ❮❮❮❮❮   ❮❙❙❙
67. ❮❮❮   ❮❮❙   ❮❮❙❙❙❙
68. ❮❮❮❙❙   ❮❙   ❮❙
69. ❮❙❙❙   ❮❙❙
70. ❮❮❮❙   ❮❙   ❙❙

For Exercises 71–80, write each number using Babylonian numerals.

71. 32
72. 23
73. 78
74. 156
75. 292
76. 514
77. 1,023
78. 1,776
79. 5,216
80. 8,200

For Exercises 81–90, write each number using Hindu-Arabic numerals.

81. XVII
82. XCIX
83. XLIII
84. CCXXI
85. LXXXVI
86. CCXXXIII
87. CDXVIII
88. MMCMXVII
89. CDXC
90. CMVI

For Exercises 91–100, write each number using Roman numerals.

91. 39
92. 142
93. 567
94. 893
95. 1,258
96. 3,720
97. 1,462
98. 2,170
99. 3,000
100. 2,222

Real-World Applications

Most movies use Roman numerals in the credits to indicate the date the film was made. Shown are some movies and their dates. Find the year the movie was made.

Movie	Year
101. Gone With the Wind	MCMXXXIX
102. Casablanca	MCMXLII
103. Animal House	MCMLXXVIII
104. Raiders of the Lost Ark	MCMLXXXI
105. Batman Begins	MMV
106. Shrek II	MMIV

Critical Thinking

107. Make up your own numeration system using your own symbols. Indicate whether it is a simple grouping, multiplicative grouping, or a positional system. Explain how to add and subtract in your numeration system.

108. Most clocks that use Roman numerals have four written incorrectly, as IIII rather than IV. Think of as many potential reasons for this as you can, then do an internet search to see if you can find the reason.

109. A colleague of mine once gave a quiz with the question "Why is it useful to learn about the Babylonian numeration system?," and one student answered "If you have any Babylonian friends, you could communicate with them about numbers." Explain why we laughed hysterically at that answer.

110. Which of the ancient numeration systems we studied (Egyptian, Babylonian, Roman) do you think is the most efficient? Why?

Section 4-2 Tools and Algorithms in Arithmetic

LEARNING OBJECTIVES

☐ 1. Multiply using the Egyptian algorithm.

☐ 2. Multiply using the Russian peasant method.

☐ 3. Multiply using the lattice method.

☐ 4. Multiply using Napier's bones.

Handheld calculators have been widely available since the early 1970s, which means that for most college students, it seems like they've always existed. Compared to your lifespan, 40 years seems like a long time, but compared to the history of mathematics, it's practically the blink of an eye. In order to have a greater appreciation of the modern tools we have, it's useful to look back at what people had to do before calculators and computers were invented. In this section, we'll look at a handful of extremely clever methods that were developed to perform multiplications. While you'll probably never use them in real life, studying them can give you insight into the type of innovations that helped advance human thought from the simple to the abstract, paving the way for all of the modern advances that we too often take for granted.

The Egyptian Algorithm

The Egyptian algorithm is an ancient method of multiplication that can be done by hand because it requires only doubling numbers and addition. We'll illustrate it with an example, then summarize.

EXAMPLE 1   **Using the Egyptian Algorithm**

Use the Egyptian algorithm to multiply 13 × 24.

SOLUTION

Step 1 Form two columns with 1 at the top of the first column and 24 at the top of the second column:

    1   24

Step 2 Double the numbers in each column, and continue to do so until the first column contains numbers that can be added to get the other number in the product, 13:

    1   24
    2   48
    4   96
    8   192

We stop here because we can get 13 from adding 1, 4, and 8.

Step 3 Add the numbers in the second column that are next to 1, 4, and 8: 24 + 96 + 192 = 312. This is the product of 13 and 24.

▼ Try This One 1

Use the Egyptian algorithm to multiply 22 × 15.

We could have put either original number at the top of the second column, but it's usually a little quicker if we put the larger number there, as we did in Example 1.

Sidelight   DIVIDING WITH THE EGYPTIAN ALGORITHM

The Egyptian algorithm can be used for dividing as well. Suppose, for example, we want to divide 1,584 by 24. Make two columns headed with 1 and 24 and double as before:

    1   24
    2   48
    4   96
    8   192
   16   384
   32   768
   64 1,536

We can stop here since the next entry would be larger than 1,584. Now find the numbers in the right column that add up to 1,584 (in this case 48 and 1,536), then add the corresponding numbers in the left column. The sum 2 + 64 = 66 is the quotient of 1,584 and 24.

This method will not work unless the numbers divide evenly, but a modified Egyptian method will work in such cases.

☑ 1. Multiply using the Egyptian algorithm.

The Egyptian Algorithm

To multiply two numbers A and B:

1. Form two columns with the numeral one at the top of the first, and one of the numbers (we'll say B) to be multiplied at the top of the second.

2. Double the numbers in each column repeatedly until the first column contains numbers that can be added to A.

3. Add the numbers in the second column that are next to the numbers in the first column that add to A. This sum is the product of A and B.

The Russian Peasant Method

Another method for multiplying by hand is known as the Russian peasant method. As you will see from Example 2, it's similar to the Egyptian algorithm, but maybe a bit simpler in that you don't have to keep searching for numbers that add to one of the factors.

EXAMPLE 2   Using the Russian Peasant Method

Use the Russian peasant method to multiply 24 × 15.

SOLUTION

Step 1 Form two columns with 24 and 15 at the top.

    24   15

Step 2 Divide the numbers in the first column by two (ignoring remainders), and double the numbers in the second column, until you reach one in the first column.

    24   15
    12   30
     6   60
     3   120
     1   240

Step 3 Add the numbers in the second column that are next to odd numbers in the first column: 120 + 240 = 360. This is the product of 24 and 15.

▼ Try This One 2

Use the Russian peasant method to multiply 18×12.

The Russian Peasant Method

To multiply two numbers A and B:

1. Form two columns with A at the top of one column and B at the top of the other.
2. Divide the numbers in the first column by two repeatedly, ignoring remainders, until you reach one. Double the numbers in the second column, with the last result next to the one in the first column.
3. Add the numbers in the second column that are next to odd numbers. The result is the product of A and B.

The Russian peasant method can be used to multiply numbers with more digits, as in Example 3.

EXAMPLE 3   **Using the Russian Peasant Method**

Use the Russian peasant method to multiply 103×19.

SOLUTION

Form the columns as described in the colored box above:

103	19
51	38
25	76
12	152
6	304
3	608
1	1,216

Now add the numbers in the second column that are next to odd numbers in the first:

$$19 + 38 + 76 + 608 + 1,216 = 1,957.$$

So $103 \times 19 = 1,957$.

▼ Try This One 3

Use the Russian peasant method to multiply 210×21.

☑ 2. Multiply using the Russian peasant method.

The Lattice Method

The lattice method for multiplication was used in both India and Persia as early as the year 1010. It was later introduced in Europe in 1202 by Leonardo of Pisa (more commonly known as Fibonacci) in his work entitled *Liber Abacii* (Book of the Abacus). The lattice method reduces multiplying large numbers into multiplying single digit numbers, as illustrated in the next two examples.

EXAMPLE 4   Using the Lattice Method

Find the product 36 × 568 using the lattice method.

SOLUTION

Step 1 Form a lattice as illustrated with one of the numbers to be multiplied across the top, and the other written vertically along the right side.

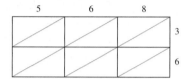

Step 2 Within each box, write the product of the numbers from the top and side that are above and next to that box. Write the first digit above the diagonal and the second below it, using zero as first digit if necessary.

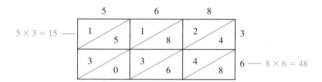

Step 3 Starting at the bottom right of the lattice, add the numbers along successive diagonals, working toward the left. If the sum along a diagonal is more than 9, write the last digit of the sum and carry the first digit to the addition along the next diagonal.

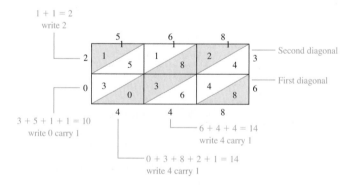

Step 4 Read the answer, starting down the left side then across the bottom:

$$36 \times 568 = 20{,}448$$

▼ Try This One 4

Find the product 53 × 844 using the lattice method.

EXAMPLE 5   **Using the Lattice Method**

Find the product 2,356 × 547 using the lattice method.

SOLUTION

Step 1 Form a lattice with one of the numbers to be multiplied across the top and the other one down the right side.

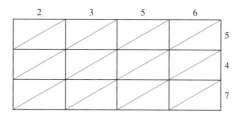

Step 2 Form the individual products in each box.

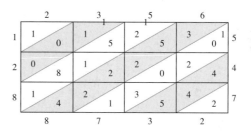

Step 3 Add along the diagonals.

Step 4 Read the answer down the left and across the bottom.

$$2,356 \times 547 = 1,288,732$$

▼ **Try This One 5**

Use the lattice method to find the product 568 × 478.

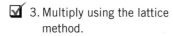 3. Multiply using the lattice method.

Napier's Bones

John Napier (1550–1617), a Scottish mathematician, introduced Napier's bones as a calculating tool based on the lattice method of multiplication. Napier's bones consist of a set of 11 rods: the first rod called the index and 1 rod for each digit 0–9, with multiples of each digit written on the rod in a lattice column as illustrated in Figure 4-3 on the next page.

The next example illustrates how Napier's bones are used to multiply by a single-digit number.

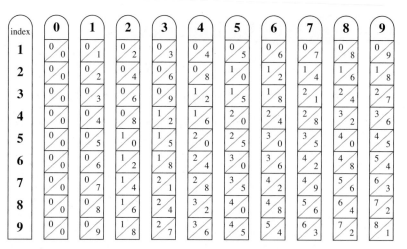

Figure 4-3

EXAMPLE 6   Using Napier's Bones

Use Napier's bones to find the product $2,745 \times 8$.

SOLUTION

Choose the rods labeled 2, 7, 4, and 5 and place them side by side; also, place the index to the left. Then locate the level for the multiplier 8, as shown in Figure 4-4.

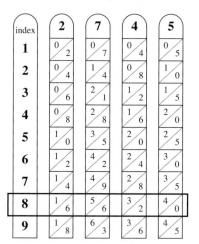

Figure 4-4

Add the numbers diagonally as in the lattice method (Figure 4-5).

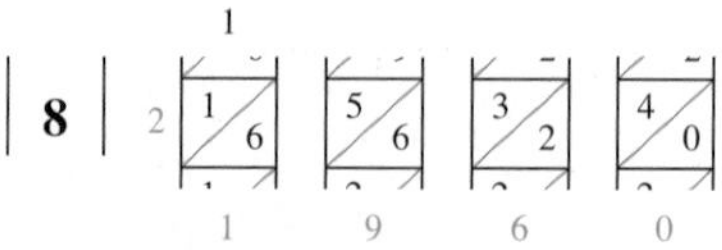

$$\begin{array}{c|cccc} & 1 & & & \\ 8 & 2 \diagdown 1 & \diagdown 5 & \diagdown 3 & \diagdown 4 \\ & \diagup 6 & \diagup 6 & \diagup 2 & \diagup 0 \\ & 1 & 9 & 6 & 0 \end{array}$$

Figure 4-5   The product is 21,960.

▼ Try This One 6

Use Napier's bones to multiply $6 \times 8,973$.

Sidelight JOHN NAPIER (1550–1617)

John Napier was born to a wealthy family in Merchiston, Scotland, in 1550. He lived in the time of Copernicus and Kepler, an age of great discoveries (and great fame) for those involved in astronomy. Napier was a young genius, entering St. Salvator's College in St. Andrews at the age of 13, but he left after two years, spending time traveling throughout Europe and studying a variety of subjects in different countries. A man of varied talents and interests, Napier found himself especially interested in simplifying the calculations with large numbers that were so crucial to the astronomical observations of the day. He is widely credited with inventing logarithms, a computational tool still in widespread use today. Napier worked with the Englishman Henry Briggs on his logarithms, and Briggs published the first logarithm table after Napier's death in 1617. Logarithm tables maintained their status as vitally important to calculations in a variety of sciences well into the 20th century, when the advent of computers reduced them to an interesting historical artifact.

EXAMPLE 7   Using Napier's Bones

Use Napier's bones to multiply 234 × 36.

SOLUTION

Choose the 2, 3, and 4 rods and place them side by side, with the index to the left. Locate the multipliers 3 and 6.

Add the diagonals as in the lattice method.

The product is 8,424.

▼ Try This One 7

Use Napier's bones to multiply 126 × 73.

☑ 4. Multiply using Napier's bones.

Answers to Try This One

1 330

2 216

3 4,410

4 44,732

5 271,504

6 53,838

7 9,198

EXERCISE SET 4-2

Writing Exercises

1. Describe the connection between the Egyptian algorithm and the Russian peasant method. How are they different?

2. Describe the connection between the lattice method and Napier's bones. How are they different?

Computational Exercises

For Exercises 3–12, use the Egyptian algorithm to multiply.

3. 12×21
4. 15×30
5. 23×17
6. 29×15
7. 34×110

8. 17×45
9. 56×8
10. 11×13
11. 18×12
12. 7×35

For Exercises 13–22, use the Russian peasant method to multiply.

13. 11×23
14. 14×32
15. 23×16
16. 29×17
17. 34×11

18. 17×42
19. 56×7
20. 11×17
21. 18×15
22. 7×45

For Exercises 23–32, use the lattice method to multiply.

23. 23×456
24. 453×938
25. $89 \times 1,874$
26. $287 \times 7,643$
27. 876×903

28. 45×583
29. 67×875
30. 359×83
31. 568×359
32. $2,348 \times 83,145$

Construct a set of Napier's bones out of poster board or construction paper and use them to do the multiplications in Exercises 33–40.

33. 9×523
34. 8×731
35. 23×45
36. 71×52

37. 47×123
38. 69×328
39. 154×236
40. 211×416

Critical Thinking

41. Perform the multiplication 38×147 three different ways: using the traditional method taught in grade school, the Egyptian algorithm, and the Russian peasant method. Did you get the same answer all three times? Which method was the fastest? If you got more than one answer, use a calculator to check. Which do you think you're most likely to get the correct answer with most often?

42. Repeat Exercise 41, this time using the multiplication 140×276, and substituting the lattice method for the Russian peasant method.

43. If you had to perform a multiplication of two 3-digit numbers without a calculator for a million dollars on a game show, and you could only do it once, what method would you use? Why?

Section 4-3 Base Number Systems

LEARNING OBJECTIVES

☐ 1. Convert between base 10 and other bases.

☐ 2. Convert between binary, octal, and hexadecimal.

In Section 4-1, we studied a variety of numeration systems other than our own. The thing that they all have in common is that they use different numerals than the ones we're all so familiar with in the Hindu-Arabic system. In this section, you'll find out that there are numeration systems that use the numerals you're familiar with, but are still different than the Hindu-Arabic system. The key difference is that all of the digits in our system are based on powers of 10. You can also define systems based on powers of other numbers. If a system uses some of our "regular" numerals, but is based on powers other than 10, we will call it a **base number system.**

The best way to get some perspective on base number systems is to review the base 10 positional system that we use, and to be completely clear on what the significance of every digit is. A number like 453 can be expanded out as

$$453 = 4 \times 100 + 5 \times 10 + 3 \times 1$$
$$= 4 \times 10^2 + 5 \times 10^1 + 3 \times 10^0$$

and we understand from experience that a 5 in the second digit from the right means five 10s. We can expand numbers in positional systems with bases other than 10 in the same way. The only difference is that the digits represent powers of some number other than 10.

Base Five System

In a base five system it is not necessary to have 10 numerals as in the Hindu-Arabic system; only five numerals (symbols) are needed. A base five number system can be formed using only the numerals 0, 1, 2, 3, and 4. Just as each digit in the Hindu-Arabic system represents a power of 10, each digit in a base five system represents a power of five. The place values for the digits in base five are:

$$\text{etc.} \mid \text{six hundred twenty-five } (5^4) \mid \text{one hundred twenty-five } (5^3) \mid \text{twenty-five } (5^2) \mid \text{five } (5^1) \mid \text{one } (5^0)$$

When writing numbers in base five, we use the subscript "five" to distinguish them from base 10 numbers, because a numeral like 423 in base 5 corresponds to a different number than the numeral 423 in base 10. (This is where understanding the difference between a number and a numeral is crucial!) Table 4-1 shows some base 10 numbers also written in base five.

This might look confusing, but it can be clarified using the reasoning in the comments next to the table. The numbers 1 through 4 are written the same in both systems. The number 5 can't be written in base five using the numeral 5 because the base five system only uses the digits 0, 1, 2, 3, and 4. So we have to write it as 10_{five}, meaning $1 \times 5 + 0 \times 1$, or 1 five and no ones. In the same way, the number 8 would be written in base five as 13_{five}, meaning 1 five and 3 ones.

TABLE 4-1 Base Five Numbers

Base 10 number	Corresponding base five number	
1	1_{five}	
2	2_{five}	
3	3_{five}	
4	4_{five}	
5	10_{five}	1 five and no ones
6	11_{five}	
7	12_{five}	
8	13_{five}	1 five and 3 ones
9	14_{five}	
10	20_{five}	2 fives and 0 ones
11	21_{five}	
25	100_{five}	1 twenty-five, no fives or ones
30	110_{five}	1 twenty-five, 1 five, no ones
50	200_{five}	
125	1000_{five}	
625	10000_{five}	

Sidelight   MATH AND THE SEARCH FOR LIFE OUT THERE

One of mankind's greatest questions is "Are we alone in the universe?" The search for life beyond our solar system is going on every hour of every day, with giant antennas listening for radio signals from outer space. In the hit movie "Contact," a scientist recognizes that a signal she's receiving must be from an intelligent source because she recognizes that it's based on mathematics (prime numbers). In fact, most scholars feel like our best chance of communicating with an alien civilization is through the universal nature of mathematics! While almost every aspect of languages is dependent on the nature and experiences of the speaker or listener, numbers may be the one true universal constant.

If you think of it, this is intimately tied to the difference between numbers and numerals: while there may be many different ways to represent numbers, the concept of a number is always the same in any language, culture, time, or place. You may then wonder how we would decipher messages from another culture based on mathematics. A good guess is in the same way historians have been able

to learn about the numeration systems of ancient cultures. The concrete nature of numbers gives us a big advantage in decoding messages, providing our best chance at finding life out there.

Converting Base Five Numbers to Base 10 Numbers

Base five numbers can be converted to base 10 numbers using the place values of the base five numbers and expanded notation. For example, the number 242_{five} can be expanded as

$$
\begin{aligned}
242_{\text{five}} &= 2 \times 5^2 + 4 \times 5^1 + 2 \times 5^0 \\
&= 2 \times 25 + 4 \times 5 + 2 \times 1 \\
&= 50 \quad\;\; + 20 \quad\;\; + 2 \\
&= 72
\end{aligned}
$$

EXAMPLE 1   Converting Numbers from Base Five to Base 10

Write each number in base 10.

(a) 42_{five}

(b) 134_{five}

(c) 4213_{five}

SOLUTION

The place value chart for base five is used in each case.

(a) $42_{\text{five}} = 4 \times 5^1 + 2 \times 1 = 20 + 2 = 22$

(b) $134_{\text{five}} = 1 \times 5^2 + 3 \times 5 + 4 \times 1$
$= 1 \times 25 + 3 \times 5 + 4 \times 1$
$= 25 + 15 + 4 = 44$

(c) $4213_{\text{five}} = 4 \times 5^3 + 2 \times 5^2 + 1 \times 5 + 3 \times 1$
$= 4 \times 125 + 2 \times 25 + 1 \times 5 + 3 \times 1$
$= 500 + 50 + 5 + 3 = 558$

▼ Try This One 1

Write each number in the base 10 system.

(a) 302_{five} (b) 1324_{five} (c) 40000_{five}

Converting Base 10 Numbers to Base Five Numbers

Base 10 numbers can be written in the base five system using the place values of the base five system and successive division. This method is illustrated in Examples 2 and 3.

EXAMPLE 2   **Converting Numbers from Base 10 to Base Five**

Write 84 in the base five system.

SOLUTION

Step 1 Identify the largest place value number (1, 5, 25, 125, etc.) that will divide into the base 10 number. In this case, it is 25.

Step 2 Divide 25 into 84, as shown.

$$\begin{array}{r} 3 \\ 25\overline{)84} \\ 75 \\ \hline 9 \end{array}$$

This tells us that there are three 25s in 84.

Step 3 Divide the remainder by the next lower place value. In this case, it is 5.

$$\begin{array}{r} 1 \\ 5\overline{)9} \\ 5 \\ \hline 4 \end{array}$$

> **Math Note**
>
> The answer can be checked using multiplication and addition:
> $3 \times 25 + 1 \times 5 + 4 \times 1$
> $= 75 + 5 + 4 = 84.$

Step 4 Continue dividing until the remainder is less than 5. In this case, it is 4, so the division process is stopped. In other words, four 1s are left. The answer, then, is 314_{five}. In 84, there are three 25s, one 5, and four 1s.

▼ Try This One 2

Write 73 in the base five system.

EXAMPLE 3   **Converting Numbers from Base 10 to Base Five**

Write 653 in the base five system.

SOLUTION

Step 1 Since 625 is the largest place value that will divide into 653, it is used first.

$$\begin{array}{r} 1 \\ 625\overline{)653} \\ 625 \\ \hline 28 \end{array}$$ *There is one 625 in 653.*

Step 2 Divide by 125.

$$\frac{0}{125\overline{)28}}$$
$$\frac{0}{28}$$
There are no 125s in 28.

Even though 125 does not divide into the 28, the zero must be written to hold its place value in the base five number system.

Step 3 Divide by 25.

$$\frac{1}{25\overline{)28}}$$
$$\frac{25}{3}$$
There is one 25 in 28.

Step 4 Divide by 5.

$$\frac{0}{5\overline{)3}}$$
$$\frac{0}{3}$$
There are no 5s in 3.

The solution is 10103_{five}.

Check: $1 \times 625 + 0 \times 125 + 1 \times 25 + 0 \times 5 + 3 \times 1 = 653.$

▼ Try This One 3

Write each number in the base five system.

(a) 52   (b) 486   (c) 1,000

Other Number Bases

Once we understand the idea of alternative bases, we can define new number systems with as few as two symbols, or digits. (Remember, we only needed digits zero through four for base five numbers.) For example, a base two, or **binary system** (used extensively in computer programming) uses only two digits, 0 and 1. The place values of the digits in the base two numeration system are powers of two:

etc. | sixteen (2^4) | eight (2^3) | four (2^2) | two (2^1) | one (2^0)

The base eight or **octal system** consists of eight digits, 0, 1, 2, 3, 4, 5, 6, and 7. The place values of the digits in the base eight system are powers of eight:

etc. | four thousand ninety-six (8^4) | five hundred twelve (8^3) | sixty-four (8^2) | eight (8^1) | one (8^0)

When the base number is greater than 10, new digits must be created to make the numbers. For example, base 16 (called the **hexadecimal system**) is used in computer technology. We need 16 digits for this system; the digits in base 16 are 0, 1, 2, 3, 4, 5, 6, 7, 8, 9, A, B, C, D, E, and F, where A represents 10, B represents 11, C represents 12, etc. (We can't use 10 through 15 because they have 2 digits!) The place values of the digits in base 16 are powers of 16:

etc.
| four thousand ninety-six (16^3)
| two hundred fifty-six (16^2)
| sixteen (16^1)
| one (16^0)

Table 4-2 shows the digits for some of the base number systems and the place values of the digits in the system. It should be pointed out that place values go on indefinitely for any base number system.

TABLE 4-2   Base Number Systems

Base two (binary system)
Digits used: 0, 1
Place values: 2^6 2^5 2^4 2^3 2^2 2^1 2^0
Numbers: 0, 1, 10 , 11, 100, 101, 110, 111, 1000, 1001, 1010, etc.

Base three
Digits used: 0, 1, 2
Place values: 3^6 3^5 3^4 3^3 3^2 3^1 3^0
Numbers: 0, 1, 2, 10, 11, 12, 20, 21, 22, 100, 101, 102, 110, etc.

Base five
Digits used: 0, 1, 2, 3, 4
Place values: 5^6 5^5 5^4 5^3 5^2 5^1 5^0
Numbers: 0, 1, 2, 3, 4, 10, 11, 12, 13, 14, 20, 21, 22, etc.

Base eight (octal system)
Digits used: 0, 1, 2, 3, 4, 5, 6, 7
Place values: 8^6 8^5 8^4 8^3 8^2 8^1 8^0
Numbers: 0, 1, 2, 3, 4, 5, 6, 7, 10, 11, 12, 13, 14, 15, 16, 17, 20, etc.

Base 10
Digits used: 0, 1, 2, 3, 4, 5, 6, 7, 8, 9
Place values: 10^6 10^5 10^4 10^3 10^2 10^1 10^0
Numbers: 0, 1, 2, 3, 4, 5, 6, 7, 8, 9, 10, 11, 12, 13, 14, 15, etc.

Base 16 (hexadecimal system)
Digits used: 0, 1, 2, 3, 4, 5, 6, 7, 8, 9, A, B, C, D, E, F
Place values: 16^6 16^5 16^4 16^3 16^2 16^1 16^0
Numbers: 0, 1, 2, 3, 4, 5, 6, 7, 8, 9, A, B, C, D, E, F, 10, 11, etc.

Looking at the table, several things become apparent. First, the number of symbols is equal to the base. Second, the place values of any base are

$$\cdots \quad \underline{b^6} \quad \underline{b^5} \quad \underline{b^4} \quad \underline{b^3} \quad \underline{b^2} \quad \underline{b^1} \quad \underline{b^0}$$

where b is the base. For example, the place values for base six are

$$\cdots \quad \underline{46{,}656} \quad \underline{7{,}776} \quad \underline{1{,}296} \quad \underline{216} \quad \underline{36} \quad \underline{6} \quad \underline{1}$$
$$\quad\quad\quad 6^6 \quad\quad 6^5 \quad\quad 6^4 \quad\quad 6^3 \quad 6^2 \quad 6^1 \quad 6^0$$

In order to convert from numbers written in bases other than 10 to base 10 numbers, expanded notation is used. This is the same procedure used in Example 1. Example 4 shows the procedure.

EXAMPLE 4   Converting Numbers to Base 10

A microphone converts sound to a voltage signal, which in turn is converted into a binary number. Each measurement is recorded as a 16-bit number and then interpreted by an amplifier.

Write each number in base 10.

(a) 132_{six}　　(b) 10110_{two}　　(c) 1532_{eight}　　(d) 2102_{three}　　(e) $5BD8_{sixteen}$

SOLUTION

(a) The place values of the digits in base six are powers of 6:

$$\begin{aligned}
132_{six} &= 1 \times 6^2 + 3 \times 6^1 + 2 \times 1 \\
&= 1 \times 36 + 3 \times 6 + 2 \times 1 \\
&= 36 + 18 + 2 = 56
\end{aligned}$$

(b) The place values of the digits in base two are powers of 2:

$$\begin{aligned}
10110_{two} &= 1 \times 2^4 + 0 \times 2^3 + 1 \times 2^2 + 1 \times 2^1 + 0 \times 1 \\
&= 1 \times 16 + 0 \times 8 + 1 \times 4 + 1 \times 2 + 0 \times 1 \\
&= 16 + 0 + 4 + 2 + 0 = 22
\end{aligned}$$

(c) The place values of the digits in base eight are powers of 8:

$$\begin{aligned}
1532_{eight} &= 1 \times 8^3 + 5 \times 8^2 + 3 \times 8^1 + 2 \times 1 \\
&= 1 \times 512 + 5 \times 64 + 3 \times 8 + 2 \times 1 \\
&= 512 + 320 + 24 + 2 = 858
\end{aligned}$$

(d) The place values of the digits in base three are powers of 3:

$$\begin{aligned}
2102_{three} &= 2 \times 3^3 + 1 \times 3^2 + 0 \times 3^1 + 2 \times 1 \\
&= 2 \times 27 + 1 \times 9 + 0 \times 3 + 2 \times 1 \\
&= 54 + 9 + 0 + 2 = 65
\end{aligned}$$

(e) The place values of the digits in base 16 are powers of 16:

$$\begin{aligned}
5BD8_{sixteen} &= 5 \times 16^3 + 11 \times 16^2 + 13 \times 16 + 8 \times 1 \\
&= 5 \times 4{,}096 + 11 \times 256 + 13 \times 16 + 8 \times 1 \\
&= 20{,}480 + 2{,}816 + 208 + 8 = 23{,}512
\end{aligned}$$

▼ Try This One 4

Write each number in base 10.

(a) 5320_{seven}　　(b) 110110_{two}　　(c) 32021_{four}　　(d) $42AE_{sixteen}$

Converting Base 10 Numbers to Other Base Numbers

In Examples 2 and 3, we used division to convert base 10 numbers to base five. The same procedure can be used to convert to other base number systems as well.

EXAMPLE 5   **Converting Numbers to Bases Other Than 10**

(a) Write 48 in base three.
(b) Write 51 in base two.
(c) Write 19,443 in base 16.

SOLUTION

(a) **Step 1** The place values for base three are powers of three. The largest power of three less than 48 is 3^3, or 27, so we divide 48 by 27.

$$\begin{array}{r} 1 \\ 27\overline{)48} \\ 27 \\ \hline 21 \end{array}$$

Step 2 Divide the remainder by 3^2 or 9.

$$\begin{array}{r} 2 \\ 9\overline{)21} \\ 18 \\ \hline 3 \end{array}$$

Step 3 Divide the remainder by 3^1 or 3.

$$\begin{array}{r} 1 \\ 3\overline{)3} \\ 3 \\ \hline 0 \end{array}$$

So, 48 is $1 \times 3^3 + 2 \times 3^2 + 1 \times 3^1 + 0 \times 3^0$, which makes it 1210_{three}.

(b) The place values for base two are 1, 2, 4, 8, 16, 32, etc. Use successive division, as shown.

$$\begin{array}{ccccc} 1 & 1 & 0 & 0 & 1 \\ 32\overline{)51} & 16\overline{)19} & 8\overline{)3} & 4\overline{)3} & 2\overline{)3} \\ 32 & 16 & 0 & 0 & 2 \\ \hline 19 & 3 & 3 & 3 & 1 \end{array}$$

So, $51 = 110011_{\text{two}}$.

(c) The place values in base 16 are 1, 16, 256 (16^2), 4096 (16^3), etc. Use successive division as shown. (Remember, in base 16, B plays the role of 11 and F plays the role of 15.)

$$\begin{array}{ccc} 4 & B & F \\ 4096\overline{)19443} & 256\overline{)3059} & 16\overline{)243} \\ 16384 & 2816 & 240 \\ \hline 3059 & 243 & 3 \end{array}$$

So $19,443 = 4BF3_{\text{sixteen}}$.

▼ Try This One 5

☑ 1. Convert between base 10 and other bases.

(a) Write 84 in base two.
(b) Write 258 in base six.
(c) Write 122 in base three.
(d) Write 874 in base 16.

Sidelight **Bar Codes**

Bar codes are a series of black and white stripes that vary in width. The width of each stripe determines a binary digit that the scanner then decodes. The most familiar bar codes are the UPC codes that appear on almost every product you buy. Most UPCs have a left and right margin that tells the reader where to begin and end, a five-digit manufacturer's code, a check digit in the middle, then a five-digit product code. Once a register reads the code and knows what the product is, it computes the price that was programmed in for that product.

Digit	Manufacturer's Number	Product Number
4	0100011	1011100
5	0110001	1001110
6	0101111	1010000
7	0111011	1000100
8	0110111	1001000
9	0001011	1110100

Notice that all of the binary numbers in the manufacturer's code begin with zero, while those in the product code begin with one. This is done so that the scan can be done from left to right, or right to left. The computer can tell the correct direction by recognizing the difference in the digits. As an example of a digit, the digit five is represented by 1001110 in the product code. This number is represented with black and white bars, with a single-width white bar representing a zero and a single-width black bar representing a one.

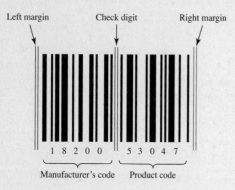

Left margin   Check digit   Right margin

1 8 2 0 0   5 3 0 4 7

Manufacturer's code   Product code

To read a UPC, you need the information in the table below. Every digit in the base 10 system is represented by a seven-digit binary number.

Digit	Manufacturer's Number	Product Number
0	0001101	1110010
1	0011001	1100110
2	0010011	1101100
3	0111101	1000010

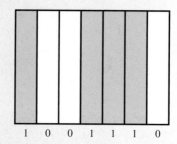

1   0   0   1   1   1   0

Notice how this matches the first four stripes to the right of the check digit in the UPC above (without the borders around the individual bars). Every digit in the left half of a UPC is represented by four stripes: white, then black, then white, then black. On the right half, it's black, then white, then black, then white. The key is to recognize the width of each stripe to decide how many bars it represents.

It takes a little bit of practice to distinguish bars that represent one, two, three, and four consecutive digits, but once you can do that, you can decode UPCs—just not as fast as a computer can.

Base Numbers and Computers

Computers use three bases to perform operations. They are base two, the binary system; base eight, the octal system; and base 16, the hexadecimal system.

Base two is used since it contains only two characters, 0 and 1. Electric circuits can differentiate two types of pulses, on and off. Early computers used one on-off vacuum tube to store one binary character. Since it is cheaper and faster to use the binary system, modern computers still use this system, and assembly language programmers must become proficient in the binary system.

The base eight system is also used by computer programmers. In computer language, 1 bit is used to represent one character, and 8 bits constitute a byte. It then becomes convenient to write numbers using a series of bytes (eight characters).

TABLE 4-3	Binary Equivalents for Octal and Hexadecimal Digits

Octal Digit	Binary Equivalent
0	000
1	001
2	010
3	011
4	100
5	101
6	110
7	111

Hex Digit	Binary Equivalent
0	0000
1	0001
2	0010
3	0011
4	0100
5	0101
6	0110
7	0111

Hex Digit	Binary Equivalent
8	1000
9	1001
A	1010
B	1011
C	1100
D	1101
E	1110
F	1111

The base 16 is used for several reasons. First of all, 16 characters consist of 2 bytes. Also, 16 is 2^4, which means one hexadecimal character can replace four binary characters. This increases the speed at which the computer is able to perform numerical applications since there are fewer characters for the computer to read and fewer operations to perform. Finally, large numbers can be written in base 16 with fewer characters than in base two or base 10, saving much needed space in the computer's memory.

There is a shortcut for converting between binary and octal or binary and hexadecimal. To use this short cut, first notice that every octal digit can be written as a three-digit binary number, and every hexadecimal digit can be written as a four-digit binary number, as illustrated in Table 4-3.

The following examples illustrate the shortcut for converting between these bases.

EXAMPLE 6	Converting between Binary and Octal

(a) Convert the binary number 1001110110_{two} to octal.
(b) Convert the octal number 7643_{eight} to binary.

SOLUTION

(a) Starting at the rightmost digit, group the digits of the binary number into groups of three (if there are not three digits that remain at the left of the number, fill them in with zeros), then use Table 4-3 to change each group to an octal digit as follows.

$$001 \quad 001 \quad 110 \quad 110$$
$$1 \quad\quad 1 \quad\quad 6 \quad\quad 6$$

So, $1001110110_{two} = 1166_{eight}$.

(b) First, convert each octal digit into a three-digit binary digit using Table 4-3, and then string them together to form a binary number.

$$7 \quad\quad 6 \quad\quad 4 \quad\quad 3$$
$$111 \quad 110 \quad 100 \quad 011$$

So, $7643_{eight} = 111110100011_{two}$.

▼ **Try This One 6**

(a) Convert 1100101_{two} to octal.   (b) Convert 6147_{eight} to binary.

EXAMPLE 4   **Adding in Base 16**

Add in base 16: $135E_{sixteen} + 21C_{sixteen}$.

SOLUTION

$$
\begin{array}{r}
\overset{1}{1}35E_{sixteen} \\
+\ 21C_{sixteen} \\
\hline
157A_{sixteen}
\end{array}
$$

— $E_{sixteen} + C_{sixteen} = 1A_{sixteen}$ Write the A and carry the 1.

— $1_{sixteen} + 5_{sixteen} + 1_{sixteen} = 7_{sixteen}$

— $3_{sixteen} + 2_{sixteen} = 5_{sixteen}$

— Bring down the 1

The sum is $157A_{sixteen}$.

▼ **Try This One 4**

☑ 1. Add in bases other than 10.

Add in base 16: $8D51_{sixteen} + 947A_{sixteen}$

Now that we know how to perform addition in other bases, we should be able to subtract as well. Addition tables can help with subtraction; the addition table for base five is below. To perform a subtraction like $12_{five} - 4_{five}$, we find 4 in the far left column of the table, then move across that row until we find 12. The number at the top of the column is the difference: $12_{five} - 4_{five} = 3_{five}$.

+	0	1	2	③	4
0	0	1	2	3	4
1	1	2	3	4	10
2	2	3	4	10	11
3	3	4	10	11	12
④	4	10	11	⑫	13

We will subtract numbers with more than one digit using a method similar to addition. When the digit to be subtracted is larger, as in the first step of Example 5, we'll need to "borrow" a one from the next larger place value.

EXAMPLE 5   **Subtracting in Base Five**

Subtract in base five:

$$
\begin{array}{r}
321_{five} \\
-\ 123_{five} \\
\hline
\end{array}
$$

SOLUTION

Step 1 Since 3 is larger than 1, it is necessary to borrow a one from the next column; this makes the subtraction $11_{five} - 3_{five} = 3_{five}$. Change 2 in the fives column to a 1.

$$
\begin{array}{r}
3\ \ \overset{1}{\cancel{2}}\ \ \overset{11}{1}_{five} \\
-1\ \ \ 2\ \ \ 3_{five} \\
\hline
3_{five}
\end{array}
$$

Step 2 In the second column, $1_{five} - 2_{five}$ requires borrowing; change 3 in the third column to 2 and take $11_{five} - 2_{five}$ to get 4_{five}.

$$
\begin{array}{rrr}
 & 2 & // \\
\cancel{3} & \cancel{2} & 1_{five} \\
-1 & 2 & 3_{five} \\
\hline
 & 4 & 3_{five}
\end{array}
$$

Step 3 Subtract $2_{five} - 1_{five}$ to get 1_{five}.

$$
\begin{array}{rrr}
 & 2 & \\
3 & 2 & 1_{five} \\
-1 & 2 & 3_{five} \\
\hline
1 & 4 & 3_{five}
\end{array}
$$

The difference is $321_{five} - 123_{five} = 143_{five}$.

> ## Math Note
>
> The answer can be checked by adding $143_{five} + 123_{five}$ and seeing if the answer is 321_{five} (which it is).

☑ 2. Subtract in bases other than 10.

▼ Try This One 5

Perform the indicated operation: $7316_{eight} - 1257_{eight}$.

The multiplication table for base five is shown next.

×	0	1	2	3	4
0	0	0	0	0	0
1	0	1	2	3	4
2	0	2	4	11	13
3	0	3	11	14	22
4	0	4	13	22	31

For example, $3_{five} \times 4_{five} = 22_{five}$ ($3 \times 4 = 12$ in base ten, which is 22_{five}).

Multiplication is done in base five using the same basic procedure you learned in base 10.

EXAMPLE 6   Multiplying in Bases Five and Two

> ## Math Note
>
> As always, you can check your answer by converting to base 10.

(a) Multiply in base five:

$$
\begin{array}{r}
314_{five} \\
\times \ 23_{five} \\
\hline
\end{array}
$$

(b) Multiply in base two:

$$
\begin{array}{r}
1011_{two} \\
\times \ 11_{two} \\
\hline
\end{array}
$$

SOLUTION

(a) First, we multiply each digit in 314_{five} by the last digit in 23_{five}.

Step 1 Multiply $4_{five} \times 3_{five} = 22_{five}$. Write the second digit and carry the first to the fives column.

$$
\begin{array}{r}
2 \\
314_{five} \\
\times \ 23_{five} \\
\hline
2_{five}
\end{array}
$$

41. 1010_{two}
       $\times\ 101_{\text{two}}$

42. 54_{eight}
       $\times\ 2_{\text{eight}}$

43. $A25_{\text{sixteen}}$
       $\times\ 4_{\text{sixteen}}$

44. 326_{eight}
       $\times\ 21_{\text{eight}}$

45. $11_{\text{two}}\overline{)1011_{\text{two}}}$

46. $6_{\text{eight}}\overline{)437_{\text{eight}}}$

47. $5_{\text{sixteen}}\overline{)37B1_{\text{sixteen}}}$

48. $10_{\text{two}}\overline{)11111_{\text{two}}}$

Critical Thinking

49. In a certain base number system, $5 + 6 = 13$. What is the base?

50. In a certain base number system, $15 - 6 = 6$. What is the base?

The American Standard Code for Information (ASCII) is used to encode characters of the alphabet as binary numbers. Each character is assigned an eight-digit binary number written in two groups of four digits as follows:

A–O are prefixed by 0100, and the second grouping starts with A = 0001, B = 0010, C = 0011, etc.

P–Z are prefixed by 0101, and the second grouping starts with P = 0000, Q = 0001, R = 0010, etc. For example, C = 0100 0011 and Q = 0101 0001.

For Exercises 51–54, find the letter of the alphabet corresponding to the binary code.

51. 0100 1100

52. 0101 0101

53. 0100 0111

54. 0101 1010

For Exercises 55–58, write each word in ASCII code.

55. DORM

56. PARTY

57. UNION

58. QUAD

CHAPTER **4** **Summary**

Section	Important Terms	Important Ideas
4-1	Number Numeral Numeration system Tally system Simple grouping system Multiplicative grouping system Digit Place value Positional system Expanded notation	**Throughout** history, people have used different numeration systems. These systems include the Egyptian, the Chinese, the Babylonian, and the Roman numeration systems. The system that is used in our world today is called the Hindu-Arabic numeration system. It uses the base 10 and 10 symbols called digits to represent numbers.
4-2	Algorithm	**There** were many methods developed for performing calculations before the development of electronic calculators. The Egyptian algorithm, the Russian peasant method, the lattice method, and Napier's bones are all procedures that can be used to multiply by hand.
4-3	Base Binary system Octal system Hexadecimal system	**Numbers** can be written using different bases. For example, the base five system has only five digits. They are 0, 1, 2, 3, and 4. The place values of the numbers written in the base five system are $5^0 = 1$, $5^1 = 5$, $5^2 = 25$, etc.
4-4		**Operations** such as addition, subtraction, multiplication, and division can be performed in other number bases the same way they are performed in base 10.

MATH IN ▶ Retail Sales REVISITED

The first UPC shown decodes as 21000 77436: this is from a staple of many college students' diet, a box of Kraft original macaroni and cheese.

The second decodes as 85909 12179: this corresponds to a 16-GB iPod Touch.

Review Exercises

Section 4-1

For Exercises 1–5, write each number using Hindu-Arabic numerals.

1. 𐤏𐄾𐄾𐄾∩∩∩I

2. 𓂣𓏤𓏤𓏤∩∩IIIIIII

3. ⟨I ⟨⟨I
4. MCXLVII
5. CDXIX
6. ⟨⟨⟨I ⟨⟨II

7. 二
千
六
百
四

8. 九
百
五
十
七

For Exercises 9–16, write each number in the system given.

9. 49 in the Egyptian system
10. 896 in the Roman system
11. 88 in the Babylonian system
12. 125 in the Egyptian system
13. 503 in the Roman system
14. 8,325 in the Chinese system
15. 165 in the Babylonian system
16. 74 in the Chinese system

For Exercises 17–18, perform the indicated operation. Leave answers in the Egyptian system.

17. ᒥᒥᒥ∩∩∩∩∩||||| + 𝆑ᒥᒥ∩∩||||||

18. 𝆑𝆑ᒥᒥᒥ∩∩||| + 𝈜𝆑∩∩|||||

Section 4-2

For Exercises 19–22, use the Egyptian algorithm to multiply.

19. 23×12
20. 13×8
21. 7×21
22. 15×16

For Exercises 23–26, multiply using the Russian peasant method.

23. 15×22
24. 12×17
25. 13×12
26. 22×45

For Exercises 27–30, use the lattice method of multiplication to find each product.

27. 23×85
28. 45×398
29. 439×833
30. 548×505

For Exercises 31–34, use Napier's bones (constructed for the exercises in Section 4-2) to find each product.

31. 31×82
32. 74×53
33. 147×95
34. 88×796

Section 4-3

For Exercises 35–44, write each number in base 10.

35. 1110111_{two}
36. 672_{eight}
37. $A03B_{twelve}$
38. 231_{four}
39. 14441_{five}
40. 2012_{three}
41. 6000_{seven}
42. 28645_{nine}
43. 555_{six}
44. $1A214_{eleven}$

For Exercises 45–54, write each number in the specified base.

45. 32 in base six
46. 105 in base 12
47. 2,001 in base nine
48. 81 in base three
49. 43 in base two
50. 213 in base eight
51. 19 in base four
52. 51 in base two
53. 343 in base seven
54. 899 in base 12

In Exercises 55–62, subscripts are omitted since the base is provided in the instructions.

For Exercises 55–58, convert each binary number to (a) octal and (b) hexadecimal.

55. 111011011
56. 10001110111
57. 1101100111
58. 111000111101

For Exercises 59 and 60, convert each octal number to binary.

59. 7324
60. 643

For Exercises 61 and 62, convert each hexadecimal number to binary.

61. A5B3
62. 9F87

Section 4-4

For Exercises 63–80, perform the indicated operation.

63. $\begin{aligned}156_{nine}\\+84_{nine}\\\hline\end{aligned}$

64. $\begin{aligned}434_{five}\\+341_{five}\\\hline\end{aligned}$

65. $\begin{aligned}101110_{two}\\+1101_{two}\\\hline\end{aligned}$

66. $\begin{aligned}5342_{six}\\+1305_{six}\\\hline\end{aligned}$

67. $\begin{aligned}6A20_{twelve}\\+B096_{twelve}\\\hline\end{aligned}$

68. $\begin{aligned}7267_{nine}\\-354_{nine}\\\hline\end{aligned}$

69. $\begin{aligned}1010011_{two}\\-100111_{two}\\\hline\end{aligned}$

70. $\begin{aligned}2120_{three}\\-1212_{three}\\\hline\end{aligned}$

71. $\begin{aligned}3312_{four}\\-2321_{four}\\\hline\end{aligned}$

72. $\begin{aligned}65602_{seven}\\-46031_{seven}\\\hline\end{aligned}$

73. $\begin{aligned}371_{nine}\\\times51_{nine}\\\hline\end{aligned}$

74. $\begin{aligned}242_{five}\\\times3_{five}\\\hline\end{aligned}$

75. $\begin{aligned}1101_{two}\\\times111_{two}\\\hline\end{aligned}$

76. $\begin{aligned}6A5_{sixteen}\\\times8_{sixteen}\\\hline\end{aligned}$

77. $3_{five}\overline{)1242_{five}}$

78. $7_{eight}\overline{)3426_{eight}}$

79. $10_{eight}\overline{)3426_{eight}}$

80. $5_{sixteen}\overline{)324_{sixteen}}$

Chapter Test

For Exercises 1–5, write each number using Hindu-Arabic numerals.

1. ☥☥ᒥᒥᒥ∩||

2. 𝈜𝈜𝆑𝆑𝆑𝆑𝆑∩∩∩|||||

3. ⟨⟨𝍦 ⟨𝍦

4. MCMLXVI

5. CDXXVI

6. 三
   百
   六
   十
   八

For Exercises 7–12, write each number in the system given.

7. 93 in the Egyptian system
8. 567 in the Roman system
9. 55 in the Babylonian system
10. 521 in the Egyptian system
11. 605 in the Roman system
12. 873 in the Chinese system

For Exercises 13–16, multiply using the given method.

13. Multiply 17×13 by the Egyptian algorithm.
14. Multiply 23×15 by the Russian peasant method.
15. Use the lattice method to multiply 364×736.
16. Use Napier's bones (constructed for the exercises in Section 4-2) to multiply 112×237.

For Exercises 17–26, write each number in base 10.

17. 341_{five}
18. 573_{eight}
19. $A07B_{twelve}$
20. 312_{four}
21. 14411_{five}
22. 21101_{three}
23. 4000_{five}
24. 1100111_{two}
25. 463_{seven}
26. $1A436_{eleven}$

For Exercises 27–36, write each number in the specified base.

27. 43 in base five
28. 183 in base 12
29. 4,673 in base nine
30. 65 in base three
31. 17 in base two
32. 316 in base eight
33. 91 in base four
34. 48 in base two
35. 434 in base seven
36. 889 in base 12

For Exercises 37 and 38 convert the binary number to (a) octal and (b) hexadecimal.

37. 111011001
38. 11000111011
39. Convert 7324_{eight} to binary.
40. Convert $A6D92_{sixteen}$ to binary.

For Exercises 41–54, perform the indicated operation.

41. $\begin{array}{r} 263_{nine} \\ + \ 18_{nine} \\ \hline \end{array}$

42. $\begin{array}{r} 341_{five} \\ +213_{five} \\ \hline \end{array}$

43. $\begin{array}{r} 111010_{two} \\ + \ 1101_{two} \\ \hline \end{array}$

44. $\begin{array}{r} 2435_{six} \\ +5013_{six} \\ \hline \end{array}$

45. $\begin{array}{r} 5A79_{twelve} \\ +B068_{twelve} \\ \hline \end{array}$

46. $\begin{array}{r} 6772_{eight} \\ - \ 735_{eight} \\ \hline \end{array}$

47. $\begin{array}{r} 11001010_{two} \\ - \ 110011_{two} \\ \hline \end{array}$

48. $\begin{array}{r} 2212_{three} \\ -1202_{three} \\ \hline \end{array}$

49. $\begin{array}{r} 3213_{four} \\ -2123_{four} \\ \hline \end{array}$

50. $\begin{array}{r} 20665_{seven} \\ -10364_{seven} \\ \hline \end{array}$

51. $\begin{array}{r} 254_{six} \\ \times \ \ 3_{six} \\ \hline \end{array}$

52. $\begin{array}{r} 413_{five} \\ \times \ 21_{five} \\ \hline \end{array}$

53. $7_{eight}\overline{)1342_{eight}}$

54. $2_{three}\overline{)1012_{three}}$

Project

In this project, we'll test various methods of multiplication, with a goal of making an individual decision on which method is most effective. We'll consider both ease of use, amount of time needed, and likelihood of getting the correct product. You will need a calculator to check the products you compute, as well as a watch to time each calculation.

(a) **Two-digit multiplication** Multiply the first two digits of your social security number and the last two digits using (i) the Egyptian algorithm, (ii) the Russian peasant method, (iii) the lattice method, (iv) Napier's bones, and (v) the method you learned in grade school. In each case, time how long it takes the method from start to finish, and make note of whether you got the right answer for each.

If you are working in a group, each group member should repeat the above steps. If you are working on your own, repeat the process, multiplying the first two digits of your phone number by the last two, then again multiplying the first two digits of your zip code by the last two.

(b) **Three-digit multiplication** Repeat question 1, but this time choose numbers this way: turn to a random page past this one in the book and note the page number, then to another page at least 100 pages further on and note that page number. Use each method of multiplication again. If you are working in a group, each group member should choose different page numbers. If you are working on your own, choose three sets of random pages.

(c) Calculate the average amount of time it took to perform all calculations with each of the five methods, and rank them in order from fastest to slowest.

(d) Calculate the percentage of problems in which the correct answer was obtained for each method, and rank them from highest to lowest.

(e) Based on your experience in using the methods, and your rankings in questions 3 and 4, write a short essay identifying the method that you think is most effective, and justify that choice.

CHAPTER **8**

Consumer Mathematics

Outline

MATH IN › **Home Buying**

Home buying shows have become very popular in the last couple of years. It's interesting to watch people looking for just the right home, and maybe more interesting to find out what homes are selling for in other parts of the country. The downside as a viewer is that it can be pretty intimidating to find out just how much houses cost. Almost everyone wonders at some point "Will I ever be able to afford a home of my own?"

This might lead you to come to a larger realization: long ago, survival depended on overcoming physical challenges that modern humans can only imagine, but today, survival is more about navigating the waters of the modern financial system. There are over 300 million people in the United States, and at any given time, probably half of them are trying to figure out a way to separate you from your hard-earned money. That's why this chapter is about some aspects of our financial system that are particularly important to the average adult. Success in this chapter will help you to be a well-informed consumer, which makes it less likely that those 150 million people will succeed in getting your cash.

We begin with a thorough look at percents, which play a big role in almost all areas of consumer mathematics. Then we'll study loans and investments, two topics of particular interest in the current financial climate. The goal is to help you take the guesswork out of financial planning, so that rather than hoping you're doing the right things for your future, you can be sure that you are.

Now to return to the original question: how much can you afford to pay for a home? Many financial experts suggest that typical home buyers can afford to pay 28% of their gross monthly income on housing. Obviously, this determines how much house you can afford. Below is a description of a hypothetical young couple. Using the math you learn in this chapter, you should be able to help them determine the price range they can afford.

Troy and Lisa have a combined annual income of $72,000, and while renting for the first 4 years of their marriage, have managed to save $15,000 for a down payment. How much can they afford to pay for a house if they qualify for a 30-year mortgage with an interest rate of 6.0%? Assume that 5% of income will go to property tax and insurance on the home.

For answers, see Math in Home Buying Revisited on page 475

Section 8-1 Percents

LEARNING OBJECTIVES

☐ 1. Convert between percent, decimal, and fraction form.

☐ 2. Perform calculations involving percents.

☐ 3. Solve real-world problems involving percents.

☐ 4. Find percent increase or decrease.

☐ 5. Evaluate the validity of claims based on percents.

Have you ever been shopping, come across a clearance rack that said something like "40% off lowest ticketed price," and had to ask someone what the discounted price of a certain item would be? If so, you're certainly not alone. Any math teacher will tell you that people ask them questions like that all of the time.

Percents are a math topic with a huge number of applications to everyday life, so they should be high on our priority list if we're trying to learn about math in our world. In this section, we'll learn about percents: what they really mean, how to use them in calculations, and even how they can be deceptively misused.

The word "percent" can be translated literally as "per hundred."

Percent means hundredths, or per hundred. That is, $1\% = \dfrac{1}{100}$.

For example, the International Mass Retail Association reported that 20% of adults plan to buy Valentine's Day cards next year. Of those who plan to buy them, 36% of women and 26% of men plan to buy romantic cards. This tells us that 20 out of every 100 adults plan to buy a card. Also, 26 out of 100 men who buy a card will choose a romantic one, and 36 out of 100 women will do so.

Percent Conversions

To work with percents in calculations, we will need to convert them to either decimal or fractional form. But to interpret the answers to calculations, we will want to convert them back into percents.

Converting Percents to Decimals

In order to change a percent to a decimal, drop the % sign and move the decimal point two places to the left.

EXAMPLE 1   Changing Percents to Decimals

Change each percent to a decimal.

(a) 84%   (c) 37.5%
(b) 5%   (d) 172%

SOLUTION

(Drop the % sign and move the decimal point two places to the left.)

(a) $84\% = 84.\% = 0.84\% = 0.84$ *Put decimal point in if necessary.*

(b) $5\% = 5.\% = 0.05\% = 0.05$

(c) $37.5\% = 0.375\% = 0.375$

(d) $172\% = 172.\% = 1.72\% = 1.72$

Math Note

Moving the decimal point two places to the left is the same as dividing by 100.

▼ Try This One 1

Change each percent to a decimal.

(a) 62.5%   (b) 3%   (c) 250%

Converting Percents to Fractions

A percent can be converted to a fraction by dropping the percent sign and using the percent number as the numerator of a fraction whose denominator is 100.

Be sure to reduce fractions to lowest terms when possible.

EXAMPLE 2   **Changing Percents to Fractions**

Change each percent to a fraction.

(a) 42%   (c) $37\frac{1}{2}\%$

(b) 6%   (d) 15.8%

SOLUTION

(a) $42\% = \dfrac{42}{100} = \dfrac{21 \cdot \cancel{2}}{50 \cdot \cancel{2}} = \dfrac{21}{50}$

(b) $6\% = \dfrac{6}{100} = \dfrac{3 \cdot \cancel{2}}{50 \cdot \cancel{2}} = \dfrac{3}{50}$

(c) When converting fractional or decimal percents, it might be helpful to multiply by some number over itself to clear fractions or decimals. In this case, multiplying by $\frac{2}{2}$ is helpful:

$$\frac{37\frac{1}{2}}{100} \times \frac{2}{2} = \frac{75}{200} = \frac{\cancel{25} \cdot 3}{\cancel{25} \cdot 8} = \frac{3}{8}$$

(d) $15.8\% = \dfrac{15.8}{100} = \dfrac{15.8}{100} \cdot \dfrac{10}{10} = \dfrac{158}{1,000} = \dfrac{79 \cdot \cancel{2}}{500 \cdot \cancel{2}} = \dfrac{79}{500}$

▼ Try This One 2

Change each percent to a fraction.

(a) 90%   (b) 16.5%   (c) 130%

Converting a Decimal to a Percent

To change a decimal to a percent, move the decimal point two places to the right and add a percent sign.

EXAMPLE 3   **Changing Decimals to Percents**

Change each decimal to a percent.

(a) 0.74   (b) 0.05   (c) 1.327   (d) 5.463

Math Note

Moving the decimal point two places to the right is the same as multiplying by 100.

SOLUTION

(a) $0.74 = 074.\% = 74\%$

(b) $0.05 = 005.\% = 5\%$

(c) $1.327 = 132.7\% = 132.7\%$

(d) $5.463 = 546.3\% = 546.3\%$

▼ Try This One 3

Change each decimal to a percent.

(a) 0.974   (b) 0.04   (c) 3.75

Changing a Fraction to a Percent

To change a fraction to a percent, first change the fraction to a decimal, and then change the decimal to a percent.

EXAMPLE 4   **Changing Fractions to Percents**

Math Note

Recall that to change a fraction to a decimal, we divide the numerator by the denominator.

Convert each fraction to a percent.

(a) $\dfrac{7}{8}$ (b) $\dfrac{3}{4}$ (c) $\dfrac{5}{6}$ (d) $1\dfrac{1}{2}$

SOLUTION

(a) $\dfrac{7}{8} = 7 \div 8 = 0.875 = 87.5\%$

(b) $\dfrac{3}{4} = 3 \div 4 = 0.75 = 75\%$

(c) $\dfrac{5}{6} = 0.83\overline{3} = 83.\overline{3}\%$

(d) $1\dfrac{1}{2} = 1.5 = 150\%$

Calculator Guide

Calculators come in very handy when converting fractions to percents. For $\frac{5}{6}$:

Standard Scientific Calculator

5 ÷ 6 =

Standard Graphing Calculator

5 ÷ 6 Enter

In each case, the display will show something like 0.83333333333. This needs to be interpreted as the repeating decimal $0.8\overline{3}$.

▼ Try This One 4

Change each fraction to a percent.

(a) $\dfrac{5}{16}$ (b) $\dfrac{7}{9}$ (c) $1\dfrac{3}{4}$

Problems Involving Percents

The most common calculations involving percents involve finding a percentage of some quantity. To understand how to do so, consider the following example. You probably know that 50% of 10 is 5. Let's rewrite that statement, then turn it into a calculation:

50% of 10 is 5

$0.5 \times 10 = 5$

When writing a percentage statement in symbols, the word "of" becomes multiplication, and the word "is" becomes an equal sign. Also, we must change the percent into decimal or fractional form. The next three examples show how to use this procedure to set up calculations.

☑ 1. Convert between percent, decimal, and fraction form.

EXAMPLE 5   **Finding a Certain Percentage of a Whole**

In a class of 66 students, 32% got a B on the first exam. How many students got a B?

SOLUTION

First write 32% in decimal form, as 0.32. The question is "what is 32% of 66?" which we translate into symbols:

32% of 66 is _____
$0.32 \times 66 = 21.12$

We can't have 0.12 students, so we interpret the answer as 21 students got a B.

▼ **Try This One 5**

In another section of the same course, 19% of the 54 students got a B. How many students got a B?

CAUTION

In calculations with percents, it's very common for the result to contain digits after a decimal point, like 21.12 in Example 5. You should always think about what quantity your answer represents to decide if it's appropriate to round to the nearest whole number.

EXAMPLE 6   **Finding a Percentage from a Portion**

Of these 5 kittens, 2 are mostly gray. What percent are gray?

Of 60 runners who started a 5k race, 45 finished the race in under 40 minutes. What percent is that?

SOLUTION

Write the statement in the form we discussed above:

45 is what percent of 60?
$45 = \quad x \quad \times 60 \qquad$ *x is the percent in decimal form.*

This is the equation $60x = 45$, which we solve for x.

$$60x = 45 \qquad \textit{Divide both sides by 60.}$$
$$\frac{60x}{60} = \frac{45}{60}$$
$$x = \frac{45}{60} = 0.75$$

The decimal 0.75 corresponds to 75%, so 75% finished in under 40 minutes.

▼ **Try This One 6**

In 2008, 21 out of 50 states had a population of 5 million or higher. What percent is that?

Sidelight   MONEY, BANKS, AND CREDIT CARDS

Long before money existed, people bartered for goods and services. For example, if you needed the roof of your hut fixed, you might pay the repair person two chickens. The first known coins were made over 2,500 years ago in Western Turkey. They consisted of a mixture of gold and silver and were stamped to guarantee uniformity. These coins were first accepted by the merchants of the area. Also around that time, coins were made in India and China.

Paper money was first made in China about 1,400 years ago; however, when Marco Polo brought the idea to Europe, it was rejected by the people. It wasn't until the 1600s that banks in Europe began to issue paper money to their depositors and borrowers.

In the United States, early settlers used tobacco, beaver skins, and foreign coins as currency. A popular coin was the Spanish dollar, called "pieces of eight." For purchases of less than one dollar, the coin was cut into eight pieces. Each piece was called a "bit" and was worth $12\frac{1}{2}$ cents. Hence 25 cents became known as "two bits," 50 cents as "four bits," etc.

During the Revolutionary War, the Continental Congress authorized the printing of paper money to pay war debts. The government printed more money than it could back up with gold and silver, and the dollar became virtually worthless. The phrase "not worth a Continental dollar" is still used today.

The U.S. Mint opened on April 2, 1792, in Washington, D.C., to mint coins. Gold was used for the $10.00, $5.00, and $2.50 coins. Silver was used for the $1.00, $0.50, $0.25, $0.10, and the $0.05 coins, and copper was used for the 1 cent and $\frac{1}{2}$ cent.

Most paper money was issued by state banks until 1863 when Congress established national banks to issue currency notes. In 1913, the Federal Reserve System was established to issue notes, which became our standard currency.

Banking began in ancient Babylon about 2000 BCE when people kept their money in temples. They thought that if the temples were robbed, the gods would punish the robbers. In medieval times, money was kept in vaults in castles and protected by the armies of the nobles. The first bank was established in 1148 in Genoa, Italy. It was called the Bank of San Giorgio. The first bank in the United States was established in 1781 in Philadelphia and was called the Bank of North America.

Credit cards were first issued by large hotels in the early 1900s. These cards were considered to be prestigious and were issued only to customers who spent a lot of money at the hotel. Department stores and gasoline companies began to issue credit cards around 1915. During World War II, the United States forbade the use of credit cards. Banks began to issue credit cards in the 1950s. Finally, in the late 1960s, banks agreed to sponsor credit cards such as Master Card, Visa, etc.

EXAMPLE 7   Finding a Whole Amount Based on a Percentage

A medium-sized company reported that it had to cut its work force back to 70% of what it was last year. If it has 63 workers now, how many did it have a year ago?

SOLUTION

Convert 70% to a decimal: 70% = 0.70. Now write as a question and translate to symbols:

$$70\% \text{ of what number is } 63?$$
$$0.70 \quad \times \quad x \quad = 63$$

This gives us the equation $0.70x = 63$, which we solve for x.

$$0.70x = 63 \qquad \textit{Divide both sides by 0.70.}$$
$$\frac{0.70x}{0.70} = \frac{63}{0.70}$$
$$x = 90$$

The company had 90 workers a year ago.

▼ Try This One 7

After a really rotten year in 2008, a baseball team won 120% as many games in 2009, which was 84 games. How many games did they win in 2008?

☑ 2. Perform calculations involving percents.

Applications of Percents

Many aspects of consumer mathematics deal with finding parts of a whole. For example, you may want to leave a 15% tip, you may want to figure out a 33% markup, or you may want to calculate an 8% commission on sales. Some applications are shown in Examples 8 through 10.

EXAMPLE 8   **Calculating Sales Tax**

Math Note

In Example 8, you can find the total by multiplying the cost by 1.07 (i.e., 107%). 1.07($89.95) = $96.25 (rounded).

The sales tax in Allegheny County, Pennsylvania, is 7%. What is the tax on a calculator that costs $89.95? What is the total amount paid?

SOLUTION

Find 7% of $89.95: Write 7% as 0.07 in decimal form, then multiply.

$$0.07 \times \$89.95 = \$6.30 \text{ (rounded)}$$

The sales tax is $6.30. The total amount paid is

$$\$89.95 + \$6.30 = \$96.25$$

▼ Try This One 8

The sales tax in Atlanta, Georgia, is 5%. Find the amount of tax and the total cost of a portable DVD player on sale for $149.

EXAMPLE 9   **Calculating Cost of Sale from Commission**

A real estate agent receives a 7% commission on all home sales. How expensive was the home if she received a commission of $5,775.00?

SOLUTION

In this case, the problem can be written as $5,775.00 is 7% of what number?

$$\$5,775 \text{ is } 7\% \text{ of } x$$
$$5,775 = 0.07 \times x \qquad \textit{Divide both sides by 0.07.}$$
$$\frac{5,775}{0.07} = \frac{0.07 \times x}{0.07}$$
$$82,500 = x$$

The home was purchased for $82,500.00.

▼ Try This One 9

A sales clerk receives a 9% commission on all sales. Find the total sales the clerk made if his commission was $486.00.

☑ 3. Solve real-world problems involving percents.

Sometimes it is useful to find the percent increase or the percent decrease in a specific situation. In this case, we can use the following method.

Procedure for Finding Percent Increase or Decrease

Step 1   Find the amount of the increase or the decrease.

Step 2   Make a fraction as shown:

$$\frac{\text{Amount of increase}}{\text{Original amount}} \quad \text{or} \quad \frac{\text{Amount of decrease}}{\text{Original amount}}$$

Step 3   Change the fraction to a percent.

EXAMPLE 10   **Finding a Percent Change**

A large latte at the Caffeine Connection sells at a regular price of \$3.50. Today it is on sale for \$3.00. Find the percent decrease in the price.

SOLUTION

The original price is \$3.50.

Step 1   Find the amount of decrease. \$3.50 − \$3.00 = \$0.50.

Step 2   Make a fraction as shown

$$\frac{\text{Amount of decrease}}{\text{Original price}} = \frac{\$0.50}{\$3.50}$$

Step 3   Change the fraction to a percent.

$$\frac{0.50}{3.50} \approx 0.1428 = 14.3\% \text{ (rounded)}$$

The decrease in price is 14.3%.

☑ 4. Find percent increase or decrease.

▼ Try This One 10

In 2008 the population of the town of Oak Creek was 23,258. In 2009, the population increased to 23,632. Find the percent increase in the population.

Percent increase or decrease is often misused, sometimes intentionally, sometimes not. In Example 11, we'll look at a common deceptive use of percents in advertising.

EXAMPLE 11   **Recognizing Misuse of Percents in Advertising**

A department store advertised that certain merchandise was reduced 25%. Also, an additional 10% discount card would be given to the first 200 people who entered the store on a specific day. The advertisement then stated that this amounted to a 35% reduction in the price of an item. Is the advertiser being honest?

SOLUTION

Let's say that an item was originally priced at \$50.00. (Note: any price can be used.) First find the discount amount.

$$\begin{aligned}
\text{Discount} &= \text{rate} \times \text{selling price} \\
&= 25\% \times \$50.00 \\
&= 0.25 \times \$50.00 \\
&= \$12.50
\end{aligned}$$

Then find the reduced price.

$$\text{Reduced price} = \text{original price} - \text{discount}$$
$$= \$50.00 - \$12.50$$
$$= \$37.50$$

Next find 10% of the reduced price.

$$\text{Discount} = \text{rate} \times \text{reduced price}$$
$$= 10\% \times \$37.50$$
$$= \$3.75$$

Find the second reduced price.

$$\text{Reduced price} = \$37.50 - \$3.75$$
$$= \$33.75$$

Now find the percent of the total reduction.

$$\frac{\text{Reduction}}{\text{Original price}} = \frac{\$12.50 + \$3.75}{\$50.00} = \frac{16.25}{50.00} = 0.325 = 32.5\%$$

The total percent of the reduction was 32.5%, and not 35% as advertised.

✓ 5. Evaluate the validity of
claims based on percents.

▼ Try This One 11

A department store offered a 20% discount on all television sets. They also stated that the fist 50 customers would receive an additional 5% discount. Find the total percent discount. You can use any selling price for the televisions.

Answers to Try This One

1 (a) 0.625 (b) 0.03 (c) 2.50

2 (a) $\frac{9}{10}$ (b) $\frac{33}{200}$ (c) $\frac{13}{10}$

3 (a) 97.4% (b) 4% (c) 375%

4 (a) 31.25% (b) 77.$\overline{7}$% (c) 175%

5 10

6 42%

7 70

8 Tax: $7.45; total cost: $156.45

9 $5,400

10 1.6%

11 24%

EXERCISE SET 8-1

Writing Exercises

1. What exactly does the word "percent" mean?
2. Explain how to change percents into decimal and fraction form.
3. Explain how to change decimals and fractions into percent form.
4. Explain how the word "of" plays an important role in calculations involving percents.
5. How do you find the percent increase or decrease of a quantity?
6. Is it possible to have more than 100% of a quantity? Explain.

Computational Exercises

For Exercises 7–18, express each as a percent.

7. 0.63   8. 0.87   9. 0.025   10. 0.0872

11. 1.56   12. 3.875   13. $\frac{1}{5}$ 14. $\frac{5}{8}$

15. $\frac{2}{3}$ 16. $\frac{1}{6}$ 17. $1\frac{1}{4}$ 18. $2\frac{3}{8}$

For Exercises 19–26, express each as a decimal.

19. 18%   20. 23%   21. 6%   22. 2%

23. 62.5%   24. 75.6%   25. 320%   26. 275%

For Exercises 27–36, express each as a fraction or mixed number.

27. 24%   28. 36%   29. 9%   30. 4%   31. 236%

32. 520%   33. $\frac{1}{2}$%   34. $12\frac{1}{2}$%   35. $16\frac{2}{3}$%   36. $4\frac{1}{6}$%

Real-World Applications

37. Find the sales tax and total cost of a laser printer that costs $299.99. The tax rate is 5%.
38. Find the sales tax and total cost of an espresso machine that costs $59.95. The tax rate is 7%.
39. Find the sales tax and total cost of a Sony Playstation that costs $149.99. The tax rate is 6%.
40. Find the sales tax and total cost of a wireless mouse that costs $19.99. The tax rate is 4.5%.
41. A diamond ring was reduced from $999.99 to $399.99. Find the percent of the reduction in the price.
42. An MP3 player was reduced from $109.99 to $99.99. Find the percent reduction in price.
43. A 20-inch flat panel computer monitor is on sale for $249.99. It was reduced $80.00 from the original price. Find the percent reduction in price.
44. The sale price of a spring break vacation package was $179.99, and the travel agent said by booking early, you saved $20. Find the percent reduction in price.
45. A luggage set was selling for $159.99, and the ad states that it has now been reduced 40%. Find the sale price.
46. If a sales clerk receives a 7% commission on all sales, find the commission the clerk receives on the sale of a computer system costing $1,799.99.
47. If the cost of a gas grill is $199.99 and it is on sale for 25% off, find the sale price.
48. If the commission for selling a 52-inch high-definition television set is 12%, find the commission on a television set that costs $2,499.99.
49. Milo receives a commission of 6% on all sales. If his commission on a sale was $75.36, find the cost of the item he sold.

50. The sales tax in Pennsylvania is 6%. If the tax on an item is $96, find the cost of the item.
51. For a certain year, 19% of all books sold were self-help books. If a bookstore sold 12,872 books, about how many were self-help books?
52. You saved $200 on your new laptop because you bought it online. If this was a 25% savings from the original price, find the original cost of the laptop.
53. The average teachers' and superintendents' salaries in a school district in western Pennsylvania was $50,480. Five years later, the new average was $54,747. Find the percent increase.
54. In 2000 there were 97 million cell phone subscribers. Four years later, there were 169.5 million cell phone subscribers. Find the percent increase.
55. In the 1992–1993 school year in Pennsylvania, there were 20 teachers' strikes. In the 2006–2007 school year, there were 8 teachers' strikes. Find the percent decrease.
56. In 1998, the winning competitor in the Nathan's hot dog eating contest ate 19 hot dogs. In 2008, the winner ate 59 hot dogs. Find the percent increase.
57. The website forsalebyowner.com reported that total real estate commissions in 2007 were $55 billion, an increase of $19 million over the year 2000. What was the percent increase?
58. In the 2004–2005 school year, the average cost of tuition, fees, room, and board for a public 4-year university was $12,127 and in the 2007–2008 school year, the average cost was $13,589. Find the percent increase.

Critical Thinking

59. A store has a sale with 30% off every item. When you enter the store, you receive a coupon that states that you receive an additional 20% off. Is this equal to a 50% discount? Explain your answer.
60. You purchase a stock at $100 per share. It drops 30% the next day; however, a week later, it increases in value by 30%. If you sell it, will you break even? Explain your answer.
61. Suppose a friend planning a shopping spree on the day after Thanksgiving tells you he plans to buy a 65-inch plasma TV, and you say "There's no way you

can afford that!" He then tells you that the store is offering 50% off any one item, and he has an Internet coupon good for 50% off any price, even a discounted one. So that's 100% off, and he'll get it for free! Explain why your friend will come home very disappointed.

62. A store that used to sell a grill for $90 now offers it at $60, and advertises "33% off our best-selling grill!" An amusement park used to have 60 rides, and now boasts 90 rides, claiming "50% more rides this year!" Which one of them is lying?

Section 8-2 Simple Interest

LEARNING OBJECTIVES

☐ 1. Compute simple interest and future value.

☐ 2. Compute principal, rate, or time.

☐ 3. Compute interest using the Banker's rule.

☐ 4. Compute the true rate for a discounted loan.

The topic of the next two sections is of interest to anyone who plans to buy a house or a car, have a credit card, invest money, have a savings account—in short, pretty much everyone. This interesting topic is interest—a description of how fees are calculated when money is borrowed, and how your money grows when you save. Unless you don't mind being separated from your hard-earned money, this is a topic you should be eager to understand well.

Interest is a fee paid for the use of money. For example, if you borrow money from a bank to buy a car, you must not only pay back the amount of money that you borrowed, but also an additional amount, called the interest, for the use of the bank's money. On the other hand, if you deposit money in a savings account, the bank will pay you interest for saving money since it will be using your money to provide loans, mortgages, etc. to people who are borrowing money. The stated rate of interest is generally given as a yearly percentage of the amount borrowed or deposited.

There are two kinds of interest. *Simple interest* is a one-time percent of an amount of money. *Compound interest* is a percentage of an original amount, as well as a percentage of the new amount including previously calculated interest. We will study simple interest in this section, and compound interest in the next.

Simple Interest

In order to compute simple interest, we will need three pieces of information: the *principal,* the *rate,* and the *time.*

> **Math Note**
>
> Remember: *P* (principal) is the beginning amount borrowed or invested, and *A* (future value) is the final amount repaid or accumulated.

Interest (I) is the fee charged for the use of money.
Principal (P) is the amount of money borrowed or placed into a savings account.
Rate (r) is the percent of the principal paid for having money loaned, or earned for investing money. Unless indicated otherwise, rates are given as a percent for a term of 1 year.
Time (t) or **term** is the length of time that the money is being borrowed or invested. When the rate is given as a percent per year, time has to be written in years.
Future value (A) is the amount of the loan or investment plus the interest paid or earned.

The basic formulas for computing simple interest use principal, rate, and time as follows:

> **Math Note**
>
> The formula $A = P(1 + rt)$ can be used to find future value without explicitly computing the interest first.

Formulas for Computing Simple Interest and Future Value

1. Interest = principal × rate × time:

$$I = Prt$$

2. Future value = principal + interest:

$$A = P + I \quad \text{or} \quad A = P(1 + rt)$$

EXAMPLE 1 | Computing Simple Interest

Find the simple interest on a loan of $3,600.00 for 3 years at a rate of 8% per year.

SOLUTION

Change the rate to a decimal and substitute into the formula $I = Prt$:

$$8\% = 0.08$$
$$I = Prt$$
$$= (\$3,600.00)(0.08)(3)$$
$$= \$864.00$$

The interest on the loan is $864.00.

▼ Try This One 1

Find the simple interest on a $12,000 loan for 5 years at 7%.

EXAMPLE 2 | Finding Future Value

Find the future value for the loan in Example 1.

SOLUTION

Substitute into the formula $A = P + I$

$$A = P + I$$
$$= \$3,600.00 + \$864.00$$
$$= \$4,464.00$$

The total amount of money to be paid back is $4,464.00.

ALTERNATE SOLUTION

Substitute into the formula $A = P(1 + rt)$

$$A = P(1 + rt)$$
$$= \$3,600(1 + 0.08 \cdot 3)$$
$$= \$4,464.00$$

▼ Try This One 2

Find the future value of the loan in Try This One 1.

Since rates are typically given in terms of percent per year, when the time of a loan or investment is given in months, we need to divide it by 12 to convert to years.

EXAMPLE 3 | Computing Simple Interest for a Term in Months

To meet payroll during a down period, United Ceramics Inc. needed to borrow $2,000.00 at 4% simple interest for 3 months. Find the interest.

SOLUTION

Change 3 months to years by dividing by 12, and change the rate to a decimal. Substitute in the formula $I = Prt$.

$$I = (\$2,000.00)(0.04)\left(\frac{3}{12}\right) \quad 4\% = 0.04$$

$$= \$20.00$$

The interest is $20.00.

▼ Try This One 3

Marta needs some quick cash for books at the beginning of spring semester, so she borrows $600 at 11% simple interest for 2 months. How much interest will she pay?

☑ 1. Compute simple interest and future value.

Often, a simple interest loan is paid off in monthly installments. To find the monthly payment, divide the future value of the loan by the number of months in the term of the loan.

EXAMPLE 4   Computing Monthly Payments

Admiral Chauffeur Services borrowed $600.00 at 9% simple interest for $1\frac{1}{2}$ years to repair a limousine. Find the interest, future value, and the monthly payment.

SOLUTION

Step 1 Find the interest.

$$I = Prt$$
$$= (\$600.00)(0.09)\left(1\frac{1}{2}\right) \quad 9\% = 0.09$$
$$= \$81$$

The interest is $81.00.

Step 2 Find the future value of the loan.

$$A = P + I$$
$$= \$600.00 + \$81.00$$
$$= \$681.00$$

Step 3 Divide the future value of the loan by the number of months. Since $1\frac{1}{2}$ years = 18 months, divide $681.00 by 18 to get $37.83. The monthly payment is $37.83.

▼ Try This One 4

The Lookout Restaurant took out a loan for $5,000.00. The simple interest rate was 6.5%, and the term of the loan was 3 years. Find the interest, future value, and monthly payment.

Finding the Principal, Rate, and Time

In addition to finding the interest and future value for a loan or investment, we can find the principal, the rate, and the time period by substituting into the formula $I = Prt$ and solving for the unknown.

Examples 5–7 show how to find the principal, rate, and time.

EXAMPLE 5   **Computing Principal**

Calculator Guide

In the calculation for Example 5, order of operations is very important.

Standard Scientific Calculator

93.5 ÷ (.055 × 2) =

Standard Graphing Calculator

93.5 ÷ (.055 × 2) Enter

Phillips Health and Beauty Spa is replacing one of its workstations. The interest on a loan secured by the spa was $93.50. The money was borrowed at 5.5% simple interest for 2 years. Find the principal.

SOLUTION

$$I = \$93.50, r = 5.5\% = 0.055, \text{ and } t = 2$$

$$I = Prt$$

$$\$93.50 = P(0.055)(2)$$

Divide both sides by (0.055)(2).

$$\frac{\$93.50}{(0.055)(2)} = \frac{P(0.055)(2)}{(0.055)(2)}$$

$$P = \$850$$

The amount of the loan was $850.00.

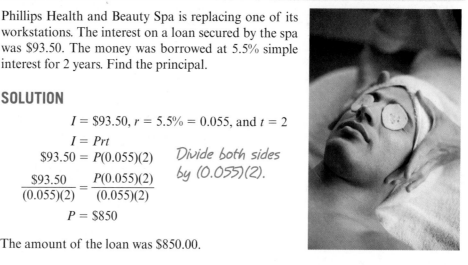

▼ Try This One 5

Find the principal on a savings account that paid $76.50 in simple interest at 6% over 3 years.

The same formulas can be used for investments as well. Example 6 shows this.

EXAMPLE 6   **Computing Interest Rate**

R & S Furnace Company invested $15,250.00 for 10 years and received $9,150.00 in simple interest. What was the rate that the investment paid?

SOLUTION

$$P = \$15,250, t = 10, \text{ and } I = \$9,150$$

$$I = Prt$$

$$\$9,150 = (\$15,250)(r)(10)$$

Divide both sides by ($15,250)(10).

$$\frac{\$9,150}{(\$15,250)(10)} = \frac{(\$15,250)(r)(10)}{(\$15,250)(10)}$$

$$0.06 = r$$

$$r = 0.06 \text{ or } 6\%$$

The interest paid on the investment was 6%.

▼ Try This One 6

If you invest $8,000 for 30 months and receive $1,000 in simple interest, what was the rate?

CAUTION   Be sure to change the decimal to a percent since rates are given in percents.

EXAMPLE 7 **Computing the Term of a Loan**

Judi and Laura borrowed $4,500.00 at $8\frac{3}{4}\%$ to put in a hot tub. They had to pay $2,756.25 interest. Find the term of the loan.

SOLUTION

$$P = \$4,500, \ r = 8\tfrac{3}{4}\% = 0.0875, \text{ and } I = \$2,756.25$$

$$I = Prt$$

$$\$2,756.25 = (\$4,500)(0.0875)t$$

$$\frac{\$2,756.25}{(\$4,500)(0.0875)} = \frac{(\$4,500)(0.0875)t}{(\$4,500)(0.0875)} \qquad \textit{Divide both sides by (\$4,500)(0.0875).}$$

$$7 = t$$

The term of the loan was 7 years.

▼ Try This One 7

☑ 2. Compute principal, rate, or time.

A pawn shop offers to finance a guitar costing $750 at 4% simple interest. The total interest charged will be $150. What is the term of the loan?

The Banker's Rule

Simple interest for short term loans is sometimes computed in days. For example, the term of a loan may be 90 days. In this case, the time would be $\frac{90 \text{ days}}{365 \text{ days}} = \frac{90}{365}$ since there are 365 days in a year. However, many lending institutions use what is called the *Banker's rule*. The Banker's rule treats every month like it has 30 days, so it uses 360 days in a year. They claim that the computations are easier to do. When a lending institution uses 360 days instead of 365, how does that affect the amount of interest? For example, on a $5,000 loan at 8% for 90 days, the interest would be

$$I = Prt$$

$$= (\$5,000)(0.08)\left(\frac{90}{365}\right) \qquad \textit{8\% = 0.08; 90 days is } \frac{90}{365} \textit{ year.}$$

$$= \$98.63$$

Using the Banker's rule, the interest is

$$I = Prt$$

$$= (\$5,000)(0.08)\left(\frac{90}{360}\right) \qquad \textit{We used a 360 day year here.}$$

$$= \$100.00$$

We can see why this is called the Banker's rule and not the customer's rule!

Sidelight **AN OUTDATED RULE**

The Banker's rule is very old, and there was a time when it made sense. Originally, interest on savings and loans had to be calculated by hand, and standardizing every month to 30 days did in fact make the calculations a lot simpler. But those types of calculations haven't been done by hand for over 50 years, and in the age of computers, it's just plain silly to worry about how difficult it is to compute the interest. That's exactly why computers are called computers—they're really good at computing things! So why do some lenders still use the Banker's rule? Because they can, probably, and it makes them more money.

EXAMPLE 8   **Using the Banker's Rule**

Find the simple interest on a $1,800 loan at 6% for 120 days. Use the Banker's rule.

SOLUTION

$$P = \$1,800, r = 6\% = 0.06, t = \frac{120}{360}$$

$$I = Prt$$

$$= (\$1,800)(0.06)\left(\frac{120}{360}\right) = \$36$$

The interest using the Banker's rule is $36.

▼ Try This One 8

☑ 3. Compute interest using the Banker's rule.

Find the simple interest on a $2,200 loan at 7% interest for 100 days. Use the Banker's rule.

Discounted Loans

Sometimes the interest on a loan is paid upfront by deducting the amount of the interest from the amount the bank gives you. This type of loan is called a **discounted loan.** The interest that is deducted from the amount you receive is called the **discount.** Example 9 illustrates how it works.

EXAMPLE 9   **Finding the True Rate of a Discounted Loan**

A student obtained a 2-year $4,000 loan for college tuition. The rate was 9% simple interest and the loan was a discounted loan.

(a) Find the discount.
(b) Find the amount of money the student received.
(c) Find the true interest rate.

SOLUTION

(a) The discount is the total interest for the loan.

$$P = \$4,000, r = 9\%, t = 2 \text{ years}$$

$$I = Prt$$

$$= (\$4,000)(0.09)(2) \quad 9\% = 0.09$$

$$= \$720$$

The discount is $720.

(b) The student received $4,000 − $720 = $3,280.
(c) The true interest rate is calculated by finding the rate on a $3,280 loan with $720 interest.

$$I = Prt$$

$$\$720 = (\$3,280)r(2) \quad \textit{Multiply.}$$

$$\$720 = \$6,560r \quad \textit{Divide both sides by \$6,560.}$$

$$r = \frac{\$720}{\$6,560} = 0.1098 \text{ (rounded)}$$

The true interest rate is approximately 10.98%.

Sidelight WHO GETS THE DISCOUNT?

Everyone likes getting discounts, so "discounted loan" sounds great, right? This is just another way that lenders can take advantage of customers. Since you're paying the interest up front, out of the amount you're borrowing, the effect is that you're borrowing less money and paying the same amount of interest. As Example 9 shows, the actual interest rate you end up paying is quite a bit higher than the rate you're quoted. The only thing they're really "discounting" is your ability to make smart financial decisions.

▼ Try This One 9

☑ 4. Compute the true rate for a discounted loan.

Mary Dixon obtained a $5,000 discounted loan for 3 years at 6% simple interest.

(a) Find the discount.
(b) Find the amount of money Mary received.
(c) Find the true interest rate.

Answers to Try This One

1 $4,200

2 $16,200

3 $11

4 $975, $5,975, $165.97

5 $425

6 5%

7 5 years

8 $42.78

9 (a) $900
   (b) $4,100
   (c) 7.32%

EXERCISE SET 8-2

Writing Exercises

1. Describe what interest is, and how simple interest is calculated.
2. What do the terms "principal" and "future value" refer to?
3. What is meant by the term of a loan?
4. How is the rate of a loan or a savings account typically described?
5. What is the Banker's rule? Does it help borrowers or lenders?
6. What does it mean for a loan to be discounted?

Computational Exercises

For Exercises 7–26, find the missing value.

	Principal	Rate	Time	Simple Interest
7.	$12,000	6%	2 years	_____
8.	$25,000	8.5%	6 months	_____
9.	$1,800	10%	_____	$360
10.	$600	4%	_____	$72
11.	$4,300	_____	6 years	$1,290
12.	$200	_____	3 years	$45
13.	_____	9%	4 years	$354.60

Principal	Rate	Time	Simple Interest
14. _____	15%	7 years	$65,625
15. $500	_____	2.5 years	$40
16. $1,250	5%	_____	$375
17. $900	$9\frac{1}{2}$%	18 months	_____
18. $420	_____	30 months	$31
19. $660	12%	_____	$514.80
20. $1,975	7.2%	$3\frac{1}{2}$ years	_____
21. $14,285	_____	6 years	$8,571
22. $650	15%	_____	$877.50
23. $325	_____	8 years	$156
24. $15,000	11%	_____	$742.50
25. $700	$6\frac{3}{4}$%	_____	$141.75
26. $135	7%	6.5 years	_____

For Exercises 27–32, find the future value of the loan

27. $P = \$800$, $r = 4\%$, $t = 5$ years
28. $P = \$15,000$, $r = 9\%$, $t = 7$ years
29. $P = \$700$, $r = 10\%$, $t = 6$ years
30. $P = \$1,250$, $r = 8\frac{1}{2}\%$, $t = 6$ months

31. $P = \$475$, $r = 13\%$, $t = 3$ months
32. $P = \$3,360$, $r = 5.5\%$, $t = 2$ years

For Exercises 33–38, find the interest on each loan using the Banker's rule.

33. $P = \$220$, $r = 3\%$, $t = 90$ days
34. $P = \$3,800$, $r = 9\%$, $t = 60$ days
35. $P = \$500$, $r = 14\%$, $t = 180$ days
36. $P = \$760$, $r = 6.2\%$, $t = 270$ days
37. $P = \$1,100$, $r = 8\frac{1}{4}\%$, $t = 105$ days
38. $P = \$420$, $r = 12\%$, $t = 150$ days

For Exercises 39–44, the loans are discounted. For each exercise, find (a) the discount, (b) the amount of money received, and (c) the true interest rate.

39. $P = \$3,000$, $r = 8\%$, $t = 3$ years
40. $P = \$1,750$, $r = 4\frac{1}{2}\%$, $t = 6$ years
41. $P = \$22,000$, $r = 5\%$, $t = 4$ years
42. $P = \$600$, $r = 2\%$, $t = 10$ years
43. $P = \$780$, $r = 6\%$, $t = 9$ years
44. $P = \$1,850$, $r = 3\%$, $t = 5$ years

Real-World Applications

For Exercises 45–64, assume that all interest is simple interest.

45. In addition to working and her family's contribution, Jane had to borrow $8,000 over the course of 6 years to complete her education. The interest is $4,046.40. Find the rate.

46. Fred started a new e-Commerce business and borrowed $15,000 for 12 years to get the business up and running. The interest is $18,000. Find the rate.

47. To take advantage of a going-out-of-business sale, the College Corner Furniture Store had to borrow some money. It paid back a total of $150,000 on a 6-month loan at 12%. Find the principal.

48. To purchase two new copiers, the campus bookstore paid $1,350 interest on a 9% loan for 3 years. Find the principal.

49. To train employees to use new equipment, Williams Muffler Repair had to borrow $4,500.00 at $9\frac{1}{2}\%$. The company paid $1,282.50 in interest. Find the term of the loan.

50. Berger Car Rental borrowed $8,650.00 at 6.8% interest to cover the increasing cost of auto insurance. Find the term of the loan if the interest is $441.15.

51. To pay for new supplies, Jiffy Photo Company borrowed $9,325.00 at 8% and paid $3,170.50 in interest. Find the term of the loan.

52. Mary Beck earned $216 interest on a savings account at 8% over 2 years. Find the principal.

53. John White has savings of $4,300, which earned $9\frac{3}{4}\%$ interest for 5 years. Find the interest.

54. Ed Bland had savings of $816 invested at $4\frac{1}{2}\%$ for 3 years. Find the interest.

55. Matt's Appliance Store borrowed $6,200 for 3 years for repairs. The rate was 6%. Find the future value of the loan.

56. Adrienne's Pub borrowed $12,000 for 6 years at 9%. Find the future value of the loan.

57. Sally borrowed $600 for 90 days at 4%. Find the interest using the Banker's rule.

58. Harry borrowed $950 for 120 days at $6\frac{3}{4}\%$. Find the interest using the Banker's rule.

59. The West Penn Finance group secured an $18,000 discounted loan to remodel its offices. The rate was 5% and the term was 6 years. Find

  (a) The discount.
  (b) The amount of money the group received.
  (c) The true interest rate.

60. The University Center obtained a $20,000 discounted loan for 3 years to remodel the student game room. The rate was 9%. Find

  (a) The discount.
  (b) The amount of money the center received.
  (c) The true interest rate.

61. Susan would like to buy a new car. Which loan would have the higher interest amount: a personal loan of $10,000 at 9% for 6 years or an auto loan of $10,000 at 8% for 60 months? Why?

62. Sea Drift Motel is converting its rooms into privately owned condominiums. The interest on a $1,000,000, 20-year construction loan is $98,000. What is the rate of interest? Does the rate seem unreasonable?

63. The Laurel Township Fire Department must decide whether to purchase a new tanker truck or repair the one they now use. For a new truck loan, the interest rate on $25,000 is 18% for a 10-year period; to repair the existing truck, the department must borrow $18,000 at $12\frac{1}{2}$% for 8 years. Which loan is less expensive?

64. A local miniature golf course owner must recarpet his fairways and replace the golf clubs his customers use. A bank will lend the owner the necessary $7,800 at 9.5% interest over 48 months. A savings and loan company will lend the owner $7,800 at 8.5% interest for 54 months. Which loan will be less expensive for the golf course owner to assume?

Critical Thinking

65. Suppose that you have a choice of two loans: one at 5% simple interest for 6 years, and one at 6% simple interest for five years. Which will result in the smaller future value? Does it depend on the principal?

66. When a loan is discounted, is it better or worse for the borrower if the term is longer? Try some specific examples and make a conjecture.

Section 8-3 Compound Interest

LEARNING OBJECTIVES

☐ 1. Compute compound interest.

☐ 2. Compute the effective interest rate of an investment.

☐ 3. Compare the effective rate of two investments.

☐ 4. Find the future value of an annuity.

☐ 5. Compute the periodic payment needed to meet an investment goal.

If you think about simple interest over a long period of time, it doesn't sound like a great deal for the investor. Suppose you put $1,000 into an account that pays 5% simple interest, and you keep it untouched for 30 years. Each year, you're getting 5% of $1,000 in interest. But for all that time, the bank could have been increasing your money through loans and investments, and they're still paying interest only on the original amount.

This is where compound interest comes into play. It seems more fair for the bank to pay interest on the actual value of the account each year, not just the original amount. When interest is computed on the principal *and* any previously earned interest, it is called **compound interest.** Let's look at an example that compares simple and compound interest.

EXAMPLE 1 Comparing Simple and Compound Interest

Suppose that $5,000 is invested for 3 years at 8%.

(a) Find the amount of simple interest.
(b) Find the compound interest if interest is calculated once per year.

SOLUTION

(a) Using the formula $I = Prt$ with $P = \$5,000$, $r = 0.08$, and $t = 3$, we get

$$I = \$5,000 \times 0.08 \times 3 = \$1,200 \quad \textit{Simple interest over 3 years}$$

(b) **First year** For the first year, we have $P = \$5,000$, $r = 0.08$ and $t = 1$:

$$I = Prt = \$5,000 \times 0.08 \times 1 = \$400$$

The interest for the first year is $400.
Second year At the beginning of the second year, the account now contains $5,400, so we use this as principal for the second year. The rate and time remain the same.

$$I = Prt = \$5,400 \times 0.08 \times 1 = \$432$$

The interest for the second year is $432.
Third year The principal is now $5,400 + $432 = $5,832.

$$I = Prt = \$5,832 \times 0.08 \times 1 = \$466.56$$

EXAMPLE 8   Finding the Weekly Payment for an Annuity

Suppose you've always dreamed of opening your own tattoo parlor, and decide it's time to do something about it. A financial planner estimates that you would need a $35,000 initial investment to start the business, and you plan to save that amount over the course of 5 years by investing in an annuity that pays 7.5% compounded weekly. How much would you need to invest each week?

SOLUTION

We know the following values: $A = 35,000$, $r = 7.5\% = 0.075$, $t = 5$, and $n = 52$.

$$R = \frac{A\left(\frac{r}{n}\right)}{\left[\left(1 + \frac{r}{n}\right)^{nt} - 1\right]}$$

$$R = \frac{35,000\left(\frac{0.075}{52}\right)}{\left(1 + \frac{0.075}{52}\right)^{52 \cdot 5} - 1} \qquad \textit{Reduce error by not rounding } \frac{0.075}{52}.$$

$$= \frac{\frac{2,625}{52}}{\left(1 + \frac{0.075}{52}\right)^{260} - 1} = 111.04$$

A payment of $111.04 per week would be necessary to save the required $35,000.

▼ Try This One 8

☑ 5. Compute the periodic payment needed to meet an investment goal.

Find the monthly payment needed to save a $6,000 down payment for a car in an annuity that pays 5.5% interest compounded monthly over 2 years.

Answers to Try This One

1 (a) $24,000
   (b) $26,247.70

2 $183.63

3 $152,569.20

4 8.24%

5 3.25% semiannually

6 $1,371.94

7 $4,979.15

8 $237.07

EXERCISE SET 8-3

Writing Exercises

1. Describe the difference between simple interest and compound interest.

2. What does it mean to say that interest is compounded quarterly? What about compounded monthly?

3. What is the effective rate of an investment?

4. Describe how an annuity works.

Computational Exercises

For Exercises 5–14, find the compound interest and future value for each.

	Principal	Rate	Compounded	Time
5.	$825	4%	Annually	10 years
6.	$3,250	2%	Annually	5 years
7.	$75	3%	Semiannually	6 years
8.	$1,550	5%	Semiannually	7 years
9.	$625	8%	Quarterly	12 years
10.	$2,575	4%	Quarterly	2 years
11.	$1,995	5%	Semiannually	6 years
12.	$460	6%	Quarterly	7 years
13.	$750	9%	Daily	1 year
14.	$3,500	11%	Daily	$4\frac{1}{2}$ years

For Exercises 15–24, find the future value of each annuity.

	Payment	Rate	Compounded	Time
15.	$200	9%	Annually	9 years
16.	$750	3%	Annually	12 years
17.	$1,250	6.8%	Semiannually	3 years
18.	$375	5%	Quarterly	4 years
19.	$1,530	4.5%	Quarterly	8 years

	Principal	Rate	Compounded	Time
20.	$1,750	10%	Annually	12 years
21.	$1,425	2%	Semiannually	6 years
22.	$3,500	6%	Semiannually	2 years
23.	$240	4%	Quarterly	7 years
24.	$175	7%	Annually	5 years

For Exercises 25–28, find the effective interest rate.

25. Rate: 6%   Compounded: Quarterly
26. Rate: 10%   Compounded: Semiannually
27. Rate: 6.5%   Compounded: Quarterly
28. Rate: 9.55%   Compounded: Semiannually

For Exercises 29–32, determine which is the better investment.

29. 4.5% compounded semiannually or 4.25% compounded quarterly.
30. 7% compounded monthly or 7.2% compounded semiannually.
31. 3% compounded daily or 3.1% compounded quarterly.
32. 5.74% compounded semiannually or 5.6% compounded daily.

Real-World Applications

33. A couple decides to set aside $5,000 in a savings account for a second honeymoon trip. It is compounded quarterly for 10 years at 9%. Find the amount of money they will have in 10 years.

34. In order to pay for college, the parents of a child invest $20,000 in a bond that pays 8% interest compounded semiannually. How much money will there be in 18 years?

35. A 25-year-old plans to retire at age 50. She decided to invest an inheritance of $60,000 at 7% interest compounded semiannually. How much will she have at age 50?

36. To pay for new machinery in 5 years, a company owner invests $10,000 at $7\frac{1}{2}$% compounded quarterly. How much money will be available in 5 years?

37. A husband and wife plan to save money for their daughter's college education in 4 years. They decide to purchase an annuity with a semiannual payment earning 7.5% compounded semiannually. Find the future value of the annuity in 4 years if the semiannual payment is $2,250.

38. A business owner decided to purchase an annuity to pay for new copy machines in 3 years. The payment is $600 quarterly at 8% interest compounded quarterly. Find the future value of the annuity in 3 years.

39. Find the future value of an annuity if you invest $200 quarterly for 20 years at 5% interest compounded quarterly.

40. The Washingtons decide to save money for a vacation in 2 years. They purchase an annuity with semi-annual payments of $200 at 9% interest compounded semiannually. Find the amount of money they can spend for the vacation.

41. The owner of the Campus Café plans to open a second location on the satellite campus in 5 years. She purchases an annuity that pays 10.5% interest compounded annually. If the payment is $4,000 a year, find the future value of the annuity in 5 years.

42. Titan Thigh, the owner of Work-it-out Fitness, wants to buy an annuity that pays 4% interest compounded quarterly for 4 years. If the quarterly payment is $160, find the future value of the annuity.

43. In order to plan for their retirement, a married couple decides to purchase an annuity that pays 8% interest compounded semiannually. If the semiannual payment is $2,000, how much will they have saved in 10 years?

44. The Wash-n-Surf, an Internet café and laundromat, plans to replace two wash and surf hubs in 3 years. If the owner purchases an annuity at 6% interest compounded annually with an annual payment of $800, find the value of the annuity in 3 years.

45. Petty Marine Co. has a long-term plan to expand to a second location that's actually near some water, so they want to start a monthly annuity to save $150,000 in capital over 5 years. The best rate they can find is 7%. Find the monthly payment.

46. Suppose you plan to work right after you graduate, but still save money for grad school. You decide to save $10,000 before starting, and find a weekly annuity that pays 6.5% interest for 4 years. How much will you need to pay each week?

47. The Massive Chemical Corporation starts an annuity to pay for the huge government penalties they expect in 10 years when a pending case finally gets litigated. Their lead attorney informs them that they can expect a $4,000,000 fine. An investment house offers 11% interest on annuities of that size, compounded semiannually. What will the semiannual payment be on this annuity?

48. A 25-year-old decides that her goal is to retire at age 50 with at least $2,000,000 in savings. The company investment annuity offers 7.4% annual returns, compounded monthly. What amount will she need to invest each month?

Critical Thinking

49. A person deposits $5,000 into an account paying 4% compounded semiannually. Two years later the person deposited $2,000 into the same account. How much money was there at the end of 5 years?

50. Sam deposited $3,500 into a savings account paying 3% compounded quarterly. Two years later he withdrew $800. How much money was in the account at the end of 6 years?

51. Akish deposited $900 into a savings account paying 2% compounded quarterly. Two years later, she deposited $400 into the same account. One year after that, she withdrew $200. How much money was in the account at the end of 6 years?

52. Find the future value of a $15,000 investment at 6% compounded monthly for 5 years. Then calculate the monthly payment that would be needed to accumulate that amount in a 6% monthly annuity. Finally, calculate the total amount that would be paid into the annuity. What can you conclude about the value of a lump-sum investment versus an annuity?

Section 8-4 Installment Buying

LEARNING OBJECTIVES

☐ 1. Find amount financed, total installment price, and finance charge for a fixed installment loan.

☐ 2. Use a table to find APR for a loan.

☐ 3. Compute unearned interest and payoff amount for a loan paid off early.

☐ 4. Compute credit card finance charges using the unpaid balance method.

☐ 5. Compute credit card finance charges using the average daily balance method.

A lot of people celebrate their college graduation by getting a new car. Unless you're very wealthy, you won't be plunking down a stack of crisp hundred dollar bills to make that happen—you'll need to get a loan. In this case, you'll be doing what is called **installment buying.** This is when an item is purchased and the buyer pays for it by making periodic partial payments, or installments.

There are natural advantages and disadvantages to installment buying. The most obvious advantage is that it allows you to buy an item that you don't have enough money to pay for, and use it while you're raising that money. The most obvious disadvantage is that you pay interest on the amount borrowed, so you end up paying more for the item—in some cases a *lot* more.

Fixed Installment Loans

A **fixed installment loan** is a loan that is repaid in equal payments. Sometimes the buyer will pay part of the cost at the time of purchase. This is known as a **down payment.** The other terms used to describe installment loans are defined next.

The **amount financed** is the amount a borrower will pay interest on.

Amount financed = Price of item − Down payment

The **total installment price** is the total amount of money the buyer will ultimately pay.

Total installment price = Sum of all payments + Down payment

The **finance charge** is the interest charged for borrowing the amount financed.

Finance charge = Total installment price − Price of item

EXAMPLE 1   Calculating Information About a Car Loan

Cat bought a 2-year old Santa Fe for $12,260. Her down payment was $3,000, and she will have to pay $231.50 for 48 months. Find the amount financed, the total installment price, and the finance charge.

SOLUTION

Using the formulas in the box on page 446:

$$\text{Amount financed} = \text{Cash price} - \text{Down payment}$$
$$= \$12,260 - \$3,000$$
$$= \$9,260$$

Since she paid $231.50 for 48 months and her down payment was $3,000,

$$\text{Total installment price} = \text{Total of monthly payments} + \text{Down payments}$$
$$= 48 \times \$231.50 + \$3,000 \quad \textit{48 payments at \$231.50.}$$
$$= \$14,112.00$$

Now we can find the finance charge:

$$\text{Finance charge} = \text{Total installment price} - \text{Cash price}$$
$$= \$14,112.00 - \$12,260.00$$
$$= \$1,852.00$$

The amount financed was $9,260.00; the total installment price was $14,112.00, and the finance charge was $1,852.00.

▼ Try This One 1

If you buy a used car for $8,200 with a down payment of $1,000 and 36 monthly payments of $270, find the amount financed, the total installment price, and the finance charge.

EXAMPLE 2   Computing a Monthly Payment

After a big promotion, a young couple bought $9,000 worth of furniture. The down payment was $1,000. The balance was financed for 3 years at 8% simple interest per year.

(a) Find the amount financed.
(b) Find the finance charge (interest).
(c) Find the total installment price.
(d) Find the monthly payment.

SOLUTION

(a) Amount financed = Price of item – Down payment

$$= \$9,000 - \$1,000 = \$8,000$$

(b) To find the finance charge, we use the simple interest formula:

$$I = Prt$$
$$= \$8,000 \times 0.08 \times 3 \quad \textit{8\% = 0.08}$$
$$= \$1,920$$

Math Note

The monthly payment is the total installment price minus the down payment, divided by the number of payments.

(c) In this case, the total installment price is simply the cost of the furniture plus the finance charge:

$$\text{Total installment price} = \$9,000 + \$1,920$$
$$= \$10,920$$

(d) To calculate the monthly payment, divide the amount financed plus the finance charge ($8,000 + $1,920) by the number of payments:

$$\text{Monthly payment} = \$9,920 \div 36$$
$$= \$275.56$$

In summary, the amount financed is $8,000, the finance charge is $1,920, the total installment price is $10,920, and the monthly payment is $275.56.

☑ 1. Find amount financed, total installment price, and finance charge for a fixed installment loan.

▼ **Try This One 2**

A graphic design pro buys a new iMac for $1,499 with a $200 down payment, and gets manufacturer financing for 5 years at 12% simple interest. Find (a) the amount financed, (b) the finance charge, (c) the total installment price, and (d) the monthly payment.

Annual Percentage Rate

Many lenders add upfront fees to a loan and then spread them over the life of the loan. This has the effect of making the actual interest rate that a borrower pays higher than the quoted rate. Because this can get confusing, lenders are required by law to disclose an **annual percentage rate,** or **APR,** that reflects the true interest charged. This allows consumers to compare loans with different terms. The mathematical procedures for computing APR are extremely complicated, so tables have been compiled that help you to estimate APR for a loan. A partial APR table is shown in Table 8-1. There are three steps required to find an APR from the table; they are listed at the top of the next page.

TABLE 8-1 **APR Table**

Number of Payments	Annual Percentage Rate												
	6.0%	6.5%	7.0%	7.5%	8.0%	8.5%	9.0%	9.5%	10.0%	10.5%	11.0%	11.5%	12.0%
	(Finance charge per $100 of amount financed)												
6	$1.76	$1.90	$2.05	$2.20	$2.35	$2.49	$2.64	$2.79	$2.94	$3.08	$3.23	$3.38	$3.53
12	3.28	3.56	3.83	4.11	4.39	4.66	4.94	5.22	5.50	5.78	6.06	6.34	6.62
18	4.82	5.22	5.63	6.04	6.45	6.86	7.28	7.69	8.10	8.52	8.93	9.35	9.77
24	6.37	6.91	7.45	8.00	8.54	9.09	9.64	10.19	10.75	11.30	11.86	12.42	12.98
30	7.94	8.61	9.30	9.98	10.66	11.35	12.04	12.74	13.43	14.13	14.83	15.54	16.24
36	9.52	10.34	11.16	11.98	12.81	13.64	14.48	15.32	16.16	17.01	17.86	18.71	19.57
48	12.73	13.83	14.94	16.06	17.18	18.31	19.45	20.59	21.74	22.90	24.06	25.23	26.40
60	16.00	17.40	18.81	20.23	21.66	23.10	24.55	26.01	27.48	28.96	30.45	31.96	33.47

Using the APR Table

Step 1 Find the finance charge per $100 borrowed using the formula

$$\frac{\text{Finance charge}}{\text{Amount financed}} \times \$100$$

Step 2 Find the row in the table marked with the number of payments and move to the right until you find the amount closest to the number from Step 1.

Step 3 The APR (to the nearest half percent) is at the top of the corresponding column.

EXAMPLE 3   Finding APR

Burk Carter purchased a color laser printer for $600.00. He made a down payment of $50.00 and financed the rest for 2 years with a monthly payment of $24.75. Find the APR.

SOLUTION

Step 1 Find the finance charge per $100.00. The total amount he will pay is $24.75 per month × 24 payments, or $594.00. Since he financed $550.00, the finance charge is $594.00 − $550.00 = $44.00.

$$\text{Finance charge per } \$100.00 = \frac{\text{Finance charge}}{\text{Amount financed}} \times \$100$$

$$= \frac{\$44}{\$550} \times \$100$$

$$= \$8.00$$

Step 2 Find the row for 24 payments and move across the row until you find the number closest to $8.00. In this case, it is exactly $8.00.

Step 3 Move to the top of the column to get the APR. It is 7.5%.

Math Note

There are many websites with calculators for finding APR without having to use a table. A Google search will find dozens of them, in fact.

☑ 2. Use a table to find APR for a loan.

▼ Try This One 3

Darla Connor purchased a Mercury Mariner for $19,900. Her down payment was $3,000. She financed the balance at $623 per month for 30 months. Find the APR.

One way to save money on a fixed installment loan is to pay it off early. This will allow a buyer to avoid paying the entire finance charge. The amount of the finance charge that is saved when a loan is paid off early is called **unearned interest.** There are two methods for calculating unearned interest, the **actuarial method** and the **rule of 78.** The actuarial method uses the APR table, and the following formula:

Math Note

The value h is found using Table 8-1: it is the entry in the row with the number of remaining payments and the column matching the loan's APR.

The Actuarial Method

$$u = \frac{kRh}{100 + h}$$

where u = unearned interest
          k = number of payments remaining, excluding the current one
          R = monthly payment
          h = finance charge per \$100 for a loan with the same APR and
             k monthly payments

EXAMPLE 4   Using the Actuarial Method

Our friend Burk from Example 3 decides to use part of his tax refund to pay off the full amount of his laser printer with his 12th payment. Find the unearned interest and the payoff amount.

SOLUTION

To use the formula for the actuarial method, we'll need values for k, R, and h. Half of the original 24 payments will remain, so $k = 12$. From Example 3, the monthly payment is \$24.75 and the APR is 7.5%. Using Table 8-1, we find the row for 12 payments and the column for 7.5%; the intersection shows \$4.11, so $h = \$4.11$. Now we substitute those values into the formula:

$$u = \frac{kRh}{100 + h} \qquad k = 12, R = 24.75, h = 4.11$$

$$= \frac{(12)(24.75)(4.11)}{100 + 4.11} \qquad \text{Multiply in the numerator, add in the denominator.}$$

$$= \frac{1{,}220.67}{104.11} \approx 11.72$$

The unearned interest is \$11.72.

The payoff amount is the amount remaining on the loan minus unearned interest. At this point, Burk has made 11 payments, so there would be 13 remaining if he were not paying the loan off early.

$$\text{Payoff amount} = 13 \times \$24.75 - \$11.72$$
$$= \$310.03$$

With a payment of \$310.03, Burk is the proud owner of a laser printer.

▼ Try This One 4

The buyer in Try This One 3 decided to pay off her car loan in 24 months instead of 30. Use the actuarial method to find the unearned interest and the payoff amount.

The next example will show how to find the unearned interest and payoff amount of a fixed installment loan using the rule of 78.

The Rule of 78

$$u = \frac{fk(k + 1)}{n(n + 1)}$$

where u = unearned interest
           f = finance charge
           k = number of remaining monthly payments
           n = original number of payments

Notice that the formula has the number of payments remaining in the numerator and the original number of payments in the denominator. That means as the number of remaining payments gets smaller, the unearned interest does as well. The reason it's not simply the proportion $u = \frac{fk}{n}$ is that the lenders collect more interest and less principal in the beginning of a loan.

EXAMPLE 5   Using the Rule of 78

Math Note

The reason that the rule of 78 is used is that the unearned interest for the last months of the loan is considerably smaller than the first months. The interest saved during the last three months of a 12-month loan is $\frac{3}{78} + \frac{2}{78} + \frac{1}{78} = \frac{6}{78}$ of the total interest while the interest paid for the first three months is $\frac{12}{78} + \frac{11}{78} + \frac{10}{78} = \frac{33}{78}$ of the total interest. People tend to pay off a loan early when the principal becomes small.

☑ 3. Compute unearned interest and payoff amount for a loan paid off early.

A \$5,000 car loan is to be paid off in 36 monthly installments of \$172. The borrower decides to pay off the loan after 24 payments have been made. Find the amount of interest saved by paying the loan off early. Use the rule of 78.

SOLUTION

Find the finance charge (i.e., total interest).

$172 \times 36 = \$6,192$ *\$172 × 36 payments*
$\$6,192 - \$5,000 = \$1,192$ *Total payments − Amount financed*

Substitute into the formula using $f = \$1,192$, $n = 36$, and $k = 36 - 24 = 12$.

$$u = \frac{fk(k + 1)}{n(n + 1)}$$

$$= \frac{1,192(12)(12 + 1)}{36(36 + 1)} = \frac{185,952}{1,332} \approx 139.60$$

By paying off the loan a year early, the borrower saved \$139.60.

▼ Try This One 5

A \$16,500 truck loan is to be paid off in 24 monthly installments of \$797.50. The borrower decides to pay off the loan after 20 payments have been made. Find the amount of interest saved. Use the rule of 78.

So far, we've covered examples of closed-ended credit; this is credit with a fixed number of payments and a specific payoff date. We turn our attention now to open-ended credit, where there is no fixed number of payments or payoff date. By far the most common example of this is credit cards. Since more and more people use credit cards for convenience, an understanding of open-ended credit is more important than ever.

The Unpaid Balance Method

With the **unpaid balance method,** interest is charged only on the balance from the previous month. Example 6 shows how to find the interest on the unpaid balance.

EXAMPLE 6   Computing a Credit Card Finance Charge

Math Note

The billing cycle for credit cards and loans can begin and end on any day of the month; however, for the examples given in this section, we will assume the cycle ends on the last day of the month.

For the month of April, Elliot had an unpaid balance of $356.75 at the beginning of the month and made purchases of $436.50. A payment of $200.00 was made during the month. The interest on the unpaid balance is 1.8% per month. Find the finance charge and the balance on May 1.

SOLUTION

Step 1 Find the finance charge on the unpaid balance using the simple interest formula with rate 1.8%.

$$I = Prt$$
$$= \$356.75 \times 0.018 \times 1 \quad \textit{1.8\% = 0.018}$$
$$= \$6.42 \text{ (rounded)}$$

The finance charge is $6.42.

(*Note:* Since the interest rate is given per month, the time is always equal to 1 month.)

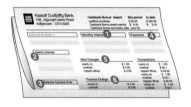

Step 2 To the unpaid balance, add the finance charge and the purchases for the month; then subtract the payment to get the new balance.

$$\text{New balance} = \$356.75 + \$6.42 + \$436.50 - \$200$$
$$= \$599.67$$

The new balance as of May 1 is $599.67.

☑ 4. Compute credit card finance charges using the unpaid balance method.

▼ Try This One 6

For the month of January, Christina has an unpaid balance of $846.50 from December. Purchases for the month were $532.86 and a payment of $350.00 was made during the month. If the interest on the unpaid balance is 2% per month, find the finance charge and the balance on February 1.

Average Daily Balance Method

Because a company that issues credit cards doesn't make as much money when users pay off the balance every month, they sometimes charge an annual fee for use of the card. Another way for them to make money from all users is to use the **average daily balance method** for computing the finance charge. In this method, the balance for each day of the month is used to compute an average daily balance, and interest is computed on that average. Example 7 shows how to compute interest using this method.

Sidelight MONEY FOR NOTHING?

Since most credit card companies either use the unpaid balance method, or don't charge interest on new purchases, if you pay off the full balance each month, you never pay any interest. In essence, you're getting to use the bank's money for nothing! But don't shed any tears for the poor banks. They charge the merchant a fee for each transaction. Also, the freedom that comes from buying stuff and walking out the door without handing over any money makes it extremely difficult for people to spend only what they can afford, especially young people using credit cards for the first time. Consider the following statistics:

- 76% of college undergrads have at least one credit card.
- 55% of credit card users keep a balance on their card.
- Total credit card debt in the United States in 2008 reached $951.7 *billion* dollars.
- The average credit card debt per borrower was $5,710.

If you find yourself spending more than you can pay off, and having to keep a balance on your card, the best approach is probably the one pictured above.

EXAMPLE 7 Computing a Credit Card Finance Charge

Betty's credit card statement showed the following transactions during the month of August.

August 1	Previous balance	$165.50
August 7	Purchases	59.95
August 12	Purchases	23.75
August 18	Payment	75.00
August 24	Purchases	107.43

Find the average daily balance, the finance charge for the month, and the new balance on September 1. The interest rate is 1.5% per month on the average daily balance.

SOLUTION

Step 1 Find the balance as of each transaction.

August 1	$165.50
August 7	$165.50 + $59.95 = $225.45
August 12	$225.45 + $23.75 = $249.20
August 18	$249.20 − $75.00 = $174.20
August 24	$174.20 + $107.43 = $281.63

Step 2 Find the number of days for each balance.

Date	Balance	Days	Calculations
August 1	$165.50	6	(7 − 1 = 6)
August 7	$225.45	5	(12 − 7 = 5)
August 12	$249.20	6	(18 − 12 = 6)
August 18	$174.20	6	(24 − 18 = 6)
August 24	$281.63	8	(31 − 24 + 1 = 8)

Math Note

Since the transaction period starts on August 1 and ends on the last day of the month, which must be included, we had to add 1 to the last period of days in step 2. The total number of days has to equal the number of days in the given month.

Step 3 Multiply each balance by the number of days, and add these products.

Date	Balance	Days	Calculations
August 1	$165.50	6	$165.50(6) = $993.00
August 7	$225.45	5	$225.45(5) = $1,127.25
August 12	$249.20	6	$249.20(6) = $1,495.20
August 18	$174.20	6	$174.20(6) = $1,045.20
August 24	$281.63	8	$281.63(8) = $2,253.04
		31	$6,913.69

Step 4 Divide the total by the number of days in the month to get the average daily balance.

$$\text{Average daily balance} = \frac{\$6,913.69}{31} \approx \$223.02$$

The average daily balance is $223.02.

Step 5 Find the finance charge. Multiply the average daily balance by the rate, which is 1.5%, or 0.015.

$$\text{Finance charge} = \$223.02 \times 0.015 \approx \$3.35.$$

Step 6 Find the new balance. Add the finance charge to the balance as of the last transaction.

$$\text{New balance:} \quad \$281.63 + \$3.35 = \$284.98$$

The average daily balance is $223.02. The finance charge is $3.35, and the new balance is $284.98.

The procedure for finding the average daily balance is summarized next.

Procedure for the Average Daily Balance Method

Step 1 Find the balance as of each transaction.

Step 2 Find the number of days for each balance.

Step 3 Multiply the balances by the number of days and find the sum.

Step 4 Divide the sum by the number of days in the month.

Step 5 Find the finance charge (multiply the average daily balance by the monthly rate).

Step 6 Find the new balance (add the finance charge to the balance as of the last transaction).

▼ **Try This One 7**

5. Compute credit card finance charges using the average daily balance method.

A credit card statement for the month of November showed the following transactions.

November 1	Previous balance	$937.25
November 4	Purchases	$531.62
November 13	Payment	$400.00
November 20	Purchases	$89.95
November 28	Payment	$100.00

(a) Find the average daily balance.

(b) Find the finance charge. The interest rate is 1.9% per month on the average daily balance.

(c) Find the new balance on December 1.

It's definitely a good idea to check with your credit card company to see what method it uses for computing finance charges. If it uses average daily balance, you will end up paying interest even if you pay off the full amount each month. There's a lot of competition out there, so if that's the case, you can probably find another card with a better deal.

Answers to Try This One

1 Amount financed, $7,200; total installment price, $10,720; finance charge, $2,520

2 (a) $1,299 (c) $2,278.40
(b) $779.40 (d) $34.64

3 8.0%

4 Unearned interest, $85.83; Payoff amount, $4,275.17

5 $88

6 Finance charge = $16.93; balance on Feb. 1 = $1,046.29

7 (a) $1,198.69
(b) $22.78
(c) $1,081.60

EXERCISE SET 8-4

Writing Exercises

1. Explain what is meant by the term "installment loan."
2. What is a finance charge?
3. What is the difference between the purchase price of an item and the amount financed?
4. What is the difference between closed-ended credit and open-ended credit?
5. What is the annual percentage rate (APR) for a loan? Why is it typically different than the stated interest rate?
6. What is the difference between the unpaid balance method and the average daily balance method for computing interest? Which is better for the consumer?

Real-World Applications

7. Mary Lee purchased a stove for $460. She made a down payment of $60 and paid $42 a month for 10 months. Find the total installment price of the stove.
8. Martin Dennis purchased a wide screen television for $1,720. He made a down payment of 15% and paid the balance over 18 months. The finance charge was 4% of the amount financed. Find the down payment and the installment price of the television and the monthly payment.
9. Joy Lansung purchased a microwave oven for $375.00. She made a down payment of 15% and financed the rest for 12 months with payments of $27.25. Find the down payment and the total installment price of the oven.
10. Mary Scherer purchased a wristwatch for $845.00. She made a down payment of $95.00 and financed the rest with six monthly payments of $128.75. Find the total installment price.
11. Hang Yo bought a treadmill for $925. He made a 20% down payment and financed the rest over 18 months. Find the monthly payment if the finance charge was 5% of the amount financed.
12. Stacie Howard purchased a water softener for $550. She made a down payment of $75 and paid the balance off in 12 monthly payments. Find the monthly payment if the interest rate was 11%.
13. Richard Johnston bought a 2010 Hummer for $39,905. He made a down payment of $15,000 and paid $614 monthly for 4 years. Find the APR.
14. Jennifer Siegel bought a new Ford Focus for $14,400. She made a down payment of $4,000 and made monthly payments of $319 for 3 years. Find the APR.
15. Erin LaRochelle bought four comforter sets for $900.00. She made a down payment of $100.00 and paid off the balance in 12 monthly payments of $71.05. Find the APR.

16. Ben King bought his wife a turquoise bracelet, earrings, and pendant for her birthday. He paid $1,125 for the set and had a down payment of $175. He paid the balance with 12 monthly payments of $84. Find the APR.

17. Matt Brawn bought a diamond engagement ring for $2,560. His down payment was $600, and he made 24 monthly payments of $90. Find the APR.

18. Mary Sinclair purchased a preowned Corvette for $27,900.00. She made a down payment of $8,000.00 and financed the rest over 5 years with monthly payments of $389.50. Find the APR.

19. In Exercise 13, Richard was able to pay off his loan at the end of 30 months. Using the actuarial method, find the unearned interest and payoff amount.

20. In Exercise 14, Jennifer decided to pay off her loan at the end of 2 years. Using the actuarial method, find the unearned interest and payoff amount.

21. In Exercise 15, Erin decided to pay off her loan at the end of 6 months. Using the actuarial method, find the unearned interest and the payoff amount.

22. In Exercise 16, Ben was able to pay off his loan at the end of 6 months. Using the actuarial method, find the unearned interest and the payoff amount.

23. In Exercise 17, Matt was able to pay off his loan at the end of 18 months. Using the actuarial method, find the unearned interest and the payoff amount.

24. In Exercise 18, Mary decided to pay off her loan at the end of 3 years. Using the actuarial method, find the unearned interest and the payoff amount.

For Exercises 25–30, use the rule of 78.

25. A $4,200.00 loan is to be paid off in 36 monthly payments of $141.17. The borrower decides to pay off the loan after 20 payments have been made. Find the amount of interest saved.

26. Fred borrowed $150.00 for 1 year. His payments are $13.75 per month. If he decides to pay off the loan after 6 months, find the amount of interest that he will save.

27. Greentree Limousine Service borrowed $200.00 to repair a limousine. The loan was to be paid off in 18 monthly installments of $13.28. After a good season, they decide to pay off the loan early. If they pay off the loan after 10 payments, how much interest do they save?

28. Household Lighting Company borrowed $600.00 to purchase items from another store that was going out of business. The loan required 24 monthly payments of $29.50. After 18 payments were made, the company decided to pay off the loan. How much interest was saved?

29. Lydia needed to have her roof repaired. She borrowed $950.00 for 10 months. The monthly payments were $99.75 each. After seven payments, she decided to pay off the balance of the loan. How much interest did she save?

30. The owners of Scottdale Village Inn decided to remodel the dining room at a cost of $3,250.00. They borrowed the money for 1 year and repaid it in monthly payments of $292.50. After eight payments were made, the owners decided to pay off the loan. Find the interest saved.

31. For the month of January, Juan had an unpaid balance on a credit card statement of $832.50 at the beginning of the month and made purchases of $675.00. A payment of $400.00 was made during the month. If the interest rate was 2% per month on the unpaid balance, find the finance charge and the new balance on February 1.

32. For the month of July, the unpaid balance on Sue's credit card statement was $1,131.63 at the beginning of the billing cycle. She made purchases of $512.58. She also made a payment of $750.00 during the month. If the interest rate was 1.75% per month on the unpaid balance, determine the finance charge and the new balance on the first day of the August billing cycle.

33. Sam is redecorating his apartment. On the first day of his credit card billing cycle, his balance was $2,364.79. He has recently made purchases totaling $1,964.32. He was able to make a payment of $1,000.00 during this billing cycle. If his interest rate is 1.67% per month on the unpaid balance, what is the finance charge and what will Sam's new balance be on the first day of the next billing cycle?

34. Janine has recently accepted a position with an upscale clothing store. On the first day of her March credit card billing cycle, her unpaid balance was $678.34. She has made clothing purchases totaling $3,479.03. She was able to make one payment of $525.00 during the billing cycle. If the interest rate is 2.25% per month on the unpaid balance, find the finance charge and the new balance on the first day of the April billing cycle.

35. Joe's credit card statement on the first day of the May billing cycle shows a balance of $986.53. During this billing cycle, he charged $186.50 to his account and made a payment of $775.00. At 1.35% interest per month on the unpaid balance, what is the finance charge? Also, find the balance on the first day of the next billing cycle.

36. Frank's credit card statement shows a balance of $638.19 on the first day of the billing cycle. If he makes a payment of $475.00 and charges $317.98 during this billing period, what will his finance charge be (the interest rate is 1.50% of the unpaid balance per month)? What will his beginning balance be at the start of the next billing cycle?

37. Mary's credit card statement showed these transactions during September:

September 1	Previous balance	$627.75
September 10	Purchase	$87.95
September 15	Payment	$200.00
September 27	Purchases	$146.22

(a) Find the average daily balance.

(b) Find the finance charge for the month. The interest rate is 1.2% per month on the average daily balance.

(c) Find the new balance on October 1.

38. Pablo's credit card statement showed these transactions during March:

March 1	Previous balance	$2,162.56
March 3	Payment	$800.00
March 10	Purchases	$329.27
March 21	Payment	$500.00
March 29	Purchases	$197.26

(a) Find the average daily balance.

(b) Find the finance charge for the month. The interest rate is 2% per month on the average daily balance.

(c) Find the new balance on April 1.

39. Mike's credit card statement showed these transactions during the month of June:

June 1	Previous balance	$157.95
June 5	Purchases	$287.62
June 20	Payment	$100.00

(a) Find the average daily balance.

(b) Find the finance charge for the month. The interest rate is 1.4% per month on the average daily balance.

(c) Find the new balance on July 1.

40. Charmaine's credit card statement showed these transactions during the month of December:

December 1	Previous balance	$1,325.65
December 15	Purchases	$287.62
December 16	Purchases	$439.16
December 22	Payment	$700.00

(a) Find the average daily balance.

(b) Find the finance charge for the month. The interest rate is 2% per month on the average daily balance.

(c) Find the new balance on January 1.

41. Ruth's credit card statement showed these transactions for the month of July:

July 1	Previous balance	$65.00
July 2	Purchases	$720.25
July 8	Payment	$500.00
July 17	Payment	$100.00
July 28	Purchases	$343.97

(a) Find the average daily balance.

(b) Find the finance charge for the month. The interest rate is 1.1% per month.

(c) Find the new balance on August 1.

42. Tamera's credit card statement showed these transactions for the month of September:

September 1	Previous balance	$50.00
September 13	Purchases	$260.88
September 17	Payment	$100.00
September 19	Purchases	$324.15

(a) Find the average daily balance.

(b) Find the finance charge for the month. The interest rate is 1.9% per month on the average daily balance.

(c) Find the new balance on October 1.

Critical Thinking

43. Find the principal on a loan at 8% for 4 years when the monthly payments are $100 per month.

44. A couple borrowed $800 for 1 year at 12% interest. Payments were made monthly. After eight payments were made, they decided to pay it off. Find the interest that was saved if it was computed equally over 12 months. Then find the interest saved using the rule of 78. Explain which is a better deal for the borrower.

Section 8-5 Home Ownership

For many people, the day they buy their first home is one of the proudest days of their life—and one of the scariest. There is nothing that compares to the feeling of looking at a house and knowing that it's all yours. But the buying process is tremendously intimidating. There are dozens of documents to sign, and the sheer numbers involved are enough to make almost everyone wonder if they're making a colossal mistake.

For the very few among us who pay cash for a house, it's not as big an issue. But almost everyone will secure a large loan to buy a home, and the most common home loans are paid over a 30-year span. That's a major commitment, and one that nobody

LEARNING OBJECTIVES

☐ 1. Find a monthly mortgage payment using a payment table.

☐ 2. Find the total interest on a home loan.

☐ 3. Compare two mortgages with different lengths.

☐ 4. Find a monthly mortgage payment using a formula.

☐ 5. Make an amortization schedule for a home loan.

should enter into without an understanding of the mathematics that go into the process. In this section, we will study that math, hopefully helping you to become a well-informed home buyer.

Mortgages

A **mortgage** is a long-term loan where the lender has the right to seize the property purchased if the payments are not made. Homes are the most common items bought using mortgages. The most common mortgage term is 30 years, but they are widely available in terms from 15 to as many as 50 years.

There are several types of mortgages. **A fixed-rate mortgage** means that the rate of interest remains the same for the entire term of the loan. The payments (usually monthly) stay the same. An **adjustable-rate mortgage** means that the rate of interest may fluctuate (i.e., increase and decrease) during the period of the loan. Some lending institutions will allow you to make **graduated payments.** This means that even though the interest does not change for the period of the loan, you can make smaller payments in the first few years and larger payments at the end of the loan period.

Finding Monthly Payments and Total Interest

One way to find the monthly payments for a fixed-rate mortgage is to use a table like Table 8-2 below. The table displays the monthly payment required for each $1,000 of a mortgage.

TABLE 8-2   **Monthly Payment per $1,000 of Mortgage (Includes Principal and Interest)**

Math Note

The word "mortgage" comes from a combination of Old French words "mort" (dead) and "gage" (pledge). It is believed the intent was that the debtor pledged the property to secure the loan, and if he or she failed to pay, the property was taken, and was therefore "dead" to the debtor.

| Rate (%) | Number of Years | | | | | |
	15	20	25	30	35	40
3.5	$7.15	$5.80	$5.01	$4.49	$4.13	$3.87
4	7.40	6.06	5.28	4.77	4.43	4.18
4.5	7.65	6.33	5.56	5.07	4.73	4.50
5	7.91	6.60	5.85	5.37	5.05	4.82
5.5	8.17	6.88	6.14	5.68	5.37	5.16
6	8.44	7.16	6.44	6.00	5.70	5.50
6.5	8.71	7.46	6.75	6.32	6.04	5.85
7	8.99	7.75	7.07	6.65	6.39	6.21
7.5	9.27	8.06	7.39	6.99	6.74	6.58
8	9.56	8.36	7.72	7.34	7.10	6.95
8.5	9.85	8.68	8.05	7.69	7.47	7.33
9	10.14	9.00	8.39	8.05	7.84	7.71
9.5	10.44	9.32	8.74	8.41	8.22	8.10
10	10.75	9.65	9.09	8.78	8.60	8.49
10.5	11.05	9.98	9.44	9.15	8.98	8.89
11	11.37	10.32	9.80	9.52	9.37	9.28

In Example 1, we'll find the monthly payment on a mortgage using the table and the procedure that follows:

Procedure for Finding the Monthly Payment for a Fixed-Rate Mortgage

Step 1 Find the down payment.

Step 2 Subtract the down payment from the cost of the home to find the principal of the mortgage.

Step 3 Divide the principal by 1,000.

Step 4 Find the number in the table that corresponds to the interest rate and the term of the mortgage.

Step 5 Multiply that number by the number obtained in step 3 to get the monthly payment.

EXAMPLE 1   Finding Monthly Mortgage Payments

The Petteys family plans to buy a home for $174,900, and have been offered a 30-year mortgage with a rate of 5.5% if they make a 20% down payment. What will their monthly payment be with this loan?

SOLUTION

Step 1 Find the down payment.

$$20\% \text{ of } \$174,900 = 0.20 \times \$174,900 = \$34,980$$

Step 2 Subtract the down payment from the cost of the home to get the principal.

$$\$174,900 - \$34,980 = \$139,920$$

Step 3 Divide by 1,000.

$$\frac{\$139,920}{1,000} = 139.92$$

Step 4 Find the value in Table 8-2 for a 30-year mortgage at 5.5%. It is $5.68.

Step 5 Multiply the value from step 3, 139.92, by $5.68.

$$139.92 \times \$5.68 \approx \$794.75$$

The monthly payment is $794.75.

▼ Try This One 1

The Trissel family agreed on a price of $229,500 for a home. Their company credit union offers a 5.0% 20-year loan with 15% down. Calculate the monthly payment.

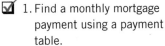

1. Find a monthly mortgage payment using a payment table.

It's an eye-opening experience to calculate the total interest on a mortgage. To do so, multiply the monthly payments by the total number of payments and then subtract the principal.

EXAMPLE 2   Finding Total Interest on a Mortgage

Find the total amount of interest the Petteys family would pay if they take the loan in Example 1.

SOLUTION

On a 30-year mortgage, there are $30 \times 12 = 360$ payments. We found that the monthly payment would be $794.75.

$$\$794.75 \times 360 = \$286,110$$

This is the total of payments. We subtract the amount financed from Example 1:

$$\$286,110 - \$139,920 = \$146,190 \quad \textit{Interest on the loan.}$$

The interest paid exceeds the principal of the loan by over $6,000!

2. Find the total interest on a home loan.

▼ Try This One 2

Find the total interest paid on the loan in Try This One 1.

Not surprisingly, the length of a loan has a profound effect on how much interest is paid. In the next example, we'll weigh the amount of extra monthly payment required versus the amount of interest saved.

EXAMPLE 3   Comparing Mortgages with Different Terms

Suppose that the Petteys family from Examples 1 and 2 is also offered a 15-year mortgage with the same rate and down payment. Find the difference in monthly payment and interest paid between the 15- and 30-year mortgages.

SOLUTION

We essentially need to rework Examples 1 and 2 with a 15-year mortgage, then compare the results. Fortunately, some of the work we did carries over. We know that the principal is $139,920, and the principal divided by 1,000 is 139.92. This time we use the 15-year column and 5.5% row in Table 8-2 to get $8.17. Now we multiply that by 139.92:

$$139.92 \times \$8.17 \approx \$1,143.15 \quad \textit{Monthly payment with 15-year term.}$$

The difference in monthly payments is

$$\$1,143.15 - \$794.75 = \$348.40 \quad \textit{\$794.75 was payment for 30 years.}$$

With a monthly payment of $1,143.15 for 15 years (which is 180 months) the total payments are

$$\$1,143.15 \times 180 = \$205,767.00$$

and the interest paid is

$$\$205,767 - \$139,920 = \$65,847$$

The interest paid on the 30-year mortgage was $146,190:

$$\$146{,}190 - \$65{,}847 = \$80{,}343$$

If the Petteys family can manage an extra $348.40 a month, they will save over $80,000 in interest!

▼ Try This One 3

☑ 3. Compare two mortgages with different lengths.

If the Trissel family from Try This One 1 chooses a 15-year mortgage instead of 20, find the increase in monthly payment and total interest saved.

There is a formula for computing monthly payments on a mortgage that can be used in place of Table 8-2. It can also be used for interest rates or terms not included in the table.

Formula for Computing Monthly Payments on a Mortgage

$$R = \frac{P\left(\frac{r}{n}\right)}{1 - \left(1 + \frac{r}{n}\right)^{-nt}}$$

R = regular monthly payment

P = amount financed, or principal

r = rate written as a decimal

n = number of payments per year

t = number of years

CAUTION

Obviously, the payment formula is pretty complicated. We will have to be extra careful in doing the calculations and take it in stages.

Sidelight THE GREAT MORTGAGE CRISIS

Throughout much of the first decade of the 21st century, homeowners were very happy people. Housing prices were rising at an almost unprecedented rate, and people watched the value of their investment soar. New homes were being built everywhere you looked, and lending institutions were practically climbing over each other to hand out home loans.

Then a funny thing happened—the housing market got oversaturated and prices started to fall. At the same time, people who took adjustable-rate mortgages to buy larger houses had their rates go up and couldn't make their payments anymore. Foreclosures (when the lending institution takes back a home) started to rise, causing even more houses to go on the market. Soon, the whole house of cards came crashing down, taking the U.S. economy with it.

There is plenty of blame to go around, but put in its simplest terms, the blame is to be shared equally between home buyers and lenders. Millions of people bought homes they couldn't afford with adjustable-rate mortgages, and the lenders gave out loans to millions of people who couldn't afford

them. The result was an economic bust that had cost over 7 million jobs by mid-2009. One lesson has been learned from this mess—lenders will be far less likely to put people in homes that they can't afford from now on.

EXAMPLE 4   Finding a Monthly Payment Using the Formula

After one hit single, a young singer unwisely decides that she needs a $2.2 million dollar mansion. With some of the proceeds from her CD, she puts down $500,000, leaving $1,700,000 to finance at 6% for 30 years. Find her monthly payment.

SOLUTION

In the formula above, use $P = 1,700,000$, $r = 0.06$, $n = 12$, and $t = 30$.

$$R = \frac{P\left(\frac{r}{n}\right)}{1 - \left(1 + \frac{r}{n}\right)^{-nt}}$$

$$R = \frac{1,700,000\left(\frac{0.06}{12}\right)}{1 - \left(1 + \frac{0.06}{12}\right)^{-12\cdot30}}$$ *Multiply in numerator. $1 + \frac{0.06}{12} = 1.005$ (in some cases, rounding might be necessary here); $-12\cdot30 = -360$.*

$$= \frac{8,500}{1 - (1.005)^{-360}}$$ *See Calculator Guide.*

$$\approx \$10,192.36$$

The monthly payment is $10,192.36, and the singer better hope her next CD does well, too.

▼ Try This One 4

☑ 4. Find a monthly mortgage payment using a formula.

Use the payment formula to find the monthly payment on the one-hit-wonder pop star's second house, a $120,000 mortgage at 5.2% for 15 years.

Computing an Amortization Schedule

After securing a mortgage, the lending institution will prepare an **amortization schedule.** This schedule shows what part of the monthly payment is paid on the principal and what part of the monthly payment is paid in interest.

In order to prepare an amortization schedule, the next procedure can be used.

Math Note

Be sure to subtract any down payment from the cost of the home before beginning the amortization schedule.

Procedure for Computing an Amortization Schedule

Step 1 Find the interest for the first month. Use $I = Prt$, where $t = \frac{1}{12}$. Enter this value in a column labeled Interest.

Step 2 Subtract the interest from the monthly payment to get the amount paid on the principal. Enter this amount in a column labeled Payment on Principal.

Step 3 Subtract the amount of the payment on principal found in step 2 from the principal to get the balance of the loan. Enter this in a column labeled Balance of Loan.

Step 4 Repeat the steps using the amount of the balance found in step 3 for the new principal.

EXAMPLE 5 **Preparing an Amortization Schedule**

Math Note

Preparing an amortization schedule makes it easy to see why more interest is paid earlier in a fixed installment loan, and more principal is paid later.

Compute the first two months of an amortization schedule for the loan in Example 1.

SOLUTION

The value of the mortage is $139,920, the interest rate is 5.5%, and the monthly payment is $794.75.

Step 1 Find the interest for month 1.

$$I = Prt$$
$$= \$139{,}920 \times 0.055 \times \frac{1}{12}$$
$$= \$641.30$$

Enter this in a column labeled Interest.

Step 2 Subtract the interest from the monthly payment.

$$\$794.75 - \$641.30 = \$153.45$$

This goes into the Payment on Principal column.

Step 3 Subtract principal payment from principal.

$$\$139{,}920 - \$153.45 = \$139{,}766.55$$

This goes into the Balance of Loan column. Now we repeat steps 1–3 using the balance of $139,766.55.

Step 4 $I = Prt$

$$= \$139{,}766.55 \times 0.055 \times \frac{1}{12}$$
$$= \$640.60$$

Step 5 $\$794.75 - \$640.60 = \$154.15$

Step 6 $\$139{,}766.55 - \$154.15 = \$139{,}612.40$

The first 2 months of the amortization schedule are:

Payment Number	Interest	Payment on Principal	Balance of Loan
1	$641.30	$153.45	$139,766.55
2	$640.60	$154.15	$139,612.40

☑ 5. Make an amortization schedule for a home loan.

▼ **Try This One 5**

Make an amortization schedule for the first 3 months for the loan in Try This One 1.

LEARNING OBJECTIVES

❑ 1. Find information from a stock listing.

❑ 2. Compute the P/E ratio for a stock.

❑ 3. Compute the total cost of a stock purchase.

❑ 4. Compute the profit or loss from a stock sale.

purchases 250 shares, then the investor owns one-quarter of the company. The investor is called a **shareholder.**

When a company makes money, it distributes part of the profit to its shareholders. This money is called a **dividend.** The stockholder receives a sum of money based on the number of shares of the stock that he or she owns. Sometimes if a company does not make a profit or its owners or managers decide to reinvest the money into the company, no dividends are paid.

Besides issuing stock, a company can also issue **bonds.** Usually bonds are issued to raise money for the company for start-up costs or special projects. A person who purchases a bond is really lending money to the company. The company, in turn, repays the owner of the bond its **face value** plus interest. As a general rule, bonds are a safer investment than stocks, but stocks have greater growth potential.

Stocks can be bought and sold on a **stock exchange.** The price of a stock varies from day to day (even from minute to minute) depending on the amount that investors are willing to pay for it. This can be affected by the profitability of the company, the economy, scandals, even global political concerns. Investors buy or sell stock through a **stockbroker.** Traditionally, this was an individual working for a brokerage firm, but it has become common for people to use online brokers, in which the investor initiates the buying and selling of stocks. In either case, the brokerage charges a fee, called a **commission,** for the service of having their representatives buy or sell the stock at an exchange. Bonds can also be bought and sold like stock.

Investors often own a combination of stocks and bonds. The set of all stocks and bonds owned is called an investor's **portfolio.** Sometimes a group of investors hire a manager to handle their investments. The manager invests in stocks and bonds, follows the activities of companies, and buys and sells in an attempt to achieve maximum profit for the group. This type of investment is called a **mutual fund.**

Stocks

In order to get information about a certain stock, you can refer to a stock table. These tables can be found in newspapers and online. The listings vary somewhat depending on the source. In this case, a stock listing for a company called Computer Programming and Systems, Inc. will be used as an example.

52 weeks								
HI	LO	STOCK	DIV	YLD%	P/E	VOL (1,000s)	CLOSE	NET CHG
31.00	17.07	CPSI	1.44	6.5%	16.8	1,244	22.25	+0.40

The first two columns give the highest and lowest selling prices for one share of stock in this company during the past 52 weeks. In this case, they are $31.00 and $17.07 respectively. The column labeled STOCK contains the letters CPSI. This is the symbol the company uses for trading. The column labeled DIV is the dividend per share that was paid to shareholders last year. In this case, it was $1.44 per share. The column labeled YLD% is the annual percentage yield: It is the dividend per share divided by the current price. In this case, it is 6.5%. This percent can be compared to other stocks as a measure of performance. The P/E column is the price-to-earnings ratio. It is the ratio of yesterday's closing price of the stock (found in the CLOSE column) to its annual earnings per share. In this case, the closing price of the stock, $22.25, is a bit less than 17 times the annual earnings per share. This concept will be explained in more detail after the first example.

The column labeled VOL (1,000s) means the number of shares in thousands that were traded yesterday. In this case, 1,244 × 1,000 = 1,244,000 shares were traded as of closing time. The column labeled NET CHG is the change in the price of the stock between the day before yesterday and yesterday at closing time. In this case, the value of the stock increased $0.40. This tells us that the value of the stock the day before yesterday was $22.25 − $0.40 = $21.85. Since the net change was positive, a + appears in the column. When … appears in this column, it means that there is no change.

EXAMPLE 1 **Reading a Stock Listing**

The following is a stock listing for the Terex Corporation. Use the listing to answer the questions.

52 weeks								
HI	LO	STOCK	DIV	YLD%	P/E	VOL (1,000s)	CLOSE	NET CHG
35	20.97	TEX	0.24	1.0	25	7,143	24.51	−0.06

(a) What was the highest price that the stock sold for during the past 52 weeks?
(b) What was the lowest price that the stock sold for during the past 52 weeks?
(c) What was the amount of the dividend per share that TEX paid last year?
(d) If you owned 250 shares of stock, how much did you make in dividends last year?
(e) How many shares were traded yesterday?
(f) What was the closing price per share the day before yesterday?

SOLUTION

(a) $35.00 *Found in the "HI" column.*

(b) $20.97 *Found in the "LO" column.*

(c) $0.24 *Found in the DIV column.*

(d) 250 × $0.24 = $60 *$0.24 dividend per share x 250 shares.*

(e) 7,143 × 1,000 = 7,143,000 *Number in VOL column x 1,000.*

(f) $24.51 + 0.06 = $24.57 *Closing price of $24.51 is 0.06 below previous day.*

▼ Try This One 1

☑ 1. Find information from a stock listing.

The following is a stock listing for Wabtec Corporation. Use the listing to answer the questions.

52 weeks								
HI	LO	STOCK	DIV	YLD%	P/E	VOL (1,000s)	CLOSE	NET CHG
22.70	16.53	WAB	0.04	0.2%	27	4,870	21.97	+0.16

(a) What was the highest price that the stock sold for during the past 52 weeks?
(b) What was the lowest price that the stock sold for during the past 52 weeks?
(c) What was the amount of the dividend per share that Wabtec paid last year?
(d) If you owned 432 shares of stock, how much did you make in dividends last year?
(e) How many shares were traded yesterday?
(f) What was the closing price per share the day before yesterday?

> **CAUTION**
>
> When finding the number of shares traded, don't forget to multiply by the units given for VOL in the table. In Example 1, it is thousands.

P/E Ratio

The P/E ratio of a stock is a comparison of the current selling price to the company's earnings per share.

Math Note

The abbreviation P/E is used to remind you that this is a ratio of Price to Earnings.

Formula for the P/E ratio

$$\text{P/E ratio} = \frac{\text{Yesterday's closing price}}{\text{Annual earnings per share}}$$

The annual earnings per share is found by dividing a company's total earnings by the number of shares that are owned by the stockholders for the last year. The annual earnings per share for a stock is found by subtracting expenses, taxes, losses, etc. from the gross revenues. These figures can be found in a company's annual reports.

EXAMPLE 2   **Computing a P/E Ratio**

If the annual earnings per share for Terex is $0.98, find the P/E ratio.

SOLUTION

$$\text{P/E ratio} = \frac{\text{Yesterday's closing price}}{\text{Annual earnings per share}} \quad \textit{Closing price from Example 1.}$$

$$= \frac{\$24.51}{\$0.98} = 25 \text{ (rounded)}$$

☑ 2. Compute the P/E ratio for a stock.

▼ Try This One 2

The most recent annual earnings per share for Wabtec, the company in Try This One 1, was $2.62. Find the updated P/E ratio for Wabtec.

Our answer to Example 2 means that the price of a share of stock is 25 times the company's annual earnings per share. If you divide $1.00 by the P/E ratio 25, you get 0.04, which means that for every dollar you invest in the company by purchasing its stock, the company makes 4¢. This however, does not mean that the company pays a dividend of 4¢. The dividends paid are determined by the board of directors of the company, and they may want to use some of the profits for other purposes, such as expansion.

Another way of looking at the P/E ratio is that you are paying the company $1.00 so it can make 4¢. Now if the P/E ratio for another company's stock is 20, then $1.00 ÷ 20 = 5¢. This means that you are paying the company $1.00 so that it can earn 5¢. Which is better? Obviously the investment in the second company is better. So in general, the lower the P/E ratio is, the better the investment, but there are many other factors to consider. Also remember that since the price of a company's stock is constantly changing, the P/E ratio also changes.

Knowing the price per share of stock and the P/E ratio, you can find the annual earnings per share for the last 12 months by using the following formula:

Math Note

This formula is obtained from solving the P/E ratio formula for earnings.

Formula for Annual Earnings per Share

$$\text{Annual earnings per share} = \frac{\text{Yesterday's closing price}}{\text{P/E ratio}}$$

EXAMPLE 3   **Computing Annual Earnings per Share**

If the closing price for Kellogg's stock was $44.23 and the P/E ratio is 15, find the annual earnings per share for last year.

SOLUTION

$$\text{Annual earnings per share} = \frac{\text{Yesterday's closing price}}{\text{P/E ratio}}$$

$$= \frac{\$44.23}{15} \approx \$2.95$$

The annual earnings per share for Kellogg's is $2.95.

▼ **Try This One 3**

Find the annual earnings per share for a stock if yesterday's closing price was $62.43 and the P/E ratio is 8.6.

The current yield for a stock can be calculated by using the following formula:

Formula for Current Yield for a Stock

$$\text{Current stock yield} = \frac{\text{Annual dividend per share}}{\text{Closing price of stock}}$$

EXAMPLE 4   **Computing Yield for a Stock**

For the CPSI stock from page 466, the annual percent yield is 6.5%. Verify the current yield by using the preceding formula.

SOLUTION

The dividend per share is $1.44 and the closing price is $22.25:

$$\text{Current yield} = \frac{\text{Annual dividend per share}}{\text{Closing price of stock}}$$

$$= \frac{\$1.44}{\$22.25} = 0.065 \text{ (rounded)} = 6.5\%$$

After rounding, the figure agrees with the 6.5% shown in the listing.

▼ Try This One 4

Find the current yield for a stock if the annual dividend per share is $1.51 and the closing price of the stock is $30.15.

There are two ways to make money from stocks: buy shares of a stock that pays dividends, or buy stock at a low price and sell it at a higher price. But of course, you can't just go buy stock at the corner store—you need to use a brokerage firm, placing an order which is then carried out by representatives at the stock exchange. In exchange for that service, the broker charges a commission, which varies among brokers. Brokers can also make recommendations concerning what stocks to buy and sell, which further justifies their commissions.

The amount that an investor receives from the sale of a stock is called the **proceeds.** The proceeds are equal to the amount of the sale minus the broker's commission. The next two examples illustrate the buying and selling of stocks.

EXAMPLE 5   Finding the Total Cost of Buying Stock

Shares of Apple Computer (AAPL) closed at $12.89 on April 1, 2004. Suppose that an investor bought 600 shares at that price using a broker that charged a 2% commission. Find the amount of commission and the total cost to the investor.

SOLUTION

Step 1 Find the purchase price.

$$600 \text{ shares} \times \$12.89 = \$7,734.00$$

Step 2 Find the broker's commission.

$$2\% \text{ of purchase price} = 0.02 \times \$7,734.00$$
$$= \$154.68$$

Step 3 Add the commission to the purchase price.

$$\$7,734.00 + \$154.68 = \$7,888.68$$

The investor paid a total of $7,888.68 for the transaction.

▼ Try This One 5

Apple closed at $38.45 on January 3, 2005. If 250 shares were bought at that price through a broker with a 1.6% commission, find the commission and total cost to the investor.

☑ 3. Compute the total cost of a stock purchase.

EXAMPLE 6   Finding the Amount Made from Selling Stock

On May 1, 2008, shares of Apple stock reached $192.24. If the investor in Example 5 sold all of his Apple stock at that point, and the broker also charges a 2% commission on sales, find the commission, proceeds, and the amount of profit made by the investor.

SOLUTION

Step 1 Find the total amount of the sale.

$$600 \text{ shares} \times \$192.24 = \$115,344.00$$

Step 2 Find the commission.

$$2\% \text{ of } \$115,344.00 = 0.02 \times \$115,344.00 = \$2,306.88$$

Step 3 Subtract the commission amount from the total amount of the sale to get the proceeds.

$$\$115,344.00 - \$2,306.88 = \$113,037.12$$

Step 4 The profit is the proceeds minus the total cost from Example 5.

$$\$113,037.12 - \$7,888.68 = \$105,148.44$$

▼ Try This One 6

When the market tanked at the end of 2008, Apple stock reached a low of $78.20 on January 20, 2009. If the investor in Try This One 5 sold all of his Apple stock that day, and the broker charges 1.6% for sales, find the commission, proceeds, and profit made.

> **Math Note**
>
> Stockbrokers charge commission for both buying and selling your stock, so you end up paying on both ends when investing in stock.

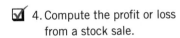 4. Compute the profit or loss from a stock sale.

Bonds

When an investor purchases bonds, the investor is lending money to the company that issues the bonds. Bonds can also be issued by local, state, and federal governments. Bonds have a **face value,** which is usually $1,000, and a fixed interest rate. Bonds can be sold just like stocks and the prices vary with the market conditions. Bonds also have a **maturity date,** which is the date that they come due. Bonds are listed in tables that are similar to stock tables. Brokers also earn commissions for buying and selling bonds. Investment procedures for bonds are similar to those for stocks.

Mutual Funds

Many times investors purchase a group of stocks and bonds called a **mutual fund.** Mutual funds are managed by professional managers and include money from other investors. The manager follows the markets and makes the decisions of when to buy or sell the stocks and bonds. Mutual funds usually consist of a large number of small investments in companies. This way, if a single stock does not perform well, only a small amount of money is lost. Sometimes mutual funds can be high return but also high risk.

Ratings for mutual funds can be found on most financial websites, and in business publications like the *Wall Street Journal*. They are rated either from A to F, or from 5 to 1, with 5 being the best. Often, two separate ratings are given. An overall rating compares the fund to all other stock funds. A category rating compares a fund to other funds that have similar holdings. For example, there are funds that invest strictly in smaller businesses, and it makes sense to compare those funds to others like them, as well as to the market as a whole.

Answers to Try This One

1
  (a) $22.70
  (b) $16.53
  (c) $0.04
  (d) $17.28
  (e) 4,870,000
  (f) $21.81

2 8.4 (rounded)

3 $7.26

4 5.0%

5 Commission = $153.80, total cost = $9,766.30

6 Commission = $312.80, proceeds = $19,237.20, profit = $9,470.90

EXERCISE SET 8-6

Writing Exercises

1. Explain in your own words what stock is.
2. What's the difference between stocks and bonds?
3. What is a mutual fund?
4. What is meant by the term P/E ratio?
5. What does a stockbroker do?
6. When selling stock, what's the difference between sale price, proceeds, and profit or loss?

Real-World Applications

Use the following information about Sunoco stock for Exercises 7–16.

| 52 weeks | | | | | | | | |
HI	LO	STOCK	DIV	YLD%	P/E	VOL (1,000s)	CLOSE	NET CHG
97.25	57.50	SUN	1.23	1.6	7	4,626	62.06	+0.77

7. What is the highest price that the stock sold for during the last 52 weeks?
8. What was the lowest price that the stock sold for during the last 52 weeks?
9. What was the amount of the dividend per share that the company paid last year?
10. If you own 175 shares, how much in dividends did you make last year?
11. How many shares were traded yesterday?
12. What was the closing price of the stock yesterday?
13. Find the annual earnings per share.
14. If you purchase 480 shares of Sunoco stock at $62.06 per share and the broker's commission is 1.5%, find the total cost of the purchase.
15. If an investor had 623 shares of Sunoco stock last year and the dividend per share was $1.23 last year, how much did the investor receive?
16. What was the closing price per share of stock the day before yesterday?

Use the following information about Wabtec stock for Exercises 17–26.

| 52 weeks | | | | | | | | |
HI	LO	STOCK	DIV	YLD%	P/E	VOL (1,000s)	CLOSE	NET CHG
40.08	24.75	WAB	0.04	0.1	20	345	29.79	+0.39

17. What was the highest price that the stock sold for during the last 52 weeks?
18. What was the lowest price that the stock sold for during the last 52 weeks?

19. What was the amount of the dividend per share that the company paid last year?
20. If you own 357 shares, how much in dividends did you make last year?
21. How many shares were traded yesterday?
22. What was the closing price of the stock yesterday?
23. Find the annual earnings per share.

24. If you purchase 1,247 shares of stock at the closing price and the broker's commission is 2.6%, find the total cost of the purchase.
25. If an investor owned 1,562 shares of Wabtec and the dividend per share was $0.10, how much income did the investor receive?
26. What was the closing price of the stock the day before yesterday?

Use the following information about Wal-Mart stock for Exercises 27–36.

52 weeks								
HI	LO	STOCK	DIV	YLD%	P/E	VOL (1,000s)	CLOSE	NET CHG
50.87	42.31	WMT	0.67	1.4	19	9,662	48.12	−0.10

27. What was the highest price that the stock sold for during the last 52 weeks?
28. What was the lowest price that the stock sold for during the last 52 weeks?
29. What was the amount of the dividend per share that the company paid last year?
30. If you own 682 shares, how much in dividends did you make last year?
31. How many shares were traded yesterday?
32. What was the closing price of the stock yesterday?
33. Find the annual earnings per share.
34. If you purchase 842 shares of Wal-Mart stock at $52.67 per share and the broker's commission is 2%, find the total cost of the purchase.
35. If an investor had 1,225 shares of Wal-Mart stock and the dividend per share was $ 0.67 last year, how much did the investor make?
36. What was the closing price of the stock the day before yesterday?
37. If the closing price of a stock is $21.92 and the annual earnings per share is $0.88, find the P/E ratio.
38. If the closing price of a stock is $6.65 and the annual earnings per share is $0.35, find the P/E ratio.
39. If the closing price of a stock is $24.19 and the annual earnings per share is $1.61, find the P/E ratio.
40. If the closing price of annual DirecTV stock is $20.18 and the annual earnings per share is $1.06, find the P/E ratio.

41. If the closing price of Gaither stock is $18.53 and the P/E ratio is 55, find the annual earnings per share.
42. If the closing price of Jacob Energy is $75.66 and the P/E ratio is 25, find the annual earnings per share.
43. If the closing price of Marine Max is $25.76 and the P/E ratio is 13, find the annual earnings per share.
44. If the closing price of Omnicare is $43.73 and the P/E ratio is 30, find the annual earnings per share.
45. An investor purchased 800 shares of stock for $63.25 per share and sold them later for $65.28 per share. The broker's commission was 2% of the purchase price and 2% of the selling price. Find the amount the investor made or lost on the stock.
46. An investor purchased 200 shares of a stock at $93.75 per share and sold it later at $89.50 per share. The broker's commission on the purchase and sale of the stock is 2.5%. Find the amount of money the investor made or lost on the sale.
47. An investor purchased 550 shares of stock at $51.60 per share. She later sold it at $49.70. The broker's commission on the purchase was 2% and 1.5% on the sale. Find the amount of money the investor made or lost on the stock.
48. An investor purchased 670 shares of a stock at $73.20 per share. Then he sold the stock at $82.35. If the broker's commission was 2.5% on the purchase and sale of the stocks, how much money did the investor make or lose on the transaction?

Critical Thinking

49. Compare the two investments below and decide which would have been the better choice.

    Investment 1: $10,000 was invested in a 24-month CD that earned 5.1% annual interest compounded daily.

    Investment 2: 1,400 shares of stock in the Lybarger Aviation Company were bought at $7.11 per share using a brokerage with a 0.75% commision rate on both buying and selling stock. Over the 2 years the stock was held, it paid a dividend of $0.48 per share in the first year and $0.36 per share in the second year. The stock was sold through the same brokerage for $7.95 per share.

CHAPTER **8** **Summary**

Section	Important Terms	Important Ideas
8-1	Percent Percent increase Percent decrease	**Percent** means "per hundred," or "hundredths." So 45% means 45 per hundred. In order to do calculations with percents, they must be changed to fractions or decimals. The word "of" is important in calculations with percents: the phrase "40% of 80 is 32" translates to the equation $0.40 \times 80 = 32$. This allows us to set up many percent calculations.
8-2	Interest Simple interest Principal Rate Term Future value Banker's rule Discounted loan	**When you** borrow money, you pay a fee for its use. This fee is called interest. Likewise, when you put money into a savings account, the bank pays interest for the use of your money. Simple interest is interest computed only as a percentage of the principal. The formula $I = Prt$ is used to compute simple interest. Future value is the sum of the principal and any interest earned.
8-3	Compound interest Effective rate Annual yield Annuity	**Compound interest** is interest calculated on both the principal and any interest previously earned. Compound interest investments earn more interest than simple interest investments at the same rate. Since the actual rate is higher when interest is compounded more than once per year, the true rate is called the effective rate or annual yield. An annuity is a savings plan where an individual or business makes the same payment each period into a compound interest account where the rate remains the same for the term of the annuity.
8-4	Fixed installment loan Finance charge Down payment Total installment price Annual percentage rate (APR) Payoff amount Actuarial method Rule of 78 Closed-ended credit Open-ended credit Unpaid balance method Average daily balance method	**A fixed** installment loan is a loan that is repaid in equal (usually monthly) payments. A down payment is a cash payment made on the purchase. Many times a finance charge is added to the amount financed. The total installment price is found by summing the monthly payments and adding the down payment. Because you pay back some of the principal each month, you do not have the full use of the money for the term of the loan. This means that the actual interest is higher than the stated interest rate. This actual interest rate is called the annual percentage rate and can be computed approximately by the constant ratio formula. When an installment loan is paid off early, the amount of interest saved can be determined by the rule of 78, or the actuarial method. Credit card companies also charge interest. There are two ways the companies compute interest. One method is computing interest on the unpaid balance. In this case you are charged interest only on last month's balance. The other method is called the average daily balance. Here the interest is computed on the average balance on all of the days of the month. This includes any purchases and payments made during the month.

8-5	Mortgage Fixed-rate mortgage Adjustable-rate mortgage Graduated payments Amortization schedule	**Because homes** cost so much, most people need a loan to buy one. A loan for which the property being bought is used as security against not making payments is called a mortgage. A table listing the amount of each payment going to pay interest, the amount toward principal, and the balance of the loan is called an amortization schedule.
8-6	Stock Shareholder Dividend Bond Face value Stock exchange Stockbroker Commission Portfolio Yield P/E ratio Proceeds Mutual fund	**Investors** can purchase stocks and bonds. A stock is a share of ownership in a company. A bond is actually a loan to a company. A mutual fund is a combination of stocks and bonds that is managed by a professional investor. Newspapers and websites show information about stocks and bonds by using tables. The tables show the 52-week high price and low price of the stocks and bonds. The table also shows the yield, the P/E ratio, the dividend, the volume of sales, the closing price, and the net change of a stock. P/E ratio is a comparison between the share price of a stock and the company's earnings per share.

MATH IN ▸ Home Buying REVISITED

Since 5% of income goes to taxes and insurance, that leaves 23% for the monthly payment. The income is $72,000 per year, which is 72,000/12, or $6,000 per month.

23% of $6,000 = 0.23 × $6,000 = $1,380

This is the monthly payment our friends can afford. Now we look in the payment chart (Table 8-2) in Section 8-5, and find the entry corresponding to 6.0% and 30 years: it is $6.00. So the payment should equal 6.0 times the mortgage amount in thousands:

$$6.0x = 1,380$$
$$x = \frac{1,380}{6.0} = 230$$

Now we multiply by 1,000 because this is the mortgage amount in thousands:

$$230 \times 1,000 = 230,000$$

This is the mortgage amount, and we add the $15,000 down payment to find that our couple can buy a $245,000 house. (We essentially did Example 1 in Section 8-5 backward.)

As a side note, 20 years ago, a 30-year mortgage could have had a rate of 9% or more. At 9% rather than 6%, the amount of home this couple could afford goes down to $186,429!

Review Exercises

Section 8-1

For Exercises 1–10, find the missing value.

Fraction	Decimal	Percent
1. $\frac{7}{8}$	_____	_____
2. _____	0.54	_____
3. _____	_____	80%

Fraction	Decimal	Percent
4. $\frac{5}{12}$	_____	_____
5. _____	_____	185%
6. _____	0.06	_____
7. $5\frac{3}{4}$	_____	_____

Fraction	Decimal	Percent
8. _____	1.55	_____
9. _____	_____	45.5%
10. $\frac{3}{8}$	_____	_____

11. Find 72% of 96.
12. 18 is what percent of 60?
13. 25% of what number is 275?
14. If the sales tax is 5% on a calculator, find the tax and the total cost if the calculator is $19.95.
15. If the sales tax on a coffee table is $3.60, find the cost of the table if the tax rate is 6%.
16. Marcia received a commission of $2,275 for selling a small home. If she receives a 7% commission, find the price of the home.
17. In 2000, households received 3.4 credit card offers per month on average. In 2005 the average was 5.9. Find the percent increase.
18. In 2001, there were 3,147 adolescents under 18 being held in state prisons. In 2005, the number was 2,226. Find the percent decrease.

Section 8-2

For Exercises 19–26, find the missing value.

	Principal	Rate	Time	Simple Interest
19.	$4,300	9%	6 years	_____
20.	$16,000	_____	3 years	$1,920
21.	$875	12%	_____	$262.50
22.	$50	6%	18 months	_____
23.	$230	_____	6.5 years	$104.65
24.	_____	3%	5 years	$63.75
25.	_____	14%	2 years	$385
26.	$785.00	_____	12 years	$1,130.40

27. Ace Auto Parts borrowed $6,000 at 6% for 5 years to enlarge its display area. Find the simple interest and future value of the loan.
28. Sam's Sound Shack borrowed $13,450 at 8% for 15 years to remodel its existing store. Find the simple interest and future value of the loan.
29. Julie earned $60.48 in simple interest on a savings account balance of $4,320.00 over a 12-month period. Find the rate of interest.
30. John has an opportunity to buy a new boat. He has to borrow $5,300 at 11% simple interest for 36 months. Find the monthly payment.
31. Find the simple interest on a $2,300 loan at 5% for 80 days. Use the Banker's rule.
32. Find the simple interest on a $8,750 loan at 8.5% for 100 days. Use the Banker's rule.

33. David obtained a 3-year, $6,000 discounted loan at 6%. Find the discount and the amount of money David received.
34. Marla obtained a 4-year $9,250 discounted loan at 12%. Find the discount and the amount of money Marla received.

Section 8-3

For Exercises 35–38, find the compound interest and future value.

	Principal	Rate	Compounded	Time
35.	$1,775	5%	annually	6 years
36.	$200	4%	semiannually	10 years
37.	$45	8%	quarterly	3 years
38.	$21,000	6%	quarterly	7 years

39. Find the effective rate when the stated rate is 12% and the interest is computed quarterly.
40. The Evergreen Landscaping Company will need to purchase a new backhoe in 7 years. The owner purchases an annuity that pays 8.3% interest compounded semiannually. If the semiannual payment is $4,000, find the future value of the annuity in 7 years.
41. Mike and Marie plan to take an African vacation in 3 years. In order to save money for the trip, they purchase an annuity that pays 3% interest compounded quarterly. Find the future value of the annuity in 3 years if their quarterly payment is $650.

Section 8-4

42. Brad Johnson purchased a washer and dryer for a total of $854. He made a 25% down payment and financed the rest with 12 monthly payments of $54.30. Find the total installment price and the finance charge.
43. Mary Cartworth purchased a four-piece luggage set for $750. She made a down payment of 15% and was charged 6% interest. Find the total installment price and the monthly payment if she paid it off in 8 months.
44. Judy Harper purchased a Cobalt for $10,900. Her down payment was $1,000. She paid the balance with monthly payments of $310 for 3 years. Find the APR.
45. Max Dunbar bought a used BMW for $20,500 on www.Autotrader.com. His down payment was $6,000. He paid off the balance with monthly payments of $311 for 5 years. Find the APR.

46. Mike purchased a mobile home for $149,500. He made a down payment of $8,000 and financed the remainder with an 8.5% simple interest loan for 25 years. Find his monthly payment.

47. In Exercise 44, Judy decided to pay off her loan at the end of 24 months. Use the actuarial method and find the unearned interest and the payoff amount.

48. In Exercise 45, Max was able to pay off his loan at the end of 3 years. Use the actuarial method and find the unearned interest and the payoff amount.

49. A loan for $1,500.00 is to be paid back in 30 monthly installments of $61.25. The borrower decides to pay off the balance after 24 payments have been made. Find the amount of interest saved. Use the rule of 78.

50. For the month of February, Pete had an unpaid balance on his credit card of $563.25 at the beginning of the month. He had purchases of $563.25 and made a payment of $350.00 during the month. Find the finance charge if the interest rate is 1.75% per month on the unpaid balance and find the new balance on March 1.

51. Sid's Used Cars had these transactions on its credit card statement:

April 1	Unpaid balance	$5,628.00
April 10	Purchases	$2,134.60
April 22	Payment	$ 900.00
April 28	Purchases	$ 437.80

Find the finance charge if the interest rate is 1.8% on the average daily balance and find the new balance for May 1.

Section 8-5

52. A home was purchased for $145,000 with a 20% down payment. The mortgage rate was 8.5% and the term of the mortgage was 25 years.

   (a) Find the amount of the down payment.
   (b) Find the amount of the mortgage.
   (c) Find the monthly payment.
   (d) Compute an amortization schedule for the first 2 months.

53. A business sold for $252,000. The down payment was 8%. The buyer financed the balance at 8.25% for 25 years. Find the monthly payment on the mortgage.

Section 8-6

Use the table shown for Exercises 54–59.

| 52 weeks | | | | | | | | |
HI	LO	STOCK	DIV	YLD%	P/E	VOL (1,000s)	CLOSE	NET CHG
34.28	27.09	TRBCQ	0.72	2.2	30	5,528	32.79	−0.25

54. What was the high price and low price of the stock for the last 52 weeks?

55. If you own 475 shares of this stock, how much was the dividend you received?

56. How many shares of the stock were sold yesterday?

57. What was the closing price of the stock the day before yesterday?

58. Find the annual earnings per share of the stock.

59. An investor purchased 90 shares of stock for $86.43 per share and later sold it for $92.27 per share. How much did she make on the stock if the broker's fee was 2% on the purchase and the sale of the stock? Ignore the dividends.

Chapter Test

1. Change $\frac{5}{16}$ to a percent.
2. Write 0.63 as a percent.
3. Write 28% as a fraction in lowest terms.
4. Change 16.7% to a decimal.
5. 32 is what percent of 40?
6. Find 87.5% of 48.
7. 45% of what number is 135?
8. Find the sales tax on a toaster oven that sells for $29.95. The tax rate is 8%.

9. If a salesperson receives a 15% commission on all merchandise sold, find the amount sold if his commission is $385.20.

10. On the first day of math class, 28 students were present. The next day, 7 more students enrolled in the class because the other section was canceled. Find the percent increase in enrollment.

11. Find the simple interest on $1,350 at 12% for 3 years.

12. Find the rate for a principal of $200 invested for 15 years if the simple interest earned is $150.

13. Ron's Detailing Service borrowed $435 at 3.75% for 6 months to purchase new equipment. Find the simple interest and future value of the loan, and the monthly payment.

14. The Express Delivery borrowed $1,535 at 4.5% for 3 months to purchase safety equipment for its employees. Find the simple interest and future value of the loan, and the monthly payment.

15. Benson Electric borrowed $1,800 at 12% for 1 year from a local bank. Find the simple interest and future value of the loan, and the monthly payment.

16. Find the simple interest on a $5,000 loan at 4% for 60 days. Use the Banker's rule.

17. Latoya obtained a 6-year $12,650 discounted loan at 7.5%. Find the discount and the amount of money Latoya received.

18. Find the interest and future value for a principal of $500 invested at 6.5% compounded semiannually for 4 years.

19. Find the interest and future value on a principal of $9,750 invested at 10% compounded quarterly for 6 years.

20. In order to purchase a motorcycle, Jayden borrowed $12,000 at 9.5% for 4 years. Find his monthly payment.

21. Find the effective rate when the stated interest rate is 8% and the interest is compounded semiannually.

22. In order to open a new branch of her business in 3 years, the owner of Quick Fit Fitness Center purchases an annuity that pays 4.5% interest compounded semiannually. If her semiannual payment is $3,000, find the future value of the annuity in 3 years.

23. Sara bought furniture for her first apartment at a price of $935. She made a down payment of 30% and financed the rest for 6 months at 10% interest. Find the total installment charge and the monthly payment.

24. Bart Johnston purchased a Mazda for $15,000 and had a down payment of $2,000. He financed the balance at $305 per month for 48 months. Find the APR.

25. In Exercise 24, Bart was able to pay off his loan at the end of 24 months. Using the actuarial method, find the unearned interest and the payoff amount.

26. A loan for $2,200 is to be paid off in 24 monthly installments of $111.85. The borrower decides to pay off the loan after 20 payments have been made. Find the amount of interest saved, using the rule of 78.

27. For the month of November, Harry had an unpaid balance of $1,250 on his credit card. During the month, he made purchases of $560 and a payment of $800. Find the finance charge if the interest rate is 1.6% per month on the unpaid balance and find the new balance on December 1.

28. Rhonda's credit card statement for the month of May shows these transactions.

May 1	Unpaid balance	$474.00
May 11	Payment	$300.00
May 20	Purchases	$ 86.50
May 25	Purchases	$120.00

Find the finance charge if the interest rate is 2% on the average daily balance and find the new balance on June 1.

29. Tamara borrowed $800.00 for tuition. She is to pay it back in 12 monthly installments of $70.70. Find the annual percentage rate.

30. A home is purchased for $180,000 with a 5% down payment. The mortgage rate is 6% and the term is 30 years.

   (a) Find the amount of the down payment.
   (b) Find the amount of the mortgage.
   (c) Find the monthly payment.
   (d) Compute an amortization schedule for the first 2 months.

31. A group of business people purchased a sporting goods store for $475,000. They made a 15% down payment and obtained a mortgage at 5.75% for 20 years. Find the monthly payment.

Use the following table for Exercises 32–36.

| 52 weeks | | | | | | | | |
HI	LO	STOCK	DIV	YLD%	P/E	VOL (1,000s)	CLOSE	NET CHG
36.98	23.17	CAT	0.20	2.7	12	1,501	27.45	+0.80

32. What were the 52-week high and low prices of the stock?

33. If you own 300 shares of stock, how much money in dividends did you receive?

34. How many shares of the stock were sold yesterday?
35. What was the closing price of the stock the day before yesterday?

36. Find the annual earnings per share of the stock.

Projects

1. Compare the investments below to decide which you think is the best. Consider such things as total profit, length of time, and amount of money needed up front.
   (a) $20,000 placed into a savings account at 3.8% compounded monthly for 10 years.
   (b) A 10-year annuity that pays 4.5% interest with monthly payments of $170.
   (c) Buying 700 shares of stock at $14.30 per share; selling 200 shares 4 years later at $25.10, and the rest 3 years after that at $28.05. The brokerage charges 1% commission on both buying and selling.
   (d) Buying a $150,000 house with $20,000 down and financing the rest with a 15-year mortgage at 5%. Then selling the house and paying off the balance of the loan in 8 years at a selling price, after commission, of $192,000. (*Hint:* You will need to calculate the monthly payment, then compute unearned interest and payoff amount.)

2. You have $1,000 to invest. Investigate the advantages and disadvantages of each type of investment.
   (a) Checking account
   (b) Money market account
   (c) Passbook savings account
   (d) Certificate of deposit

   Write a short paper indicating which type of account you have chosen and why you chose that account.

3. There are many fees involved in buying or selling a home. Some of these include an appraisal fee, survey fee, etc. Consult a real estate agency to see what is necessary to purchase a home in your area and write a short paper on the necessary closing costs.

CHAPTER 11

Probability and Counting Techniques

Outline

MATH IN ▶ Gambling

The fact that you're reading this sentence means that you're probably taking a math class right now. But maybe not . . . you could be an instructor evaluating the book, or maybe an editor looking for mistakes (unsuccessfully, we hope). Still, I would be willing to bet that you're taking a math class. The word "probably" indicates a certain likelihood of something happening, and that basic idea is the topic of this chapter. We call the study of the likelihood of events occurring *probability*.

Probability is one of the most useful concepts in math because being able to anticipate the likelihood of events can be useful in so many different areas. Games of chance, business and investing, sports, and weather forecasting are just a few samples from a seemingly limitless list of applications. What are the chances of your team winning the championship? Should you take an umbrella to the golf course today? Will stock in a company you're keeping an eye on go up or down? Is that new job offer a good opportunity, or a disaster waiting to happen? Every day you make decisions regarding possible events that are governed at least in part by chance. The more you know about the likelihood of events, the more informed your decisions are likely to be.

In order to compute probabilities of events occurring, we're going to need to know all of the possible outcomes for an event. For example, in deciding whether or not to bring an umbrella, there are only two outcomes: it will either rain, or it won't. But in considering whether or not to take a job, there are a wide variety of possible outcomes, some good, some not so good. Since counting up the number of possible outcomes is important in probability, we will begin our study with a look at methods for counting. (Don't worry—that's not quite as elementary as it sounds!) Then we'll be ready to tackle the basic concepts of probability. Along the way, we'll learn about odds and the expected value of a probability experiment, and this is where gambling comes into play.

A handful of gambling scenarios is provided below. In each case, find the expected value (that is, the average amount a person would win or lose) if placing the bet 100 times. Then rank the scenarios from best to worst in terms of your likelihood of winning or losing money.

1. At a church fair, you bet $1 and roll two dice. If the sum is 2, 3, 11, or 12, you get back your dollar plus four more. On any other roll, you lose.

2. In a casino, you bet $1 on 33 at a roulette table. There are 38 possible numbers that can come up. If you win, you get your dollar back, plus 35 more.

3. You buy a $1 ticket to a multistate lottery. If you match all six numbers, including the Mega Ball, you win the $20 million jackpot. If not, you lose. There are 175,711,536 possible combinations, and only one of them will be a winner.

4. You bet $1 on flipping a coin with your roommate. Heads, you win, tails, your roommate wins.

For answers, see Math in Gambling Revisited on page 640

Section 11-1 The Fundamental Counting Principle and Permutations

LEARNING OBJECTIVES

☐ 1. Use the fundamental counting principle.

☐ 2. Calculate the value of factorial expressions.

☐ 3. Find the number of permutations of *n* objects.

☐ 4. Find the number of permutations of *n* objects taken *r* at a time.

☐ 5. Find the number of permutations when some objects are alike.

Many problems in probability and statistics require knowing the total number of ways a sequence of events can occur. Suppose that as part of an exciting new job, you're responsible for designing a new license plate for your state. You want it to look cool, of course. But if you want to keep your job, you better make sure that the sequence of letters and numbers you choose guarantees that there are enough different combinations so that every registered vehicle has a different plate number.

In this chapter, we'll study three basic rules for counting the number of outcomes for a sequence of events. The first is the *fundamental counting principle*.

The Fundamental Counting Principle

After getting that new job, you naturally want a new apartment, and furniture to go along with it. The hip furniture boutique around the corner has the couch you want in either leather or microsuede, and each comes in your choice of four colors. How many different couches do you have to choose from?

We'll illustrate the situation with a *tree diagram,* which displays all the possible combinations.

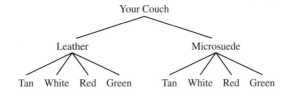

This shows us that the total number of couches possible is eight. This number can also be found by multiplying the number of materials (2) by the number of colors for each (4).

Now what if each couch can also come with or without an end recliner? Each of the eight choices in our diagram would have two more possibilities beneath it.

This would give us a total of 16 couches, which is $2 \cdot 4 \cdot 2$, or the product of the number of choices at each stage. This illustrates our first key counting principle.

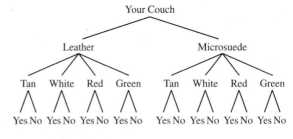

Math Note

The occurrence of the first event in no way affects the occurrence of the second event, which in turn, does not affect the occurrence of the third event, etc.

The Fundamental Counting Principle

In a sequence of *n* events in which the first event can occur in k_1 ways and the second event can occur in k_2 ways and the third event can occur in k_3 ways and so on, the total number of ways the sequence can occur is

$$k_1 \cdot k_2 \cdot k_3 \cdots \cdots k_n$$

EXAMPLE 1 **Using the Fundamental Counting Principle**

There are four blood types: A, B, AB, and O. Blood is also either Rh^+ or Rh^-. If a local blood bank labels donations according to type, Rh factor, and gender of the donor, how many different ways can a blood sample be labeled?

SOLUTION

There are four possibilities for blood type, two for Rh factor, and two for gender of the donor. Using the fundamental counting principle, there are

$$4 \cdot 2 \cdot 2 = 16$$

different ways that blood could be labeled.

▼ **Try This One 1**

A paint manufacturer plans to manufacture several different paints. The categories include

Color	Red, blue, white, black, green, brown, yellow
Type	Latex, oil
Texture	Flat, semigloss, high gloss
Use	Outdoor, indoor

How many different kinds of paint can be made if a person can select one color, one type, one texture, and one use?

When determining the number of different ways a sequence of events can occur, we'll need to know whether or not repetitions are permitted. The next example shows the difference between the two situations.

EXAMPLE 2 **Using the Fundamental Counting Principle with Repetition**

How many three-digit codes are possible if repetition is not permitted?

(a) The letters A, B, C, D, and E are to be used in a four-letter ID card. How many different cards are possible if letters are allowed to be repeated?
(b) How many cards are possible if each letter can only be used once?

SOLUTION

(a) There are four spaces to fill and five choices for each. The fundamental counting principle gives us

$$5 \cdot 5 \cdot 5 \cdot 5 = 5^4 = 625$$

(b) The first letter can still be chosen in five ways. But with no repetition allowed, there are only four choices for the second letter, three for the third, and two for the last. The number of potential cards is

$$5 \cdot 4 \cdot 3 \cdot 2 = 120$$

Hopefully, this ID card is for a pretty small organization.

▼ **Try This One 2**

The lock on a storage facility is controlled by a keypad containing digits 1 through 5.

(a) How many three-digit codes are possible if digits can be repeated?
(b) How many three-digit codes are possible if digits cannot be repeated?

☑ 1. Use the fundamental counting principle.

Factorial Notation

The next couple of counting techniques we'll learn use **factorial notation.** The symbol for a factorial is the exclamation mark (!). In general, $n!$ means to multiply the whole numbers from n down to 1. For example,

$$1! = 1 = 1$$
$$2! = 2 \cdot 1 = 2$$
$$3! = 3 \cdot 2 \cdot 1 = 6$$
$$4! = 4 \cdot 3 \cdot 2 \cdot 1 = 24$$
$$5! = 5 \cdot 4 \cdot 3 \cdot 2 \cdot 1 = 120$$

The formal definition of factorial notation is given next.

> For any natural number n
> $$n! = n(n-1)(n-2)(n-3)\cdots 3 \cdot 2 \cdot 1$$
>
> $n!$ is read as "**n factorial.**"
> 0! is defined as 1. (This might seem strange, but will be explained later.)

Some of the formulas we'll be working with require division of factorials. This will be simple if we make two key observations:

- $\frac{n!}{n!}$ is always 1.   For example, $\frac{3!}{3!} = \frac{3 \cdot 2 \cdot 1}{3 \cdot 2 \cdot 1} = \frac{6}{6} = 1$
- You can write factorials without writing all of the factors down to 1. For example, $5! = 5 \cdot 4 \cdot 3 \cdot 2 \cdot 1$, but we can also write this as $5 \cdot 4!$, or $5 \cdot 4 \cdot 3!$, etc.

In Example 3, we'll use these ideas to simplify our calculations.

EXAMPLE 3   Evaluating Factorial Expressions

Evaluate each expression:

(a) 8!   (b) $\frac{12!}{10!}$

SOLUTION

(a) $8! = 8 \cdot 7 \cdot 6 \cdot 5 \cdot 4 \cdot 3 \cdot 2 \cdot 1 = 40{,}320$

(b) First, write 12! as $12 \cdot 11 \cdot 10!$, then note that $\frac{10!}{10!} = 1$.

$$\frac{12!}{10!} = \frac{12 \cdot 11 \cdot 10!}{10!} = 12 \cdot 11 = 132$$

▼ Try This One 3

2. Calculate the value of factorial expressions.

Evaluate each expression:

(a) 6!   (b) $\frac{9!}{4!}$

CAUTION

You cannot divide factorial expressions by reducing fractions. In Example 3(b), $\frac{12!}{10!}$ is *not* equal to $\frac{6!}{5!}$.

Permutations

The second rule that we can use to find the total number of outcomes for a sequence of events is the *permutation rule*.

> An arrangement of *n* distinct objects in a specific order is called a **permutation** of the objects.

For example, suppose that a photographer wants to arrange three people, Carmen, Juan, and Christina, in a specific order for a portrait. There are six ways he could arrange them:

Carmen	Juan	Christina		Carmen	Christina	Juan
Juan	Carmen	Christina		Juan	Christina	Carmen
Christina	Juan	Carmen		Christina	Carmen	Juan

We could use the fundamental counting principle to see that there are six possible permutations as well:

$$3 \quad \cdot \quad 2 \quad \cdot \quad 1 \quad = \quad 3!$$

Choices for	Choices for	Choices for
1st position	2nd position	3rd position

In general,

> The number of permutations of *n* distinct objects using all of the objects is *n*!.

Example 4 illustrates this formula.

EXAMPLE 4 Calculating the Number of Permutations

In seven of the 10 years from 1998–2007, the five major league baseball teams in the American League East division finished in the exact same order: New York, Boston, Toronto, Baltimore, Tampa Bay. Just how unusual is this? Find the number of possible finishing orders for these five teams.

SOLUTION

This is a permutation problem since we're deciding on the number of ways to arrange five distinct objects. There are

$$5! = 120$$

possible finishing orders.

▼ **Try This One 4**

3. Find the number of permutations of *n* objects.

In how many different orders can the 11 basketball teams in the Big Ten conference finish? (Seriously, there are 11 teams in the Big Ten.)

So far, in calculating permutations, we've used all of the available objects. But what if only some of them are selected?

EXAMPLE 5 **Solving a Permutation Problem**

How many different ways can a pledge class with 20 members choose a president, vice president, and Greek Council representative? (No pledge can hold two offices.)

SOLUTION

There are 20 choices for president, 19 remaining candidates for vice president, and 18 members left to choose from for Greek Council rep. So there are $20 \cdot 19 \cdot 18 = 6{,}840$ different ways to assign these three offices.

▼ Try This One 5

How many ways can a manager and assistant manager be selected from a department consisting of 10 employees?

In Example 5, a certain number of objects (people in this case) have been chosen from a larger pool. The order of selection is important, and no repetition is allowed. (No pledge can be both president and vice president—power trip!) We call such an arrangement of objects a **permutation of *n* objects taken *r* at a time.** In the pledge problem, *n* is 20 and *r* is 3. We will use the symbol $_nP_r$ to represent this type of permutation.

We solved Example 5 using the fundamental counting principle, but the result suggests the formula below:

Permutation of *n* Objects Taken *r* at a Time

The arrangement of *n* objects in a specific order using *r* of those objects is called a **permutation of *n* objects taken *r* at a time.** It is written as $_nP_r$, and is calculated using the formula

$$_nP_r = \frac{n!}{(n-r)!}$$

EXAMPLE 6 **Solving a Permutation Problem**

How many five-digit zip codes are there with no repeated digits?

SOLUTION

This is a permutation problem because five numbers are taken from 10 possible digits, with order important and no repetition. In this case, $n = 10$ and $r = 5$.

$$_{10}P_5 = \frac{10!}{(10-5)!} = \frac{10!}{5!} = \frac{10 \cdot 9 \cdot 8 \cdot 7 \cdot 6 \cdot 5!}{5!} = 30{,}240$$

Calculator Guide

Most graphing calculators have the permutation formula built in. To find $_{10}P_5$ on a standard graphing calculator: 10 [MATH], then use right arrow to select PRB, and press [2] to select $_nP_r$, and finally 5 [ENTER].

☑ 4. Find the number of permutations of *n* objects taken *r* at a time.

▼ Try This One 6

How many six-letter passwords are there that use only lowercase letters with no letter repeated?

We now have two permutation formulas: there are $n!$ permutations of n objects using all of them, and $\frac{n!}{(n-r)!}$ using only r of the objects. We should probably make sure that these formulas are consistent with each other. To check, we'll use the second formula to calculate the number of permutations when n objects are taken n at a time. The result should be $n!$ (to match the first formula). Let's see.

If we arrange five people in order for a group picture, we can think of it as a permutation of the five people chosen five at a time; that is,

$$_5P_5 = \frac{5!}{(5-5)!} = \frac{5!}{0!}$$

This will agree with the first formula if we agree to define 0! as 1. Now we know why $0! = 1$, and we know that our two permutation formulas are consistent. This is good news, because it means we only need to remember the second permutation rule.

Problems involving permutation without duplicate objects can be solved using the fundamental counting rule; however, not all problems that can be solved with the fundamental counting rule can be solved using permutations.

When some of the objects are the same, a different permutation rule is used. Suppose that to solve a word puzzle, you need to find the number of permutations of the letters in the word *moon*. First label the letters as M, O_1, O_2, and N. This would be 4!, or 24, permutations. But since the O's without the subscripts are the same, the permutation M, O_1, O_2, N would be the same as M, O_2, O_1, N. The duplicates are eliminated by dividing 4! by the number of ways to arrange the O's (2!) to get 12. This leads to the next rule.

Permutation Rule When Objects Are Alike

The number of permutations of n objects in which k_1 objects are alike, k_2 objects are alike, etc. is

$$\frac{n!}{k_1! k_2! \ldots k_p!}$$

where $k_1 + k_2 + \cdots + k_p = n$

EXAMPLE 7 · Solving a Permutation Problem with Like Objects

How many different passwords can be made using all of the letters in the word *Mississippi*?

SOLUTION

The letters can be rearranged as M IIII SSSS PP. Then $n = 11$, $k_1 = 1$, $k_2 = 4$, $k_3 = 4$, and $k_4 = 2$.

Using our newest formula, there are

$$\frac{11!}{1!4!4!2!} = 34,650$$

different passwords.

▼ Try This One 7

5. Find the number of permutations when some objects are alike.

Find the number of different passwords using all of the letters in the word *Massachusetts*.

In summary, the formulas for permutations are used when we're looking for the number of ways to arrange objects when the order matters, and once an object is used, it can't be used again.

Sidelight WIN A MILLION OR BE STRUCK BY LIGHTNING?

Do you think you would be more likely to win a large lottery and become a millionaire or more likely to be struck by lightning? The answer is that you would be quite a bit more likely to be struck by lightning.

An article in the Associated Press noted that researchers have found that the chance of winning $1 million or more is about 1 in 1.9 million. The chances of winning $1 million in a recent Pennsylvania lottery were 1 in 9.6 million. The chances of winning a $10 million prize in Publisher's Clearinghouse Sweepstakes were 1 in 200 million. In contrast, the chances of being struck by lightning are about 1 in 600,000. In other words, a person is at least 3 times more likely to be struck by lightning than to win $1 million.

One way to guarantee winning a lottery is to buy all possible combinations of the winning numbers. In 1992, an Australian investment group purchased 5 million of the 7 million possible combinations of the lottery numbers in

a Virginia State Lottery. Because of the time, they could not purchase the other two million tickets. However, they were able to purchase the winning number and won $27 million. Their profit was about $22 million. Not bad!

States have written laws to prevent this from happening today, and they are devising lottery games with many more possibilities so that it would be impossible to purchase all the possible tickets to win.

The consequence is that your odds of winning are now even lower! There's an old joke among statisticians: lotteries are a tax on people who are bad at math.

Answers to Try This One

1 84

2 (a) 125   (b) 60

3 (a) 720   (b) 15,120

4 39,916,800

5 90

6 165,765,600

7 64,864,800

EXERCISE SET 11-1

Writing Exercises

1. Explain the fundamental counting principle in your own words.
2. What do we mean by the phrase "a permutation of n distinct objects"?
3. How does a permutation of n objects differ from a permutation of n objects taken r at a time?
4. Explain what the symbols $n!$ and $_nP_r$ represent, and explain how to compute each for given values of n and r.

Computational Exercises

Evaluate each.

5. 10!
6. 5!
7. 9!
8. 1!
9. 0!
10. 4!
11. (3!) (2!)
12. (7!) (2!)
13. $\dfrac{8!}{5!}$
14. $\dfrac{9!}{7!}$
15. $\dfrac{7!}{2!3!}$
16. $\dfrac{10!}{2!5!}$
17. $\dfrac{150!}{148!}$
18. $\dfrac{200!}{197!}$
19. $_8P_2$
20. $_7P_5$
21. $_{12}P_{12}$
22. $_5P_3$
23. $_6P_6$
24. $_6P_0$
25. $_8P_0$
26. $_8P_8$
27. $_{11}P_3$
28. $_6P_2$

Real-World Applications

29. How many different four-letter permutations can be formed from the letters in the word *decagon*?

30. Out of a group of eight students serving on the Student Government Association, how many different ways can a president, a vice president, and a treasurer be selected?

31. How many different ID cards can be made if there are six digits on a card and no digit can be used more than once?

32. How many different ways can seven types of laser printer be displayed on a shelf in a computer store?

33. How many different ways can four Super Bowl raffle tickets be selected from 50 tickets if each ticket wins a different prize?

34. How many different ways can a psychology student select five subjects from a pool of 20 subjects and assign each one to a different experiment?

35. How many website graphics can be created by using at least three of five different bitmap images?

36. A chemistry lab group has seven experiments to choose from and five members in the group. How many different ways can the experiments be assigned if only one experiment is assigned to each group member?

37. A radio DJ has a choice of seven songs in the queue. He must select three different songs to play in a certain order after the commercial break. How many ways can he select the three different songs?

38. A professor has five different tasks to assign, one to each of her five teaching assistants. In how many different ways could she make the assignments?

39. A nursing student has six different patients assigned to her. How many different ways can she see each one exactly once in the same day?

40. A store owner has 50 items to advertise, and she can select one different item each week for the next 6 weeks to put on special. How many different ways can the selection be made?

41. Out of 17 contacts in her cell phone, how many different ways can Shana set the first four speed-dial contacts?

42. How many different ways can you visit four different stores in a shopping mall?

43. How many ways can a research company select three geographic areas from a list of six geographic areas to test market its product? One area will be selected and tested in September, a different area in October, and a third area will be used in November.

44. How many different code words can be made from the symbols *, *, *, @, @, $, #, #, #, # if each word has 10 symbols?

45. How many different permutations of the letters in the word *Alabama* are there?

46. A radio station must run commercial A three times, commercial B twice, and commercial C once. How many different ways can this be done?

47. How many desktop wallpaper designs can be created from two identical red squares, three identical white squares, and two identical blue squares?

48. How many different ways can two identical television sets, three identical DVD players, and one computer be arranged on a shelf?

49. How many ways can five DVD-ROMs, three zip discs, and two flash drives be arranged in a laptop case?

50. There are 14 teams in the Atlantic Ten Conference, and 12 qualify for the conference basketball tournament. Those 12 teams are seeded 1 through 12 for the conference tournament. In how many ways could this be done?

51. There are 16 teams in the Big East Conference. How many different ways can the top four seeds for the conference basketball tournament be selected?

52. A major league baseball team has 25 players on the active roster. How many choices does a manager have for batting order, listing the nine starters from 1 through 9?

53. A professional football team has 53 players on the active roster. How many choices of 22 starting players does a coach have without regard for their positions?

54. For the new fall season, a network president has 11 shows in development, and six openings in the prime time schedule. In how many ways can she arrange new shows to fit into the schedule?

55. For Ozzfest 2008, there were nine bands scheduled to perform on the main stage. In how many different orders could the bands have been scheduled to perform? How many are possible if Ozzy Osbourne is always scheduled to perform last?

Critical Thinking

56. A campus pizzeria offers regular crust, thin crust, or pan pizzas. You can get either white or red sauce. The owner is kind of eccentric, and only sells pizzas with one topping, chosen from pepperoni, sausage, ham, onions, and ground beef. First, use a tree diagram like the one on page 574 to diagram out all possible choices of pizza. Then show that using the fundamental counting principle yields the same answer.

Section 11-2 Combinations

LEARNING OBJECTIVES

☐ 1. Distinguish between combinations and permutations.

☐ 2. Find the number of combinations of *n* objects taken *r* at a time.

☐ 3. Use the combination rule in conjunction with the fundamental counting principle.

Suppose that after waiting in line overnight, you manage to snag the last three tickets to a big concert. Sweet! The bad news is that you can only take two of your four housemates. How many different ways can you choose the two friends that get to go?

This sounds a little bit like a permutation problem, but there's a key difference: the order in which you choose two friends doesn't make any difference. They either get to go or they don't. So choosing Ruth and

Ama is exactly the same as choosing Ama and Ruth. When order matters in a selection, we call it a permutation, but when order is not important we call it a *combination*.

> A selection of objects without regard to order is called a **combination.**

In Example 1, we'll examine the difference between permutations and combinations.

EXAMPLE 1   **Comparing Permutations and Combinations**

Given four housemates, Ruth, Elaine, Ama, and Jasmine, list the permutations and combinations when you are selecting two of them.

SOLUTION

We'll start with permutations, then eliminate those that have the same two people listed.

Permutations

Ruth Elaine	Elaine Ruth	Ruth Ama
Ama Ruth	Ruth Jasmine	Jasmine Ruth
Elaine Ama	Ama Elaine	Elaine Jasmine
Jasmine Elaine	Ama Jasmine	Jasmine Ama

Combinations

Ruth Elaine	Ruth Ama	Ruth Jasmine
Elaine Ama	Elaine Jasmine	Ama Jasmine

There are 12 permutations, but only 6 combinations.

▼ Try This One 1

If you are choosing two business classes from three choices, list all the permutations and combinations.

It will be very valuable in our study of counting and probability to be able to decide if a given selection is a permutation or a combination.

EXAMPLE 2   Identifying Permutations and Combinations

Decide if each selection is a permutation or a combination.

(a) From a class of 25 students, a group of 5 is chosen to give a presentation.
(b) A starting pitcher and catcher are picked from a 12-person intramural softball team.

SOLUTION

(a) This is a combination because there are no distinct roles for the 5 group members, so order is not important.
(b) This is a permutation because each selected person has a distinct position, so order matters.

▼ Try This One 2

☑ 1. Distinguish between combinations and permutations.

Decide if each selection is a permutation or a combination.

(a) A 5-digit passcode is chosen from the numbers 0 through 9.
(b) A gardener picks 4 vegetable plants for his garden from 10 choices.

Recall that the number of combinations in Example 1 was half as great as the number of permutations. This is because once two people are selected, there are two ways to arrange them. So the number of combinations of n objects chosen r at a time should be the number of permutations divided by the number of arrangements of r objects. But we know that is $r!$. This gives us a formula for combinations.

Math Note

Notice that the combination formula is the permutation formula from Section 11-1 with an extra factor of $r!$ in the denominator.

The Combination Rule

The number of combinations of n objects taken r at a time is denoted by $_nC_r$, and is given by the formula

$$_nC_r = \frac{n!}{(n-r)!\,r!}$$

EXAMPLE 3   Using the Combination Rule

How many combinations of four objects are there taken two at a time?

SOLUTION

Since this is a combination problem, the answer is

$$_4C_2 = \frac{4!}{(4-2)!\,2!} = \frac{4!}{2!\,2!} = \frac{4 \cdot 3 \cdot 2!}{2 \cdot 1 \cdot 2!} = 6$$

This matches our result from Example 1.

Calculator Guide

Most graphing calculators have the combination formula built in. To find $_4C_2$ on a standard graphing calculator:

4 MATH, then use right arrow to select PRB, and press 3 to select $_nC_r$, and finally 2 Enter.

▼ Try This One 3

How many combinations of eight objects are there taken five at a time?

EXAMPLE 4   An Application of Combinations

> ### Math Note
>
> Some people use the terminology "10 choose 3" to describe the combination $_{10}C_3$, and it is sometimes represented using the notation $\binom{10}{3}$.

While studying abroad one semester, Tran is required to visit 10 different cities. He plans to visit 3 of the 10 over a long weekend. How many different ways can he choose the 3 to visit? Assume that distance is not a factor.

SOLUTION

The problem doesn't say anything about the order in which they'll be visited, so this is a combination problem.

$$_{10}C_3 = \frac{10!}{(10-3)!3!} = \frac{10!}{7!3!} = 120$$

☑ 2. Find the number of combinations of *n* objects taken *r* at a time.

▼ Try This One 4

An instructor posts a list of eight group projects to her website. Every group is required to do four projects at some point during the semester. How many different ways can a group choose the four projects they want to do?

In some cases, the combination rule is used in conjunction with the fundamental counting principle. Examples 5 and 6 illustrate some specific situations.

EXAMPLE 5   Choosing a Committee

At one school, the student government consists of seven women and five men. How many different committees can be chosen with three women and two men?

SOLUTION

First, we will choose three women from the seven candidates. This can be done in $_7C_3 = 35$ ways. Then we will choose two men from the five candidates in $_5C_2 = 10$ ways. Using the fundamental counting principle, there are $35 \cdot 10 = 350$ possible committees.

▼ Try This One 5

On an exam, a student must select 2 essay questions from 6 essay questions and 10 multiple choice questions from 20 multiple choice questions to answer. How many different ways can the student select questions to answer?

EXAMPLE 6   Designing a Calendar

To raise money for a charity event, a sorority plans to sell a calendar featuring tasteful pictures of some of the more attractive professors on campus. They will need to choose six models from a pool of finalists that includes nine women and six men. How many possible choices are there if they want to feature at least four women?

SOLUTION

Since we need to include at least four women, there are three possible compositions: four women and two men, five women and one man, or six women and no men.

Four women and two men:

$$_9C_4 \cdot {}_6C_2 = \frac{9!}{(9-4)!\,4!} \cdot \frac{6!}{(6-2)!\,2!} = 126 \cdot 15 = 1{,}890$$

Five women and one man:

$$_9C_5 \cdot {}_6C_1 = \frac{9!}{(9-5)!\,5!} \cdot \frac{6!}{(6-1)!\,1!} = 126 \cdot 6 = 756$$

Six women and no men:

$$_9C_6 \cdot {}_6C_0 = \frac{9!}{(9-6)!\,6!} \cdot \frac{6!}{(6-0)!\,0!} = 84 \cdot 1 = 84$$

The total number of possibilities is $1{,}890 + 756 + 84 = 2{,}730$.

▼ **Try This One 6**

A four-person crew for the international space station is to be chosen from a candidate pool of 10 Americans and 12 Russians. How many different crews are possible if there must be at least two Russians?

☑ 3. Use the combination rule in conjunction with the fundamental counting principle.

Table 11-1 summarizes all of the counting rules from sections 11-1 and 11-2. It's important to know the formulas, but it's far more important to understand the situations that each formula is needed for.

TABLE 11-1   **Summary of Counting Rules**

Rule	Definition	Formula
Fundamental counting principle	The number of ways a sequence of n events can occur if the first event can occur in k_1 ways, the second event can occur in k_2 ways, etc. (Events are unaffected by the others.)	$k_1 \cdot k_2 \cdot k_3 \cdots k_n$
Permutation rule	The number of permutations of n objects taking r objects at a time. (Order is important.)	$\dfrac{n!}{(n-r)!}$
Permutation rule for duplicate objects	The number of permutations in which k_1 objects are alike, k_2 objects are alike, etc.	$\dfrac{n!}{k_1!\,k_2!,\,\cdots,\,k_p!}$
Combination rule	The number of combinations of r objects taken from n objects. (Order is not important.)	$\dfrac{n!}{(n-r)!\,r!}$

Answers to Try This One

1 Call the classes A, B, and C:

Permutations
A B   B A   A C
C A   B C   C B

Combinations
A B   A C   B C

2 (a) Permutation

(b) Combination

3 56

4 70

5 2,771,340

6 5,665

EXERCISE SET 11-2

Writing Exercises

1. What is meant by the term combination?
2. What is the difference between a permutation and a combination?
3. Describe a real-life situation in which it would be appropriate to use combinations to count possibilities.

4. Describe a situation related to the one in Exercise 3 in which it would be appropriate to use permutations to count possibilities.

Computational Exercises

For Exercises 5–14, evaluate each expression.

5. $_5C_2$
6. $_8C_3$
7. $_7C_4$

8. $_6C_2$
9. $_6C_4$
10. $_3C_0$

11. $_3C_3$
12. $_9C_7$

13. $_{12}C_2$
14. $_4C_3$

For Exercises 15–20, find both the number of combinations and the number of permutations for the given number of objects.

15. 8 objects taken 5 at a time
16. 5 objects taken 3 at a time
17. 6 objects taken 2 at a time

18. 10 objects taken 6 at a time
19. 9 objects taken 9 at a time
20. 12 objects taken 1 at a time

For Exercises 21–28, decide whether the selection described is a combination or a permutation.

21. Ten fans at a concert are chosen to go backstage after the show.
22. From a list of 20 dishes he knows how to cook, Maurice chooses different dishes for breakfast, lunch, and dinner on his girlfriend's birthday.
23. A state elects a governor and lieutenant governor from a pool of eight candidates.
24. A state elects two senators from a pool of 12 candidates.

25. Lupe chooses an eight-letter password from the letters of the alphabet.
26. Of the six optional community service projects in a service learning course, Haylee picks three of them.
27. When looking for a new car, you read about ten different models and choose four that you would like to test drive.
28. Mark looks over the novels on his bookshelf and lists his five favorites ranked 1 through 5.

Real-World Applications

29. How many different ways can five cards be selected from a standard deck of 52 cards?
30. How many ways are there to select three math help websites from a list that contains six different websites?
31. How many ways can a student select five questions from an exam containing nine questions? How many ways are there if he must answer the first question and the last question?
32. How many ways can four finalists for a job be selected from ten interviewees?
33. If a person can select three presents from 10 presents under a Christmas tree, how many different combinations are there?
34. How many different possible tests can be made from a test bank of 20 questions if the test consists of 5 questions? (Ignore the order of questions.)

35. The general manager of a fast-food restaurant chain must select 6 restaurants from 11 for a promotional program. How many different possible ways can this selection be done?
36. How many ways can 3 cars and 4 trucks be selected from 8 cars and 11 trucks to be tested for a safety inspection?
37. During the tryouts for the school jazz band, there were four trumpet players, twelve guitar players, and seven saxophonists. How many ways can the jazz band be chosen so there are two trumpet players, five guitarists, and three saxophonists?
38. There are seven men and five women in line at a Salsa dance club. The bouncer can only admit two more men and two more women. How many ways can he choose from those in line? How many ways

can he choose if instead he is told he can admit four people and at least two must be women?

39. Coca-Cola comes in two low-calorie varieties: Diet Coke and Coke Zero. If a promoter has 10 cans of each, how many ways can she select 3 cans of each for a taste test at the local mall?

40. At the movies, Shana wants to get snacks for her friends. How many ways can she select three types of candy and two types of soda from the eight types of candy and five types of soda available?

41. Steve wants to download new music into his iPod from iTunes. How many ways can Steve select two rock songs, three alternative songs, and three rap songs from a list of eight rock songs, six alternative songs, and ten rap songs?

42. How many ways can 2 men and 2 women be selected for a debate tournament if there are 10 male finalists and 12 female finalists?

43. The state narcotics bureau must form a 5-member investigative team. If it has 25 agents to choose from, how many different possible teams can be formed?

44. How many different ways can a computer programmer select 3 jobs from a possible 15?

45. The Environmental Protection Agency must investigate nine nuclear reactors for complaints of radioactive pollution. How many different ways can a representative select five of these to investigate this week?

46. How many ways can a person select 8 DVDs from 10 DVDs?

47. How many ways can 20 students be chosen for the express line at registration if there are 30 students to choose from?

48. An advertising manager decides to have an ad campaign in which eight special items will be hidden at various locations in a shopping mall. If he has 17 locations to pick from, how many different possible combinations can he choose?

Section 11-3 Basic Concepts of Probability

LEARNING OBJECTIVES

- ☐ 1. Compute classical probabilities.
- ☐ 2. Compute empirical probabilities.

Walking into a casino without knowing anything about probability is kind of like going to a stick fight without a stick—you're likely to take a beating. Casinos aren't in the business of losing money, and the games are designed so that most people lose more than they win. But an understanding of what is likely to happen in a given situation can give you an advantage over other players, giving you a better chance of walking out the door with some cash in your pockets.

The study of probability originated in an effort to understand games of chance, like those that use coins, dice, and playing cards. Generally speaking, probability is simply a number that describes how likely an event is to occur. We will use games of chance to illustrate the ideas, but will eventually see that probability has many applications beyond simple games. In this section, we'll examine the basic concepts involved in studying probability.

Sample Spaces

Processes such as flipping a coin, rolling a die, or drawing a card from a deck are called *probability experiments*.

> A **probability experiment** is a process that leads to well-defined results called outcomes. An **outcome** is the result of a single trial of a probability experiment.

Some examples of a trial are flipping a coin once, rolling a single die, and drawing one card from a deck. When a coin is tossed, there are two possible outcomes: heads or tails. When rolling a single die, there are six possible outcomes: 1, 2, 3, 4, 5, or 6.

In a probability experiment, we can predict what outcomes are possible, but we cannot predict with certainty which one will occur. We say that the outcomes occur at random. In any experiment, the set of all possible outcomes is called the *sample space*.

A **sample space** is the set of all possible outcomes of a probability experiment.

Some sample spaces for various probability experiments are shown here.

Experiment	Sample Space
Toss one coin	{head, tail}
Roll a die	{1, 2, 3, 4, 5, 6}
Answer a true-false question	{true, false}
Toss two coins	{head/head, tail/tail, head/tail, tail/head}

It is important to realize that when two coins are tossed, there are *four* possible outcomes. Consider tossing a quarter and a dime at the same time. Both coins could fall heads up. Both coins could fall tails up. The quarter could fall heads up and the dime could fall tails up and, finally, the quarter could fall tails up and the dime could fall heads up. The situation is the same even if the coins are indistinguishable.

In finding probabilities, it is sometimes necessary to consider several outcomes of a probability experiment. For example, when a die is rolled, we may want to consider obtaining an odd number, i.e., 1, 3, or 5. Getting an odd number when rolling a die is an example of an event.

Experiment: draw a card. Sample space: 52 cards. Event: drawing an ace.

An **event** is any subset of the sample space of a probability experiment.

Classical Probability

Now we're ready to specifically define what is meant by probability. The first type we will study is called *classical probability,* because it was the first type of probability to be studied in the 17th and 18th centuries. In classical probability, we study all of the possible outcomes in a sample space and determine the probability, or likelihood, of an event occurring without actually performing experiments.

There is one key assumption we make in classical probability: that every outcome in a sample space is equally likely. For example, when a single die is rolled, we assume that each number is equally likely to come up. When a card is chosen from a deck of 52 cards, we assume that each card has the same probability of being drawn.

Math Note

Because classical probabilities are based on theory, not experiments, they are also called theoretical probabilities.

Formula for Classical Probability

Let E be an event that is a subset of the sample space S. We will write $n(E)$ to represent the number of outcomes in E, and $n(S)$ to represent the number of outcomes in S. The probability of the event E is defined to be

$$P(E) = \frac{n(E)}{n(S)} = \frac{\text{Number of outcomes in } E}{\text{Number of outcomes in } S}$$

In Example 1, we'll compute some simple probabilities using the formula above.

EXAMPLE 1   Computing Classical Probabilities

A single die is rolled. Find the probability of getting

(a) A 2.
(b) A number less than 5.
(c) An odd number.

SOLUTION

In this case, since the sample space is 1, 2, 3, 4, 5, and 6, there are six outcomes: $n(S) = 6$.

A die roll has six outcomes. If E = roll a 2, then $P(E) = \frac{1}{6}$. If E = roll an even number, then $P(E) = \frac{3}{6} = \frac{1}{2}$.

(a) There is one possible outcome that gives a 2, so $P(2) = \frac{1}{6}$.
(b) There are four possible outcomes for the event of getting a number less than 5—1, 2, 3, or 4; so $n(E) = 4$, and

$$P(\text{a number less than } 5) = \frac{n(E)}{n(S)} = \frac{4}{6} = \frac{2}{3}$$

(c) There are three possible outcomes for the event of getting an odd number: 1, 3, or 5; so $n(E) = 3$, and

$$P(\text{odd number}) = \frac{n(E)}{n(S)} = \frac{3}{6} = \frac{1}{2}$$

▼ Try This One 1

Each number from one to twelve is written on a card and placed in a box. If a card is selected at random, find the probability that the number on the card is

(a) A 7.
(b) An odd number.
(c) A number less than four.
(d) A number greater than seven.

EXAMPLE 2   Computing Classical Probabilities

Two coins are tossed. Find the probability of getting

(a) Two heads.
(b) At least one head.
(c) At most one head.

SOLUTION

The sample space is {HH, HT, TH, TT}; therefore, $n(S) = 4$.

(a) There is only one way to get two heads: HH. So

$$P(\text{two heads}) = \frac{n(E)}{n(S)} = \frac{1}{4}$$

(b) "At least one head" means one or more heads; i.e., one head or two heads. There are three ways to get at least one head: HT, TH, and HH. So $n(E) = 3$, and

$$P(\text{at least one head}) = \frac{n(E)}{n(S)} = \frac{3}{4}$$

(c) "At most one head" means no heads or one head: TT, TH, HT. So $n(E) = 3$, and

$$P(\text{at most one head}) = \frac{n(E)}{n(S)} = \frac{3}{4}$$

☑ 1. Compute classical probabilities.

▼ Try This One 2

Suppose that in a certain game, it is equally likely that you will win, lose, or tie. Find the probability of

(a) Losing twice in a row.
(b) Winning at least once in two tries.
(c) Having the same outcome twice in a row.

At this point, we can make a series of simple but important observations about probabilities. Both $n(E)$ and $n(S)$ have to be zero or positive, so *probability is never negative*. Second, since S represents all possible outcomes, and E is a subset of S, $n(E)$ is always less than or equal to $n(S)$. This means that *probability is never greater than 1*. Probabilities are usually expressed as fractions or decimals between (and including) zero and one. But sometimes we will express probabilities in percent form when it seems appropriate for a given situation.

When an event cannot possibly occur, the probability is zero, and *when an event is certain to occur, the probability is one.* For example, the probability of getting 8 when rolling a single die is zero because none of the outcomes in the sample space result in 8. The probability of getting either heads or tails when flipping a single coin is 1 because that particular event is satisfied by every outcome in the sample space.

A 10% chance of rain is not the same as no chance of rain. You would expect it to rain on roughly 1 in 10 days when a 10% chance of rain was forecast.

The sum of the probabilities of all the outcomes in the sample space will always be one. For example, when a die is rolled, each of the six outcomes has a probability of $\frac{1}{6}$, and the sum of the probabilities of the six outcomes will be one.

When the probability of an event is close to zero, the event is very unlikely to occur. When the probability of an event is close to $\frac{1}{2}$ or 0.5, the event has approximately a 50% chance of occurring. When the probability of an event is near one, the event is almost certain to occur. See Figure 11-1.

In addition to finding the probability that an event will occur, it is sometimes useful to find the probability that the event will *not* occur. For example, if a die is rolled, the probability that a 4 will not occur, symbolized by $P(4')$, is $\frac{5}{6}$ since there are five ways that a 4 will not occur; i.e., 1, 2, 3, 5, 6. The solution can also be found by finding the

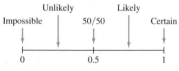

Figure 11-1

probability of getting a 4 and subtracting it from one; the sum of the probabilities of all outcomes in the sample space is one, so

$$P(4') = 1 - P(4) = 1 - \frac{1}{6} = \frac{5}{6}$$

The rule can be generalized as follows

> For any event, E, $P(E') = 1 - P(E)$, where E' is the event "E does not occur."

Probability and Sets

The theory of probability is related to the theory of sets discussed in Chapter 2. For a given probability experiment, the sample space can be considered the universal set, and an event E can be considered as a subset of the universal set.

For example, when rolling a die, the sample space is $\{1, 2, 3, 4, 5, 6\}$; so the universal set is $U = \{1, 2, 3, 4, 5, 6\}$. Let the event E be getting an odd number; i.e., 1, 3, or 5. In sets, $E = \{1, 3, 5\}$. A Venn diagram can now be drawn illustrating this example. See Figure 11-2.

Notice that set E contains 1, 3, and 5 while the numbers 2, 4, and 6 are in the universal set but not in E. So $E' = \{2, 4, 6\}$. Now recall from set theory that $E \cup E' = U$. As stated previously, the sum of the probabilities of the outcomes in the sample space is one, so $P(U) = 1$. E' represents the elements in U but not in E, so $P(E) + P(E') = 1$. Subtracting $P(E)$ from both sides, we get $P(E') = 1 - P(E)$. Additional relationships between probability theory and set theory will be shown in other sections of this chapter.

U

1   4
   3
      5   6
   E
2

$E \cup E' = U$
$P(E) + P(E') = 1$

Figure 11-2

Empirical Probability

The second type of probability we will study is computed using experimental data, rather than counting equally likely outcomes. For example, suppose 100 games into the season, your favorite baseball team has won 60 games and lost 40. You might reasonably guess that since they've won 60 of their 100 games so far, the probability of them winning any given game is about 60/100, or 0.6. This type of probability is called **empirical probability**, and is based on *observed frequencies*—that is, the number of times a particular event has occurred out of a certain number of trials. In this case, the observed frequency of wins is 60, the observed frequency of losses is 40, and the total number of trials is 60 + 40 = 100.

Sidelight YOU BET YOUR LIFE!

You probably think of gambling as betting money at a casino or on a sporting event, but people gamble all the time in many ways. In fact, people bet their lives every day by engaging in unhealthy activities like smoking, using drugs, eating a high-fat diet, and even driving too fast. Maybe people don't care about the risks involved in these activities because they don't understand the concept of probability. On the other hand, people tend to fear things that are far less likely to harm them, like flying, because the occasional negative consequence is sensationalized in the press.

In his book *Probabilities in Everyday Life* (Ivy Books, 1986), author John D. McGrevey states:

When people have been asked to estimate the frequency of death from various causes, the most overestimated causes are those involving pregnancy, tornados, floods, fire, and homicide. The most underestimated categories include death from diseases such as diabetes,

stroke, tuberculosis, asthma, and stomach cancer (although cancer in general is overestimated).

Which do you think is safer: flying across the United States on a commercial airline, or driving cross country? According to our friend McGrevey, the probability of being killed on any given airline flight is about 1/1,000,000, while the probability of being killed on a transcontinental automobile trip is just 1/8,000. That means that driving across the country is 125 times more dangerous than flying!

Math Note

The total number of trials is the sum of all observed frequencies.

Formula for Empirical Probability

$$P(E) = \frac{\text{Observed frequency of the specific event }(f)}{\text{Total number of trials }(n)} = \frac{f}{n}$$

In this coin toss, the empirical probability of heads was $\frac{6}{10}$, or $\frac{3}{5}$. With more tosses, you would expect $P(\text{heads})$ to approach $\frac{1}{2}$.

The information in the baseball problem can be written in the form of a *frequency distribution* that consists of classes and frequencies for the classes, as shown below:

Result (Class)	Observed Frequency
Win	60
Lose	40
Total	100

This technique is often helpful in working out empirical probabilities.

EXAMPLE 3   Computing an Empirical Probability

In a sample of 50 people, 21 had type O blood, 22 had type A blood, 5 had type B blood, and 2 had type AB blood. Set up a frequency distribution and find these probabilities for a person selected at random from the sample.

(a) The person has type O blood.
(b) The person has type A or type B blood.
(c) The person has neither type A nor type O blood.
(d) The person does not have type AB blood.

Source: Based on American Red Cross figures

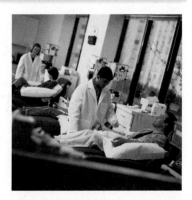

Type O negative blood is the least likely to react badly with a patient's blood. If it is not possible to test the patient's blood before a transfusion, then O negative is used.

SOLUTION

Type (class)	Observed Frequency
A	22
B	5
AB	2
O	21
Total	50

Math Note

The solution to part c could also be done as P(neither A nor O) $= 1 - P$(A or O):

$$1 - \left(\frac{22}{50} + \frac{21}{50}\right)$$

$$= 1 - \frac{43}{50} = \frac{7}{50}.$$

☑ 2. Compute empirical
   probabilities.

(a) $P(\text{O}) = \frac{f}{n} = \frac{21}{50}$

(b) The frequency of A or B is $22 + 5 = 27$. $P(\text{A or B}) = \frac{27}{50}$

(c) Neither A nor O means either B or AB; the frequency of either B or AB is $5 + 2 = 7$. $P(\text{neither A nor O}) = \frac{7}{50}$

(d) The probability of not AB is found by subtracting the probability of AB from 1.

$$P(\text{not AB}) = 1 - P(\text{AB}) = 1 - \frac{2}{50} = \frac{48}{50} = \frac{24}{25}$$

▼ Try This One 3

A bag of Hershey's Assorted Miniatures contains 18 Hershey Milk Chocolate bars, 9 Mr. Goodbars, 9 Krackel bars, and 8 Hershey's Special Dark Chocolate bars. If a bar is selected at random from the bag, find the probability that it is

(a) A Mr. Goodbar.
(b) A Krackel or a Special Dark Chocolate bar.
(c) Not a Milk Chocolate bar.

It is important to understand the relationship between classical probability and empirical probability in certain situations. In classical probability, the probability of rolling a 3 when a die is thrown is found by looking at the sample space, and is $\frac{1}{6}$. To find the probability of getting a 3 when a die is thrown using empirical probability, you would actually toss a die a specific number of times and count the number of times a 3 was obtained; then divide that number by the number of times the die was rolled. For example, suppose a die was rolled 60 times, and a 3 occurred 12 times. Then the empirical probability of getting a 3 would be $\frac{12}{60} = \frac{1}{5}$. Most of the time, the probability obtained from empirical methods will differ from that obtained using classical probability. The question is, then, "How many times should I roll the die when using empirical probability?" There is no specific answer except to say that the more times the die is tossed, the closer the results obtained from empirical probability will be to those of classical probability.

In summary, then, classical probability uses sample spaces and assumes the outcomes are equally likely. Empirical probability uses observed frequencies and the total of the number of frequencies.

Sidelight PROBABILITY AND YOUR FEARS

All of us at one time or another have thought about dying. Some people have fears of dying in a plane crash or dying from a heart attack. In the sidelight on page 591, it was explained that it is safer to fly across the United States than to drive. Statisticians who work for insurance companies (called actuaries) also calculate probabilities for dying from other causes. For example, based on deaths in the United States, the risks of dying from various other causes are shown.

Motor vehicle accident	1 in 7,000
Shot by a gun	1 in 10,000
Accident while walking across the street	1 in 60,000
Lightning strike	1 in 3 million
Shark attack	1 in 100 million

The death risk for various diseases is much higher as shown.

Heart attack	1 in 400
Cancer	1 in 600
Stroke	1 in 2,000

As you can see, the chances of dying from diseases are much higher than dying from accidents.

Answers to Try This One

1   (a) 1/12   (b) 1/2   (c) 1/4   (d) 5/12   **3**   (a) 9/44   (b) 17/44   (c) 13/22

2   (a) 1/9   (b) 5/9   (c) 1/3

EXERCISE SET 11-3

Writing Exercises

1. Define in your own words what the probability of an event means.
2. What is a sample space?
3. What is the difference between an outcome and an event?
4. What is the range of numbers that can represent probabilities? Why?
5. What is the probability of an event that can't occur? Explain why.
6. What is the probability of an event that is certain to occur? Explain why.
7. Explain the difference between classical and empirical probability.
8. Describe how to find the empirical probability of an event after conducting an experiment.

Computational Exercises

For Exercises 9–16, decide whether or not the given number could represent a probability.

9. $\frac{3}{4}$

10. 0.75

11. $-\frac{1}{2}$

12. 0

13. $\frac{41}{40}$

14. $\frac{40}{41}$

15. 72%

16. 111%

For Exercises 17–20, decide whether the probability described is classical or empirical.

17. At one school, 59% of the students having lunch in the union are women, so the probability of a randomly selected student from the campus phone directory being male is 0.41.

18. A pool table has 15 balls labeled 1 through 15. The probability of a ball made on the break having a number less than 6 is $\frac{1}{3}$.

19. The probability of a randomly selected state beginning with the letter A is $\frac{2}{25}$.

20. While at a casino, Catalina won 10 of the first 15 hands of blackjack she played, so she has a $\frac{2}{3}$ chance of winning the next hand.

Real-World Applications

21. If a die is rolled one time, find the probability of
    (a) Getting a 4.
    (b) Getting an even number.
    (c) Getting a number greater than 4.
    (d) Getting a number less than 7.
    (e) Getting a number greater than 0.
    (f) Getting a number greater than 3 or an odd number.
    (g) Getting a number greater than 3 and an odd number.

22. A couple has two children. Find the probability that
    (a) Both children are girls.
    (b) At least one child is a girl.
    (c) Both children are of the same gender.

23. On the *Price Is Right* game show, a contestant spins a wheel with numbers 1 through 7, with equally sized regions for each of these numbers. If the contestant spins once, what is the probability that the number is
    (a) A 6.
    (b) An even number.
    (c) A number greater than 4.
    (d) A number less than 8.
    (e) A number greater than 7.

24. A list contains the names of five anthropology students, two sociology students, and three psychology students. If one name is selected at random to assist in the professor's new study, find the probability that the chosen student is

    (a) An anthropology student.
    (b) A psychology student.
    (c) An anthropology student or a sociology student.
    (d) Not a psychology student.
    (e) Not an anthropology student.

25. On the shelf at the gaming store, there are five Sony Playstations and four Nintendo Wii consoles left. If one gaming system is selected at random, find the probability that the system is a Wii console.

26. If there are only 50 lottery tickets for the Big Game, one of which is a winning ticket, and you buy 7 of those tickets at random, what is the probability that you will win the super jackpot?

27. In a math class of seven women and nine men, if one person is selected at random to come to the board to show the solution to a problem, what is the probability that the student is a man?

28. A recent survey reported that 67% of Americans approve of human embryonic stem cell research. If an American is selected at random, find the probability that he or she will disagree or have no opinion on the issue.

29. The Federal Bureau of Investigation reported that in 2007, there were 7,624 incidents of hate crimes that had a bias motivation based on race, religion, sexual orientation, nationality, or disability. Of these incidents, 6,965 were committed by a "known offender," where one or more attributes is known about the offender. If one incident is selected at random, find the probability that the incident was committed by a known offender.

30. Thirty-nine of 50 states are currently under court order to alleviate overcrowding and poor conditions in one or more of their prisons. If a state is selected at random, find the probability that it is currently under such a court order.

    Source: *Harper's Index*

31. In a survey, 16% of male college students said they lied to get a woman to go out on a date with them. If a male college student is chosen at random, find the probability that he does not lie to get a date with a woman.

32. In the lost and found box at the campus security office, there were nine BlackBerry SmartPhones and seven Apple iPhones. If a phone is selected at random, find the probability that it is

    (a) A BlackBerry SmartPhone.
    (b) An Apple iPhone.

Exercises 33–35 refer to a standard deck of playing cards. If you are unfamiliar with playing cards, see the description on page 600.

33. During a game of Texas Hold'em poker, each of four players is dealt two cards, then the dealer "burns" a card (puts it face down), then deals the "flop" (three cards face up). He then burns another card, then flips over the "turn" card (one card face up). One player needs a spade on the "turn" to make a flush. No one else has a spade, and he has two in his hand and there are two on the flop. If neither of the burn cards are spades, what's the probability the turn card will be a spade?

34. During a game of Gin Rummy, Sven needs the eight of diamonds to make a straight in his hand. He and the other player have been dealt 10 cards each, the other player does not have the card he wants, and all other cards are in the deck. What is the probability that the next card picked from the deck is the eight of diamonds?

35. During a game of Blackjack, three players are dealt two cards each, and the dealer has two cards. No one has a card that is worth 10 or 11, which would be a 10, a face card, or an ace. What is the probability that the next player dealt a card would get a card worth 10 or 11?

36. A survey on campus revealed that 68% of the students felt that a new attendance policy was unfair. If a student is randomly asked to give an opinion of the new attendance policy, find the probability that the student will either think it's fair or have no opinion.

37. A survey of 25 students in line during registration revealed that 3 were math majors, 10 were history majors, 2 were psychology majors, 7 were biology majors, and the rest were undecided. If the clerk calls a name from the same line of students at random, find the probability the student would be either a history or biology major.

38. On a bookshelf, there are five Tess Gerritsen novels, three Stephen King novels, and seven John Grisham novels. If Sheri selects one while turned away to talk to her friend, find the probability she chose a Tess Gerritsen novel.

39. In a class of 35 students, 22 passed the first exam. If a student is chosen at random from the class, find the probability he failed the first exam.

40. On her way out the door to class, Li dumped five energy bars and three candy bars of the same size into her bag. During class, she got hungry, and she grabbed a bar without looking. It was an energy bar. Her friend then asked for something to eat, and she grabbed another bar without looking. Find the probability that she grabbed a candy bar.

41. On a 10-question true/false test, there are seven false questions and the rest are true. If Marcus answered the first eight questions correctly, and five of them were false, find the probability that when he answers true for the next question, his answer will be correct.

42. According to www.namestatistics.com, the five most popular male names and their percentages are as follows:

Name	Percentage
James	3.318%
John	3.271%
Robert	3.143%
Michael	2.629%
William	2.451%

   (a) If Mary meets a man at a party, find the probability his name is one of the most popular five male names in the country.

   (b) If Jane goes to the grocery store and the clerk is a man, find the probability his name would be John or Robert.

   (c) If Bob and Sue rent a new apartment and the landlord is a man, find the probability his name would be in the top three most popular male names.

43. Many people blame Wall Street greed for causing the economic crisis that gripped the nation in late 2008. In February 2009, the Harris Poll surveyed 1,010 Americans, using the statement that people on Wall Street are "as honest and moral as other people." The number giving each response is summarized in the table below:

   Agree   707
   Disagree   263
   Not sure   40

   Based on these results, if you ask a randomly selected American this question,

   (a) What is the probability that a randomly selected American thinks that people on Wall Street are less honest than other people?

   (b) What is the probability that he or she either agrees or disagrees?

44. In December 2008, 500 men and 500 women were surveyed by Omnitel about their opinion on whether federal government bailout money should be used to help homeowners in default. The number giving each response is shown below.

Response	Men	Women
Yes	195	235
No	290	220
Not sure	15	45

   (a) If a person who participated in the survey is selected at random, what is the probability that he or she answered no?

   (b) What is the probability that the person is a man who answered either yes or no?

   (c) Based on the data from the survey, if you had stopped a random woman on the street in December 2008 and asked her opinion, what is the probability that she would have said that bailout money should not be used to help homeowners in default?

45. In a survey conducted by Bank of America, college graduates were asked how much money they typically donate to their alma mater each year. The responses are summarized below:

   Nothing   58%
   Something, but less than $500   32%
   $500 or more   10%

   Based on these results:

   (a) What is the probability that a randomly selected college graduate gives at least something in a typical year?

   (b) What is the probability that a randomly selected college graduate gives less than $500 in a typical year?

46. Jockey International surveyed men to find out how old their oldest pair of underwear is. The results are summarized below:

   Less than 1 year   17%
   1–4 years   59%
   5–9 years   15%
   10–19 years   7%
   20 or more years   2%

   Based on these results:

   (a) What is the probability that a randomly selected man has a pair of underwear that is older then 4 years? 9 years?

   (b) What is the probability that a randomly selected man has no pair of underwear more than a year old?

   (c) What is the probability that a randomly selected man has no underwear more than 9 years old?

47. A student passed a fountain every day on the way to class and tossed in his good luck penny with a wish. He then retrieved it because he couldn't bear to part with the penny. Out of 100 consecutive tosses of this same penny, he noticed the penny landed on tails 73 times. Can he conclude his good luck penny is unbalanced?

48. A professor stated that with a certain method of teaching statistics, a student has about a 50% chance of passing her class. She justified this by saying, "Either a student will pass or he won't pass." Comment on this statement.

49. The students at a university are classified by a 0 for freshman, a 1 for sophomores, a 2 for juniors, a 3 for seniors, and a 4 for graduate students. There are two extra scholarships to assign, so an administrator randomly selects from a box with only the numbers 0, 1, 2, 3, and 4 to choose the class of the first recipient. She then puts the number back into the box and randomly selects a number for the class of the second recipient. Find the sample space, and then find the probability of the following events:

   (a) An odd number is chosen first and an even number is chosen second. (*Note:* 0 is considered an even number.)

(b) The sum of the two numbers selected is greater than 4.

(c) For both selections, an even number is drawn.

(d) The sum of the two numbers selected is odd.

(e) The same number is drawn twice.

50. Only six students attended a school charity event, so each of their names was placed into three boxes for the three raffles for the event. What is the probability that the same student's name will be drawn from each box?

Section 11-4 Tree Diagrams, Tables, and Sample Spaces

LEARNING OBJECTIVES

☐ 1. Use tree diagrams to find sample spaces and compute probabilities.

☐ 2. Use tables to find sample spaces and compute probabilities.

Math Note

Recall that we used tree diagrams to illustrate the fundamental counting principle back in Section 11-1.

For centuries, people have tried a wide variety of techniques, some of them pretty bizarre, to try and influence the gender of their children. The truth is, without the aid of cutting-edge science, you don't get to choose. But that doesn't stop many young couples from planning the type of family they hope to have. Suppose that one couple would like to have three children, but they definitely want to have at least one boy and one girl. What is the probability that they'll get their wish without having to go beyond three kids?

When working with classical probabilities, we know that we need to decide on the sample space for an event, and then find how many individual outcomes are in that event. When situations start to get complicated, it might not always be apparent how to do so. That's where tree diagrams and tables can help.

Tree Diagrams

A **tree diagram** consists of branches corresponding to the outcomes of two or more probability experiments that are done in sequence.

When constructing a tree diagram, use branches emanating from a single point to show the outcomes for the first experiment, and then show the outcomes for the second experiment using branches emanating from each branch that was used for the first experiment, etc.

In Example 1, we'll use a tree diagram to find the sample space for our hopeful young couple.

EXAMPLE 1   Using a Tree Diagram to Find a Sample Space

Use a tree diagram to find the sample space for the genders of three children in a family.

SOLUTION

Math Note

The genders of the children are usually listed in their birth order. For example, the outcome GGB means the firstborn was a girl, the second a girl, and the third a boy.

There are two possibilities for the first child, boy or girl, two for the second, boy or girl, and two for the third, boy or girl. So the tree diagram can be drawn as shown in Figure 11-3.

After a tree diagram is drawn, the outcomes can be found by tracing through all of the branches. In this case, the sample space would be {BBB, BBG, BGB, BGG, GBB, GBG, GGB, GGG}.

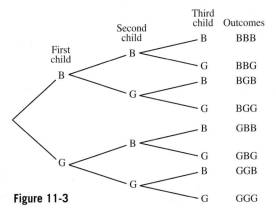

Figure 11-3

▼ Try This One 1

A soda machine dispenses both Coke and Pepsi products, in both 12-ounce cans and 20-ounce bottles. For each brand, it has a regular cola, diet cola, and lemon-lime drink. Use a tree diagram to find the sample space for all the drinks dispensed.

Once a tree diagram is drawn and the sample space is found, you can compute the probabilities for various events.

EXAMPLE 2   Computing a Probability

If a family has three children, find the probability that all three children are the same gender; that is, all boys or all girls. (Assume that all outcomes are equally likely.)

SOLUTION

The sample space shown in Example 1 has eight outcomes, and there are two possible ways to have three children of the same gender, BBB or GGG. So, the probability of the three children being of the same gender is $\frac{2}{8}$ or $\frac{1}{4}$.

▼ Try This One 2

Suppose the soda machine from Try This One 1 goes berserk and starts dispensing drinks randomly. If you want a diet cola, what is the probability that you'll get one?

EXAMPLE 3   Using a Tree Diagram to Compute Probabilities

A coin is tossed, and then a die is rolled. Use a tree diagram to find the probability of getting heads on the coin and an even number on the die.

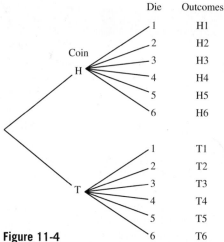

Figure 11-4

SOLUTION

First, we'll use a tree diagram to find the sample space. The coin will land on either heads or tails, and there are six outcomes for the die: 1, 2, 3, 4, 5, or 6. The tree diagram is shown in Figure 11-4.

The sample space is {H1, H2, H3, H4, H5, H6, T1, T2, T3, T4, T5, T6}.

The total number of outcomes for the experiment is 12. The number of ways to get a head on the coin and an even number on the die is 3: H2, H4, or H6. So, the probability of getting a head and an even number when a coin is tossed and a die is rolled is $\frac{3}{12}$, or $\frac{1}{4}$.

1. Use tree diagrams to find sample spaces and compute probabilities.

▼ Try This One 3

In order to collect information for a student survey, a researcher classifies students according to eye color (blue, brown, green), gender (male, female), and class rank (freshman, sophomore). A folder for each classification is then made up (e.g., freshman/female/green eyes). Find the sample space for the folders using a tree diagram. If a folder is selected at random, find the probability that

(a) It includes students with blue eyes.
(b) It includes students who are female.
(c) It includes students who are male freshmen.

In constructing tree diagrams, not all branches have to be the same length. For example, suppose two players, Alice and Diego, play chess, and the first one to win two games wins the tournament. The tree diagram would be like the one shown in Figure 11-5. For any game, A means that Alice wins, and D means that Diego wins.

Notice that if Alice wins the first two games, the tournament is over. So the first branch is shorter than the second one. But if Alice wins the first game and Diego wins the second game, they need to play a third game in order to decide who wins the tournament. Similar reasoning can be applied to the rest of the branches.

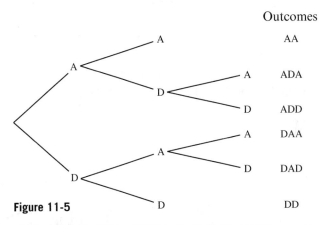

Figure 11-5

Outcomes:
AA
ADA
ADD
DAA
DAD
DD

Sidelight MATH AND THE DRAFT LOTTERY

Today there are many state lotteries that offer patrons a chance to win money. At one time, there was a national lottery not to win money but to see who would be drafted for military service. During the Vietnam War, men were drafted based on their age and their birthday. The oldest men were drafted first. Men born in the last months of the year could avoid the draft since they were younger in months and days than those born earlier in the year.

In 1970, the United States decided to change the system and draft men based on a lottery. The days of the year were numbered one through 366 (leap year), placed in a barrel, and mixed up. Then numbers corresponding to birth dates were selected one at a time and men were drafted on the basis of their draft number.

It was assumed that the drawing was random. However, mathematicians found that the drawing was not random since those born later in the year had a higher chance of being drafted than those born earlier in the year. It was concluded that the capsules containing the numbers were not thoroughly mixed and that the numbers placed in the barrel last were on the top of the pile. They were selected first.

> **CAUTION**
>
> When the branches of a tree diagram are not equal in length, the outcomes are not equally likely even if the probability of every individual trial is $\frac{1}{2}$. In the tournament example above, if each player is equally likely to win any given game, the outcomes AA and DD both have probability $\frac{1}{4}$, while the outcomes ADA, ADD, DAA, and DAD all have probability $\frac{1}{8}$.

Tables

Another way of determining a sample space is by making a **table.** Consider the sample space of selecting a card from a standard deck of 52 cards. (The cards are assumed to be shuffled to make sure that the selection occurs at random.) There are four suits—hearts, diamonds, spades, and clubs, and 13 cards of each suit consisting of the denominations ace (A), 2, 3, 4, 5, 6, 7, 8, 9, 10, and 3 picture or face cards—jack (J), queen (Q), and king (K). The sample space is shown in Figure 11-6.

	A	2	3	4	5	6	7	8	9	10	J	Q	K
♥	A♥	2♥	3♥	4♥	5♥	6♥	7♥	8♥	9♥	10♥	J♥	Q♥	K♥
♦	A♦	2♦	3♦	4♦	5♦	6♦	7♦	8♦	9♦	10♦	J♦	Q♦	K♦
♠	A♠	2♠	3♠	4♠	5♠	6♠	7♠	8♠	9♠	10♠	J♠	Q♠	K♠
♣	A♣	2♣	3♣	4♣	5♣	6♣	7♣	8♣	9♣	10♣	J♣	Q♣	K♣

Figure 11-6

EXAMPLE 4   Using a Table to Compute Probabilities

A card is drawn from an ordinary deck. Use the sample space shown in Figure 11-6 to find the probabilities of getting

(a) A jack.   (b) The 6 of clubs.   (c) A 3 or a diamond.

SOLUTION

(a) There are four jacks and 52 possible outcomes, so

$$P(\text{jack}) = \frac{4}{52} = \frac{1}{13}$$

(b) Since there is only one 6 of clubs, the probability of getting a 6 of clubs is

$$P(\text{6 of clubs}) = \frac{1}{52}$$

(c) There are four 3s and 13 diamonds, but the 3 of diamonds is counted twice in this listing. So, there are 16 possibilities of drawing a 3 or a diamond, and

$$P(\text{3 or diamond}) = \frac{16}{52} = \frac{4}{13}$$

▼ Try This One 4

A single card is drawn at random from a well-shuffled deck. Using the sample space shown in Figure 11-6, find the probability that the card is

(a) An ace.   (c) A club.   (e) A 6 and a spade.
(b) A face card.   (d) A 4 or a heart.

When two dice are rolled, how many outcomes are in the sample space? Assume for the purpose of illustration that one die is red and the other is blue. The sample space for the red die is {1, 2, 3, 4, 5, 6}, and the sample space for the blue die is also {1, 2, 3, 4, 5, 6}. Now if the outcomes for each die are combined, the sample space will consist of 36 outcomes, as shown in Figure 11-7. Note that the color indicates which die the number comes from.

The outcome (3, 6) means the 3 was obtained on the red die and a 6 was obtained on the blue die. The sum of the spots on the faces then would be 3 + 6 = 9.

Math Note

The sample space for rolling two dice is the same regardless of the color of the dice. Color helps distinguish between (2, 4) and (4, 2).

	Blue die					
	1	**2**	**3**	**4**	**5**	**6**
1	(1, 1)	(1, 2)	(1, 3)	(1, 4)	(1, 5)	(1, 6)
2	(2, 1)	(2, 2)	(2, 3)	(2, 4)	(2, 5)	(2, 6)
3	(3, 1)	(3, 2)	(3, 3)	(3, 4)	(3, 5)	(3, 6)
4	(4, 1)	(4, 2)	(4, 3)	(4, 4)	(4, 5)	(4, 6)
5	(5, 1)	(5, 2)	(5, 3)	(5, 4)	(5, 5)	(5, 6)
6	(6, 1)	(6, 2)	(6, 3)	(6, 4)	(6, 5)	(6, 6)

Red die (label on left side)

Figure 11-7

EXAMPLE 5   Using a Table to Compute Probabilities

When two dice are rolled, find the probability of getting

(a) A sum of 8.
(b) Doubles.
(c) A sum less than 5.

SOLUTION

Using the sample space shown in Figure 11-7, there are 36 possible outcomes.

(a) There are five ways to get a sum of 8: (2, 6), (3, 5), (4, 4), (5, 3), and (6, 2). So $n(E) = 5$, $n(S) = 36$, and

$$P(\text{sum of 8}) = \frac{n(E)}{n(S)} = \frac{5}{36}$$

(b) There are six ways to get doubles: (1, 1), (2, 2), (3, 3), (4, 4), (5, 5), and (6, 6). So $n(E) = 6$, $n(S) = 36$, and

$$P(\text{doubles}) = \frac{n(E)}{n(S)} = \frac{1}{6}$$

(c) A sum less than 5 means a sum of 4 or 3 or 2. The number of ways this can occur is 6, as shown.

Sum of 4: (1, 3), (2, 2), (3, 1)
Sum of 3: (1, 2), (2, 1)
Sum of 2: (1, 1)
$n(E) = 6$, $n(S) = 36$, and so

$$P(\text{sum less than 5}) = \frac{6}{36} = \frac{1}{6}$$

▼ Try This One 5

2. Use tables to find sample spaces and compute probabilities.

Two dice are rolled. Use the sample space shown in Figure 11-7 to find the probability of

(a) Getting a sum of 9.
(b) Getting a sum that is an even number.
(c) Getting a sum greater than 6.

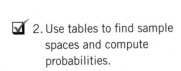

Answers to Try This One

1 Sample Space: {Coke, can, cola; Coke, can, diet cola; Coke, can, lemon-lime; Coke, bottle, cola; Coke, bottle, diet cola; Coke, bottle, lemon-lime; Pepsi, can, cola; Pepsi, can, diet cola; Pepsi, can, lemon-lime; Pepsi, bottle, cola; Pepsi, bottle, diet cola; Pepsi, bottle, lemon-lime}.

2 $\frac{1}{3}$

3 Sample space: {blue, male, freshman; blue, male, sophomore; blue, female, freshman; blue, female, sophomore; brown, male, freshman; brown, male, sophomore; brown, female, freshman; brown, female, sophomore; green, male, freshman; green, male, sophomore; green, female, freshman; green, female, sophomore}.

(a) $\frac{1}{3}$ (b) $\frac{1}{2}$ (c) $\frac{1}{4}$

4 (a) $\frac{1}{13}$ (c) $\frac{1}{4}$ (e) $\frac{1}{52}$
      (b) $\frac{3}{13}$ (d) $\frac{4}{13}$

5 (a) $\frac{1}{9}$ (b) $\frac{1}{2}$ (c) $\frac{7}{12}$

EXERCISE SET 11-4

Writing Exercises

1. Explain how to draw a tree diagram, and how tree diagrams help to find sample spaces.

2. Think of an example, other than the one provided in the section, where a tree diagram would have branches of different lengths.

Real-World Applications

3. There are three computers on a table that are either Dells or Gateways. Using a sample space similar to the one in Example 1, find the probability that

    (a) There will be exactly two Dells.
    (b) All three will be Gateways.
    (c) There will be at least one Dell.

4. There was a die and a quarter sitting on a table, and Klutzy Kramer knocked both off the table at the same time when he passed by. Using a sample space similar to Example 3, find the probability that as each landed on the floor,

    (a) There was a head on the coin and an odd number on the die.
    (b) There was a head on the coin and a prime number on the die.
    (c) There was a tail on the coin and a number less than 5 on the die.

5. After the incident in Exercise 4, the professor got smart and dropped the die and the quarter in a box to prevent Klutzy Kramer from knocking them onto the floor again. Using a sample space similar to

Example 3, find the probability that as each landed in the box,

    (a) There was a tail on the coin and a number greater than 1 on the die.
    (b) There was a head on the coin and an even number on the die.
    (c) There was a tail on the coin and a number divisible by 3 on the die.

6. Sara came across a new website that featured a "live" fortune-teller. She typed in three questions and found (shockingly) that the fortune-teller could only answer yes or no to her questions. Draw a tree diagram for all possible answers for her three questions. Find the probability that

    (a) All answers will be yes or all answers will be no.
    (b) The answers will alternate (i.e., Yes–No–Yes or No–Yes–No).
    (c) Exactly two answers will be yes.

7. After a late night studying, Ebony decides to grab a latte before class so she can stay awake through the

lecture. She has only a one-dollar bill, a five-dollar bill, and a ten-dollar bill in her wallet. She pulls one out and looks at it, but then she puts it back. Distracted by a flyer for a new campus organization, she randomly hands a bill from her wallet to the clerk. Draw a tree diagram to determine the sample space and find the probability that

(a) Both bills have the same value.
(b) The second bill is larger than the first bill.
(c) The value of each of the two bills is even.
(d) The value of exactly one of the bills is odd.
(e) The sum of the values of both bills is less than $10.

8. When Frank threw his jeans into the washer after getting them muddy during an impromptu mud-wrestling match at the fraternity house, four coins fell out onto the floor. Find the probability that

(a) Exactly three coins land heads up.
(b) All coins land tails up.
(c) Two or more coins land heads up.
(d) No more than two coins land tails up.
(e) At least one coin lands tails up.

9. Mark and Raul play three rounds of Mortal Kombat. They are equal in ability. Draw a tree diagram to determine the sample space and find the probability that

(a) Either Mark or Raul win all three games.
(b) Either Mark or Raul win two out of three games.
(c) Mark wins only two games in a row.
(d) Raul wins the first game, loses the second game, and wins the third game.

10. Sofia is in line at the Simpsons ride at Universal Studios and notices a box containing a Bart keychain, a Homer keychain, a Marge keychain, and a Lisa keychain. She selects a keychain from the box and then puts it back. She then blindly selects another keychain from the box. Draw a tree diagram to determine the sample space and find the probability that

(a) Both key chains are the same character.
(b) The key chains are different characters.
(c) At least one is a Marge keychain.
(d) Both are Bart keychains.
(e) One keychain is Marge and the other is Homer.

11. The pool table in the student lounge is broken, and when Carrie puts her quarter into the slot, only the balls numbered 1 through 5 come down the chute. She selects one without looking and puts it on the table. She then selects another without looking. Draw a tree diagram to determine the sample space and find the probability that

(a) The sum of the numbers of the balls is odd.
(b) The number on the second ball is larger than the number on the first ball.

(c) The sum of the numbers on the balls is greater than 4.

12. Akira wants to purchase his first new car and can select one option from each category:

Model	Engine Type	Color
Ford Focus	Hybrid	Burnt copper
Honda Civic	E-85	Cobalt blue
Toyota Corolla		Metallic green

Draw a tree diagram and find the sample space for all possible choices. Find the probability that the car, if chosen at random,

(a) Has an E-85 engine.
(b) Is a burnt copper Ford Focus.
(c) Is a metallic green hybrid Honda Civic.
(d) Is cobalt blue.
(e) Is either a metallic green or cobalt blue Toyota Corolla.

13. Kimberly goes onto Dell's website to order a custom-made Tablet PC. She can select one option from each category:

Operating System	Processor	Wireless Options
Windows Vista Ultimate	Intel Core 2 Duo	Dell Wireless Mini Card
Windows Vista Home Premium	Intel Celeron 540	Bluetooth 2.0
Windows Vista Home Basic		

Draw a tree diagram to determine the sample space and find the probability that her Tablet PC, if chosen at random, will have

(a) An Intel Celeron 540 Processor.
(b) A Windows Vista Home Premium operating system and an Intel Core 2 Duo Processor.
(c) An Intel Core 2 Duo Processor with a Bluetooth 2.0 wireless option.

14. To choose the order of bands for the finals of the campus Battle of the Bands competition, Freddy puts a penny, a nickel, a dime, a quarter, and a half-dollar into five separate envelopes and has one band choose an envelope. Another band then chooses from the envelopes remaining. Draw a tree diagram to determine the sample space and find the probability that

(a) The amount of the first coin is less than the amount of the second coin.
(b) Neither coin is a quarter.
(c) One coin is a penny and the other coin is a nickel or a dime.
(d) The sum of the amounts of both coins is even.
(e) The sum of the amounts of both coins is less than $0.40.

15. At the beginning of a magic trick, The Great Mancini shuffles an ordinary deck of 52 cards as shown in Figure 11-6, and has the nearest person in the audience draw a single card. Using the sample space for drawing a single card from this deck, find the probability that the contestant got

    (a) A 10.
    (b) A club.
    (c) The ace of hearts.
    (d) A 3 or a 5.
    (e) A 6 or a spade.
    (f) A queen or a club.
    (g) A diamond or a club.
    (h) A red king.
    (i) A black card or an 8.
    (j) A red 10.

16. After a rowdy game of 52 pickup, Lauren cleans up the mess of 52 cards from a standard deck from the floor. Use the sample space for drawing a single card from an ordinary deck as shown in Figure 11-6 to find the probability that the first card Lauren picked up was

    (a) The 6 of clubs.
    (b) A black card.
    (c) A queen.
    (d) A black 10.
    (e) A red card or a 3.
    (f) A club and a 6.

(g) A 2 or an ace.
(h) A club, diamond, or spade.
(i) A diamond face card.
(j) A red ace.

17. In between classes, Jade plays a game of online Monopoly on her laptop. Using the sample space for rolling two dice shown in Figure 11-7, find the probability that when Jade rolls the two dice, she gets a

    (a) Sum of 5.
    (b) Sum of 7 or 11.
    (c) Sum greater than 9.
    (d) Sum less than or equal to 5.
    (e) Three on one die or on both dice.
    (f) Sum that is odd.
    (g) A prime number on one or both dice.
    (h) A sum greater than 1.

18. During a charity Las Vegas Casino Night, Rosie plays craps and gets to roll the dice. Using the sample space for rolling two dice as shown in Figure 11-7, find the probability she rolled a

    (a) Sum of 8.
    (b) Sum that is prime.
    (c) Five on one or both dice.
    (d) Sum greater than or equal to 7.
    (e) Sum that is less than 3.
    (f) Sum greater than 12.
    (g) Six on one die and 3 on the other die.

Critical Thinking

19. An online math quiz made up of true-false questions starts every student out with two questions. If they get both wrong, they're done. If they get at least one right, they get a third question. Suppose that a student guesses on all questions. Draw a tree diagram and find the sample space for all possible results. Then explain why every outcome is not equally likely.

20. To get past security at a club, potential patrons must answer a series of four questions. If they get any of the first three wrong, they get no more questions and

don't get in. Draw a tree diagram and find the sample space for all possible results. Then explain why all of the outcomes are not equally likely.

21. Consider the sample space when three dice are rolled. How many different outcomes would there be?

22. When three dice are rolled, how many ways can a sum of 6 be obtained?

23. When three dice are rolled, find the probability of getting a sum of 6.

Section 11-5 Probability Using Permutations and Combinations

Sometimes a friendly game of poker can become less friendly when someone seems just a bit too lucky. Suppose one player in such a game gets dealt all four aces in one hand. Would you suspect that something fishy was going on? What is the probability of that happening?

In Section 11-4, we used tree diagrams and tables to find sample spaces and the number of outcomes in certain events. This was a pretty good strategy, but when the number of possibilities gets larger, diagrams can get out of hand. Fortunately, we know about counting techniques that are tailor-made for answering questions about

probability. If our job is to find how many ways something can happen, the combination and permutation rules from Section 11-2 will be our best friends.

Our general game plan will be to use these rules to find the number of outcomes that satisfy a certain event, as well as the total number of outcomes in the sample space. Then we can divide the first number by the second to obtain the probability of the event occurring.

LEARNING OBJECTIVES

☐ 1. Compute probabilities using combinations.

☐ 2. Compute probabilities using permutations.

| EXAMPLE 1 | **Using Combinations to Compute Probability** |

Stacy has the option of selecting three books to read for a humanities course. The suggested book list consists of 10 biographies and five current events books. She decides to select the three books at random. Find the probability that all three books selected will be current events books.

SOLUTION

Since there are five current events books and Stacy will need to select three of them, then there are $_5C_3$ ways of doing this.

$$_5C_3 = \frac{5!}{(5-3)!3!} = \frac{5 \cdot 4 \cdot \cancel{3!}}{2 \cdot 1 \cdot \cancel{3!}} = 10 \quad \textit{10 ways to choose 3 current events books.}$$

The total number of outcomes in the sample space is $_{15}C_3$ since she has to select three books from 15 books.

$$_{15}C_3 = \frac{15!}{(15-3)!3!} = \frac{15!}{12!3!} = \frac{15 \cdot 14 \cdot 13 \cdot \cancel{12!}}{\cancel{12!} \cdot 3 \cdot 2 \cdot 1} = 455 \quad \textit{455 total choices.}$$

The probability of selecting three current events books is

$$\frac{10}{455} = \frac{2}{91} \approx 0.022$$

▼ Try This One 1

There are 12 women and 8 men in a seminar course. If the professor chooses five-person groups at random, what is the probability that the first group chosen will consist of all women?

Now back to that poker game . . .

| EXAMPLE 2 | **Using Combinations to Compute Probability** |

What is the probability of getting 4 aces when drawing 5 cards from a standard deck of 52 cards?

SOLUTION

First, we'll figure out how many five-card hands have four aces. Since there are only four aces in the deck, there's only one way to get all four of them in your hand. At that point there are 48 cards left for the other card in the hand. Using the fundamental counting principle, there are $1 \cdot 48$ ways to be dealt four aces.

The total number of hands is the combinations of 5 cards chosen from 52, or $_{52}C_5$.

$$_{52}C_5 = \frac{52!}{(52-5)!5!} = \frac{52!}{47!5!} = \frac{52 \cdot 51 \cdot 50 \cdot 49 \cdot 48 \cdot \cancel{47!}}{\cancel{47!} \cdot 5 \cdot 4 \cdot 3 \cdot 2 \cdot 1} = 2,598,960$$

The probability of getting four aces is

$$\frac{48}{2,598,960} = \frac{1}{54,145} \approx 0.0000185$$

We hate to accuse your friend of cheating, but to say the least, it's unlikely that she would draw a hand with 4 aces.

☑ 1. Compute probabilities using combinations.

▼ Try This One   2

Suppose the deck of cards in Example 2 has all 32 cards with numbers less than 10 removed, so that only 10s, jacks, queens, kings, and aces remain. Now what is the probability of getting 4 aces when drawing 5 cards?

Example 3 uses the permutation rule.

EXAMPLE 3   Using Permutations to Compute Probability

Permutations determine the number of combinations that can open a combination lock.

A combination lock has 40 numbers on it, from zero to 39. Find the probability that if the combination to unlock it consists of three numbers, it will contain the numbers 1, 2, and 3 in some order. Assume that numbers cannot be repeated in the combination. (It's interesting to note that a combination lock should really be called a permutation lock since the order of the numbers is important when you are unlocking the lock.)

SOLUTION

The number of combinations for the lock containing 1, 2, and 3 is $_3P_3$.

$$_3P_3 = \frac{3!}{(3-3)!} = \frac{3!}{0!} = \frac{3 \cdot 2 \cdot 1}{1} = 6$$

The total number of combinations is a permutation of the 40 numbers taken 3 at a time, or $_{40}P_3$.

$$_{40}P_3 = \frac{40!}{(40-3!)} = \frac{40!}{37!} = \frac{40 \cdot 39 \cdot 38 \cdot \cancel{37!}}{\cancel{37!}} = 59,280$$

The probability of the combination containing 1, 2, and 3 is $\frac{6}{59,280} \approx 0.000101$

▼ Try This One   3

A different "permutation" lock has letters from A through L on it, and the combination consists of four letters with no repeats. What is the probability that the combination is I, J, K, and L in some order?

☑ 2. Compute probabilities using permutations.

In Example 4, we will again need to use the fundamental counting principle.

EXAMPLE 4   Using Combinations to Compute Probability

A store has six different fitness magazines and three different news magazines. If a customer buys three magazines at random, find the probability that the customer will pick two fitness magazines and one news magazine.

SOLUTION

There are $_6C_2$ or 15 ways to select two fitness magazines from six fitness magazines, as shown:

$$_6C_2 = \frac{6!}{(6-2)!2!} = \frac{6!}{4!2!} = \frac{6 \cdot 5 \cdot \cancel{4!}}{\cancel{4!} \cdot 2 \cdot 1} = 15$$

There are $_3C_1$ or three ways to select one magazine from three news magazines:

$$_3C_1 = \frac{3!}{(3-1)!1!} = \frac{3!}{2! \cdot 1!} = \frac{3 \cdot \cancel{2!}}{\cancel{2!} \cdot 1} = 3$$

Using the fundamental counting principle, there are $15 \cdot 3$ or 45 ways to select two fitness magazines *and* one news magazine.

Next, there are $_9C_3$ or 84 ways to select three magazines from nine magazines:

$$_9C_3 = \frac{9!}{(9-3)!3!} = \frac{9!}{6!3!} = \frac{9 \cdot 8 \cdot 7 \cdot \cancel{6!}}{\cancel{6!} \cdot 3 \cdot 2 \cdot 1} = 84$$

The probability of selecting two fitness magazines and one news magazine is

$$\frac{45}{84} \approx 0.536$$

▼ Try This One 4

A box contains 24 imported cell phones and four of them are defective. If three phones are selected at random, find the probability that

(a) Exactly two are defective.   (c) All three are defective.
(b) None are defective.

Now we see why Chapter 11 began with a study of permutations and combinations: a large variety of probability problems can be solved using permutations and combinations in conjunction with the probability rules.

Sidelight THE CLASSICAL BIRTHDAY PROBLEM

What do you think the chances are that in a classroom with 23 students, two students have the same birthday (day and month)? Most people think that the probability would be very low since there are 365 days in a year. You may be surprised to find out that it is greater than 0.5, or 50%! Furthermore, as the number of people increases, the probability becomes even greater than 0.5 very rapidly. In a room of 30 students, there is a greater than 70% chance that two students have the same birthday. If you have 50 students in the room, the probability jumps to 97%!

The problem can be solved by using probability and permutation rules. It must be assumed that all birthdays are equally likely, but this assumption will have little effect on the answers. The way to solve the problem is to find the probability that no two people have the same birthday, and then subtract this probability from one. In other words, P(two students have the same birthday) $= 1 - P$(all students have different birthdays).

For example, suppose that there were only three students in a room. Then the probability that each would have a different birthday is

$$\frac{365}{365} \cdot \frac{364}{365} \cdot \frac{363}{365} = \frac{_{365}P_3}{365^3} \approx 0.992$$

So the probability that at least two of the three students have the same birthday is

$$1 - 0.992 = 0.008$$

In general, in a room with k people, the probability that at least two people have the same birthday is

$$1 - \frac{_{365}P_k}{365^k}$$

In a room with 23 students, then, the probability that at least two students will have the same birthday is

$$1 - \frac{_{365}P_{23}}{365^{23}} \approx 0.507 \text{ or } 50.7\%$$

It is interesting to note that two presidents, James K. Polk and Warren G. Harding, were both born on November 2. Also, John Adams and Thomas Jefferson both died on July 4. The unusual thing about this is that they died on the same day of the same year, July 4, 1826.

Answers to Try This One

1   33/646 ≈ 0.051

2   1/969 ≈ 0.00103

3   1/495 ≈ 0.002

4   (a) 15/253 ≈ 0.059

(b) 285/506 ≈ 0.56

(c) 1/506 ≈ 0.002

EXERCISE SET   11-5

Writing Exercises

1. Explain how combinations and permutations are useful in computing probabilities.

2. What is the biggest advantage of combinations and permutations over tree diagrams when computing probability?

Real-World Applications

3. A student-faculty government committee of 4 people is to be formed from 20 student volunteers and 5 faculty volunteers. Find the probability that the committee will consist of the following, assuming the selection is made at random:

   (a) All faculty members.
   (b) Two students and two faculty members.
   (c) All students.
   (d) One faculty member and three students.

4. In a company there are seven executives: four women and three men. Three are selected to attend a management seminar. Find these probabilities.

   (a) All three selected will be women.
   (b) All three selected will be men.
   (c) Two men and one woman will be selected.
   (d) One man and two women will be selected.

5. A city council consists of 10 members. Four are Republicans, three are Democrats, and three are Independents. If a committee of three is to be selected, find the probability of selecting

   (a) All Republicans.   (b) All Democrats.
   (c) One of each party.
   (d) Two Democrats and one Independent.
   (e) One Independent and two Republicans.

6. In a class of 18 students, there are 11 men and seven women. Four students are selected to present a demonstration on the use of graphing calculators. Find the probability that the group consists of

   (a) All men.
   (b) All women.
   (c) Three men and one woman.
   (d) One man and three women.
   (e) Two men and two women.

7. Fred needs to print his term paper. He pulls down a box of twelve ink cartridges and recalls that three of them have no more ink. If he selects four cartridges from the box, find the probability that

   (a) No cartridge has ink.
   (b) One cartridge has no ink.
   (c) Three cartridges have no ink.

8. There are 50 tickets sold for a raffle for the Student Art Auction, and there are two prizes to be awarded. If Dionte buys two tickets, find the probability that he will win both prizes.

9. An engineering company has four openings and the applicant pool consists of six database administrators and eight network engineers. If the hiring is done without regard for the specific qualifications of the applicants, find the probability that the four hired will be

   (a) All network engineers.
   (b) Two database administrators and two network engineers.
   (c) All database administrators.
   (d) Three database administrators and one network engineer.
   (e) One database administrator and three network engineers.

10. At the coffee kiosk in the mall, there are eight coffee drinks, five tea drinks, and two smoothies. Nora wants to buy three drinks for herself and her friends. Find the probability that she buys

   (a) All coffee drinks.
   (b) Two smoothie drinks.
   (c) All tea drinks.
   (d) One of each type of drink.
   (e) Two coffee drinks and one tea drink.

11. Find the probability of getting any triple-digit number where all the digits are the same in a lottery game that consists of selecting a three-digit number.

12. Binh is choosing from eight YouTube videos and nine online role-playing games to link to his MySpace page. If he randomly picks seven links total, find the probability that Binh chooses three YouTube videos and four online role-playing games.

13. Drew is on a fitness kick, so he's walking around with four protein bars and eight lowfat cereal bars in his backpack. If he reaches in and randomly grabs five bars, find the probability that he gets two protein bars and three cereal bars.

14. To win a state lottery, a person must select 5 numbers from 40 numbers. Find the probability of winning if a person buys one ticket. (*Note:* The numbers can be selected in any order.)

15. A five-digit identification card is made. Find the probability that the card will contain the digits 0, 1, 2, 3, and 4 in any order.

16. The combination lock in Example 3 has 40 numbers from zero to 39, and a combination consists of 3 numbers in a specific order with no repeats. Find the probability that the combination consists only of even numbers.

Exercises 17–22 refer to poker hands consisting of 5 cards dealt at random from a standard deck of 52 cards. Find the probability of getting each hand.

17. A full house (three of one denomination and two of another)

18. A flush (five cards of the same suit)

19. Three of a kind (exactly three of one denomination, remaining cards are two different denominations)

20. Four of a kind (four of the same denomination)

21. A royal flush (ten, jack, queen, king, and ace of the same suit)

22. A straight flush (five cards of the same suit that are consecutive in denomination)

Critical Thinking

23. At a carnival game, the player pays a dollar, then flips a quarter, rolls two dice, and draws two cards from a standard deck. If the result is tails, 12, and a pair of aces, he wins $1,000. What is the probability of this happening?

Section 11-6 Odds and Expectation

LEARNING OBJECTIVES

☐ 1. Compute the odds in favor of and against an outcome.

☐ 2. Compute odds from probability.

☐ 3. Compute probability from odds.

☐ 4. Compute expected value.

The Pittsburgh Steelers won the Super Bowl on February 1, 2009, and by the time the ink dried on newspapers reporting the victory, oddsmakers in Las Vegas had listed the odds against the Steelers winning it again in 2010 as 9 to 1. But what exactly does that mean? The term "odds" is used all the time in describing the likelihood of something happening, but a lot of people don't understand exactly what a given set of odds means.

Odds are used by casinos, racetracks, and other gambling establishments to determine the payoffs when bets are made or lottery tickets are purchased. They're also used by insurance companies in determining the amount to charge for premiums. The formulas for computing odds are similar to the formula we've been using for classical probability, and shortly we will see a strong connection between the two concepts.

> If an event E has a favorable outcomes and b unfavorable outcomes, then
>
> 1. The odds in favor of event E occurring $= \frac{a}{b}$
>
> 2. The odds against event E occurring $= \frac{b}{a}$

CAUTION Do not confuse the formula for odds in favor of an event with the formula for classical probability. The probability formula is the number of favorable outcomes over the *total* number of outcomes, while the one for odds is the number of favorable outcomes over the number of *unfavorable* outcomes.

Odds can be expressed as a fraction or a ratio. For example, the odds against Pittsburgh repeating as Super Bowl champion could be listed as $\frac{9}{1}$, 9:1, or 9 to 1. In common usage, the phrase "the odds of" really means "the odds against"; if we are told that the odds of rolling a 12 with two dice are 35 to 1, it means that the odds against rolling 12 are 35 to 1. So by setting Pittsburgh's odds at 9:1, the oddsmakers are predicting that if the season were played 10 times, Pittsburgh would win the Super Bowl 1 time, and not win it 9 times.

EXAMPLE 1   Computing Odds

A card is drawn from a standard deck of 52 cards.

(a) Find the odds in favor of getting an ace.
(b) Find the odds against getting an ace.

SOLUTION

(a) In a deck of cards there are 52 cards and there are 4 aces, so $a = 4$ and $b = 52 - 4 = 48$. (In other words, there are 48 cards that are not aces.)

The odds in favor of an ace $= \frac{4}{48} = \frac{1}{12}$

(b) The odds against an ace $= \frac{48}{4} = \frac{12}{1}$.

The odds in favor of an ace are 1:12 and the odds against an ace are 12:1.

> ### ▼ Try This One 1
>
> What are the odds in favor of rolling a prime number sum with a roll of two dice? What are the odds against? (Figure 11-7 on page 601 will help.)

Math Note

Notice that if the odds in favor of an event occurring are $a:b$, the odds against it occurring are $b:a$.

☑ 1. Compute the odds in favor of and against an outcome.

When an event E has a favorable and b unfavorable outcomes, there are $a + b$ total outcomes, and the probability of E is

$$P(E) = \frac{a}{a + b}$$

The probability of E not occurring is

$$1 - P(E), \quad \text{or} \quad \frac{b}{a + b}$$

If we divide these two probabilities, we get

$$\frac{P(E)}{1 - P(E)} = \frac{\dfrac{a}{a + b}}{\dfrac{b}{a + b}} = \frac{a}{a + b} \cdot \frac{a + b}{b} = \frac{a}{b}$$

The result is the odds in favor of event E. This gives us a strong connection between probability and odds.

Formulas for Odds in Terms of Probability

$$\text{Odds in favor} = \frac{P(E)}{1 - P(E)}$$

$$\text{Odds against} = \frac{P(E')}{1 - P(E')}$$

where $P(E)$ is the probability that event E occurs and $P(E')$ is the probability that the event E does not occur.

Math Note

Recall that
$P(E') = 1 - P(E)$.

EXAMPLE 2	**Finding Odds from Probability**

The probability of getting exactly one pair in a five-card poker hand is 0.423. Find the odds in favor of getting exactly one pair, and the odds against.

SOLUTION

This is a direct application of the formula relating probability and odds. The odds in favor of getting exactly one pair are

$$\frac{P(\text{getting exactly one pair})}{1 - P(\text{getting exactly one pair})} = \frac{0.423}{1 - 0.423} = \frac{0.423}{0.577}$$

We can convert this into fraction form by multiplying both the numerator and denominator by 100.

$$\frac{0.423}{0.577} \cdot \frac{100}{100} = \frac{423}{577}$$

So the odds in favor of getting exactly one pair are 423:577, and the odds against are 577:423.

▼ Try This One 2

2. Compute odds from probability.

According to the American Cancer Society, the probability of an American female developing some type of cancer at some point in her life is about $\frac{1}{3}$. Find the odds in favor of and against an American woman developing cancer.

In Example 2, the odds for an event were found when the probabilities were known. As we saw on page 610, when the odds of an event are given, the probability of an event can be found.

Math Note

When the odds are 1:1, a game is said to be fair. That is, both parties have an equal chance of winning or losing.

Formula for Probability in Terms of Odds

If the odds in favor of an event E are $a:b$, then the probability that the event will occur is

$$P(E) = \frac{a}{a + b}$$

EXAMPLE 3	**Finding Probability from Odds**

According to the National Safety Council, the odds of dying due to injury at some point in your life are about 10:237. Find the probability of dying from injury.

SOLUTION

In the formula for converting to probability, the odds in favor are $a:b$. In this case, those odds are 10:237, so $a = 10$ and $b = 237$.

$$P(\text{dying from injury}) = \frac{10}{10 + 237} = \frac{10}{247} \approx 0.040$$

▼ Try This One 3

3. Compute probability from odds.

When two dice are rolled, the odds in favor of getting a sum of 9 are 1:8. Find the probability of not getting a sum of 9 when two dice are rolled.

Sidelight ODDS AND BETTING

In almost any gambling enterprise, from Vegas to a church raffle, odds are used to determine what the payouts will be. Let's use the game of roulette as an example. There are 38 partitions on a roulette wheel, with a small ball that is equally likely to land in any of them. Players make various bets on where the ball will land. If you simply bet on a particular number, the odds against you are 37:1. If you win, the casino will pay 35 times what you bet. So if you bet a dollar on each spin, on average, in 38 spins, you would lose 37 times and win once, meaning you'd be two dollars in the hole. That doesn't sound like the recipe for the casino making a lot

of money, but when you consider the large number of people in a typical casino, and the fact that they're placing multiple bets at frequent intervals, it starts to make more sense.

This is where it becomes clear that state lotteries are an awful bet. In the Ohio lottery's "Classic Lotto" game, for example, the odds in favor of matching 5 of 6 numbers are 1:54,021. So to make the game completely fair, the payout should be in the neighborhood of $54,000 on a $1 ticket. The actual payout? Just $1,500! Any gambler or statistician will tell you that lotteries offer the worst odds of just about any game of chance.

Expected Value

Another concept related to odds and probability is **expectation,** or **expected value.** Expected value is used to determine the result that would be expected over the long term in some sort of gamble. It is used not only for games of chance, but in areas like insurance, management, engineering, and others. *The key element is that the events in question must have numerical outcomes.*

For example, rolling a die has a numerical outcome (1 through 6), and expected value can be used to determine what the average long-run result is likely to be. (We'll find out in Example 4.)

To find expected value, multiply the numerical result of each outcome by the corresponding probability of the outcome, then add those products.

Expected Value

The expected value for the outcomes of a probability experiment is

$$E = X_1 \cdot P(X_1) + X_2 \cdot P(X_2) + \cdots + X_n \cdot P(X_n)$$

where the X's correspond to the numerical outcomes and the $P(X)$'s are the corresponding probabilities of the outcomes.

EXAMPLE 4   Computing Expected Value

Math Note

In Example 4, a die cannot show 3.5 spots: It can only show 1, 2, 3, 4, 5, or 6 spots. However, in this case, the expected value would be the long run average—that is, if you add up the total number of spots, then divide by the number of times the die is rolled, the average would be close to 3.5.

When a single die is rolled, find the expected value of the outcome.

SOLUTION

Since each numerical outcome, 1 through 6, has a probability of $\frac{1}{6}$, the expected value is

$$E = 1 \cdot \frac{1}{6} + 2 \cdot \frac{1}{6} + 3 \cdot \frac{1}{6} + 4 \cdot \frac{1}{6} + 5 \cdot \frac{1}{6} + 6 \cdot \frac{1}{6} = \frac{21}{6} = 3.5$$

▼ Try This One 4

If seven cards are numbered with integers from -2 to 4, then placed into a box and picked out at random, find the expected value.

In gambling games, the expected value is found by multiplying the amount won, or net gain, and the amount lost by the corresponding probabilities and then finding the sum.

EXAMPLE 5   **Computing Expected Value**

One thousand tickets are sold at $1 each for a color television valued at $350. What is the expected value if a person purchases one ticket?

SOLUTION

We begin with two notes. First, for a win, the net gain is $349, since the person does not get the cost of the ticket ($1) back. Second, for a loss, the gain is represented by a negative number, in this case, $-$1.

The problem can then be set up as follows:

	Win	Lose
Gain, X	$349	$-$1
Probability, $P(X)$	$\dfrac{1}{1,000}$	$\dfrac{999}{1,000}$

The solution, then, is

$$E(X) = \$349 \cdot \frac{1}{1,000} + (-\$1) \cdot \frac{999}{1,000} = -\$0.65$$

▼ Try This One 5

With his house in foreclosure, a homeowner comes up with a plan to salvage the situation: he sells 10,000 raffle tickets at $50 each for the home, which is valued at $200,000. Find the expected value from buying one ticket.

Note that the expectation in Example 5 is $-$0.65. This does not mean that a person would ever actually lose 65 cents, since the person can only win a television set valued at $350 or lose $1 on the ticket. What this expectation means is that the average of the losses is $0.65 for each of the 1,000 ticket holders. Here is another way of looking at this situation: If a person purchased one ticket each week over a long period of time, the average loss would be $0.65 per ticket, since theoretically, on average, that person would win the television set once for each 1,000 tickets purchased.

Sidelight MATH AND SLOT MACHINES

Today most slot machines are run electronically, much the same as video games are. However, early slot machines were mechanical in nature. The first slot machines were invented by the Fey Manufacturing Company of San Francisco in 1895. They consisted of three large wheels, which were spun when the handle on the side of the machine was pulled. In order to control the number of wins and the payoffs, each wheel contains 20 symbols. However, the number of the same symbols is not the same on each wheel. For example, there may be two oranges on wheel 1, six oranges on wheel 2, and no oranges on wheel 3. When a person gets two orange symbols, he may think that he almost won; i.e., 2 out of 3. However, since there is no orange symbol on the third wheel, the probability of getting three oranges is zero! The higher the probability of getting three oranges, the lower the payoff. Using probability theory, the owner of the machines can determine his long-run profit.

EXAMPLE 6   Computing Expected Value

A stock you bought two years ago with high hopes is now selling for less than you paid, and things look grim for the company. Do you sell, or hold on and hope it will come back to the original price before you sell?

A model economists use for such situations is a game no one wants to play: Suppose you have a choice: lose $100, or take a $\frac{50}{50}$ chance between losing nothing, and losing $300. Which do you choose? Find the expected value for each strategy over 10 trials. (See Exercise 24.)

☑ 4. Compute expected value.

One thousand tickets are sold at $1 each for four prizes of $100, $50, $25, and $10. What is the expected value if a person purchases two tickets?

SOLUTION

Find the expected value if the person purchases one ticket.

Gain, x	$99	$49	$24	$9	−$1
Probability, $P(x)$	$\frac{1}{1,000}$	$\frac{1}{1,000}$	$\frac{1}{1,000}$	$\frac{1}{1,000}$	$\frac{996}{1,000}$

$$E(x) = \$99 \cdot \frac{1}{1,000} + \$49 \cdot \frac{1}{1,000} + \$24 \cdot \frac{1}{1,000} + \$9 \cdot \frac{1}{1,000} - \$1 \cdot \frac{996}{1,000} = -\$0.815$$

Now multiply by 2 since two tickets were purchased.

$$-\$0.815(2) = -\$1.63$$

▼ Try This One 6

A small ski resort loses $70,000 per season when it does not snow very much and makes $250,000 profit when it does snow a lot. The probability of it snowing at least 75 inches (i.e., a good season) is 40%. Find the expectation for the profit.

Math Note

In American roulette, there are 22 different types of bet you can place, but it is interesting to note that all but one of them have the exact same expected value: −$0.053 on a $1 bet. (Betting on 0, 00, 1, 2, and 3, called a five-number bet, is worse, at −$0.079.)

In gambling games, if the expected value of the gain is 0, the game is said to be fair. If the expected value of the gain of a game is positive, then the game is in favor of the player. That is, the player has a better-than-even chance of winning. If the expected value of the gain is negative, then the game is said to be in favor of the house. That is, in the long run, the players will lose money. Can you guess what the sign of the expected value is for every game in a casino?

Answers to Try This One

1 In favor: 5:7; against: 7:5	**3** $\frac{8}{9}$	**5** −$30
2 In favor: 1:2; against: 2:1	**4** 1	**6** $58,000

EXERCISE SET 11-6

Writing Exercises

1. Explain the difference between the odds in favor of an event and the odds against an event.

2. Explain the numerical relationship between the odds in favor of an event and the odds against an event.

3. Explain the meaning of odds in a gambling game.

4. Explain how to find the probability of an event occurring when given the odds in favor of an event.

5. Explain what is meant by the expected value of an event.

6. Why does every game in a casino have a negative expected value for the player?

Real-World Applications

7. In planning a gambling booth for a charity festival, Antoine needs to know the odds of various combinations in order to decide on payouts that will be high enough that people want to play, but low enough that the charity will make money. If the player rolls two dice, find the odds

   (a) In favor of getting a sum of 10.
   (b) In favor of getting a sum of 12.
   (c) Against getting a sum of 7.
   (d) Against getting a sum of 3.
   (e) In favor of getting doubles.

8. If the game in Exercise 7 has players who roll only one die, find the odds

   (a) In favor of getting a 3.
   (b) In favor of getting a 6.
   (c) Against getting an odd number.
   (d) Against getting an even number.
   (e) In favor of getting a prime number.

9. Steve shuffled a deck of 52 cards and asked Sally to draw one card to start a magic trick. Find the odds

   (a) In favor of getting a queen.
   (b) In favor of getting a face card.
   (c) Against getting a club.
   (d) In favor of getting an ace.
   (e) In favor of getting a black card.

10. While cleaning her dorm room, Monica mistakenly pushed three coins off the desk. When they land on the chair below, find the odds

    (a) In favor of getting exactly three heads.
    (b) In favor of getting exactly three tails.
    (c) Against getting exactly two heads.
    (d) Against getting exactly one tail.
    (e) In favor of getting at least one tail.

11. Your friends have taken bets on whether you will pass this class. (Sounds like maybe you need new friends.) Find the probability that you will pass given these odds:

    (a) 7:4 in favor of you passing
    (b) 2:5 against you passing
    (c) 3:1 in favor of you passing
    (d) 1:4 against you passing

12. Find the probability that you will win a Wii bowling tournament given these odds:

    (a) 3:4 in favor of you winning
    (b) 1:7 against you winning
    (c) 5:4 in favor of you winning
    (d) 6:5 in favor of you winning

13. If the odds against a horse winning a race are 9:5, find the probability that the horse will win the race.

14. A person rolls two dice and wins if he or she throws doubles. What are the odds in favor of the event? What are the odds against the event?

15. A cash prize of $5,000 is to be awarded at a fundraiser. If 2,500 tickets are sold at $5 each, find the expected value.

16. You start your shift as a cashier with your drawer containing ten $1 bills, five $2 bills, three $5 bills, one $10 bill, and one $100 bill. Find the expectation if one bill is selected.

17. In a scratch-off game, if you scratch the two dice on the ticket and get doubles, you win $5. For the game to be fair, how much should you pay to play the game?

18. At this year's State Fair, there was a dice rolling game. If you rolled two dice and got a sum of 2 or 12, you won $20. If you rolled a 7, you won $5. Any other roll was a loss. It cost $3 to play one game with one roll of the dice. What is the expectation of the game?

19. Melinda buys one raffle ticket at the Spring Fling since there is one $1,000 prize, one $500 prize, and five $100 prizes. There were a total of 1,000 tickets sold at $3 each. What is Melinda's expectation?

20. If Melinda buys two tickets to the raffle in Exercise 19, what is her expectation?

21. For a daily lottery, a person selects any three-digit number from 000 to 999. If a person plays for $1, the person can win $500. Find the expectation. In the same daily lottery, if a person boxes a number, the person can win $80. Find the expectation if the number 123 is played for $1 and boxed. (When a number is "boxed," it can win when the digits occur in any order.)

22. If a 60-year-old buys a $1,000 life insurance policy at a cost of $60 and has a probability of 0.972 of living to age 61, find the expectation of the policy until the person reaches 61.

Critical Thinking

23. Consider the following problem: You stop on the street between errands to engage in a shell game with a street vendor. The vendor shows you a two-headed penny under one shell, a two-tailed penny under the second shell and a fair penny (one head and one tail) under the third shell. He shuffles the shells around and then

you choose a shell. He shows you that under the shell is a penny with the head side up. He is willing to bet you $5 that it is the two-headed penny. He says it cannot be the two-tailed penny because a head is showing. Therefore, he says there is a 50-50 chance of it being the two-headed coin. Should you take the bet?

24. Stuck in a bad situation, you're given a choice: lose $100, or take a 50-50 chance between losing nothing and losing $300. Choose the option that sounds better to you, then find the expected value of each option over 10 trials.

25. Since expected value only applies to numerical outcomes, it takes some ingenuity to use it for flipping a coin.

  (a) Choose any two numbers at random, assigning one to heads and another to tails. Then find the expected value of flipping the coin.

(b) Repeat part (a) for two different numbers. What can you conclude?

26. Chevalier de Mere, a famous gambler, won money when he bet unsuspecting patrons that in four rolls of a die, he could get at least one 6, but he lost money when he bet that in 24 rolls of two dice, he could get a double 6. Using the probability rules, find the probability of each event and explain why he won the majority of the time on the first game but lost the majority of the time when playing the second game.

27. A roulette wheel has 38 numbers: 1 through 36, 0, and 00. A ball is rolled, and it falls into one of the 38 slots, giving a winning number. If a player bets $1 on a number and wins, the player gets $35 plus his $1 back. Otherwise, he loses the $1 he bet. Show that the expected value of the game matches that shown in the Math Note on page 614.

Section 11-7 The Addition Rules for Probability

LEARNING OBJECTIVES

☐ 1. Decide if two events are mutually exclusive.

☐ 2. Use the addition rule for mutually exclusive events.

☐ 3. Use the addition rule for events that are not mutually exclusive.

Many interesting problems in probability involve finding the probability of more than one event. Usually, some careful thought is required. For example, when the U.S. House of Representatives is in session, suppose that a political commentator feels like a certain bill is most likely to be supported by women and Democrats. She would likely be interested in the probability that a member of the House

is either a woman or a Democrat. She could find the number of women representatives, and the number of Democratic representatives easily, but then what? Should she add those numbers and divide by the total number of representatives? What about those who are both women *and* Democrats? They would get counted twice.

The situation would be simpler if the commentator were interested in the probability of a representative being either a Republican or an Independent. The key difference is that any individual has to be one or the other. These two events are called *mutually exclusive,* which indicates that either one or the other must occur, but not both.

> Two events are **mutually exclusive** if they cannot both occur at the same time. That is, the events have no outcomes in common.

EXAMPLE 1   Deciding if Two Events Are Mutually Exclusive

In drawing cards from a standard deck, determine whether the two events are mutually exclusive or not.

(a) Drawing a 4, drawing a 6.   (b) Drawing a 4, drawing a heart.

SOLUTION

(a) Every card has just one denomination, so a card can't be both a 4 and a 6. The events are mutually exclusive.
(b) You could draw the 4 of hearts, which is one outcome satisfying both events. The events are not mutually exclusive.

▼ Try This One 1

☑ 1. Decide if two events are mutually exclusive.

If student government picks students at random to win free books for a semester, determine whether the two events are mutually exclusive or not.

(a) The winner is a sophomore or a business major.
(b) The winner is a junior or a senior.

If you select one of these T-shirts at random in the morning, the probability that it is blue or red is $\frac{1}{5} + \frac{1}{5}$.

The probability of two or more events occurring can be determined by using the **addition rules.** The first addition rule is used when the events are mutually exclusive.

Addition Rule 1

When two events A and B are mutually exclusive, the probability that A or B will occur is

$$P(A \text{ or } B) = P(A) + P(B)$$

In Exercise 2, you will examine why this formula makes sense.

EXAMPLE 2 | Using Addition Rule 1

A restaurant has three pieces of apple pie, five pieces of cherry pie, and four pieces of pumpkin pie in its dessert case. If a customer selects at random one kind of pie for dessert, find the probability that it will be either cherry or pumpkin.

SOLUTION

The events are mutually exclusive. Since there is a total of 12 pieces of pie, five of which are cherry and four of which are pumpkin,

$$P(\text{cherry or pumpkin}) = P(\text{cherry}) + P(\text{pumpkin})$$
$$= \frac{5}{12} + \frac{4}{12} = \frac{9}{12} = \frac{3}{4}$$

Math Note

Sometimes it's a bad idea to reduce fractions in the individual probabilities when using the addition rule: you'll need a common denominator to add them. Your final answer should always be reduced if possible, though.

▼ Try This One 2

A liberal arts math class contains 7 freshmen, 11 sophomores, 5 juniors, and 2 seniors. If the professor randomly chooses one to present a homework problem at the board, find the probability that it's either a junior or senior.

EXAMPLE 3   **Using Addition Rule 1**

A card is drawn from a standard deck. Find the probability of getting an ace or a queen.

SOLUTION

The events are mutually exclusive. There are four aces and four queens; therefore,

$$P(\text{ace or queen}) = P(\text{ace}) + P(\text{queen})$$
$$= \frac{4}{52} + \frac{4}{52} = \frac{8}{52} = \frac{2}{13}$$

▼ Try This One 3

At a political rally, there are 20 Republicans, 13 Democrats, and 6 Independents. If a person is selected at random, find the probability that he or she is either a Democrat or an Independent.

The addition rule for mutually exclusive events can be extended to three or more events as shown in Example 4.

EXAMPLE 4   **Using the Addition Rule with Three Events**

A card is drawn from a deck. Find the probability that it is either a club, a diamond, or a heart.

SOLUTION

In the deck of 52 cards there are 13 clubs, 13 diamonds, and 13 hearts, and any card can be only one of those suits. So

$$P(\text{club, diamond, or heart}) = P(\text{club}) + P(\text{diamond}) + P(\text{heart})$$
$$= \frac{13}{52} + \frac{13}{52} + \frac{13}{52} = \frac{39}{52} = \frac{3}{4}$$

▼ Try This One 4

In rolling two dice, find the probability that the sum is 2, 3, or 4.

☑ 2. Use the addition rule for mutually exclusive events.

In Example 4, we used an extended version of addition rule 1:

$$P(A \text{ or } B \text{ or } C) = P(A) + P(B) + P(C)$$

When two events are not mutually exclusive, any outcomes that are common to two events are counted twice. We account for this by subtracting the probability of both events occurring, which results in addition rule 2.

Math Note

Addition rule 2 can actually be used when events are mutually exclusive, too—in that case, $P(A \text{ and } B)$ will always be zero, and you'll get addition rule 1 back. But it's still important to distinguish between the two situations.

Addition Rule 2

When two events A and B are not mutually exclusive, the probability that A or B will occur is

$P(A \text{ or } B) = P(A) + P(B) - P(A \text{ and } B)$

EXAMPLE 5   **Using Addition Rule 2**

A single card is drawn from a standard deck of cards. Find the probability that it is a king or a club.

SOLUTION

In this case, there are 4 kings and 13 clubs. However, the king of clubs has been counted twice since the two events are not mutually exclusive. When finding the probability of getting a king or a club, the probability of getting the king of clubs (i.e., a king and a club) must be subtracted, as shown.

$$P(\text{king or club}) = P(\text{king}) + P(\text{club}) - P(\text{king and club})$$
$$= \frac{4}{52} + \frac{13}{52} - \frac{1}{52} = \frac{16}{52} = \frac{4}{13}$$

▼ **Try This One 5**

A card is drawn from an ordinary deck. Find the probability that it is a heart or a face card.

EXAMPLE 6   **Using Addition Rule 2**

Two dice are rolled. Find the probability of getting doubles or a sum of 6.

SOLUTION

Using the sample space shown in Section 11-2, there are six ways to get doubles: (1, 1), (2, 2), (3, 3), (4, 4), (5, 5), (6, 6). So $P(\text{doubles}) = \frac{6}{36}$. There are five ways to get a sum of 6: (1, 5), (2, 4), (3, 3), (4, 2), (5, 1). So $P(\text{sum of 6}) = \frac{5}{36}$. Notice that there is one way of getting doubles and a sum of 6, so $P(\text{doubles and a sum of 6}) = \frac{1}{36}$. Finally,

$$P(\text{doubles or a sum of 6}) = P(\text{doubles}) + P(\text{sum of 6}) - (\text{doubles and sum of 6})$$
$$= \frac{6}{36} + \frac{5}{36} - \frac{1}{36} = \frac{10}{36} = \frac{5}{18}$$

▼ **Try This One 6**

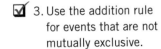
3. Use the addition rule for events that are not mutually exclusive.

When two dice are rolled, find the probability that both numbers are more than three, or that they differ by exactly two.

In many cases, the information in probability problems can be arranged in table form in order to make it easier to compute the probabilities for various events. Example 7 uses this technique.

EXAMPLE 7   **Using a Table and Addition Rule 2**

In a hospital there are eight nurses and five physicians. Seven nurses and three physicians are females. If a staff person is selected, find the probability that the subject is a nurse or a male.

SOLUTION

The sample space can be written in table form.

Staff	Females	Males	Total
Nurses	7	1	8
Physicians	3	2	5
Total	10	3	13

Looking at the table, we can see that there are 8 nurses and 3 males, and there is one person who is both a male and a nurse. The probability is

$$P(\text{nurse or male}) = P(\text{nurse}) + P(\text{male}) - P(\text{male and a nurse})$$

$$= \frac{8}{13} + \frac{3}{13} - \frac{1}{13} = \frac{10}{13}$$

▼ Try This One 7

In a class of students, there are 15 freshmen and 10 sophomores. Six of the freshmen are males and four of the sophomores are males. If a student is selected at random, find the probability that the student is a sophomore or a male.

Probability and Sets

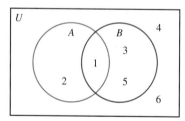

(a) Mutually exclusive events
$A \cap B = \varnothing$
$P(A \cup B) = P(A) + P(B)$

The addition rules for probability can be represented by Venn diagrams. First, consider two mutually exclusive events. For example, we will use the probability experiment of rolling a die. Let A be the event of getting a number less than 3 and B be the event of getting a number greater than 3. In set notation, $U = \{1, 2, 3, 4, 5, 6\}$, $A = \{1, 2\}$, and $B = \{4, 5, 6\}$. The Venn diagram for mutually exclusive events is shown in Figure 11-8(a). Notice that $A \cup B = \{1, 2\} \cup \{4, 5, 6\} = \{1, 2, 4, 5, 6\}$; now $P(A \cup B) = P(A) + P(B)$ or in probability language, $P(A \text{ or } B) = P(A) + P(B)$. Since $P(A) = \frac{2}{6}$, and $P(B) = \frac{3}{6}$, then $P(A \text{ or } B) = \frac{5}{6}$.

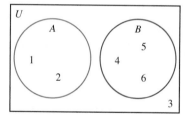

(b) Events not mutually exclusive
$A \cap B \neq \varnothing$
$P(A \cup B) = P(A) + P(B) - P(A \cap B)$

Figure 11-8

Next, consider two events that are not mutually exclusive. Let A be the event of getting a number less than 3 and B be the event of getting an odd number. The sample space for A is $\{1, 2\}$. The sample space for B is $\{1, 3, 5\}$. The Venn diagram for this example is shown in Figure 11-8(b). We can see that 4 of the 6 outcomes are in $A \cup B$, so $P(A \cup B) = \frac{4}{6}$. Also, there are 2 outcomes in A, 3 in B, and 1 in $A \cap B$, so $P(A) = \frac{2}{6}$, $P(B) = \frac{3}{6}$, and $P(A \cap B) = \frac{1}{6}$. Then

$$P(A \cup B) = P(A) + P(B) - P(A \cap B)$$

$$= \frac{2}{6} + \frac{3}{6} - \frac{1}{6} = \frac{4}{6} = \frac{2}{3}$$

In probability notation, this is equivalent to $P(A \text{ or } B) = P(A) + P(B) - P(A \text{ and } B)$.

Answers to Try This One

1 (a) Not mutually exclusive
    (b) Mutually exclusive

2 $\frac{7}{25}$

3 $\frac{19}{39}$

4 $\frac{1}{6}$

5 $\frac{11}{26}$

6 $\frac{5}{12}$

7 $\frac{16}{25}$

EXERCISE SET 11-7

Writing Exercises

1. Explain how to tell if two events are mutually exclusive or not.

For Exercises 2–8, determine whether or not the events are mutually exclusive, and explain your answer.

2. Roll a die: Get an even number, or get a number less than 3.

3. Roll a die: Get a prime number (2, 3, 5), or get an odd number.

4. Roll a die: Get a number greater than 3, or get a number less than 3.

5. Select a student in your class: the student has blond hair, or the student has blue eyes.

6. Select a student in your college: the student is a sophomore, or the student is a business major.

7. Select any course: It is a calculus course, or it is an English course.

8. Select a registered voter: The voter is a Republican, or the voter is a Democrat.

Real-World Applications

9. A young couple who plan to marry decide to select a month for their wedding. Find the probability that it will be April or May. Assume that all months have an equal opportunity of being selected.

10. At the animal shelter where Miguel volunteers on the weekends, there were two Siamese cats, four tabby cats, sixteen mixed-breed dogs, and four iguanas in their cages. If a customer picks any of these animals at random, find the probability that the animal is either a mixed-breed dog or a Siamese cat.

11. When Milo went to register for classes at the last minute, the only classes left to take were seven math courses, five computer science courses, three statistics courses, and four science courses. He shut his eyes and picked one at random. Find the probability that Milo selected either a science course or a math course. (The probability that Milo will ever graduate using this strategy is an interesting question, too.)

12. When Shana looked at the favorites list on her boyfriend's MP3 player, there were 10 songs she liked, 7 songs she'd heard but did not like, and 5 songs she hadn't heard. She let the MP3 player select a song at random. What is the probability that the selected song was one she liked or one she'd heard but did not like?

13. The bookstore has eight red school jerseys, nine blue school jerseys, and three black school jerseys to choose from. If a student selects one at random, find the probability that it is

   (a) A red or a blue jersey.
   (b) A red or a black jersey.
   (c) A blue or a black jersey.

14. In my Tae Kwon Do class, there are two black belts, three red belts, five blue belts, three green belts, and six yellow belts. If the sensei selects a student at random to lead the warm-up, find the probability that the person is
   (a) Either a green belt or a yellow belt.

   (b) Either a black belt or a blue belt.
   (c) Either a black belt, a green belt, or a yellow belt.

15. On a small college campus, there are five English professors, four mathematics professors, two science professors, three psychology professors, and three history professors. If a professor is selected at random, find the probability that the professor is

   (a) An English or psychology professor.
   (b) A mathematics or science professor.
   (c) A history, science, or mathematics professor.
   (d) An English, mathematics, or history professor.

16. A deck of cards is randomly dealt by the computer during a game of Spider Solitaire. Find the probability the first card dealt is

   (a) A 4 or a diamond.
   (b) A club or a diamond.
   (c) A jack or a black card.

17. In a statistics class there are 18 juniors and 10 seniors; 6 of the seniors are females, and 12 of the juniors are males. If a student is selected at random, find the probability of selecting

   (a) A junior or a female.
   (b) A senior or a female.
   (c) A junior or a senior.

18. A cell phone company gets a good deal on 400 new Motorola phones. Of them, 250 have digital cameras and 150 have touch screens. Of the phones that have digital cameras, 140 are lime green and the rest are metallic orange. Of the phones that have touch screens, 80 are lime green and the rest are metallic orange. If a phone is selected at random, find the probability that it will

   (a) Be lime green or have a digital camera.
   (b) Be metallic orange or have a touch screen.

19. BlueFly.com, an online designer clothing marketplace, purchases items from Kenneth Cole, Michael

Kors, and Vera Wang. The most recent purchases are shown here:

Product	Kenneth Cole	Michael Kors	Vera Wang
Dresses	24	18	12
Jeans	13	36	15

If one item is selected at random, find these probabilities:

(a) It was purchased from Kenneth Cole or is a dress.

(b) It was purchased from Michael Kors or Vera Wang.

(c) It is a pair of jeans or it was purchased from Kenneth Cole.

20. In a recent campus survey, the following data were obtained in response to the question "Do you think there should be harsher penalties for underage drinking on campus?"

	Yes	No	No opinion
Males	72	81	5
Females	103	68	7

If a person is selected at random, find these probabilities:

(a) The person has no opinion.

(b) The person is a male or is against the issue.

(c) The person is a female or favors the issue.

21. A grocery store employs cashiers, stock clerks, and deli personnel. The distribution of employees according to marital status is shown next.

Marital status	Cashiers	Stock clerks	Deli personnel
Married	8	12	3
Not married	5	15	2

If an employee is selected at random, find these probabilities:

(a) The employee is a stock clerk or married.

(b) The employee is not married.

(c) The employee is a cashier or is not married.

22. Students were surveyed on campus about their study habits. Some said they study in the morning, others study during the day between classes, and others study at night. Some students always study in a group and others always study alone. The distribution is shown below:

How students study	Morning	Between classes	Evening
Study in a group	2	3	1
Study alone	3	4	2

If a student who was surveyed is selected at random, find these probabilities:

(a) The student studies in the evening.

(b) The student studies in the morning or in a group.

(c) The student studies in the evening or studies alone.

23. Three cable channels (95, 97, and 103) air quiz shows, comedies, and dramas. The numbers of shows aired are shown here.

Type of show	Channel 95	Channel 97	Channel 103
Quiz show	5	2	1
Comedy	3	2	8
Drama	4	4	2

If a show is selected at random, find these probabilities:

(a) The show is a quiz show or it is shown on Channel 97.

(b) The show is a drama or a comedy.

(c) The show is shown on Channel 103 or it is a drama.

24. A local postal carrier distributed first-class letters, advertisements, and magazines. For a certain day, she distributed the following number of each type of item.

Delivered to	First-class letters	Ads	Magazines
Home	325	406	203
Business	732	1,021	97

If an item of mail is selected at random, find these probabilities:

(a) The item went to a home.

(b) The item was an ad or it went to a business.

(c) The item was a first-class letter or it went to a home.

25. As part of her major in microbiology, Juanita spent 3 weeks studying the spread of a disease in the jungles of South America. When she returned, she found that she had many e-mails sent to her home account and her school account, and that the e-mails were either spam, school announcements, or messages from friends as follows:

Delivered to	School announcements	Spam	Messages from friends
Home	325	406	203
School	732	1,021	97

If an e-mail is selected at random, find these probabilities:

(a) The e-mail was sent to her home.

(b) The e-mail was a school announcement or it was sent to her school account.

(c) The e-mail was spam or it was sent to her home account.

26. During a windstorm, the two large dice atop a new casino in Las Vegas crash into the pool below. Find the probabilities the dice landed with

(a) A sum of 6, 7, or 8.

(b) Doubles or a sum of 4 or 6.

(c) A sum greater than 9 or less than 4 or equal to 7.

27. Before a Walk for the Cure 10-mile walk, participants could choose a T-shirt from a box with six red shirts, two green shirts, one blue shirt, and one white shirt. When the first participant randomly selects a shirt from the box, what is the probability she will select a red shirt or a white shirt?

28. Colby tosses the contents of his jeans onto a table before putting them into the washer. Among the things thrown are three dice. Find the probability that the dice landed so that

   (a) All three have the same number showing.
   (b) The three numbers sum to 5.

Critical Thinking

29. The probability that a customer selects a pizza with mushrooms or pepperoni is 0.55, and the probability that the customer selects mushrooms only is 0.32. If the probability that he or she selects pepperoni only is 0.17, find the probability of the customer selecting both items.

30. In building new homes, a contractor finds that the probability of a buyer selecting a two-car garage is 0.70 and of selecting a one-car garage is 0.20. Find the probability that the buyer will select no garage. The builder does not build houses with garages for three or more cars.

31. In Exercise 30, find the probability that the buyer will not want a two-car garage.

32. In this exercise, we will attempt to justify addition rule 1. When two dice are rolled, we will find the probability of getting a sum of 5 or 10.

   (a) Explain why the two events are mutually exclusive.
   (b) How many total outcomes are possible when two dice are rolled?
   (c) How many outcomes result in a sum of either 5 or 10?
   (d) Find the probability of rolling a sum of 5 or 10 without the addition rule, using your answers from parts b and c.
   (e) Find the probability of rolling a sum of 5.
   (f) Find the probability of rolling a sum of 10.
   (g) Add your answers from parts e and f, then explain why the calculations from parts d and g will always be the same for any pair of mutually exclusive events.

Section 11-8 The Multiplication Rules and Conditional Probability

LEARNING OBJECTIVES

❑ 1. Find the probability of two or more independent events all occurring.

❑ 2. Find the probability of two or more dependent events all occurring.

❑ 3. Find conditional probabilities.

Based on data collected from 1960–2000, the probability of it raining on any given day during March in Daytona Beach, Florida, is about 1/5. So you head to Daytona for spring break, and you're more than a little disappointed when it rains the first 2 days. Trying to remain upbeat, you say "With only a $\frac{1}{5}$ chance of rain, what are the chances of it raining 3 days in a row?"

That's actually a much more interesting question than you think. One reason is that many people would say that it's less likely to rain the third day because it already rained 2 days in a row, but that's not the case. Assuming that there's not a massive storm system lasting for 3 days, what happened on Saturday has no effect on whether or not it rains on Monday, so the probability of rain on the third day is $\frac{1}{5}$ regardless of what happened the first 2 days.

Returning to the original question, the probability of it raining 3 days in a row, we see that a rule for finding the probability of consecutive events occurring would be helpful. As we will see, the probability of consecutive events depends on whether the first event affects the second.

> Two events A and B are **independent** if the fact that A occurs has no effect on the probability of B occurring.

Based on our description above, rain on Saturday and rain on Monday are independent events.

Each day a professor selects a student at random to work out a problem from the homework. If the student is selected regardless of who already went, the events are independent. If the student is selected from the pool of students who haven't gone yet, the events are dependent.

Here are other examples of independent events:

Rolling a die and getting a 6, and then rolling a second die and getting a 3.

Drawing a card from a deck and getting a queen, replacing it, and drawing a second card and getting a queen.

On the other hand, when the occurrence of the first event changes the probability of the occurrence of the second event, the two events are said to be *dependent*. For example, suppose a card is drawn from a deck and *not* replaced, and then a second card is drawn. The probability for the second card is changed since the sample space contains only 51 cards when the first card is not replaced.

> Two events A and B are **dependent** if the outcome of A has some effect on the probability of B occurring.

Here are some examples of dependent events:

Drawing a card from a deck, not replacing it, and then drawing a second card.

Selecting a lottery ball from a tumbler, not replacing it, and then drawing a second ball.

Parking in a no-parking zone and getting a parking ticket.

When a coin is flipped twice, the outcomes of the first and second flips are independent, and in each case, the probability of getting tails is $\frac{1}{2}$. The sample space for the two flips is {HH, TT, HT, TH}, and the probability of getting tails twice is $\frac{1}{4}$. Notice that $\frac{1}{4} = \frac{1}{2} \cdot \frac{1}{2}$. This shows that the probability of two consecutive tails is the product of the probabilities of getting tails in each individual trial. This result is our first *multiplication rule*.

Multiplication Rule 1

When two events A and B are independent, the probability of both occurring is

$$P(A \text{ and } B) = P(A) \cdot P(B)$$

EXAMPLE 1   Using Multiplication Rule 1

A coin is flipped and a die is rolled. Find the probability of getting heads on the coin and a 4 on the die.

SOLUTION

The two events, the coin landing on heads and the die showing 4, are independent. We know from earlier examples that the probability of heads is $\frac{1}{2}$ and the probability of getting 4 with one die is $\frac{1}{6}$. Using the multiplication rule:

$$P(\text{heads and } 4) = P(\text{heads}) \cdot P(4) = \frac{1}{2} \cdot \frac{1}{6} = \frac{1}{12}$$

Math Note

The problem in Example 1 could be solved using standard sample space methods, but as outcomes get more complicated, it can be extremely difficult to list sample spaces. That's why the multiplication rules are so helpful.

▼ Try This One   1

If the probability of your alarm not going off is $\frac{1}{20}$, and the probability of getting a ticket on your way to work is $\frac{1}{200}$, find the probability that both will happen.

EXAMPLE 2   Using Multiplication Rule 1

As part of a psychology experiment on perception and memory, colored balls are picked from an urn. The urn contains three red balls, two green balls, and five white balls. A ball is selected and its color is noted. Then it is replaced. A second ball is selected and its color is noted. Find the probability of each of these.

(a) Selecting two green balls.
(b) Selecting a green ball and then a white ball.
(c) Selecting a red ball and then a green ball.

SOLUTION

Remember, selection is done with replacement, which makes the events independent.

(a) The probability of selecting a green ball on each trial is $\frac{2}{10}$, so

$$P(\text{green and green}) = P(\text{green}) \cdot P(\text{green}) = \frac{2}{10} \cdot \frac{2}{10} = \frac{4}{100} = \frac{1}{25}$$

(b) The probability of selecting a green ball is $\frac{2}{10}$ and the probability of selecting a white ball is $\frac{5}{10}$, so

$$P(\text{green and white}) = P(\text{green}) \cdot P(\text{white}) = \frac{2}{10} \cdot \frac{5}{10} = \frac{10}{100} = \frac{1}{10}$$

(c) The probability of selecting a red ball is $\frac{3}{10}$ and the probability of selecting a green ball is $\frac{2}{10}$, so

$$P(\text{red and green}) = P(\text{red}) \cdot P(\text{green}) = \frac{3}{10} \cdot \frac{2}{10} = \frac{6}{100} = \frac{3}{50}$$

▼ Try This One 2

As part of a card trick, a card is drawn from a deck and replaced; then a second card is drawn. Find the probability of getting a queen and then an ace.

EXAMPLE 3   *Finding Probabilities for Three Independent Events*

Math Note

Multiplication rule 1 can be extended to three or more independent events using the formula

$$P(A_1 \text{ and } A_2 \text{ and } A_3 \cdots \text{ and } A_n)$$
$$= P(A_1) \cdot P(A_2) \cdot P(A_3) \cdots \cdot P(A_n)$$

Three cards are drawn from a deck. After each card is drawn, its denomination and suit are noted and it is replaced before the next card is drawn. Find the probability of getting

(a) Three kings.
(b) Three clubs.

SOLUTION

(a) Since there are four kings, the probability of getting a king on each draw is $\frac{4}{52}$ or $\frac{1}{13}$. The probability of getting three kings is

$$\frac{1}{13} \cdot \frac{1}{13} \cdot \frac{1}{13} = \frac{1}{2{,}197}$$

(b) Since there are 13 clubs, the probability of getting a club is $\frac{13}{52}$ or $\frac{1}{4}$. The probability of getting three clubs in a row is

$$\frac{1}{4} \cdot \frac{1}{4} \cdot \frac{1}{4} = \frac{1}{64}$$

▼ Try This One 3

Given that the probability of rain on any given day in March in Daytona Beach is $\frac{1}{5}$, find the probability that

(a) It rains three straight days in March.
(b) It rains on March 10 and 12, but not March 11.

Assume that weather on any day is independent of the others.

When a few subjects are selected from a large number of subjects in a sample space, and the subjects are not replaced, the probability of the event occurring changes so slightly that, for the most part, it is considered to remain the same. Example 4 illustrates this concept.

EXAMPLE 4　**Using Multiplication Rule 1 with Large Samples**

According to a Gallup Poll in 2007, 47 percent of all parents in America with children under 18 feel frequent stress. If three parents are chosen randomly, find the probability that all three will say they feel frequent stress.

SOLUTION

Let S denote the event that the chosen parents feel stress.

$$P(S \text{ and } S \text{ and } S) = P(S) \cdot P(S) \cdot P(S) = (0.47)(0.47)(0.47) \approx 0.104$$

☑ 1. Find the probability of two or more independent events all occurring.

▼ Try This One 4

According to a report from the National Institute of Justice, 64% of males arrested for any reason in 2000 tested positive for illegal drugs. If four prisoners at random were chosen, find the probability that all four test positive.

CAUTION

Even though the three events in Example 4 are not independent, because parents were not replaced after being chosen, there are millions and millions of parents, so having one or two fewer in the sample has a negligible effect. Make sure to carefully consider the situation before using multiplication rule 1.

When we are interested in finding the probability of consecutive events that are dependent, we can still use the multiplication rule, but with a minor modification. For example, let's say we draw two cards at random from a standard deck. The probability of getting an ace on the first draw is $\frac{4}{52}$. But if the first card is not put back into the deck, that changes the probability of drawing another ace—it's now $\frac{3}{51}$. Using the multiplication rule, the probability of both events occurring is

$$\frac{4}{52} \cdot \frac{3}{51} = \frac{12}{2,652} = \frac{1}{221}.$$

We can summarize this procedure as multiplication rule 2.

Multiplication Rule 2

When two events are dependent, the probability of both occurring is

$$P(A \text{ and } B) = P(A) \cdot P(B \text{ given that } A \text{ has already occurred})$$

EXAMPLE 5   Using Multiplication Rule 2

An appliance store gets a shipment of 25 plasma TVs, and 3 of them are defective. If two of the TVs are chosen at random, find the probability that both are defective. (The first TV is not replaced after it's tested.)

SOLUTION

Since there are 3 defective TVs out of a total of 25, the probability of the first being defective is $\frac{3}{25}$. After the first one is found to be defective and not replaced, there are 2 defective sets left out of 24, so the probability of the second being defective given that the first one is defective is $\frac{2}{24}$. Using multiplication rule 2, the probability that both are defective is

$$P(\text{1st defective and 2nd defective}) = P(\text{1st}) \cdot P(\text{2nd given 1st})$$

$$= \frac{3}{25} \cdot \frac{2}{24} = \frac{6}{600} = \frac{1}{100}$$

▼ Try This One 5

The 2009 NCAA men's basketball tournament field had (among 64 teams) 7 teams from the Big East conference, 7 from the Big Ten, 6 from the Big 12, and 3 from the Southeastern conference. If you were randomly assigned two teams in a dorm pool, find the probability that

(a) Both were from the Big East.
(b) The first was from the Southeastern conference and the second was from the Big 12.

Multiplication rule 2 can be extended to three or more events as shown in Example 6.

EXAMPLE 6   Using Multiplication Rule 2 with Three Events

Three cards are drawn from an ordinary deck and not replaced. Find the probability of

(a) Getting three jacks.
(b) Getting an ace, a king, and a queen in order.
(c) Getting a club, a spade, and a heart in order.
(d) Getting three clubs.

SOLUTION

(a) $P(\text{three jacks}) = \frac{4}{52} \cdot \frac{3}{51} \cdot \frac{2}{50} = \frac{24}{132,600} = \frac{1}{5,525}$

(b) $P(\text{ace and king and queen}) = \frac{4}{52} \cdot \frac{4}{51} \cdot \frac{4}{50} = \frac{64}{132,600} = \frac{8}{16,575}$

(c) $P(\text{club and spade and heart}) = \frac{13}{52} \cdot \frac{13}{51} \cdot \frac{13}{50} = \frac{2,197}{132,600} = \frac{169}{10,200}$

(d) $P(\text{three clubs}) = \frac{13}{52} \cdot \frac{12}{51} \cdot \frac{11}{50} = \frac{1,716}{132,600} = \frac{11}{850}$

☑ 2. Find the probability of two or more dependent events all occurring.

▼ Try This One 6

When drawing four cards from a deck, what is the probability that

(a) All four are aces?   (b) All four are clubs?

Conditional Probability

We know that to find the probability of two dependent events occurring, it's important to find the probability of the second event occurring given that the first has already occurred. We call this the **conditional probability** of event B occurring given that event A has occurred, and denote it $P(B \mid A)$.

Now that we have a symbol to represent the probability of event B given that A has occurred, we can rewrite multiplication rule 2, and solve the equation for $P(B \mid A)$:

$$P(A \text{ and } B) = P(A) \cdot P(B \mid A)$$

$$P(B \mid A) = \frac{P(A \text{ and } B)}{P(A)}$$

This gives us a formula for conditional probability.

> **Math Note**
>
> We use the term conditional probability because the condition that A has already occurred affects the probability of B.

Formula for Conditional Probability

The probability that the second event B occurs given that the first event A has occurred can be found by dividing the probability that both events occurred by the probability that the first event has occurred. The formula is

$$P(B \mid A) = \frac{P(A \text{ and } B)}{P(A)}$$

Example 7 illustrates the use of this rule.

EXAMPLE 7   Finding a Conditional Probability

Military strategies (and other types of strategies) use conditional probability. If A occurs, how likely is B? How likely is B if A doesn't occur?

Suppose that your professor goes stark raving mad and chooses your final grade from A, B, C, D, F, or Incomplete totally at random. Find the probability of getting an A given that you get a letter grade higher than D.

SOLUTION

We are asked to find $P(\text{A} \mid \text{letter grade higher than D})$.

Method 1 Knowing that you got a letter grade higher than D reduces the sample space to {A, B, C}, which has three outcomes. One of them is an A, so $P(\text{A} \mid \text{letter grade higher than D}) = \frac{1}{3}$.

Method 2 With the full sample space of {A, B, C, D, F, I}, $P(\text{A}) = \frac{1}{6}$, and $P(\text{letter grade higher than D}) = \frac{3}{6}$. Using the formula for conditional probability,

$$P(\text{A} \mid \text{letter grade higher than D}) = \frac{\frac{1}{6}}{\frac{3}{6}} = \frac{1}{6} \cdot \frac{6}{3} = \frac{1}{3}$$

▼ Try This One 7

A group of buses is rented for an away game, and they are numbered from 1–8. All students are randomly assigned to a bus. What is the probability that you get an even–numbered bus given that your bus number is less than 6?

EXAMPLE 8 **Finding a Conditional Probability**

Hate crimes are defined to be crimes in which the victim is targeted because of one or more personal characteristics, such as race, religion, or sexual orientation. The table below lists the motivation for certain crimes as reported by the FBI for 2007.

Motivation	Crimes against persons	Crimes against property	Crimes against society
Race	3,031	1,686	7
Religion	421	1,054	2
Sexual orientation	1,039	418	3
Total	4,491	3,158	12

(a) Find the probability that a hate crime was racially motivated given that it was a crime against persons.
(b) Find the probability that a hate crime was against property given that it was motivated by the victim's sexual orientation.

SOLUTION

(a) Since we are interested only in crimes against persons, we only need to look at that column. There were 4,491 such crimes total, and 3,031 were racially motivated, so the probability is

$$\frac{3,031}{4,491} \approx 0.675$$

(b) This time we are given that the crime was motivated by sexual orientation, so we only need to look at that row. There were 1,460 such crimes total, and 418 were against property, so the probability is

$$\frac{418}{1,460} \approx 0.286$$

☑ 3. Find conditional probabilities.

▼ Try This One 8

Based on the data in the above table, find the probability that

(a) A crime was motivated by either race or religion given that it was a crime against society.
(b) A crime was against persons given that it was motivated by religion or sexual orientation.

Answers to Try This One

1 $\frac{1}{4,000}$

2 $\frac{1}{169}$

3 (a) $\frac{1}{125}$ (b) $\frac{4}{125}$

4 Approximately 0.168

5 (a) $\frac{1}{96}$ (b) $\frac{1}{224}$

6 (a) $\frac{1}{270,725}$ (b) $\frac{11}{4,165}$

7 $\frac{2}{5}$

8 (a) $\frac{3}{4}$ (b) $\frac{1,460}{2,937} \approx 0.497$

EXERCISE SET 11-8

Writing Exercises

1. What is the difference between independent and dependent events? Give an example of each.
2. What is meant by the term conditional probability?
3. Describe two methods for computing conditional probability.
4. Explain why the probability of two consecutive events occurring couldn't possibly be the sum of the two individual probabilities.

In Exercises 5–12, decide whether the events are independent or dependent, and explain your answer.

5. Tossing a coin and drawing a card from a deck.
6. Drawing a ball from an urn, not replacing it, and then drawing a second ball.
7. Getting a raise in salary and purchasing a new car.
8. Driving on ice and having an accident.
9. Having a large shoe size and having a high IQ.
10. A father being left-handed and a daughter being left-handed.
11. Smoking excessively and having lung cancer.
12. Eating an excessive amount of ice cream and smoking an excessive amount of cigarettes.

Real-World Applications

13. If 18% of students on campus said they were voting for Homer Simpson for the next President of the United States, find the probability that if three students were randomly selected on campus and asked whom they were voting for in the presidential election, all would say they were voting for Homer Simpson.
14. A national study of patients who were overweight found that 56% also have elevated blood pressure. If two overweight patients are selected, find the probability that both have elevated blood pressure.
15. According to the National Highway Traffic Safety Administration, 83% of Americans used seat belts regularly in 2008. If four people are selected at random, find the probability that all four regularly use seat belts.
16. A computer salesperson at Best Buy claims that she has a 20% chance of selling a computer when helping out a customer. If this is true and she talks to four customers before lunch, find the probability that all four will buy computers.
17. If 25% of Michael's graduating class are not U.S. citizens, find the probability that two randomly selected graduating students are not U.S. citizens.
18. If two people are selected at random, what is the probability that they were both born in December?
19. If two people are selected at random, find the probability that they were born in the same month.
20. If three people are selected, find the probability that all three were born in March.
21. If half of Americans believe that the federal government should take "primary responsibility" for eliminating poverty, find the probability that three randomly selected Americans will agree that it is the federal government's responsibility to eliminate poverty.
22. What is the probability that a husband, wife, and daughter have the same birthday?
23. A telecommunications company has six satellites, two of which are sending a weak signal. If two are selected at random without replacement find the probability that both are sending a weak signal.

24. In Exercise 23, find the probability that one satellite sends a strong signal and the other sends a weak signal.
25. The U.S. Department of Justice reported that in 2005, 50.8% of all murders are committed with a handgun. If three murder cases are selected at random, find the probability that a handgun was used in all three.
26. In a department store there are 120 customers, 90 of whom will buy at least one item. If five customers are selected at random, one by one, find the probability that all will buy at least one item.
27. During a game of online hearts, three cards are dealt, one at a time without replacement, from a shuffled, ordinary deck of cards. Find these probabilities:

    (a) All are jacks.
    (b) All are clubs.
    (c) All are red cards.

28. In a group of eight Olympic track stars, five are hurdlers. If three are selected at random without replacement, find the probability they are all hurdlers.
29. In Exercise 28, find the probability none of them are hurdlers.
30. In a class consisting of 15 men and 12 women, two different homework papers were selected at random. Find the probability that both papers belonged to women.
31. While practicing juggling with a die, a quarter, and a spoon, Ken drops the quarter first and then the die and is left holding the spoon. Find the probability of getting a 3 on the die given that the coin landed heads up.
32. Juan draws a black card from an ordinary deck as the first card for a game of Gin Rummy. What is the probability the card was a king?
33. At a carnival gambling booth, two dice are rolled, and a sum of seven wins double your money. Find the probability that the sum is 7 if it is given that one of the numbers was a 6.
34. Frank flips a coin to see who will pick up the pizza from Pizza Hut, and then Sun rolls a die to see how much the person picking up the pizza has to pay toward the meal. Find the probability that the coin landed on tails and the number on the die was odd.

35. A computer randomly deals an ordinary deck of cards for a game of FreeCell, and the first card dealt is a face card. Find the probability that the card was also a diamond.
36. During a backgammon game, Kelly rolled the two dice on the board. Find the probability that the sum obtained was greater than 8 given that the number on one die was a 6.

Use this information for Exercises 37–40.
Three red cards are numbered 1, 2, and 3. Three black cards are numbered 4, 5, and 6.
The cards are placed in a box and one card is selected at random.

37. Find the probability that a red card was selected given that the number on the card was an odd number.
38. Find the probability that a number less than 5 was selected given that the card was a black card.
39. Find the probability that a number less than 5 was selected given that the card was red.
40. Find the probability that a black card was selected given that the number on the card was an even number.

Use the following information for Exercises 41–44.
A survey of 200 college students shows the average number of minutes that people talk on their cell phones each month.

	Less than 600	600–799	800–999	1,000 or more
Men	56	18	10	16
Women	61	18	13	8

If a person is selected at random, find these probabilities:

41. The person talked less than 600 minutes if it is known that the person was a woman.
42. The person talked 1,000 or more minutes if it is known that the person was a man.
43. The person was a woman if it is known that the person talked between 600 and 799 minutes.
44. The person was a man if it is known that the person talked between 600 and 999 minutes.

Critical Thinking

45. A magician is carrying his box of tricks and out spill three dice. What is the probability that the three dice sum to 9?
46. In a rush to pay for her latte, Shelly dropped her change purse and five coins fell out. What is the probability that as the coins fell to the floor, there was at least one head?
47. During a comedy show, the comedian selected three people at random from the audience. What is the probability that the three people will have the same birthday? (Ignore the year.)
48. Suppose that I roll two dice and tell you that the result is definitely even, then offer you 3 to 1 odds that the total isn't 4. Draw a diagram to illustrate the outcomes, then use the diagram to compute the conditional probability. Finally, decide if the given odds are in your favor or not.

Section 11-9 The Binomial Distribution

Many probability problems involve situations that have only two outcomes. When a baby is born, it will be either male or female. When a coin is tossed, it will land either heads or tails. When the New York Yankees play, they either win or they lose. That cute girl that sits behind you in class will either go out with you or she won't.

Other situations can be reduced to two outcomes. For example, medical procedures can be classified as either successful or unsuccessful. An answer to a multiple choice exam question can be classified as correct or incorrect even though there may be four answer choices.

Situations like these are called *binomial experiments*.

LEARNING OBJECTIVES

☐ 1. Identify binomial experiments.

☐ 2. Compute probabilities of outcomes in a binomial experiment.

☐ 3. Construct a probability distribution.

A **binomial experiment** is a probability experiment that satisfies the following requirements:

1. Each trial can have only two outcomes, or outcomes that can be reduced to two outcomes. These outcomes can be considered as either a success or a failure.
2. The outcomes must be independent of each other.
3. There must be a fixed number of trials.
4. The probability of a success must remain the same for all trials of the experiment.

EXAMPLE 1   Deciding if an Experiment is Binomial

Decide whether or not each is a binomial experiment.

(a) Drawing a card from a deck and seeing what suit it is
(b) Answering a question on a true-false test
(c) Asking 100 people whether or not they smoke
(d) Selecting cards at random from a deck without replacement and deciding if they are red or black cards

SOLUTION

(a) No, since there are four outcomes: heart, diamond, spade, or club.
(b) Yes, there are only two outcomes: correct and incorrect.
(c) Yes, there are only two outcomes: yes or no.
(d) No, since the cards are not being replaced, the probability changes on each draw.

▼ Try This One 1

Decide whether or not each experiment is a binomial experiment.

(a) Selecting a colored ball with replacement from an urn containing three balls of different colors, and seeing if the chosen ball is orange
(b) Selecting a number from a bingo machine
(c) Selecting a card at random from a deck with replacement and noting its color, red or black
(d) Tossing a die and getting a 3

☑ 1. Identify binomial experiments.

Consider the following experiment. A box contains four colored balls—one each of red, black, white, and green. A ball is randomly selected and its color is recorded. It is then replaced and a second ball is randomly selected and its color is recorded. The tree diagram for this experiment is shown in Figure 11-9.

The probability of selecting two green balls is $\frac{1}{16}$ since there is only one way to select two green balls, namely (G, G), and there are 16 total possible outcomes in the sample space. The probability of selecting exactly one green is $\frac{6}{16}$ or $\frac{3}{8}$ since there are 6 outcomes that contain one green ball: (R, G), (B, G), (W, G), (G, R), (G, B), and (G, W). The probability of selecting no green balls is $\frac{9}{16}$ since there are 9 outcomes that contain no green balls.

A table for the probabilities can be shown.

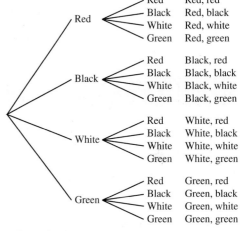

Outcome	Probability
0 green balls	$\frac{9}{16}$
1 green ball	$\frac{6}{16} = \frac{3}{8}$
2 green balls	$\frac{1}{16}$
Sum	$\frac{16}{16} = 1$

The experiment can be considered a binomial experiment since it meets the four conditions of a binomial experiment:

Figure 11-9

1. Each trial has only two outcomes. The ball chosen is either green or it is not green.

2. The outcomes are independent of each other: each ball is replaced before the second ball is selected.

3. There is a fixed number of trials. In this case, there are two draws.

4. The probability of a success remains the same in each case. In this case, since there is only one green ball and a total of four balls, $P(S) = \frac{1}{4}$ and $P(F) = 1 - \frac{1}{4} = \frac{3}{4}$. (Getting a green ball is considered a success. Getting any other colored ball is considered a failure.)

The probability of a given outcome for a binomial experiment can be found using the binomial probability formula.

The Binomial Probability Formula

The probability of exactly x successes in n trials is

$$P(x) = {}_nC_x \cdot p^x \cdot q^{n-x}$$

where p = the probability of a success

q = the probability of a failure ($q = 1 - p$)

Since p is the probability of success on any given trial, using the multiplication rule, p^x is the probability of x successes. The same reasoning shows that q^{n-x} is the probability of $n - x$ failures. We also need to multiply by the number of different ways we can get x successes in n trials, which is ${}_nC_x$: the number of combinations of n objects taken x at a time.

In our example of drawing balls from a box, let's find the probability of getting one green ball in two draws. In this case, $n = 2$, $x = 1$, and $n - x = 1$. The probability of success (p) is $\frac{1}{4}$, and the probability of failure (q) is $\frac{3}{4}$. Using the binomial probability formula,

$$P(1 \text{ green ball}) = {}_nC_x \cdot p^x \cdot q^{n-x}$$
$$= {}_2C_1 \cdot \left(\frac{1}{4}\right)^1 \cdot \left(\frac{3}{4}\right)^1$$
$$= \frac{2!}{(2-1)!1!} \cdot \frac{1}{4} \cdot \frac{3}{4}$$
$$= 2 \cdot \frac{3}{16} = \frac{3}{8}$$

This matches the probability found using a tree diagram.

EXAMPLE 2   Using the Binomial Probability Formula

Suppose that the morning after your birthday, you remember that you have a 20 question true or false quiz in your early class. Uh oh! Completely unprepared and a little woozy, you decide to guess on every question. What is the probability that you'll get 16 out of 20 right?

SOLUTION

Because the questions are true or false, and you're arbitrarily guessing, the probability of getting any given question right is $\frac{1}{2}$. The number of trials is $n = 20$, and the number of successes is $x = 16$. The probability of success is $p = \frac{1}{2}$, and the probability of failure is then $q = 1 - \frac{1}{2}$. Substituting these values into the binomial probability formula, we get

$$P(16 \text{ right}) = {}_nC_x \cdot p^x \cdot q^{n-x}$$
$$= {}_{20}C_{16} \cdot \left(\frac{1}{2}\right)^{16} \cdot \left(\frac{1}{2}\right)^{20-16}$$
$$= \frac{20!}{(20-16)!16!} \cdot \left(\frac{1}{2}\right)^{16} \cdot \left(\frac{1}{2}\right)^4$$
$$= 4{,}845 \cdot \frac{1}{1{,}048{,}576} \approx 0.0046$$

In short, your chances are not good.

Math Note

Notice that because there are 20 trials in Example 2, it would be cumbersome (to say the very least!) to use a tree diagram to find the probability.

▼ Try This One 2

What is the probability of getting exactly 6 questions right when guessing on a 10 question true or false quiz?

EXAMPLE 3   Using the Binomial Probability Formula

A box contains three red balls and two yellow balls. Five balls are selected with each ball being replaced before the next ball is selected. Find the probability of getting

(a) Exactly two yellow balls
(b) Fewer than two yellow balls

SOLUTION

(a) Use the binomial probability formula with $n = 5$, $x = 2$, $p = \frac{2}{5}$, and $q = \frac{3}{5}$.

$$P(2 \text{ yellow}) = {}_5C_2 \left(\frac{2}{5}\right)^2 \left(\frac{3}{5}\right)^3$$

$$= \frac{5!}{(5-2)!2!} \cdot \frac{4}{25} \cdot \frac{27}{125}$$

$$= 0.3456$$

(b) Fewer than two yellow balls means 0 or 1 yellow ball, so we will find each probability and add the answers.

$$P(0 \text{ yellow}) = {}_5C_0 \left(\frac{2}{5}\right)^0 \left(\frac{3}{5}\right)^5$$

$$= \frac{5!}{(5-0)!0!}(1)\left(\frac{243}{3,125}\right)$$

$$= 0.07776$$

$$P(1 \text{ yellow}) = {}_5C_1 \left(\frac{2}{5}\right)^1 \left(\frac{3}{5}\right)^4$$

$$= \frac{5!}{(5-1)!1!}\left(\frac{2}{5}\right)\left(\frac{81}{625}\right)$$

$$= 0.2592$$

$$P(0 \text{ or } 1 \text{ yellow}) = 0.07776 + 0.2592 = 0.33696$$

▼ Try This One 3

For the experiment in Example 3, find the probability of getting

(a) Exactly one red ball
(b) More than three red balls

When several subjects are selected without replacement from a large group of subjects, theoretically the selections are not independent and the binary probability formula doesn't apply. However, since the individual probabilities of a subject selected change only slightly, binomial probabilities can be used. This is shown in the next example.

EXAMPLE 4   Using the Binary Probability Formula with a Large Sample

Forty-two percent of individuals surveyed said that a man should always pay for the first date. If 10 people are randomly selected, find the probability that 3 randomly selected people will agree that a man should pay.

SOLUTION

Since the population is large, the binomial distribution can be used even though there's no replacement. In this case, $n = 10$, $x = 3$, $n - x = 7$, $p = 0.42$ and $q = 1 - 0.42 = 0.58$.

$$P(x) = {}_nC_x \cdot p^x \cdot q^{n-x}$$

$$P(3 \text{ people agree}) = {}_{10}C_3(0.42)^3(0.58)^7$$

$$= \frac{10!}{(10-7)!3!}(0.42)^3(0.58)^7$$

$$\approx 120(0.074)(0.022)$$

$$\approx 0.195$$

☑ 2. Compute probabilities of outcomes in a binomial experiment.

▼ Try This One 4

In a large community, it was determined that 44% of the residents use the public library at least once a year. If 10 people are selected, find the probability that exactly 2 people have used the library during the last year.

To describe all of the outcomes in a probability experiment, we can build a *probability distribution*.

A **probability distribution** consists of a list of all outcomes and the corresponding probabilities for a probability experiment.

EXAMPLE 5   Constructing a Probability Distribution

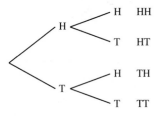

Figure 11-10

Construct a probability distribution for the possible number of tails when you flip two coins.

SOLUTION

When two coins are tossed, the outcomes can be shown using a tree diagram. See Figure 11-10.

The sample space is {HH, HT, TH, TT}. Each outcome has a probability of $\frac{1}{4}$. Notice that the outcome "No tails" is HH, and $P(HH) = \frac{1}{4}$. The outcome of one tail consists of HT and TH, and $P(HT, TH) = \frac{1}{4} + \frac{1}{4} = \frac{1}{2}$. The outcome of two tails is TT and $P(TT) = \frac{1}{4}$. Now a probability distribution can be constructed by considering the outcomes as the number of tails. The probability distribution is

Number of tails, x	0	1	2
Probability, $P(x)$	$\frac{1}{4}$	$\frac{1}{2}$	$\frac{1}{4}$

Math Note

In Example 5, the number of trials was small enough that a tree diagram was more efficient than using the binomial probability formula three times.

☑ 3. Construct a probability distribution.

▼ Try This One 5

Three cards are numbered 1, 2, 3 and placed into a bag. Another bag is set up the same way, then one card is drawn from each bag and the numbers are added. Find all possible totals, and construct a probability distribution for the experiment.

Answers to Try This One

1 (a) Yes   (b) No   (c) Yes   (d) Yes

2 $\frac{105}{512} \approx 0.205$

3 (a) 0.0768 (b) 0.33696

4 ≈0.084

5

Total	2	3	4	5	6
Probability	$\frac{1}{9}$	$\frac{2}{9}$	$\frac{1}{3}$	$\frac{2}{9}$	$\frac{1}{9}$

EXERCISE SET 11-9

Writing Exercises

1. What are the four requirements for a probability experiment to be a binomial experiment?
2. Give a brief description of how an experiment with several outcomes can be reduced to one with two outcomes.
3. What is a probability distribution?
4. In a binomial experiment, given the probability of any trial being a success, explain how to find the probability of a failure.

Computational Exercises

Find the probability of each using the binary probability formula.

5. $n = 3$, $p = 0.40$, $x = 2$
6. $n = 5$, $p = 0.80$, $x = 3$
7. $n = 10$, $p = 0.66$, $x = 4$
8. $n = 5$, $p = 0.20$, $x = 8$

9. $n = 20$, $p = 0.93$, $x = 12$
10. $n = 13$, $p = 0.16$, $x = 7$
11. $n = 9$, $p = 0.33$, $x = 5$
12. $n = 6$, $p = 0.58$, $x = 2$

13. $n = 4$, $p = 0.72$, $x = 0$
14. $n = 7$, $p = 0.25$, $x = 1$

Real-World Applications

15. During a game of Yahtzee, a player needs three sixes. She rolls the same die three times. What is the probability she got three sixes?
16. A cooler held three energy drinks. One was a Monster, another was a Red Bull, and the third was Atomic X. Simon selects an energy drink at random, puts it back, then selects another, puts it back and then selects a third drink. Find the probability that

    (a) No Red Bull drinks are selected.
    (b) Exactly one Atomic X drink is selected.
    (c) Exactly three Monster drinks are selected.

17. Of all identity thefts, 27% are solved in 1 day or less. If 10 cases are selected, find the probability that exactly 5 are solved in 1 day or less.
18. Of all people who do banking, 16% prefer to use ATMs. Of 20 people who are banking customers, find the probability that exactly 4 prefer to use the ATM.
19. According to the Bureau of Labor Statistics, among married-couple families where both the husband and wife have earnings, 26% of wives earned more than their husbands. If 18 wives are selected, find the probability that exactly 6 of them earn more than their husbands.
20. It is reported that 41% of people surveyed said that they eat meals while driving. If 12 drivers are selected, find the probability that exactly 6 will say that they eat meals while driving.
21. An instructor gives a 10-question true-false exam. If a student does not study and guesses, find the probability of getting exactly five correct answers.
22. A multiple-choice quiz consists of five questions. Each question has four responses, and only one of the answers is correct. Find the probability of guessing and getting exactly three correct answers.
23. Approximately 45% of people who eat at fast food places choose McDonald's. If 10 randomly selected people are surveyed, find the probability that 5 selected McDonald's.
24. About 30% of people who listen to commercial radio change the station in 1 to 2 minutes after the commercials begin. If six people are randomly selected, find the probability that two will change the station within 1 to 2 minutes after the commercials begin.
25. A survey shows that 65% of workers ages 42 to 60 would select excellent retirement benefits over a high salary when seeking a job. If 15 people are randomly selected, find the probability that 9 would select excellent benefits over a high salary.
26. About 22% of people selected Yahoo for instant messaging services during a selected year. If six randomly selected people are asked what instant messaging service they use, find the probability that one will say that he or she uses Yahoo. (Source: Nielson/net Ratings.)
27. A survey done by Zoomerang found that 30% of the people who were planning to remodel were planning to remodel the family room or den. If 12 people planning to remodel are selected, find the probability that 5 are planning to remodel the family room or den.
28. Approximately 20% of all college students in the United States do not have health insurance. If 10 college students are randomly selected in the United States, find the probability that 3 will not have health insurance.

29. A survey found that 55% of people said that a diet was harder to stick to than a budget. (Source: Kelton Research for Medifast.) If 20 people are randomly selected, find the probability that 10 will say that a diet is harder to stick to than a budget.

30. A survey done by Harris found that 40% of the people surveyed said that their children will have between $5,001 and $20,000 in debt when they graduate from college. If 25 people are selected, find the probability that 14 will say that their children will have a debt between $5,001 and $20,000 when they graduate from college.

31. A survey done by Harris International QUICK-QUERY found the 10% of women had a fear of flying. If 50 women are selected, find the probability that 6 will have a fear of flying.

32. In a Harris survey, 40% of the people surveyed said that they received error messages from doing online transactions. If 18 people are randomly selected, find the probability that 5 or 6 people would have received error messages while doing online transactions.

33. A survey found that 33% of people earning between $30,000 and $75,000 said that they were very happy. If 6 people are selected at random, find the probability that at most 2 people who earn between $30,000 and $75,000 would consider themselves very happy.

34. In a recent survey, 2% of the people selected stated that they would keep their current job if they won a multi-million-dollar lottery. If 20 people are selected, find the probability that 3, 4, or 5 of them would keep their job.

Critical Thinking

35. Using coins, cards, colored balls, etc., design a binomial experiment.

C H A P T E R **11** **Summary**

Section	Important Terms	Important Ideas
11-1	Fundamental counting principle Factorial notation Permutation Permutation rule Tree diagram	**In order** to determine the total number of outcomes for a sequence of events, the fundamental counting rule or the permutation rule can be used. When the order or arrangement of the objects in a sequence of events is important, then the result is called a permutation of the objects.
11-2	Combination Combination rule	**When the** order of the objects is not important, then the result is called a combination.
11-3	Probability experiment Outcome Sample space Event Classical probability Empirical probability Observed frequency	**Flipping coins,** drawing cards from a deck, and rolling a die are examples of probability experiments. The set of all possible outcomes of a probability experiment is called a sample space. The two types of probability are classical and empirical. Classical probability uses sample spaces. Empirical probability uses frequency distributions and is based on observation. Probability is a number that represents how likely it is that something will occur. Probability can be zero, one, or any number in between. When the probability of an event is close to zero, the event is highly unlikely to occur. When the probability of an event is near one, the event is almost certain to occur.
11-4		**When sample** spaces are difficult to identify, it is often helpful to use tree diagrams or tables to identify all possible outcomes for a probability experiment.
11-5		**Probabilities** of events can be found by using the fundamental counting principle, the permutation rule, or the combination rule, depending on the situation.
11-6	Odds Expectation (expected value)	**In order** to determine payoffs, gambling establishments give odds. There are two ways to compute odds for a game of chance. They are "odds in favor of an event" and "odds against the event." Another concept related to probability and odds is the concept of expectation or expected value. Expected value is used to determine what happens over the long run. It is found by multiplying the outcomes of a probability experiment by their corresponding probabilities and then finding the sum of the products.
11-7	Mutually exclusive events Addition rules	**Two events** are said to be mutually exclusive if they cannot occur at the same time. To find the probability of one event or another event occurring, one of two addition rules can be used, depending on whether or not the events are mutually exclusive.

	Multiplication rules Independent events Dependent events Conditional probability	**Events can** be classified as independent or dependent. Events are said to be independent if the occurrence of the first event does not affect the probability of the occurrence of the next event. If the probability of the second event occurring is changed by the occurrence of the first event, then the events are dependent. To find the probability of one event and another event occurring, one of the two multiplication rules can be used, depending on whether the two events are independent or dependent. If the probability of an event B occurring is affected by an event A occurring, then we say that a condition has been imposed on the event and the probability of event B occurring given that A has occurred is called a conditional probability.
11-8		
11-9	Binomial experiment Probability distribution	**Many probability** experiments have two outcomes or can be reduced to two outcomes. If the trials are independent, fixed in number, and have the same probability of a success, then the experiment can be considered a binomial experiment. These problems can be solved using the binomial probability formula. For some probability experiments, a probability distribution can be constructed, listing all outcomes with the corresponding probabilities.

MATH IN Gambling REVISITED

1. Using the table for rolling two dice on page 601, the probability of rolling 2, 3, 11, or 12 is $\frac{1}{6}$, meaning the probability of losing is $\frac{5}{6}$. So the two outcomes are $+\$4$ with probability $\frac{1}{6}$, and $-\$1$ with probability $\frac{5}{6}$. The expected value of each trial is then

$$+4 \cdot \frac{1}{6} + (-1) \cdot \frac{5}{6} = -\frac{1}{6}$$

In 100 trials, you would expect to lose $\$100\left(\frac{1}{6}\right)$, or $\$16.67$.

2. The probability of winning $\$35$ is $\frac{1}{38}$, and the probability of losing $\$1$ is $\frac{37}{38}$. The expected value of each spin is

$$+35 \cdot \frac{1}{38} + (-1) \cdot \frac{37}{38} = -\frac{2}{38} = -\frac{1}{19}$$

In 100 trials, you would expect to lose $\$100\left(\frac{1}{19}\right)$, or $\$5.26$.

3. Using the same idea as scenarios 1 and 2, the expected value of each ticket is

$$+20{,}000{,}000 \cdot \frac{1}{175{,}711{,}536} + (-1) \cdot \frac{175{,}711{,}535}{175{,}711{,}536}$$

$$\approx -\$0.8862$$

Buying 100 tickets, you would expect to lose $\$100(-0.8862)$, or $\$88.62$.

4. You would win $\$1$ with probability $\frac{1}{2}$, and lose $\$1$ with probability $\frac{1}{2}$, so the expected value of each flip is

$$1 \cdot \frac{1}{2} + (-1) \cdot \frac{1}{2} = 0$$

In 100 flips you would expect to break even.

The best, by far is flipping a coin, followed by roulette, the church fair dice game, and, bringing up the rear by quite a bit, the multistate lottery. Notice that under the best of circumstances, you are likely to break even!

Review Exercises

Section 11-1

1. Compute $\frac{14!}{11!}$.
2. Compute $_{12}P_6$.
3. An automobile license plate consists of three letters followed by four digits. How many different plates can be made if repetitions are allowed? If repetitions are allowed in the letters but not in the digits?
4. How many different arrangements of the letters in the word *bread* are there?
5. How many different arrangements of the letters in the word *cheese* are there?
6. How many different three-digit odd numbers use only the digits 0, 1, 2, 3, 4?

Section 11-2

7. Compute $_9C_6$.
8. Find both the number of combinations and the number of permutations of 10 objects taken 4 at a time.
9. Describe the difference between combinations and permutations.
10. How many different three-digit combinations can be made by using the numbers 1, 3, 5, 7, and 9 without repetitions if the "right" combination can open a safe? Does a combination lock really use combinations?
11. How many two-card pairs (i.e., the same rank) are there in a standard deck?
12. How many ways can five different television programs be selected from 12 programs?
13. A quiz consists of six multiple-choice questions. Each question has three possible answer choices. How many different answer keys can be made?
14. How many different ways can a buyer select four television models from a possible choice of six models?

Section 11-3

15. Which of the following numbers could represent a probability?
    (a) $\frac{3}{2}$
    (b) $\frac{2}{3}$
    (c) 0.1
    (d) $-\frac{1}{2}$
    (e) 80%
16. When a die is rolled, find the probability of getting
    (a) A 5.   (b) A 6.   (c) A number less than 5.

17. When a card is drawn from a deck, find the probability of getting
    (a) A heart.
    (b) A 7 and a club.
    (c) A 7 or a club.
    (d) A jack.
    (e) A black card.
18. In a survey conducted at the food court in the local mall, 20 people preferred Panda Express, 16 preferred Sbarro Pizza, and 9 preferred Subway for lunch. If a person is selected at random, find the probability that he or she prefers Sbarro Pizza.
19. If a die is rolled one time, find these probabilities:
    (a) Getting a 7
    (b) Getting an odd number
    (c) Getting a number less than 3
20. In a recent survey in a college dorm that has 1,500 rooms, 850 have an Xbox 360. If a room in this dorm is randomly selected, find the probability that it has an Xbox 360.
21. During a Midnight Madness sale at Old Navy, 16 white cargo pants, 3 khaki cargo pants, 9 tan cargo pants, and 7 black cargo pants were sold. If a customer who made a purchase during the sale is selected at random, find the probability that he or she bought
    (a) A pair of tan cargo pants.
    (b) A pair of black cargo pants or a pair of white cargo pants.
    (c) A pair of khaki, tan, or black cargo pants.
    (d) A pair of cargo pants that was not white.
22. In a survey of college students who reported they used a search engine that day, 16 reported they used Google, 4 used MSN, 3 used Yahoo! Search, and 7 used Ask Jeeves. If a student from the survey is selected at random and the student used one search engine that day, find the probability he or she used
    (a) Yahoo! Search.
    (b) MSN or Ask Jeeves.
    (c) Google or Yahoo! Search or Ask Jeeves.
    (d) A search engine that was not MSN.
23. When two dice are rolled, find the probability of getting
    (a) A sum of 5 or 6.
    (b) A sum greater than 9.
    (c) A sum less than 4 or greater than 9.
    (d) A sum that is divisible by 4.
    (e) A sum of 14.
    (f) A sum less than 13.

24. Two dice are rolled. Find the probability of getting a sum of 8 if the number on one die is a 5.

Section 11-4

25. A person rolls an eight-sided die and then flips a coin. Draw a tree diagram and find the sample space.

26. A student can select one of three courses at 8:00 A.M.: English, mathematics, or chemistry. The student can select either psychology or sociology at 11:00 A.M. Finally, the student can select either world history or economics at 1:00 P.M. (a) Draw a tree diagram and find all the different ways the student can make a schedule. (b) Repeat part (a), but include the condition that the student will take classes only at 8 A.M. and 11 A.M. if his first class is chemistry.

27. As an experiment in probability, a two-question multiple choice quiz is given at the beginning of class, but the answers are all written in Hebrew, which none of the students can read. This forces everyone to guess. Each question has choices A, B, C, D, and E. Construct a table that displays the sample space, then use the table to find the probability that both questions in a randomly selected quiz were answered with D or E (either D-E, or E-D).

Section 11-5

28. A card is selected from a deck. Find the probability that it is a diamond given that it is a red card.

29. A person has six bond accounts, three stock accounts, and two mutual fund accounts. If three investments are selected at random, find the probability that one of each type of account is selected.

30. A newspaper advertises five different movies, three plays, and two baseball games. If a couple selects three activities at random, find the probability they will attend two plays and one movie.

31. In putting together the music lineup for an outdoor spring festival, Fast Eddie can choose from 4 student bands and 12 nonstudent bands. There are five time slots for bands; the first at 3 P.M., the others on the hour until 7 P.M. If Eddie chooses the bands randomly, find the probability that no student bands will be picked.

Section 11-6

32. Find the odds for an event E when $P(E) = \frac{1}{4}$.
33. Find the odds against an event E when $P(E) = \frac{5}{6}$.
34. Find the probability of an event when the odds for the event are 6:4.
35. The table lists five outcomes for a probability experiment with the corresponding probabilities. Find the expected value.

Outcome	5	10	15	20	25
Probability	0.5	0.2	0.1	0.1	0.1

36. Ishi has a penny, a nickel, a dime, a quarter, and a half-dollar in her wallet. One falls out onto the counter as she is paying for gas. Find the expected value of the event.

37. A person selects a card from a deck. If it is a red card, he wins $1. If it is a black card between and including 2 and 10, he wins $5. If it is a black face card, he wins $10, and if it is a black ace, he wins $100. Find the expectation of the game.

Section 11-7

In Exercises 38–40, decide if the two events are mutually exclusive.

38. You meet someone while out; she gives you her phone number or her email address.
39. You complete a course and either pass or fail.
40. You spend a weekend in Las Vegas; you either win money, lose money, or break even.
41. If one of the 50 states is selected at random to be the site of a new nuclear power plant,

    (a) Find the probability that the state either borders Canada or Mexico.
    (b) Find the probability that the state begins with either A or ends with S.

42. During Halloween, Seth collected six Snickers bars, three Twix bars, two packages of M&M's, and two boxes of Nerds while trick-or-treating in the dorm. If one candy is selected from his candy stash, find the probability of getting a package of M&M's or a Twix bar.

Section 11-8

In Exercises 43–46, decide if the two events are independent.

43. Missing 3 straight days of class and failing the next test.
44. Missing 3 straight days of class and getting overloaded with spam e-mails.
45. Drawing an ace from a standard deck, then drawing a second ace.
46. Drawing an ace from a standard deck, then replacing that card, shuffling, and drawing another ace.
47. In a family of three children, find the probability that all the children will be girls if it is known that at least one of the children is a girl.
48. A Gallup Poll found that 78% of Americans worry about the quality and healthfulness of their diet. If five people are selected at random, find the probability that all five worry about the quality and healthfulness of their diet.

Source: *The Book of Odds,* Michael D. Shook and Robert C. Shook (New York: Penguin Putnam, Inc., 1991), p. 33.

49. Twenty-five percent of the engineering graduates of a university received a starting salary of $50,000 or more. If three of the graduates are selected at random, find the probability that all have a starting salary of $50,000 or more.

50. Three cards are drawn from an ordinary deck *without* replacement. Find the probability of getting

   (a) All black cards.
   (b) All spades.
   (c) All queens.

51. A coin is tossed and a card is drawn from a deck. Find the probability of getting

   (a) A head and a 6.
   (b) A tail and a red card.
   (c) A head and a club.

52. The data in the table below are based on a nationwide exit poll taken on November 4, 2008. The numbers are based on an average sample of 1,000 voters. The rows represent the political affiliation of voters, and the columns represent how they voted.

	Obama	McCain	Other
Democrat	347	39	4
Republican	32	285	3
Independent	151	128	11

(a) Find the probability that a randomly selected person voted for Obama given that he or she was not Republican.
(b) Find the probability that a randomly selected person voted for either Obama or McCain given that he or she was Independent.
(c) Find the probability that a randomly selected person was a Republican given that he or she voted for McCain.

Section 11-9

53. Use the binomial probability formula to find the probability of five successes in six trials when the probability of success on each trial is 1/3.

54. A survey found that 24% of families eat at home as a family five times a week. If 10 families are selected, find the probability that exactly 3 will say that they eat at home as a family five times a week.

55. According to a survey, 45% of teenagers said that they have seen passengers in an automobile encouraging the driver to speed. If 16 teens are selected, find the probability that exactly 6 will say that they have seen passengers encouraging the driver to speed.

56. Construct a probability distribution for the possible number of heads when tossing a coin three times.

Chapter Test

In Exercises 1–4, compute the requested value.

1. $\frac{20!}{18!}$

2. $_7C_5$

3. $_{12}P_5$

4. The probability of 8 successes in 10 trials when the probability of success on each trial is $\frac{1}{4}$.

5. If someone saw the title of Chapter 11 in this book and asked you "What is probability?" what would you say?

6. Describe a situation where combinations would be used to count possibilities and one where permutations would be used.

7. One company's ID cards consist of five letters followed by two digits. How many cards can be made if repetitions are allowed? If repetitions are not allowed?

8. A physics test consists of 25 true-false questions. How many different possible answer keys can be made?

9. At Blockbuster Video, there are seven DVDs in a box. How many different ways can four DVDs be selected?

10. How many ways can five sopranos and four altos be chosen for the university chorus from seven sopranos and nine altos?

11. Eight students at graduation are in line to take their seats. How many ways can they be seated in a row?

12. A soda machine servicer must restock and collect money from 15 machines, each one at a different location. How many ways can she select four machines to service in one day?

13. How many different ways can three cell phone covers be drawn from a box containing four differently colored cell phone covers, if

   (a) Each cell phone cover is replaced after it has been drawn?
   (b) There is no replacement?

14. If a man can wear a shirt or a sweater and a pair of dress slacks or a pair of jeans, how many different outfits can he wear?

15. When a card is drawn from an ordinary deck, find the probability of getting

   (a) A jack.   (b) A 4.

(c) A card less than 6 (an ace is considered above 6).

16. When a card is drawn from a deck, find the probability of getting

    (a) A diamond.
    (b) A 5 or a heart.
    (c) A 5 and a heart.
    (d) A king.
    (e) A red card.

17. At a sporting goods store, 12 people purchased blue rollerblades, 8 purchased green rollerblades, 4 purchased gray rollerblades, and 7 bought black rollerblades. If a customer is selected at random, find the probability he or she purchased

    (a) A pair of blue rollerblades.
    (b) A pair of green or gray rollerblades.
    (c) A pair of green or black or blue rollerblades.
    (d) A pair of rollerblades that was not black.

18. When two dice are rolled, find the probability of getting

    (a) A sum of 6 or 7.
    (b) A sum greater than 3 or greater than 8.
    (c) A sum less than 3 or greater than 8.
    (d) A sum that is divisible by 3.
    (e) A sum of 16.
    (f) A sum less than 11.

19. There are six cards numbered 1, 2, 3, 4, 5, and 6. A person flips a coin. If it lands heads up, he will select a card with an odd number. If it lands tails up, he will select a card with an even number. Draw a tree diagram and find the sample space.

20. Of the physics graduates of a university, 30% received a starting salary of $60,000 or more. If five of the graduates are selected at random, find the probability that all had a starting salary of $60,000 or more.

21. Five cards are drawn from an ordinary deck *without* replacement. Find the probability of getting

    (a) All red cards.
    (b) All diamonds.
    (c) All aces.

22. Four coins are tossed. Find the probability of getting four heads if it is known that two of the four coins landed heads up.

23. A card is drawn from a deck. Find the probability of getting a club if it is known that the card selected was a black card.

24. A die is rolled. Find the probability of getting a four if it is known that the result of the roll was an even number.

25. A coin is tossed and a die is rolled. Find the probability of getting a head on the coin if it is known that the number on the die is even.

26. Nurses at one hospital can be classified according to gender (male, female), income (low, medium, high), and rank (staff nurse, charge nurse, head nurse). Draw a tree diagram and show all possible outcomes.

27. The National Gaming Association can select one of four cities for its Pac Man tournament next year. The cities are Miami, San Francisco, Philadelphia, and Houston. The following year, it can hold the tournament in Chicago or Indianapolis. How many different possibilities are there for the next 2 years? Draw a tree diagram and show all possibilities.

28. Find the odds in favor of an event E when $P(E) = \frac{3}{8}$.

29. Find the odds against an event E when $P(E) = \frac{4}{9}$.

30. Find the probability of an event when the odds against the event are 3:7.

31. There are six cards placed face down in a box. Each card has a number written on it. One is a 4, one is a 5, one is a 2, one is a 10, one is a 3, and one is a 7. A person selects a card. Find the expected value of the draw.

32. A person selects a card from an ordinary deck of cards. If it is a black card, she wins $2. If it is a red card between or including 3 and 7, she wins $10. If it is a red face card, she wins $25, and if it is a black jack, she wins an additional $100. If it is any other card, she wins nothing. Find the expectation of the game.

33. In a soda machine in the student union, there are five Diet Cokes, four Mountain Dews, and two Dr. Peppers. If a person selects three sodas at random, find the probability that the selection will include one Diet Coke, one Mountain Dew, and one Dr. Pepper.

34. At Sally's freshman orientation, there were six computer science majors, four electrical engineering majors, and three architecture majors in her group. If four students are selected at random to receive a free tote bag with the school's logo, find the probability that the selection will include two computer science majors, one electrical engineering major, and one architecture major.

35. The results of a survey revealed that 30% of the people surveyed said that they would buy home electronic equipment at post-holiday sales. If 20 people are selected, find the probability that exactly 8 will purchase home electronic equipment after the holidays.

Projects

1. Make a set of three cards—one with the word "heads" on both sides, one with the word "tails" on both sides, and one with "heads" on one side and "tails" on the other side. With a partner, play the game described in Exercise 23 of Section 11-6 (page 615) 100 times and record how many times your partner wins. (*Note:* Do not change options during the 100 trials.)

   (a) Do you think the game is fair (i.e., does one person win approximately 50% of the time)?

   (b) If you think the game is unfair, explain what the probabilities might be and why.

2. Take a coin and tape a small weight (e.g., part of a paper clip) to one side. Flip the coin 100 times and record the results. Do you think you have changed the probabilities of the results of flipping the coin?

3. This game is called "Diet Fractions." Roll two dice and use the numbers to make a fraction less than or equal to one. Player A wins if the fraction cannot be reduced; otherwise, player B wins.

   (a) Play the game 100 times and record the results.

   (b) Decide if the game is fair or not. Explain why or why not.

   (c) Using the sample space for two dice, compute the probabilities of player A winning and player B winning. Do these agree with the results obtained in part a?

   Source: George W. Bright, John G. Harvey, and Margariete Montaque Wheeler, "Fair Games, Unfair Games." Chapter 8, *Teaching Statistics and Probability. NCTM 1981 Yearbook.* Reston, Virginia: The National Council of Teachers of Mathematics, Inc., 1981, p. 49. Used with permission.

4. Remember looking through cereal boxes for toys when you were a kid? It always seemed like you didn't get the exact one you wanted. Let's say that there was a certain toy you wanted, and five others that you could take or leave, all packed one per box at random. About how many boxes would you expect to have to buy to get the toy you wanted? Of course, you might have gotten it in the first box. Or you might have exhausted mom and dad's savings without ever getting it. These are the extremes.

   (a) You can simulate this experience using a single die, and rolling until a particular number of your choice comes up. Keep track of how many rolls it took, then repeat 99 more times, and find the average number of times it took.

   (b) If there were 10 different choices, you could simulate that by using the ace through 10 of a certain suit. Pick a certain card, shuffle the deck, and start dealing out the cards, keeping track of how many it takes to get the one you picked. Repeat 99 times and find the average.

   (c) Summarize your findings for both experiments.

   (d) Call getting the number or card you wanted a value of 2, and not getting it a value of 1. Then find the probability of each on any given roll or draw, and find the expected value for each experiment. How does it compare to the experimental results?

CHAPTER **12**

Statistics

Outline

MATH IN ▶ Sociology

Broadly defined, sociology is the study of human behavior within society. One important branch is criminology. This is not about investigating crimes, but rather studying patterns of criminal behavior and their effect on society. One of the main tools used by sociologists is statistics. This important area of math allows researchers to study patterns of behavior objectively, by analyzing information gathered from a mathematical perspective, not a subjective one.

It all begins with the gathering of data. Data are measurements or observations that are gathered for a study of some sort. Let's look at an example. There is an old adage in police work that violent crime increases with the temperature. A statement like "My cousin Jed is a cop, and he told me that there are more violent crimes during the summer" is not evidence, nor is it data. It's the subjective opinion of one individual. In order to study whether this phenomenon is legitimate, we would need to gather information about the number of violent crimes at different times during the year, as well as temperature information, and study those numbers objectively to see if there appears to be a connection. This is one of the most important topics in this chapter.

Data on its own isn't good for very much unless we develop methods for organizing, studying, and displaying that data. These are the methods that make up the bulk of this chapter. After discussing methods of gathering data, we will learn effective methods for organizing and displaying data so that it can be presented in a meaningful, understandable way. We will then turn our attention to techniques of analyzing data that will help us to unlock the secrets of what sets of data may be trying to tell us.

As for math in sociology, in an attempt to study the phenomena of violent crime and temperature increase, the data below were gathered. The table shows the number of homicides committed in each month of 2008 in Columbus, Ohio, along with the average high temperature for each of those months.

Month	Avg. high temp.	Homicides
1	36	6
2	40	8
3	51	5
4	63	7
5	73	7
6	82	12
7	85	9
8	84	12
9	77	11
10	66	15
11	53	9
12	41	7

After you've finished this chapter, you should be able to answer the following questions.

1. Based on a graph of the data called a scatter plot, does there appear to be a relationship between temperature and homicide rate?

2. Can you conclude, using a measure called the correlation coefficient, with 95% certainty that there is in fact a relationship between the data sets? What about with 99% certainty?

3. Do the results indicate that warmer temperatures cause people to behave in a more violent manner?

For answers, see Math in Sociology Revisited on page 711

Section 12-1 Gathering and Organizing Data

One of the big issues being discussed over the last 10 years or so in higher education is grade inflation—the perception that college students in general are getting much higher grades than they used to. But perception and reality are often two different things, so how could we decide if this is actually taking place? And if so, what are some possible reasons? Are students just getting smarter? Are professors lowering their standards?

In order to examine questions like this, it would be very valuable to gather some *data*.

LEARNING OBJECTIVES

☐ 1. Define data and statistics.

☐ 2. Explain the difference between a population and a sample.

☐ 3. Describe four basic methods of sampling.

☐ 4. Construct a frequency distribution for a data set.

☐ 5. Draw a stem and leaf plot for a data set.

> **Data** are measurements or observations that are gathered for an event under study.

Gathering data plays an important role in many different areas. In college sports, recruiters look at past performance to help them decide which high school players will be stars in college. In public health, administrators keep track of the number of residents in a certain area who contract a new strain of the flu. In education, researchers might try to determine if a new method of teaching is an improvement over traditional methods. Media outlets report the results of Nielsen, Harris, and Gallup polls. All of these studies begin with collecting data.

Once data have been collected, in order to get anything of value from it, the data need to be organized, summarized, and presented in a form that allows observers to draw conclusions. This is what the study of statistics is all about:

☑ 1. Define data and statistics.

> **Statistics** is the branch of mathematics that involves collecting, organizing, summarizing, and presenting data and drawing general conclusions from that data.

Populations and Samples

In the case of grade inflation, relevant data might be average grade point averages for students in several different years. Table 12-1 shows some GPA data from the website Gradeinflation.com.

TABLE 12-1	**Average GPAs for the Years 1991–1992 to 2006–2007 at Some American Universities**

School Year	Average undergraduate GPA
1991–1992	2.93
1996–1997	2.99
2001–2002	3.07
2006–2007	3.11

The numbers certainly appear to indicate that grade inflation is real. But where did the data come from? Does this factor in *all* colleges, or just some?

When statistical studies are performed, we usually begin by identifying the *population* for the study.

A **population** consists of all subjects under study.

In our example, the population is all colleges in the United States. If you were interested in study habits of the students at your school, the population would be all of the students at the school. More often than not, it's not realistic to gather data from every member of a population. In that case, a smaller representative group of the population would be selected. This group is called a *sample*.

☑ 2. Explain the difference between a population and a sample.

A **sample** is a representative subgroup or subset of a population.

The GPA data in Table 12-1 were gathered from a sample of 70 schools. The reason the data are compelling is that the sample is *representative* of the population as a whole. The schools chosen vary in size, cost, and geographic location. Some are public, and some are private. In order to ensure that a sample is representative, researchers use a variety of methods. Four of these sampling methods are explained next.

Sampling Methods

We will study four basic sampling methods that can be used to obtain a representative sample: random, systematic, stratified, and cluster.

In order to obtain a **random sample,** each subject of the population must have an equal chance of being selected. The best way to obtain a random sample is to use a list of random numbers. Random numbers can be obtained from a table or from a computer or calculator. Subjects in the population are numbered, and then they are selected by using the corresponding random numbers.

Using a random number generator such as a calculator, computer, or table of random numbers is like selecting numbers out of a hat. The difference is that when random numbers are generated by a calculator, computer, or table, there is a better chance that every number has an equally likely chance of being selected. When numbers are placed in a hat and mixed, you can never be sure that they are thoroughly mixed so that each number has an equal chance of being chosen.

A **systematic sample** is taken by numbering each member of the population and then selecting every kth member, where k is a natural number. For example, the researcher from gradeinflation.com might have numbered all of the colleges in the country and chosen every tenth one. When using systematic sampling, it's important that the starting number is selected at random.

When a population is divided into groups where the members of each group have similar characteristics (like large public schools, large private schools, small public schools, and small private schools) and members from each group are chosen at random, the result is called a **stratified sample.** The grade inflation researcher might have decided to choose five schools from each of those groups. Since 20 is a relatively small sample, it's possible that 15 or more came from large public schools. This would jeopardize the study because it may be the case that grade inflation is more or less likely at large public schools than schools in the other categories. So the purpose of a stratified sample is to ensure that all groups will be properly represented.

When an existing group of subjects that represent the population is used for a sample, it is called a **cluster sample.** For example, an inspector may select at random one carton of calculators from a large shipment and examine each one to determine how many are defective. The group in this carton represents a cluster. In this case, the researcher assumes that the calculators in the carton represent the population of all calculators manufactured by the company.

Samples are used in the majority of statistical studies, and if they are selected properly, the results of a study can be generalized to the population.

Wildlife biologists capture and tag animals to study how they live in the wild. The population is all the animals of the species in this region. The tagged animals constitute the sample. If the sample is not representative of the species the data will be skewed, and possibly misleading.

EXAMPLE 1   Choosing a Sample

A student in an education class is given an assignment to find out how late typical students at his campus stay up to study. He decides to stop by the union before his 9 A.M. class and ask everyone sitting at a table how late they were up studying the night before.

(a) What method of sampling is he using?
(b) Do you think he's likely to get a representative sample?

SOLUTION

(a) Since he is choosing all students in a particular place at a particular time, he has chosen a cluster sample.
(b) The sample is unlikely to be representative. Since he's polling people early in the morning, those that tend to stay up very late studying are less likely to be included in the sample.

☑ 3. Describe four basic methods of sampling.

▼ Try This One 1

To study the number of credit hours taken by a typical student, Shawna asks the registrar to provide e-mail addresses for 10 freshmen, 10 sophomores, 10 juniors, and 10 seniors. From each group, she asks for one whose student ID ends in 0, one whose ends in 1, and so forth.

(a) What method of sampling did she use?
(b) Do you think the sample will be representative?

Descriptive and Inferential Statistics

There are two main branches of statistics: descriptive and inferential. Statistical techniques that are used to *describe* data are called **descriptive statistics.** For example, a researcher may wish to determine the average age of the full-time students enrolled in your college and the percentage who own automobiles.

Sidelight   MATH IN THE COURTROOM

Mathematicians are often called on to testify in court, and often it's to interpret the statistical likelihood of some event. In one case in Los Angeles, a couple was convicted of robbery based almost entirely on statistics! There were witnesses who saw the robbers leaving the scene, but they could not positively identify the suspects: just certain characteristics, like race, hair color, facial hair, and type of vehicle. A mathematician calculated that there was just one chance in 12 million of a second couple with the exact characteristics as the suspects being in the same area at that time. Despite a lack of any hard evidence, the couple was convicted.

When the conviction was appealed, the appellate judge was somewhat less impressed by the statistical argument than the jury had been. The conviction was overturned based on faulty calculations and the lack of other evidence.

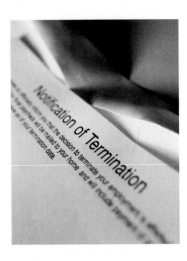

Statistical techniques used to make *inferences* are called **inferential statistics.** For example, every month the Bureau of Labor and Statistics estimates the number of people in the United States who are unemployed. Since it would be impossible to survey every adult resident of the United States, the Bureau selects a sample of adult individuals in the United States to see what percent are unemployed. In this case, the information obtained from a sample is used to estimate a population measure.

Another area of inferential statistics is called *hypothesis testing.* A researcher tries to test a hypothesis to see if there is enough evidence to support it. Here are some research questions that lend themselves to hypothesis testing:

Is one brand of aspirin better than another brand?
Does taking vitamin C prevent colds?
Are children more susceptible to ear infections than adults?

A third aspect of inferential statistics is determining whether or not a relationship exists between two or more variables. This area of statistics is called *correlation and regression;* for example:

Is caffeine related to heart trouble?
Is there a relationship between a person's age and his or her blood pressure?
Is these a connection between hours spent studying and grades on a final exam?

Frequency Distributions

The data collected for a statistical study are called **raw data.** In order to describe situations and draw conclusions, the researcher must organize the data in a meaningful way.

Two methods that we will use are *frequency distributions* and *stem and leaf plots.* There are two types of frequency distributions, the categorical frequency distribution and the grouped frequency distribution.

A categorical frequency distribution is used when the data are categorical rather than numerical. Example 2 shows how to construct a **categorical frequency distribution.**

EXAMPLE 2   Constructing a Frequency Distribution

Twenty-five volunteers for a medical research study were given a blood test to obtain their blood types. The data follow.

A	B	B	AB	O
O	O	B	AB	B
B	B	O	A	O
AB	A	O	B	A
A	O	O	O	AB

Construct a frequency distribution for the data.

SOLUTION

Step 1 Make a table as shown, with all categories represented.

Type	Tally	Frequency
A		
B		
O		
AB		

Step 2 Tally the data using the second column.

Step 3   Count the tallies and place the numbers in the third column. The completed frequency distribution is shown.

Type	Tally	Frequency
A	卌	5
B	卌 //	7
O	卌 ////	9
AB	////	4

▼ Try This One 2

A health-food store recorded the type of vitamin pills 35 customers purchased during a 1-day sale. Construct a categorical frequency distribution for the data.

C	C	C	A	D	E	C
E	E	A	B	D	C	E
C	E	C	C	C	D	A
B	B	C	C	A	A	E
E	E	E	A	B	C	B

Another type of frequency distribution that can be constructed uses numerical data and is called a **grouped frequency distribution.** In a grouped frequency distribution, the numerical data are divided into classes. For example, if you gathered data on the weights of people in your class, there's a decent chance that no two people have the exact same weight. So it would be reasonable to group people into weight ranges, like 100–119 pounds, 120–139 pounds, and so forth. In the 100–119 pound class, we call 100 the lower limit and 119 the upper limit. When deciding on classes, here are some useful guidelines:

1. Try to keep the number of classes between 5 and 15.

2. Make sure the classes do not overlap.

3. Don't leave out any numbers between the lowest and highest, even if nothing falls into a particular class.

4. Make sure the range of numbers included in a class is the same for each one. (For example, don't have the first class go from 100–120 pounds and the second from 121–130 pounds.)

Example 3 demonstrates the steps for building a grouped frequency distribution.

EXAMPLE 3   Constructing a Frequency Distribution

These data represent the record high temperatures for each of the 50 states in degrees Fahrenheit. Construct a grouped frequency distribution for the data.

112	100	127	120	134	105	110	109	112	118
110	118	117	116	118	114	114	105	109	122
107	112	114	115	118	118	122	106	110	117
116	108	110	121	113	119	111	104	111	120
120	113	120	117	105	118	112	114	114	110

Source: *The World Almanac Book of Facts*

SOLUTION

Step 1   Subtract the lowest value from the highest value: $134 - 100 = 34$.

Step 2   If we use a range of 5 degrees, that will give us seven classes, since the entire range (34 degrees) divided by 5 is 6.8. This is certainly not the only choice for the number of classes: if we choose a range of 4 degrees, there will be 9 classes.

Step 3   Start with the lowest value and add 5 to get the lower class limits: 100, 105, 110, 115, 120, 125, 130, 135.

Step 4   Set up the classes by subtracting one from each lower class limit except the first lower class limit.

Step 5   Tally the data and record the frequencies as shown.

Class	Tally	Frequency
100–104	//	2
105–109	///// ///	8
110–114	///// ///// ///// ///	18
115–119	///// ///// ///	13
120–124	///// //	7
125–129	/	1
130–134	/	1

☑ 4. Construct a frequency distribution for a data set.

▼ **Try This One 3**

In one math class, the data below represent the number of hours each student spends on homework in an average week. Construct a grouped frequency distribution for the data using six classes.

1	2	6	7	12	13	2	6	9	5
18	7	3	15	15	4	17	1	14	5
4	16	4	5	8	6	5	18	5	2
9	11	12	1	9	2	10	11	4	10
9	18	8	8	4	14	7	3	2	6

Stem and Leaf Plots

Another way to organize data is to use a **stem and leaf plot** (sometimes called a stem plot). Each data value or number is separated into two parts. For a two-digit number such as 53, the tens digit, 5, is called the *stem,* and the ones digit, 3, is called its *leaf.* For the number 72, the stem is 7, and the leaf is 2. For a three-digit number, say 138, the first two digits, 13, are used as the stem, and the third digit, 8, is used as the leaf. Example 4 shows how to construct a stem and leaf plot.

EXAMPLE 4   **Drawing a Stem and Leaf Plot**

The data below show the number of games won by the Chicago Cubs in each of the 21 seasons from 1988–2008, with the exception of 1994, which was a short season because of a player strike. Draw a stem and leaf plot for the data.

97	85	66	79	89	88	67	88	65	67	90	68
76	73	84	78	77	77	93	77			

SOLUTION

Notice that the first digit ranges from 6 to 9, so we set up a table with stems 6, 7, 8, 9:

Stems	Leaves
6	
7	
8	
9	

Now we go through the data one value at a time, putting the appropriate leaf next to the matching stem. For 97, we put a 7 under leaves, next to the stem 9 (shown in color below). For 85, we put a 5 under leaves, next to the stem 8, and so on, until all data values have been included.

The stem and leaf plot for number of wins by the Cubs is

Stems	Leaves
6	6 7 5 7 8
7	9 6 3 8 7 7 7
8	5 9 8 8 4
9	7 0 3

This is an efficient way of organizing the data. We can easily see that the most common class of wins is from 70–79, and the least common is 90–99. We can also see that 77 is the number of wins that occurred most often, three times.

☑ 5. Draw a stem and leaf plot for a data set.

Math Note

Remember, when drawing a stem and leaf plot with three-digit numbers, the first two digits are the stem. So for 119, the stem is 11 and the leaf is 9.

▼ **Try This One 4**

It's no secret that gas prices have fluctuated wildly in the last few years, but from 1980–1999, they were surprisingly stable. According to the Energy Information Administration, the data below represent the average price (in cents) per gallon of regular unleaded gas for those years. Draw a stem and leaf plot of the data.

119	131	122	113	112	86	90	90	100	115
114	113	111	111	115	123	123	123	106	117

Answers to Try This One

1 (a) Stratified sample
(b) The population is likely to be representative since the last digit of a student's ID number is likely to be completely random.

2

Type	Tally	Frequency
A	||||| /	6
B	|||||	5
C	||||| ||||| //	12
D	///	3
E	||||| ////	9

3

Class	Tally	Frequency
1–3	✕✕✕✕✕ ✕✕✕✕✕	10
4–6	✕✕✕✕✕ ✕✕✕✕✕ ////	14
7–9	✕✕✕✕✕ ✕✕✕✕✕	10
10–12	✕✕✕✕✕ /	6
13–15	✕✕✕✕✕	5
16–18	✕✕✕✕✕	5

4

8	6
9	0 0
10	0 6
11	9 3 2 5 4 3 1 1 5 7
12	2 3 3 3
13	1

EXERCISE SET 12-1

Writing Exercises

1. What are *data?*
2. Define *statistics.*
3. Explain the difference between a population and a sample.
4. How is a random sample selected?
5. How is a systematic sample selected?
6. How is a stratified sample selected?
7. How is a cluster sample selected?
8. What are the similarities between a grouped frequency distribution and a stem and leaf plot?

For Exercises 9–14, classify each sample as random, systematic, stratified, or cluster and explain your answer.

9. In a large school district, all teachers from two buildings are interviewed to determine whether they believe the students have less homework to do now than in previous years.

10. Every seventh customer entering a shopping mall is asked to select his or her favorite store.
11. Nursing supervisors are selected using random numbers in order to determine annual salaries.
12. Every hundredth hamburger manufactured is checked to determine its fat content.
13. Mail carriers of a large city are divided into four groups according to gender (male or female) and according to whether they walk or ride on their routes. Then 10 are selected from each group and interviewed to determine whether they have been bitten by a dog in the last year.
14. For the draft lottery that was conducted from 1969 to 1975, the days of the year were written on pieces of paper and put in plastic capsules. The capsules were then mixed in a barrel and drawn out one at a time, with the day recorded.

Real-World Applications

15. At a college financial aid office, students who applied for a scholarship were classified according to their class rank: Fr = freshman, So = sophomore, Jr = junior, Se = senior. Construct a frequency distribution for the data.

Fr	Fr	Fr	Fr	Fr
Jr	Fr	Fr	So	Fr
Fr	So	Jr	So	Fr
So	Fr	Fr	Fr	So
Se	Jr	Jr	So	Fr
Fr	Fr	Fr	Fr	So
Se	Se	Jr	Jr	Se
So	So	So	So	So

16. A questionnaire about how students primarily get news resulted in the following responses from 25 people. Construct a frequency distribution for the data. (I = Internet, N = newspaper, R = radio, T = TV.)

T I I N I I N I R T N I
I T R I I N I R T N I I

17. Twenty-five fans of reality TV were asked to rate four shows, and the data below reflect which one each rated highest. Construct a frequency distribution for the data. (S = *Survivor*, P = *Project Runway*, B = *Big Brother*, A = *The Amazing Race.*)

S S B P P B S P A B A A S
B A P B A S A P B B S A

18. The new rap artist, Funky Fido, has had some success, although not as much as he'd like. The number of downloads per week of his hit, "Bark Up My Tree," is listed below. Construct a frequency distribution for the data using six classes.

373	254	237	243	308	210	266	253	201	266
239	114	224	373	286	329	236	284	247	273
198	361	416	207	243	326	251	169	360	311
215	189	344	268	363	21	270	165	240	48
150	300	207	314	197	209	210	260	327	

19. The ages of the signers of the Declaration of Independence are shown here. (Age is approximate since only the birth year appeared in the source, and one has been omitted since his birth year is unknown.) Construct a frequency distribution for the data using seven classes.

41	54	47	40	39	35	50	37	49	42	70	32
44	52	39	50	40	30	34	69	39	45	33	52
44	62	60	27	42	34	50	42	52	38	36	45
35	43	48	46	31	27	55	63	46	33	60	62
35	46	45	34	53	50	50					

Source: *The Universal Almanac*

20. The percentage of people killed in car accidents who were not wearing seatbelts in 2006 is shown for 27 states. Construct a frequency distribution using five classes.

56.9	59.1	33.1	43.3	62.3	36.3	74.4	64.0	60.0
56.8	45.5	38.2	71.0	46.6	42.4	39.3	46.0	60.4
52.5	69.2	63.9	60.5	47.5	43.3	62.3	67.1	39.8

Source: *Statemaster.com*

21. The data (in cents) are the cigarette taxes per pack imposed by each state as of April 1, 2009. Construct a frequency distribution. Use 0–39, 40–79, 80–119, etc.

42.5	200	200	115	87	84	200	115	33.9	37
200	57	98	99.5	136	79	60	36	200	200
251	200	150.4	18	17	170	64	80	133	257.5
91	275	35	44	125	103	118	135	246	7
153	62	141	69.5	199	30	202.5	55	177	60

Source: *National Conference at State Legislatures*

22. The acreage (in thousands of acres) of the 39 U.S. National Parks is shown here. Construct a frequency distribution for the data using eight classes.

41	66	233	775	169
36	338	233	236	64
183	61	13	308	77
520	77	27	217	5
650	462	106	52	52
505	94	75	265	402
196	70	132	28	220
760	143	46	539	

Source: *The Universal Almanac*

23. The heights in feet above sea level of the major active volcanoes in Alaska are given here. Construct a frequency distribution for the data using 10 classes.

4,265	3,545	4,025	7,050	11,413
3,490	5,370	4,885	5,030	6,830
4,450	5,775	3,945	7,545	8,450
3,995	10,140	6,050	10,265	6,965
150	8,185	7,295	2,015	5,055
5,315	2,945	6,720	3,465	1,980
2,560	4,450	2,759	9,430	
7,985	7,540	3,540	11,070	
5,710	885	8,960	7,015	

Source: *The Universal Almanac*

24. During the 1998 baseball season, Mark McGwire and Sammy Sosa both broke Roger Maris's home run record of 61. The distances in feet for each home run follow. Construct a frequency distribution for each player using the same eight classes.

McGwire				Sosa			
306	370	370	430	371	350	430	420
420	340	460	410	430	434	370	420
440	410	380	360	440	410	420	460
350	527	380	550	400	430	410	370
478	420	390	420	370	410	380	340
425	370	480	390	350	420	410	415
430	388	423	410	430	380	380	366
360	410	450	350	500	380	390	400
450	430	461	430	364	430	450	440
470	440	400	390	365	420	350	420
510	430	450	452	400	380	380	400
420	380	470	398	370	420	360	368
409	385	369	460	430	433	388	440
390	510	500	450	414	482	364	370
470	430	458	380	400	405	433	390
430	341	385	410	480	480	434	344
420	380	400	440	410	420		
377	370						

Source: *USA Today*

25. The data (in millions of dollars) are the values of the 32 National Football League franchises in 2009. Construct a frequency distribution for the data using seven classes.

937	1,178	872	1,064	1,076	941	1,116	1,612
861	1,035	929	1,040	1,016	888	876	1,010
994	839	1,125	1,044	1,170	865	885	1,324
1,061	1,015	1,053	1,538	914	917	1,023	1,062

26. Twenty-nine executives reported the number of telephone calls made during a randomly selected week as shown here. Construct a stem and leaf plot for the data and analyze the results.

22	14	12	9	54	12
16	12	14	49	10	14
8	21	37	28	36	22
9	33	58	31	41	19
3	18	25	28	52	

27. The National Insurance Crime Bureau reported that these data represent the number of registered

vehicles per car stolen for 35 selected cities in the United States. For example, in Miami, one automobile is stolen for every 38 registered vehicles in the city. Construct a stem and leaf plot for the data and analyze the distribution. (The data have been rounded to the nearest whole number.)

38	53	53	56	69	89	94
41	58	68	66	69	89	52
50	70	83	81	80	90	74
50	70	83	59	75	78	73
92	84	87	84	85	84	89

Source: *USA Today*

28. As an experiment in a botany class, 20 plants are placed in a greenhouse, and their growth in centimeters after 20 days is recorded, with the results shown below. Construct a stem and leaf plot for the data.

20	12	39	38
41	43	51	52
59	55	53	59
50	58	35	38
23	32	43	53

29. The data shown represent the percentage of unemployed males for a sample of countries of the world. Using whole numbers as stems and the decimals as leaves, construct a stem and leaf plot.

8.8	1.9	5.6	4.6	1.5
2.2	5.6	3.1	5.9	6.6
9.8	8.7	6.0	5.2	5.6
4.4	9.6	6.6	6.0	0.3
4.6	3.1	4.1	7.7	

Source: *The Time Almanac*

Critical Thinking

For Exercises 30–34, decide whether descriptive or inferential statistics is being used.

30. A recent study showed that eating garlic can lower blood pressure.
31. The average number of students in a class at White Oak University is 22.6.
32. It is predicted that the average number of automobiles each household owns will increase next year.
33. Last year's total attendance at Long Run High School's football games was 8,325.
34. The chance that a person will be robbed in a certain city is 15%.

35. In addition to the four basic sampling methods, other methods are also used. Some of these methods are *sequence sampling, double sampling,* and *multiple sampling.* Look up these methods on the Internet and explain the advantages and disadvantages of each method.
36. For the data in Exercise 25, draw a stem and leaf plot, and compare your result to the frequency distribution. Which do you think provides more useful information, and why? What are the strengths and weaknesses of each?

Section 12-2 Picturing Data

LEARNING OBJECTIVES

☐ 1. Draw bar graphs and pie charts.

☐ 2. Draw histograms and frequency polygons.

☐ 3. Draw time series graphs.

Now we've gathered some data, and we think maybe some of it has an interesting story to tell. How can we most effectively present that data? In Section 12-1, we displayed data in table form, using frequency distributions, and using stem and leaf plots. All are perfectly valid, but... they don't exactly *pop.* The graphic on this page displays data related to identity theft complaints that could have been put in table form:

Identity Theft is Sneaking Up

Consumers made nearly twice as many identity theft complaints in 2008 as in 2002.

Complaints:

313,982

161,977

'02 '03 '04 '05 '06 '07 '08

Source: Federal Trade Commission, February 2009

Year	2002	2003	2004	2005	2006	2007	2008
Complaints in thousands	162	215	247	256	246	258	314

The information is the same, but with the graph, just a quick glance is enough to see that identity theft rose sharply for a couple of years, then sort of leveled off, before another sharp rise. Simply put, if you want your data to really catch someone's eye, you can't do much better than a nice graphical representation. In this section, we'll study several methods for accomplishing this goal.

Bar Graphs and Pie Charts

The first type of frequency distribution we studied in Section 12-1 was the categorical frequency distribution. When data are representative of certain categories, rather than numerical, we often use bar graphs or circle graphs (commonly known as pie charts) to illustrate that data. We will start with a bar graph in Example 1.

EXAMPLE 1   Drawing a Bar Graph to Represent Data

The marketing firm Deloitte Retail conducted a survey in 2008 of grocery shoppers. The frequency distribution below represents the responses to the survey question "How often do you bring your own bags when grocery shopping?" Draw a vertical bar graph to represent the data.

Response	Frequency
Always	10
Never	39
Frequently	19
Occasionally	32

SOLUTION

Step 1 Draw and label the axes. We were asked for a vertical bar graph, so the responses go on the horizontal axis, and the frequencies on the vertical.

Step 2 Draw vertical bars with heights that correspond to the frequencies.

The completed graph is shown in Figure 12-1.

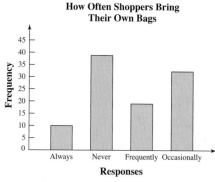

Figure 12-1

▼ Try This One   1

The frequency distribution below represents responses to a survey on whether or not the posting of calorie information at fast food restaurants affects what customers order. Draw a vertical bar graph to illustrate the data.

Response	Frequency
Great impact	40
Some impact	42
Not much impact	11
None at all	7

CAUTION   In drawing a vertical bar graph, it's very important that the scale on the vertical axis begins at zero, and has consistent spacing. As you will see in the supplement on misuse of statistics, an improperly labeled axis can lead to a deceptive graph.

Another type of graph that can be drawn for the data that are categorical in nature is the **circle graph** or **pie chart.** A pie chart is a circle that is divided into sections in proportion to the frequencies corresponding to the categories. The purpose of a pie chart is to show the relationship of the parts to the whole by visually comparing the size of the sections. Example 2 shows the procedure for constructing a pie chart.

EXAMPLE 2   Drawing a Pie Chart to Represent Data

Draw a pie chart for the frequency distribution from Example 1. The distribution is repeated below.

Response	Frequency
Always	10
Never	39
Frequently	19
Occasionally	32

> **Math Note**
>
> Spreadsheet programs, like Microsoft Excel, have built-in commands that generate bar graphs and pie charts when you enter frequency distributions in table form.

SOLUTION

Step 1 Find the number of degrees corresponding to each slice using the formula

$$\text{Degrees} = \frac{f}{n} \cdot 360°$$

where f is the frequency for each class and n is the sum of the frequencies. In this case, $n = 100$, so the degree measures are:

Always $\quad \frac{10}{100} \cdot 360° = 36°$

Never $\quad \frac{39}{100} \cdot 360° = 140.4°$

Frequently $\quad \frac{19}{100} \cdot 360° = 68.4°$

Occasionally $\quad \frac{32}{100} \cdot 360° = 115.2°$

Step 2 Using a protractor, graph each section on the circle using the calculated angles, as shown in Figure 12-2. Notice the labeling that makes it clear what each slice represents.

Step 3 Calculate the percent of the circle covered by each slice.

Always: $\frac{10}{100} = 10\%$ Never: $\frac{39}{100} = 39\%$

Frequently: $\frac{19}{100} = 19\%$ Occasionally: $\frac{32}{100} = 32\%$

Label each section with the percent, as shown in Figure 12-2.

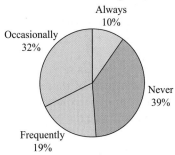

How Often Shoppers Bring Their Own Bags

Figure 12-2

☑ 1. Draw bar graphs and pie charts.

▼ Try This One 2

Draw a pie chart that illustrates the frequency distribution from Try This One 1.

Histograms and Frequency Polygons

When data are organized into grouped frequency distributions, two types of graphs are commonly used to represent them: *histograms* and *frequency polygons.*

A **histogram** is similar to a vertical bar graph in that the heights of the bars correspond to frequencies. The difference is that class limits are placed on the horizontal axis, rather than categories. The procedure is illustrated in Example 3.

EXAMPLE 3   Drawing a Histogram

The frequency distribution to the right is for the closing price of General Motors stock in dollars for each of the first 74 trading days of 2009. Draw a histogram for the data.

Class	Frequency	Class	Frequency
1.01–1.50	1	3.01–3.50	12
1.51–2.00	18	3.51–4.00	8
2.01–2.50	14	4.01–4.50	5
2.51–3.00	16		

SOLUTION

Step 1 Write the scale for the frequencies on the vertical axis and the class limits on the horizontal axis.

Step 2 Draw vertical bars with heights that correspond to the frequencies for each class. See Figure 12-3.

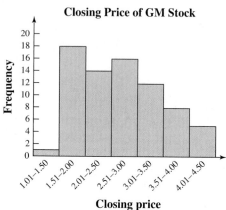

Figure 12-3

> **Math Note**
>
> When drawing a histogram, make sure that the bars touch (unlike a bar graph) and that every class is included, even if the frequency is zero.

▼ Try This One 3

Draw a histogram for the frequency distribution to the right, which represents the number of losses by the team that won the NCAA men's basketball championship for the years from 1939–2009.

Losses	Frequency	Losses	Frequency
0–1	13	6–7	9
2–3	27	8–9	2
4–5	17	10–11	3

A **frequency polygon** is similar to a histogram, but instead of bars, a series of line segments is drawn connecting the midpoints of the classes. The heights of those points match the heights of the bars in a histogram. In Example 4, we'll draw a frequency polygon for the frequency distribution from Example 3 so you can compare the two.

EXAMPLE 4   Drawing a Frequency Polygon

> **Math Note**
>
> Once you have the first midpoint, you can get all of the others by just adding the size of each class to the previous. For example, the second midpoint is the first, 1.255, plus the size of the classes, 0.50.

Draw a frequency polygon for the frequency distribution from Example 3. The distribution is repeated here.

Class	Frequency	Class	Frequency
1.01–1.50	1	3.01–3.50	12
1.51–2.00	18	3.51–4.00	8
2.01–2.50	14	4.01–4.50	5
2.51–3.00	16		

SOLUTION

Step 1 Find the midpoints for each class. This is accomplished by adding the upper and lower limits and dividing by 2. For the first two classes, we get:

$$\frac{1.50 + 1.01}{2} = 1.255$$

$$\frac{2.00 + 1.51}{2} = 1.755$$

The remaining midpoints are 2.255, 2.755, 3.255, 3.755, and 4.255.

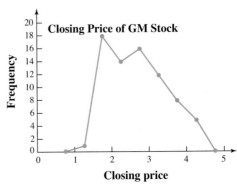

Figure 12-4

Math Note

A frequency polygon should always touch the horizontal axis at both ends to indicate that the frequency is zero for any values not included on the graph.

Step 2 Write the scale for the frequencies on the vertical axis, and label a scale on the horizontal axis so that all midpoints will be included.

Step 3 Plot points at the midpoints with heights matching the frequencies for each class, then connect those points with straight lines.

Step 4 Finish the graph by drawing a line back to the horizontal axis at the beginning and end. The horizontal distance to the axis should equal the distance between the midpoints. In this case, that distance is 0.5, so we extend back to 0.755 and forward to 4.755. See Figure 12-4.

☑ 2. Draw histograms and frequency polygons.

▼ Try This One 4

Draw a frequency polygon for the frequency distribution from Try This One 3.

Time Series Graphs

A **time series graph** can be drawn for data collected over a period of time. This type of graph is used primarily to show trends, like prices rising or falling, for the time period. There are three types of trends. Secular trends are viewed over a long period of time, such as yearly. Cyclical trends show oscillating patterns. Seasonal trends show the values of a commodity for shorter periods of the year, such as fall, winter, spring, and summer. Example 5 shows how to draw a time series graph.

EXAMPLE 5   Drawing a Time Series Graph

Identity theft has increased as more people are shopping online. The table below shows the number of identify theft complaints made to the FTC in thousands between 2002 and 2008. Draw a time series graph for the data.

Year	2002	2003	2004	2005	2006	2007	2008
Complaints in thousands	162	215	247	256	246	258	314

Source: Federal Trade Commission

Math Note

Notice how this time series graph matches the one at the beginning of this section.

SOLUTION

Label the horizontal axis with years, and the vertical axis with the number of complaints in thousands, then plot the points from the table and connect them with line segments. See Figure 12-5.

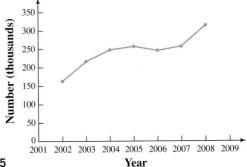

Figure 12-5

students enrolled in specific fields. Draw a pie chart for the data and analyze the results.

Major field	Number
Preschool	893
Elementary	605
Middle	245
Secondary	1,096

13. For 108 randomly selected college applicants, the frequency distribution shown here for entrance exam scores was obtained. Draw a histogram and frequency polygon for the data.

Class	Frequency
90–98	6
99–107	22
108–116	43
117–125	28
126–134	9

14. For 75 employees of a large department store, the distribution shown here for years of service was obtained. Draw a histogram and frequency polygon for the data.

Class	Frequency
1–5	21
6–10	25
11–15	15
16–20	0
21–25	8
26–30	6

15. Thirty cars and trucks were tested by the EPA for fuel efficiency in miles per gallon (mpg). The frequency distribution shown here was obtained. Draw a histogram and frequency polygon for the data.

Class	Frequency
8–12	3
13–17	5
18–22	15
23–27	5
28–32	2

16. In a study of reaction times of dogs to a specific stimulus, an animal trainer obtained these data, given in seconds. Draw a histogram and frequency polygon for the data and analyze the results.

Class	Frequency
2.3–2.9	10
3.0–3.6	12
3.7–4.3	6
4.4–5.0	8
5.1–5.7	4
5.8–6.4	2

17. The data below represent the number of people admitted to graduate programs in mechanical engineering by year. Draw a time series graph for the data.

Year	2004	2005	2006	2007	2008
Number	1,981	2,895	3,027	1,651	1,432

18. The data below represent the number of laptops sold by a local computer store for the years listed. Draw a time series graph for the data.

Year	Number
1999	201
2000	256
2001	314
2002	379
2003	450
2004	576
2005	681
2006	799
2007	873
2008	1,012

19. The data below represent the number of downloads per year of a popular shareware program. Draw a time series graph for the data.

Year	2000	2002	2004	2006	2008
Downloads	12,413	15,160	18,201	20,206	19,143

Critical Thinking

In Exercises 20–25, state which type of graph (bar graph, pie chart, or time series graph) would most appropriately represent the given data.

20. The number of students enrolled at a local college each year for the last 5 years.

21. The budget for the student activities department at your college.

22. The number of students who get to school by automobile, bus, train, or by walking.

Step 2 Write the scale for the frequencies on the vertical axis, and label a scale on the horizontal axis so that all midpoints will be included.

Step 3 Plot points at the midpoints with heights matching the frequencies for each class, then connect those points with straight lines.

Step 4 Finish the graph by drawing a line back to the horizontal axis at the beginning and end. The horizontal distance to the axis should equal the distance between the midpoints. In this case, that distance is 0.5, so we extend back to 0.755 and forward to 4.755. See Figure 12-4.

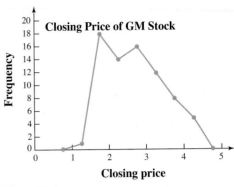

Figure 12-4

☑ 2. Draw histograms and frequency polygons.

▼ Try This One 4

Draw a frequency polygon for the frequency distribution from Try This One 3.

Time Series Graphs

A **time series graph** can be drawn for data collected over a period of time. This type of graph is used primarily to show trends, like prices rising or falling, for the time period. There are three types of trends. Secular trends are viewed over a long period of time, such as yearly. Cyclical trends show oscillating patterns. Seasonal trends show the values of a commodity for shorter periods of the year, such as fall, winter, spring, and summer. Example 5 shows how to draw a time series graph.

EXAMPLE 5   Drawing a Time Series Graph

Identity theft has increased as more people are shopping online. The table below shows the number of identify theft complaints made to the FTC in thousands between 2002 and 2008. Draw a time series graph for the data.

Year	2002	2003	2004	2005	2006	2007	2008
Complaints in thousands	162	215	247	256	246	258	314

Source: Federal Trade Commission

SOLUTION

Label the horizontal axis with years, and the vertical axis with the number of complaints in thousands, then plot the points from the table and connect them with line segments. See Figure 12-5.

Figure 12-5

☑ 3. Draw time series graphs.

Math Note

It's especially important to scale the vertical axis appropriately when drawing a time series graph. See Exercise 27 for some perspective on why.

▼ **Try This One 5**

The number of bankruptcy filings (in millions) in the United States from 2002 to 2008 is shown in the table. Draw a time series graph for the data.

Year	2002	2003	2004	2005	2006	2007	2008
Filings (millions)	1.58	1.66	1.60	2.08	0.62	0.85	1.12

This section provided just a sampling of the many types of charts and graphs used to picture data. A Google search for the string *picturing data* will help you find a more comprehensive list.

Answers to Try This One

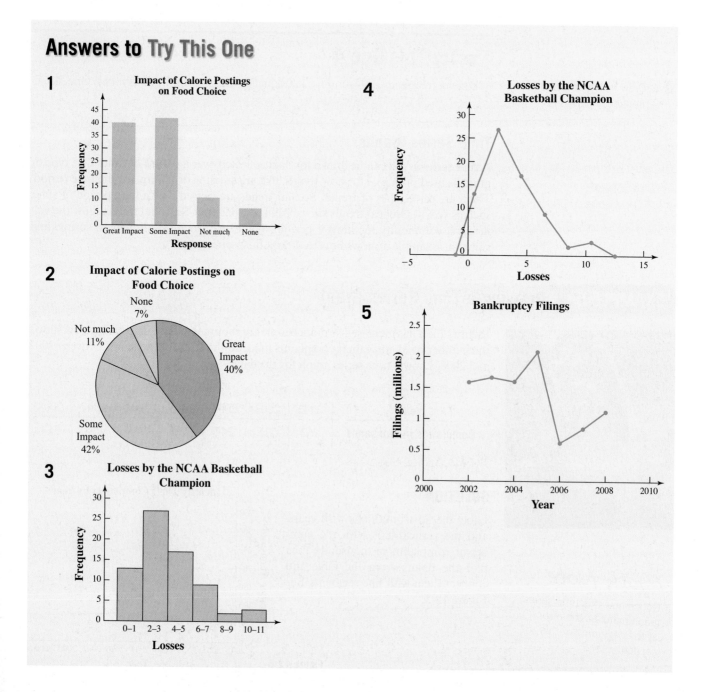

1 Impact of Calorie Postings on Food Choice

2 Impact of Calorie Postings on Food Choice

3 Losses by the NCAA Basketball Champion

4 Losses by the NCAA Basketball Champion

5 Bankruptcy Filings

EXERCISE SET 12-2

Writing Exercises

1. Describe how to draw a bar graph and a pie chart given a frequency distribution.
2. Explain why bar graphs and pie charts are typically used for categorical frequency distributions, while histograms are used for grouped frequency distributions.
3. How are histograms and frequency polygons similar? How are they different?
4. Describe the purpose of a time series graph.

Real-World Applications

5. Draw a bar graph for the number of transplants of various types performed in the United States in 2008.

Type	Number
Kidney	13,743
Liver	5,273
Pancreas	370
Heart	1,802
Lung	1,221

Source: *Infoplease.com*

6. The data below show the number of students visiting a university health care center during finals week who suffered from certain conditions. Draw a bar graph to illustrate the data.

Condition	Number
Flu	48
Panic attack	36
Bronchitis	32
Headache	32
Broken bone	19
Cold/sniffles	17
Rash	16
Pneumonia	11
Ear infection	9

7. Draw a bar graph for the number of registered taxicabs in 2008 in the selected cities.

City	Number
New York	13,087
Washington, D.C.	7,000
Chicago	7,000
Los Angeles	2,300
Atlanta	1,600

Source: *Wikipedia*

8. Draw a bar graph for the number of unemployed people in the selected states for February 2009.

State	Number
Texas	772,000
New York	760,000
Pennsylvania	486,000
Florida	886,000
Ohio	567,000

Source: *Bureau of Employment Statistics*

9. The number of students at one campus who had a 4.0 GPA is shown below, organized by class. Draw a pie chart for the data.

Rank	Frequency
Freshman	12
Sophomore	25
Junior	36
Senior	17

10. In an insurance company study of the causes of 1,000 deaths, these data were obtained. Draw a pie chart to represent the data.

Cause of death	Number of deaths
Heart disease	432
Cancer	227
Stroke	93
Accidents	24
Other	224
	1,000

11. In a survey of 100 college students, the numbers shown here indicate the primary reason why the students selected their majors. Draw a pie chart for the data and analyze the results.

Reason	Number
Interest in subject	62
Future earning potential	18
Pressure from parents	12
Good job prospects	8

12. A survey of the students in the school of education at a large university obtained the following data for

students enrolled in specific fields. Draw a pie chart for the data and analyze the results.

Major field	Number
Preschool	893
Elementary	605
Middle	245
Secondary	1,096

13. For 108 randomly selected college applicants, the frequency distribution shown here for entrance exam scores was obtained. Draw a histogram and frequency polygon for the data.

Class	Frequency
90–98	6
99–107	22
108–116	43
117–125	28
126–134	9

14. For 75 employees of a large department store, the distribution shown here for years of service was obtained. Draw a histogram and frequency polygon for the data.

Class	Frequency
1–5	21
6–10	25
11–15	15
16–20	0
21–25	8
26–30	6

15. Thirty cars and trucks were tested by the EPA for fuel efficiency in miles per gallon (mpg). The frequency distribution shown here was obtained. Draw a histogram and frequency polygon for the data.

Class	Frequency
8–12	3
13–17	5
18–22	15
23–27	5
28–32	2

16. In a study of reaction times of dogs to a specific stimulus, an animal trainer obtained these data, given in seconds. Draw a histogram and frequency polygon for the data and analyze the results.

Class	Frequency
2.3–2.9	10
3.0–3.6	12
3.7–4.3	6
4.4–5.0	8
5.1–5.7	4
5.8–6.4	2

17. The data below represent the number of people admitted to graduate programs in mechanical engineering by year. Draw a time series graph for the data.

Year	2004	2005	2006	2007	2008
Number	1,981	2,895	3,027	1,651	1,432

18. The data below represent the number of laptops sold by a local computer store for the years listed. Draw a time series graph for the data.

Year	Number
1999	201
2000	256
2001	314
2002	379
2003	450
2004	576
2005	681
2006	799
2007	873
2008	1,012

19. The data below represent the number of downloads per year of a popular shareware program. Draw a time series graph for the data.

Year	2000	2002	2004	2006	2008
Downloads	12,413	15,160	18,201	20,206	19,143

Critical Thinking

In Exercises 20–25, state which type of graph (bar graph, pie chart, or time series graph) would most appropriately represent the given data.

20. The number of students enrolled at a local college each year for the last 5 years.

21. The budget for the student activities department at your college.

22. The number of students who get to school by automobile, bus, train, or by walking.

23. The record high temperatures of a city for the last 30 years.
24. The areas of the five lakes in the Great Lakes.
25. The amount of each dollar spent for wages, advertising, overhead, and profit by a corporation.
26. Use the Internet or a library to find a reference describing what a pictograph is, then describe its purpose.

27. Redraw the time series graph from Example 5, but make the scale on the vertical axis range from 150 to 350 rather than from 0 to 350. Why does this make the graph deceiving?

Section 12-3 Measures of Average

LEARNING OBJECTIVES

- ☐ 1. Compute the mean of a data set.
- ☐ 2. Compute the median of a data set.
- ☐ 3. Compute the mode of a data set.
- ☐ 4. Compute the midrange of a data set.
- ☐ 5. Compare the four measures of average.

Are you an average college student? What does that even mean? According to a variety of sources found on the Web, the average college student is 20 years old, lives on campus, and works off campus during the school year. She is female, talks to her parents every day, and comes from a family with an annual income between $50,000 and $100,000. She sleeps 6 hours a night, has $2,700 in credit card debt, and will leave college with $21,000 in total debt.

If this doesn't sound exactly like anyone you know, don't feel bad. As we will learn in this section, the word *average* is ambiguous—there are a variety of ways to describe an average. So what one source considers average might not match someone else's thoughts, and with so many different facets to a person, it's possible that nobody exactly meets all of the average criteria.

Our goal in Section 12-3 will be to understand the different measures of average. In casual terms, average means the most typical case, or the center of the distribution. Measures of average are also called *measures of central tendency,* and include the *mean, median, mode,* and *midrange.*

The Mean

The *mean,* also known as the arithmetic average, is found by adding the values of the data and dividing by the total number of values. The Greek letter Σ (sigma) is used to represent the sum of a list of numbers. If we use the letter X to represent data values, then ΣX means to find the sum of all values in a data set. Using this notation:

> The **mean** is the sum of the values in a data set divided by the number of values. If $X_1, X_2, X_3, \ldots X_n$ are the data values, we use $\overline{X}$ to stand for the mean, and
>
> $$\overline{X} = \frac{X_1 + X_2 + X_3 + \cdots + X_n}{n} = \frac{\Sigma X}{n}$$

EXAMPLE 1 Finding the Mean of a Data Set

In 2003, there were 12 inmates on death row who were proven innocent and freed. In the 5 years after that, there were 6, 2, 1, 3, and 4. Find the mean number of death row inmates proven innocent for the 6 years from 2003 to 2008.

SOLUTION

$$\overline{X} = \frac{\sum X}{n} = \frac{12 + 6 + 2 + 1 + 3 + 4}{6} = \frac{28}{6} \approx 4.7$$

The mean is about 4.7.

▼ Try This One 1

To test a customer's Internet connection, a tech records how long it takes for 10 different websites to load completely. The times in seconds are shown below. Find the mean time.

   20.68   16.22   16.76   16.90   20.98   18.84   14.18   40.04   24.92   22.96

The procedure for finding the mean for grouped data uses the midpoints and the frequencies of the classes as shown in Example 2. This procedure will give only an approximate value for the mean, and it is used when the data set is very large or when the original raw data are unavailable but have been grouped by someone else.

> **Formula for Finding the Mean for Grouped Data:**
>
> $$\overline{X} = \frac{\sum(f \cdot X_m)}{n}$$
>
> where f = frequency
>
> X_m = midpoint of each class
>
> $n = \sum f$ or sum of the frequencies

EXAMPLE 2   Finding the Mean for Grouped Data

Find the mean for the price of GM stock for the first 74 days of trading in 2009. The frequency distribution is below.

Class	Frequency	Class	Frequency
1.01–1.50	1	3.01–3.50	12
1.51–2.00	18	3.51–4.00	8
2.01–2.50	14	4.01–4.50	5
2.51–3.00	16		

SOLUTION

We found the midpoint of each class in Example 4 of Section 12-2: the midpoints are 1.255, 1.755, 2.255, 2.755, 3.255, 3.755, and 4.255. Now we multiply each midpoint by the frequency:

Midpoint (X_m)	Frequency (f)	$f \cdot X_m$
1.255	1	1.255
1.755	18	31.59
2.255	14	31.57
2.755	16	44.08
3.255	12	39.06
3.755	8	30.04
4.255	5	21.275
Sums	74	198.87

Now we divide $\Sigma(f \cdot X_m)$ by the sum of the frequencies to get the mean:

$$\overline{X} = \frac{198.87}{74} \approx 2.69$$

The mean closing price was $2.69.

☑ 1. Compute the mean of a data set.

▼ Try This One 2

Find the mean for the number of losses by the NCAA men's basketball champion for the years from 1939–2009. The frequency distribution is below.

Losses	Frequency	Losses	Frequency
0–1	13	6–7	9
2–3	27	8–9	2
4–5	17	10–11	3

The Median

According to payscale.com, the *median* salary for all federal government employees as of early 2009 was $60,680. This measure of average means that half of all government employees made less than $60,680, and half made more.

Simply put, the **median** is the halfway point of a data set when it is arranged in order. When a data set is ordered, it is called a **data array.** The median will either be a specific value in the data set, or will fall between two values, as shown in Examples 3 and 4.

Steps in Computing the Median of a Data Set

Step 1 Arrange the data in order, from smallest to largest.

Step 2 Select the middle value. If the number of data values is odd, the median is the value in the exact middle of the list. If the number of data values is even, the median is the mean of the two middle data values.

EXAMPLE 3   Finding the Median of a Data Set

The mean and median age for this group are different. The grandfather's age pulls up the mean, while the four children bring down the median.

The weights of the five starting offensive linemen for the Pittsburgh Steelers in Super Bowl XLIII were 345, 340, 315, 285, and 317. Find the median weight.

SOLUTION

Step 1 Arrange the data in order.

285   315   317   340   345

Step 2 Select the middle value.
The median weight was 317 pounds.

▼ Try This One 3

The high temperatures for seven consecutive days in April, 2009 in Cincinnati were 60°, 49°, 67°, 73°, 76°, 59°, and 59°. Find the median temperature.

EXAMPLE 4   Finding the Median of a Data Set

One of the authors of this book conducts a campus food drive at the end of each semester. The amount of food in pounds gathered over the last eight semesters is shown below. Find the median weight.

1,675   1,209   1,751   1,700   1,532   2,171   2,292   3,211

SOLUTION

Step 1 Arrange the data in order.

1,209   1,532   1,675   1,700   1,751   2,171   2,292   3,211

Step 2 Find the middle value: in this case, it is in between 1,700 and 1,751, so we find the mean of those two values.

$$\frac{1,700 + 1,751}{2} = 1,725.5$$

The median weight is 1,725.5 pounds.

▼ Try This One 4

The data below are the number of fatalities in the United States caused by tornadoes for the years 1999–2008. Find the median number of fatalities.

125   81   67   39   66   54   55   44   41   94

CAUTION   When finding the median of a data set, make sure the data values are arranged in order!

☑ 2. Compute the median of a data set.

The Mode

The third measure of average is called the *mode.* The mode is sometimes said to be the most typical case.

The value that occurs most often in a data set is called the **mode.**

A data set can have more than one mode or no mode at all. These situations will be shown in some of the examples that follow.

EXAMPLE 5   Finding the Mode of a Data Set

These data represent the duration (in days) of U.S. space shuttle voyages for the years 2002–2008. Find the mode.

10   10   13   10   13   15   13   12   11   12   13   12   15   12   15   13   15

Source: Wikipedia

SOLUTION

If we construct a frequency distribution, it will be easy to find the mode—it's simply the value with the greatest frequency. The frequency distribution for the data is shown to the right, and the mode is 13.

Days	Frequency	Days	Frequency
10	3	13	5
11	1	15	4
12	4		

▼ Try This One 5

The data below represent the number of fatal commercial airline incidents in the United States for each year from 1998–2008. Find the mode.

    1 2 3 6 0 2 2 3 2 1 2

EXAMPLE 6   **Finding the Mode of a Data Set**

Math Note

When there is no mode, don't say that the mode is zero. That would be incorrect because for some data, such as temperature, zero can be an actual value.

Six strains of bacteria were tested by the Centers for Disease Control to see how long they could remain alive outside their normal environment. The time, in minutes, is recorded below. Find the mode.

    2   3   5   7   8   10

SOLUTION

Since each value occurs only once, there is no mode.

▼ Try This One 6

The final exam scores for 10 students in a seminar course are listed below. Find the mode.

    91   74   66   93   76   85   86   90   71   89

EXAMPLE 7   **Finding the Mode of a Data Set**

Math Note

When a data set has two modes, it is called *bimodal*.

The number of wins in a 16-game season for the Cincinnati Bengals from 1997–2008 is listed below. Find the mode.

    7   3   4   4   6   2   8   8   11   8   7   4

SOLUTION

There are two numbers that occur three times: 4 and 8. No number occurs more than three times, so the data set has two modes, 4 and 8.

▼ Try This One 7

The table below lists the average high temperature in degrees Fahrenheit for each month of the year on the island of Antigua. Find the mode.

Month	Jan	Feb	Mar	Apr	May	Jun	Jul	Aug	Sep	Oct	Nov	Dec
High	81	82	82	83	85	86	87	87	87	86	84	82

The mode is the only measure of central tendency that can be used in finding the most typical case when the data are classified by groups or categories, like those shown in Example 8.

EXAMPLE 8 **Finding the Mode for Categorical Data**

A survey of the junior class at Fiesta State University shows the following number of students majoring in each field. Find the mode.

Business	1,425
Liberal arts	878
Computer science	632
Education	471
General studies	95

SOLUTION

The values here are not the numbers, but the categories: business, liberal arts, computer science, education, and general studies. The value that appears most often is business, so that is the mode.

The winner of an election by popular vote is the mode.

☑ 3. Compute the mode of a data set.

▼ Try This One 8

Five hundred college graduates were asked how much they donate to their alma mater on an annual basis. Find the mode of their responses, summarized below.

$500 or more	45
Between 0 and $500	150
Nothing	275
Refused to answer	30

The Midrange

The midrange is a very quick and rough estimate of the middle of a data set. It is found by adding the lowest and highest values and dividing by 2.

Finding the Midrange for a Data Set
$\text{Midrange} = \dfrac{\text{Lowest value} + \text{highest value}}{2}$

The midrange is not terribly reliable since it can be greatly affected by just one extremely high or low data value.

EXAMPLE 9 **Finding the Midrange**

In Example 1, we saw that the number of death row inmates proven innocent for the years 2003–2008 was 12, 6, 2, 1, 3, and 4. Find the midrange.

SOLUTION

The lowest value is 1 and the highest is 12, so the midrange is

$$\text{Midrange} = \frac{12 + 1}{2} = 6.5.$$

☑ 4. Compute the midrange of a data set.

▼ Try This One 9

The number of earthquakes worldwide measuring at least 6.0 on the Richter scale from 2000–2008 is shown below. Find the midrange.

173   142   143   155   157   151   153   200   178

In Example 1, we found that the mean for the data set in Example 9 is 4.7. The midrange is much higher because the data value 12 is so much higher than the rest. This brings up an interesting question: how do our four measures of average compare for a data set?

EXAMPLE 10   Comparing the Four Measures of Average

The table below lists the number of golfers who finished the Masters tournament with a better score than Tiger Woods between 1997 and 2009.

Year	Number	Year	Number
1997	0	2004	21
1998	7	2005	0
1999	17	2006	2
2000	4	2007	1
2001	0	2008	1
2002	0	2009	5
2003	14		

Find the mean, median, mode, and midrange for the data.

SOLUTION

It will be helpful to arrange the numbers in order:

0   0   0   0   1   1   2   4   5   7   14   17   21

$$\text{Mean} = \frac{\sum X}{n} = \frac{0 + 0 + 0 + 0 + 1 + 1 + 2 + 4 + 5 + 7 + 14 + 17 + 21}{13} \approx 5.54$$

$$\text{Median} = 2$$

$$\text{Mode} = 0$$

$$\text{Midrange} = \frac{21 + 0}{2} = 10.5$$

So which is the best indicator of average performance? That's open to interpretation, but all four measures of average are very different.

▼ Try This One 10

☑ 5. Compare the four measures of average.

Tiger's final scores in relation to par for the 13 Masters tournaments from 1997 to 2009 are listed below. Find the mean, median, mode, and midrange.

−18   −3   +1   −4   −16   −12   +2   +2   −12   −4   +3   −5   −8

To conclude the section, Table 12-2 summarizes some of the strengths and weaknesses of each measure of average.

TABLE 12-2   **A Comparison of Measures of Average**

Measure	Strengths	Weaknesses
Mean	• Unique—there's exactly one mean for any data set • Factors in all values in the set • Easy to understand	• Can be adversely affected by one or two unusually high or low values • Can be time-consuming to calculate for large data sets
Median	• Divides a data set neatly into two groups • Not affected by one or two extreme values	• Can ignore the effects of large or small values even if they are important to consider
Mode	• Very easy to find • Describes the most typical case • Can be used with categorical data like candidate preference, choice of major, etc.	• May not exist for a data set • May not be unique • Can be very different from mean and median if the most typical case happens to be near the low or high end of the range
Midrange	• Very quick and easy to compute • Provides a simple look at average	• Dramatically affected by extremely high or low values in the data set • Ignores all but two values in the set

Sidelight THE BIRTH OF STATISTICS

The study of statistics has its origin in censuses taken by the Babylonians and Egyptians almost 6,000 years ago. "Birth" is an appropriate word to use in describing the beginning of statistics, since it started with birth records. The infancy of statistics occurred much later, some time around 27 BCE, when the Roman emperor Augustus conducted surveys on births and deaths of citizens, as well as the amount of livestock each owned and the crops each had harvested. Suddenly, a large amount of data was wanted, and methods had to be developed to collect, organize, and summarize that data.

The adolescence of statistics is probably sometime around the 14th century, when people began keeping detailed records of births, deaths, and accidents in order to determine insurance rates. Over the next 600 years or so, statistics grew up, with a wide variety of methods developed to fill needs in biology, physics, astronomy, commerce, and many other areas.

The true adulthood of statistics coincides with the rise of computer technology. Today, with just a few clicks of a mouse, statisticians can process and analyze amounts of data that would have taken the pioneers in the field centuries.

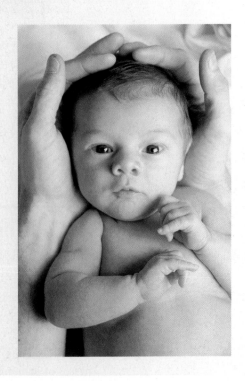

Answers to Try This One

1 21.248 seconds

2 3.63 losses

3 60°

4 60.5 fatalities

5 2 incidents

6 There is no mode.

7 The modes are 82° and 87°.

8 The mode is donating nothing.

9 171 earthquakes

10 Mean: −5.69; median: −4; mode: −12, −4, +2; midrange: −7.5

EXERCISE SET 12-3

Writing Exercises

1. If someone asked you before covering this section what the word "average" meant, what would you have said? What would your response be now?
2. Describe how to find the mean of a data set.
3. Describe how to find the median of a data set.
4. What is meant by the term *mode of a data set?*
5. Describe how to find the midrange of a data set.
6. Which of the measures of average can be used to describe the average for categorical data? Why?

Real-World Applications

For exercises 7–18, find the mean, median, mode, and midrange.

7. These data are the number of on-campus burglaries reported in 2008 for nine western Pennsylvania universities.

   61 11 1 3 2 30 18 3 7

8. The data below show the number of attorneys employed by the ten largest law firms in Pittsburgh.

   87 109 57 221 175 123 170 80 66 80

9. A graduate student in social work surveyed students at 10 colleges in a Midwestern state to find how many are single parents. The results are the data below.

   700 298 638 260 1,380 280 270 1,350 380 570

10. The number of wins for the teams that won college football bowl games at the end of the 2008 season is

    8 7 8 8 7 11 7 7 9 9 9 8 8 10
    8 10 10 8 9 7 8 8 9 8 10 9 7
    8 11 12 10 13 12 13

11. The average number of cigarettes smoked per person in a year in the top ten countries for smoking are shown next.

Greece	4,313	Malta	2,668
Hungary	3,265	Bulgaria	2,574
Kuwait	3,062	Belarus	2,571
Japan	3,023	Belgium	2,428
Spain	2,779	Turkey	2,394

12. The number of existing home sales in millions for the months from August 2007 to February 2009 are shown below.

    5.5 5.1 5.1 5.0 4.9 4.9 5.0 4.9 4.9 5.0
    4.9 5.0 4.9 5.1 4.9 4.5 4.7 4.5 4.7

13. The number of bids for the five most popular products under concert tickets on eBay for a day in April is shown below.

    340 75 123 259 151

14. The number of sales of single-family homes in the largest metropolitan areas of Florida in 2008 was

    321 307 338 200 141 115 518 185 258
    276 31 116 881 72 181 175 490 162
    1,235 369

15. From 1992 to 2004, the number of violent crimes committed per 1,000 students in U.S. schools each year was

    10 12 13 9 9 8 9 7 5 6 6 5

16. The average amount of tuition, fees, room and board for full-time students at public 4-year institutions in 2005–2006 in states starting with "M" was

    $12,865 $15,253 $15,199 $14,519 $13,719
    $10,040 $12,588 $11,292

17. The annual number of murders in the United States from 1995 to 2007 was as follows:

Year	Murders	Year	Murders
1995	21,610	2002	16,229
1996	19,650	2003	16,528
1997	18,208	2004	16,148
1998	16,914	2005	16,740
1999	15,522	2006	17,030
2000	15,586	2007	16,929
2001	16,037		

18. The 10 states with the highest unemployment rates in February 2009 and their rates of unemployment are given below:

State	Rate
Michigan	12.0
South Carolina	11.0
Oregon	10.8
Rhode Island	10.5
Nevada	10.1
North Carolina	10.7
California	10.5
District of Columbia	9.9
Florida	9.4
Indiana	9.4

For Exercises 19–26, find the mean of the data set.

19. For 50 students in the student union at one campus, the distribution of the students' ages was obtained as shown.

Class	Frequency	Class	Frequency
18–20	20	24–26	8
21–23	18	27–29	4

20. Thirty new automobiles were tested for fuel efficiency by the EPA (in miles per gallon). This frequency distribution was obtained:

Class	Frequency	Class	Frequency
8–12	3	23–27	5
13–17	5	28–32	2
18–22	15		

21. In a study of the time it takes an untrained mouse to run a maze, a researcher recorded these data in seconds.

Class	Frequency
2.1–2.7	5
2.8–3.4	7
3.5–4.1	12
4.2–4.8	14
4.9–5.5	16
5.6–6.2	8

22. Eighty randomly selected lightbulbs were tested to determine their lifetimes (in hours). The frequency distribution was obtained as shown.

Class	Frequency
53–63	6
64–74	12
75–85	25
86–96	18
97–107	14
108–118	5

23. These data represent the net worth (in millions of dollars) of 45 national corporations.

Class	Frequency
10–20	2
21–31	8
32–42	15
43–53	7
54–64	10
65–75	3

24. The cost per load (in cents) of 35 laundry detergents tested by *Consumer Reports* is shown here.

Class	Frequency
13–19	2
20–26	7
27–33	12
34–40	5
41–47	6
48–54	1
55–61	0
62–68	2

25. The frequency distribution shown represents the commission earned (in dollars) by 100 salespeople employed at several branches of a large chain store.

Class	Frequency	Class	Frequency
150–158	5	186–194	20
159–167	16	195–203	15
168–176	20	204–212	3
177–185	21		

26. This frequency distribution represents the data obtained from a sample of 75 copy machine service technicians. The values represent the days between service calls for various copy machines.

Class	Frequency	Class	Frequency
16–18	14	25–27	10
19–21	12	28–30	15
22–24	18	31–33	6

Critical Thinking

27. For each of the characteristics of the average college student listed on page 665, decide which measure of average you think was used, and explain your choices.

28. For these situations, state which measure of average—mean, median, or mode—should be used.

   (a) The most typical case is desired.
   (b) The data are categorical.
   (c) The values are to be divided into two approximately equal groups, one group containing the larger and one containing the smaller values.

For Exercises 29–34, describe which measure of average— mean, median, or mode—was probably used in each situation.

29. Half of the factory workers make more than $5.37 per hour and half make less than $5.37 per hour.
30. The average number of children per family in the Plaza Heights is 1.8.
31. Most people prefer red convertibles to any other color.
32. The average person cuts the lawn once a week.
33. The most common fear today is fear of speaking in public.
34. The average age of college professors is 42.3 years.

Section 12-4 Measures of Variation

LEARNING OBJECTIVES

☐ 1. Find the range of a data set.

☐ 2. Find the variance and standard deviation of a data set.

☐ 3. Interpret standard deviation.

Now that we know about measures of average, we'll consider the fact that there's more to the story told by a data set than just the average. For an example, consider the two pictures of dogs on this page.

If we look only at measures of average, particularly the mean, we might be fooled into thinking that the two groups are very similar, when clearly they are not. The difference, of course, is that all of the dogs in the first picture are of similar size, while those in the second picture have many different weights. Because there are some small dogs and one very large one, the mean weight in both groups is probably similar.

In this section we will study *measures of variation,* which will help to describe how the data within a set vary. The three most commonly used measures of variation are *range, variance,* and *standard deviation.*

The two groups of dogs have about the same mean size, but the range of sizes is quite different.

Range

The *range* is the simplest of the three measures of variation that we will study.

> The **range** of a data set is the difference between the highest and lowest values in the set.
>
> Range = Highest value − lowest value

EXAMPLE 1   **Finding the Range of a Data Set**

The first list below is the weights of the dogs in the first picture, and the second is the weights of the dogs in the second picture. Find the mean and range for each list.

70   73   58   60
30   85   40   125   42   75   60   55

SOLUTION

For the first list,

$$\text{Mean} = \frac{70 + 73 + 58 + 60}{4} = 65.25 \text{ lb}$$

$$\text{Range} = 73 - 58 = 15 \text{ lb}$$

For the second list,

$$\text{Mean} = \frac{30 + 85 + 40 + 125 + 42 + 75 + 60 + 55}{8} = 64 \text{ lb}$$

$$\text{Range} = 125 - 30 = 95 \text{ lb}$$

As we suspected, the means are very close, but the ranges are very different.

▼ **Try This One 1**

The monthly average high temperatures from January to December in Aruba are shown below. Find the range.

85°   85°   86°   87°   88°   89°   88°   89°   89°   89°   87°   85°

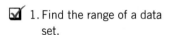   1. Find the range of a data set.

Variance and Standard Deviation

The range is a limited measure of variation because it ignores all the data except the highest and lowest values. If most of the values are similar, but there's just one unusually high value, the range will make it look like there's a lot more variation than there actually is. For this reason, we will next define *variance* and *standard deviation,* which are much more reliable measures of variation.

Variance and standard deviation are a little tricky to compute. In the box below, we'll explain how to find them. Later in the section, we'll discuss their significance.

Procedure for Finding the Variance and Standard Deviation

Step 1   Find the mean.

Step 2   Subtract the mean from each data value in the data set.

Step 3   Square the differences.

Step 4   Find the sum of the squares.

Step 5   Divide the sum by $n - 1$ to get the variance, where n is the number of data values.

Step 6   Take the square root of the variance to get the standard deviation.

EXAMPLE 2 **Finding Variance and Standard Deviation**

The heights in inches of the top six scorers for the Cleveland Cavaliers during the 2008–2009 season are listed below. Find the variance and standard deviation.

80   73   87   74   83   74

SOLUTION

Step 1 Find the mean height.

$$\text{Mean} = \frac{\sum X}{n} = \frac{80 + 73 + 87 + 74 + 83 + 74}{6} = 78.5 \text{ inches}$$

Step 2 Subtract the mean from each data value.

$80 - 78.5 = 1.5$	$87 - 78.5 = 8.5$	$83 - 78.5 = 4.5$
$73 - 78.5 = -5.5$	$74 - 78.5 = -4.5$	$74 - 78.5 = -4.5$

Step 3 Square each result.

$(1.5)^2 = 2.25$	$(8.5)^2 = 72.25$	$(4.5)^2 = 20.25$
$(-5.5)^2 = 30.25$	$(-4.5)^2 = 20.25$	$(-4.5)^2 = 20.25$

Step 4 Find the sum of the squares.

$$2.25 + 30.25 + 72.25 + 20.25 + 20.25 + 20.25 = 165.5$$

Step 5 Divide the sum by $n - 1$ to get the variance, where n is the sample size. In this case, n is 6, so $n - 1 = 5$.

$$\text{Variance} = \frac{165.5}{5} = 33.1$$

Step 6 Take the square root of the variance to get standard deviation.

$$\text{Standard deviation} = \sqrt{33.1} \approx 5.75 \text{ inches}$$

To organize the steps, you might find it helpful to make a table with three columns: The original data, the difference between each data value and the mean, and their squares. Then you just add the entries in the last column and divide by $n - 1$ to get the variance.

Data (X)	$X - $ mean	$(X - $ mean$)^2$
80	1.5	2.25
73	-5.5	30.25
87	8.5	72.25
74	-4.5	20.25
83	4.5	20.25
74	-4.5	20.25
		165.5

▼ **Try This One 2**

The heights in inches for the eight nonpitchers in the starting lineup for the New York Mets on opening day 2008 are listed below. Find the variance and standard deviation.

73   74   72   75   73   74   73   71

To understand the significance of standard deviation, we'll look at the process one step at a time.

Step 1 *Compute the mean.* Variation is a measure of how far the data vary from the mean, so it makes sense to begin there.

Step 2 *Subtract the mean from each data value.* In this step, we are literally calculating how far away from the mean each data value is. The problem is that since some are greater than the mean and some less, their sum will always add up to zero. (Try it!) So that doesn't help much.

Step 3 *Square the differences.* This solves the problem of those differences adding to zero—when we square, they're all positive.

Step 4 *Add the squares.* In the next two steps, we're getting an approximate average of the squares of the individual variations from the mean. First we add them, then . . .

Step 5 *Divide the sum by $n - 1$.* It's a bit technical to explain why we divide by $n - 1$ rather than n, but in any case we now have the approximate average of the squares of the individual variations from the mean.

Step 6 *Take the square root of the sum.* This "undoes" the square we did in step 3. It will return the units of our answer to the units of the original data, giving us a good measure of how far the typical data value varies from the mean.

Now we'll formally define these two key measures of variation.

☑ 2. Find the variance and standard deviation of a data set.

The **variance** for a data set is an approximate average of the square of the distance between each value and the mean. If X represents individual values, $\overline{X}$ is the mean and n is the number of values:

$$\text{Variance} = \frac{\sum (X - \overline{X})^2}{n - 1}$$

The **standard deviation** is the square root of the variance.

Interpreting Standard Deviation

Since standard deviation measures how far typical values are from the mean, its size tells us how spread out the data are. We'll examine this idea in Example 3.

EXAMPLE 3   **Interpreting Standard Deviation**

A professor has two sections of Math 115 this semester. The 8:30 A.M. class has a mean score of 74% with a standard deviation of 3.6%. The 2 P.M. class also has a mean score of 74%, but a standard deviation of 9.2%. What can we conclude about the students' averages in these two sections?

SOLUTION

In relative terms, the morning class has a small standard deviation and the afternoon class has a large one. So even though they have the same mean, the classes are quite different. In the morning class, most of the students probably have scores relatively close to the mean, with few very high or very low scores. In the afternoon class, the scores vary more widely, with a lot of high scores and a lot of low scores that average out to a mean of 74%.

▼ **Try This One 3**

☑ 3. Interpret standard deviation.

For the dogs in the two pictures on page 675, discuss what you think the standard deviations might be in comparison to one another, then check your answer by computing the standard deviation for each group.

Answers to Try This One

1   4°

2   Variance ≈ 1.55 inches; standard deviation ≈ 1.25 inches

3   The second group should have a much larger standard deviation than the first since the weights are more spread out. The actual standard deviation for the first group is 7.37 lb and for the second group it is 30.7 lb.

EXERCISE SET   12-4

Writing Exercises

1. Name three measures of variation.
2. What is the range?
3. Why is the range not usually the best measure of variation?
4. What is the relationship between the variance and standard deviation?
5. Explain the procedure for finding the standard deviation for data.
6. Explain how the variation of two data sets can be compared by using the standard deviations.

For Exercises 7–10, discuss the relative sizes of the standard deviations for the two data sets.

7. Data set 1:   12   15   13   10   16   13   12   13
   Data set 2:   5   26   31   2   10   25   6   33

8. Data set 1:   40-yard dash times for starting running backs in the National Football League
   Data set 2:   40-yard dash times for every student in your math class
9. Data set 1:   Average monthly high temperature in Chicago
   Data set 2:   Average monthly high temperature in Los Angeles
10. Data set 1:   Weights of all the dogs at a golden retriever rescue shelter
    Data set 2:   Weights of all the dogs for sale in a pet store

Real-World Applications

For Exercises 11-26, find the range, variance, and standard deviation.

11. These data are the number of junk e-mails Lena received for 9 consecutive days.

    61   1   1   3   2   30   18   3   7

12. The number of hospitals in the five largest hospital systems is shown here.

    340   75   123   259   151

    Source: USA Today

13. Ten used trail bikes are randomly selected from a bike shop, and the odometer reading of each is recorded as follows.

    1,902   103   653   1,901   788   361   216   363   223   656

14. Fifteen students were selected and asked how many hours each studied for the final exam in statistics. Their answers are recorded here.

    8   6   3   0   0   5   9   2   1   3   7   10   0   3   6

15. The weights of nine players from a college football team are recorded as follows.

    206   215   305   297   265   282   301   255   261

16. Shown here are the numbers of stories in the 11 tallest buildings in St. Paul, Minnesota.

    37   46   32   32   33   25   17   27   21   25   33

    Source: The World Almanac and Book of Facts

17. The heights (in inches) of nine male army recruits are shown here.

    78   72   68   73   75   69   74   73   72

18. The number of calories in 12 randomly selected microwave dinners is shown here.

    560   832   780   650   470   920   1,090   970
    495   550   605   735

19. The table below shows the average price of a gallon of regular unleaded gas in U.S. dollars for various cities in June 2007.

City	Price
Chicago	2.69
Paris	6.52
Toronto	3.28
Moscow	2.89
São Paulo	4.89
Seoul	6.06

20. The number of attorneys in 10 law firms in Pittsburgh is 87, 109, 57, 221, 175, 123, 170, 80, 66, and 80.

    Source: *Pittsburgh Tribune Review*

21. The stock prices for eight major grocery store chains in early 2009 were: $18.28, $20.32, $9.34, $11.57, $15.21, $48.04, $48.84, and $28.23.

22. The table reflects consumer priorities worldwide for a variety of expenditures:

Global Priority	U.S. Currency (in billions)
Cosmetics in the United States	8
Ice cream in Europe	11
Perfumes in Europe and the United States	12
Pet foods in Europe and the United States	17
Business entertainment in Japan	35
Cigarettes in Europe	50
Alcoholic drinks in Europe	105
Narcotic drugs in the world	400
Military spending in the world	780

Source: www.globalissues.org

23. The number of flu breakouts in 2009 in various regions of the U.S. were

    429   690   884   827   914   176   565   479   569

    Source: cdc.gov

24. The five teams in baseball's National League eastern division had the following number of wins in 2008: 92, 89, 84, 72, 59.

25. The number of workplace fatalities in the United States from 2000 to 2007 were as follows:

Year	Fatalities	Year	Fatalities
2000	5,920	2004	5,764
2001	5,915	2005	5,734
2002	5,534	2006	5,840
2003	5,575	2007	5,488

Source: *bls.gov*

26. From 1992 to 2004, the number of violent crimes committed per 1,000 students in U.S. schools each year was

    10   12   13   9   9   8   9   7   5   6   6   5

Critical Thinking

27. The three data sets have the same mean and range, but is the variation the same? Explain your answer.

    (a)   5   7   9   11   13   15   17
    (b)   5   6   7   11   15   16   17
    (c)   5   5   5   11   17   17   17

28. Using this set—10, 20, 30, 40, and 50,
    (a) Find the standard deviation.
    (b) Add 5 to each value and then find the standard deviation.

    (c) Subtract 5 from each value and then find the standard deviation.
    (d) Multiply each value by 5 and then find the standard deviation.
    (e) Divide each value by 5 and then find the standard deviation.
    (f) Generalize the results of (a)–(e).

Section 12-5 Measures of Position

LEARNING OBJECTIVES

☐ 1. Compute the percentile rank for a data value.

☐ 2. Find a data value corresponding to a given percentile.

☐ 3. Use percentile rank to compare values from different data sets.

☐ 4. Compute quartiles for a data set.

So you managed to survive 4 years of college and escape with that long-awaited diploma. But maybe the thought of entering the real world starts to look a little less appealing, and you realize that a couple more years of college might suit you. Next step: take the GRE (Graduate Record Examination), which is like the SAT for grad school.

When you get your score back, you see that it's 1120. How do you know if that's a good score? The quickest way is to look at the *percentile rank* on the report, which in this case would probably be 60%. Does this mean that you only got 60% of the questions right? That wouldn't be a very good score! In fact, that's not at all what it means, and you did just fine.

The term percentile is used in statistics to measure the position of a data value in a data set.

> A **percentile,** or percentile rank, of a data value indicates the percent of data values in a set that are below that particular value.

In this case, your percentile rank of 60% means that 60% of all students who took the GRE scored lower than you did. Not bad! Scores on standardized tests are one of the most common uses for percentiles because they help you to put a raw score like 1120 into context.

Percentiles are also used very commonly in health care, especially pediatrics. To monitor a child's development, doctors compare the child's height, weight, and head size at a certain age to measurements of other children at the same age. If a child's percentiles suddenly change radically, the doctor might suspect a problem in his or her development.

Percentiles were originally used to analyze data sets with 100 or more values. But when statistical techniques were developed for smaller data sets, the percentile concept came into use for those sets as well. There are several methods that can be used for computing percentiles, and sometimes the answers vary slightly, especially with small data sets. In this section, we will use a basic method that works well for smaller data sets.

EXAMPLE 1 Finding the Percentile Rank of a Data Value

Math Note

In order to keep our study of percentiles relatively simple, we'll work with data sets with no repeated values. More complicated techniques are used to find percentiles for data sets with repeated values.

Suppose you score 77 on a test in a class of 10 people, with the 10 scores listed below. What was your percentile rank?

93 82 64 75 98 52 77 88 90 71

SOLUTION

Step 1 Arrange the scores in order.

52 64 71 75 77 82 88 90 93 98

Step 2 Find the number of data values below 77. There are 4 values below 77.

Step 3 Divide the number below the score by the total number of data values and change the answer to a percent.

$$\frac{4}{10} = 0.40 = 40\%$$

A test score of 77 is equivalent to the 40th percentile.

☑ 1. Compute the percentile rank for a data value.

▼ Try This One 1

The weights in pounds for the 12 members of a college gymnastics team are below. Find the percentile rank of the gymnast who weighs 97 pounds.

101 120 88 72 75 80 98 91 105 97 78 85

In Example 1, we saw how to find the percentile rank for a given data value. In Example 2, we'll examine the opposite question—finding the data value that corresponds to a given percentile.

| EXAMPLE 2 | Finding a Data Value Corresponding to a Given Percentile |

The number of words in each of the last 10 presidential inaugural addresses is listed below. Find the length that corresponds to the 30th percentile.

2,406   2,073   1,571   2,170   1,507   2,283   2,546   2,463   1,087   1,668

SOLUTION

Step 1 We are asked to find the number on the list that has 30% of the numbers below it. There are 10 numbers, and 30% of 10 is 3.

Step 2 Arrange the data in order from smallest to largest, and find the value that has 3 values below it.

1,087   1,507   1,571   1,668   2,073   2,170   2,283   2,406   2,463   2,546

The 30th percentile is the speech that consisted of 1,668 words.

▼ Try This One 2

The average monthly rainfall in inches for St. Petersburg, Florida, is shown in the chart below. Which month is at the 75th percentile?

Jan	Feb	Mar	Apr	May	Jun	Jul	Aug	Sep	Oct	Nov	Dec
2.3	2.8	3.4	1.6	2.6	5.7	7.0	7.8	6.1	2.5	1.9	2.2

☑ 2. Find a data value corresponding to a given percentile.

Percentile ranks are particularly useful in comparing data that come from two different sets, as shown in Example 3.

| EXAMPLE 3 | Using Percentiles to Compare Data from Different Sets |

Two students are competing for one remaining spot in a law school class. Miguel ranked 51st in a graduating class of 1,700, while Dustin ranked 27th in a class of 540. Which student's position was higher in his class?

SOLUTION

This is an ideal application of percentile rank. Miguel ranked 51st out of 1,700, so there were $1,700 - 51 = 1,649$ students ranked below him. His percentile rank is

$$\frac{1,649}{1,700} = 0.97 \text{ or } 97\%$$

Dustin had $540 - 27 = 513$ students ranked below him, so his percentile rank is

$$\frac{513}{540} = 0.95 \text{ or } 95\%$$

Both are excellent students, but Miguel's ranking is higher.

▼ **Try This One 3**

3. Use percentile rank to compare values from different data sets.

In the 2007–2008 school year, West Virginia University finished the season ranked sixth out of 119 Division IA football teams, and ranked 17th out of 346 Division I basketball teams. Which team had the higher percentile rank?

In Section 12-3, we saw that the median of a data set divides the set into equal halves. Another statistical measure we will study is the **quartile,** which divides a data set into quarters. The second quartile is the same as the median, and divides a data set into an upper half and a lower half. The first quartile is the median of the lower half, and the third quartile is the median of the upper half. We use the symbols Q_1, Q_2, and Q_3 for the first, second, and third quartiles respectively.

EXAMPLE 4   **Finding Quartiles for a Data Set**

Find Q_1, Q_2, and Q_3 for the number of aircraft stolen during a recent 8-year period.

| 14 | 11 | 20 | 21 | 42 | 24 | 36 | 35 |

Source: USA Today

SOLUTION

Step 1 Arrange the data in order.

| 11 | 14 | 20 | 21 | 24 | 35 | 36 | 42 |

Step 2 Find the median. This is Q_2.

11   14   20   21   24   35   36   42
↑
$Q_2 = 22.5$

Step 3 Find the median of the data values less than Q_2. This is Q_1.

11   14   20   21
↑
$Q_1 = 17$

Step 4 Find the median of the data values above Q_2. This is Q_3.

24   35   36   42
↑
$Q_3 = 35.5$

In summary, $Q_1 = 17$, $Q_2 = 22.5$, and $Q_3 = 35.5$.

✓ 4. Compute quartiles for a data set.

▼ **Try This One 4**

Find Q_1, Q_2, and Q_3 for the data shown.

18   32   54   36   27   42   31   15   60   25

In this section, we studied two measures of position, percentile and quartile. In Section 12-6, the concept of position plays a very important role when we study a third measure of position, the z score.

Answers to Try This One

1 58th percentile

2 September

3 Basketball

4 $Q_1 = 25$, $Q_2 = 31.5$, $Q_3 = 42$

EXERCISE SET 12-5

Writing Exercises

1. If your score in your math class puts you in the 60th percentile, what exactly does that mean?
2. Does a score in the 90th percentile mean that you got 90% of the questions right on a test? Explain.
3. Explain what quartiles are.
4. What is the connection between the second quartile and the median for a data set? Explain.

Real-World Applications

5. The scores for 20 students on a 50-point math test are 42, 48, 50, 36, 35, 27, 47, 38, 32, 43, 24, 33, 39, 49, 44, 40, 29, 30, 41, and 37.

   (a) Find the percentile rank for a score of 32.
   (b) Find the percentile rank for a score of 44.
   (c) Find the percentile rank for a score of 36.
   (d) Find the percentile rank for a score of 27.
   (e) Find the percentile rank for a score of 49.

6. The heights (in inches) of the 12 students in a seminar course are 73, 68, 64, 63, 71, 70, 65, 67, 72, 66, 60, and 61.

   (a) Find the percentile rank for a height of 67 in.
   (b) Find the percentile rank for a height of 70 in.
   (c) Find the percentile rank for a height of 63 in.
   (d) Find the percentile rank for a height of 68 in.
   (e) Find the percentile rank for a height of 66 in.

7. In a class of 500 students, Carveta's rank was 125. Find her percentile rank.

8. In a class of 400 students, John's rank was 80. Find his percentile rank.
9. In a charity marathon to raise money for AIDS research, Chen finished 43rd out of 200 entrants. Find her percentile rank.
10. In a speed boat race, there were 25 participants. Nate came in 4th place. What is his percentile rank?
11. On an exam, Angela scored in the 20th percentile. If there were 50 students in the class, how many students scored lower than she did?
12. Out of 600 applicants to a graduate program at an Ivy League school, Marissa's GRE score was in the 25th percentile. How many applicants scored lower than she did?
13. Lea's percentile rank on an exam in a class of 600 students is 60. Maurice's class rank is 220. Who is ranked higher?
14. In an English class of 30 students, Audrelia's percentile rank is 20. Maranda's class rank is 20. Whose rank is higher?

15. In an evening statistics class, the ages of 20 students are as follows.

18   24   19   20   33   42   43   27   31   39
21   44   26   32   37   34   23   35   28   25

(a) What is the percentile rank of 33?
(b) What is the rank (from the top) of 33?
(c) What age corresponds to the 20th percentile?

16. Twenty subjects in a psychology class experiment scored the following on an IQ test.

95   107   110   101   122   96   94   104   131   90
111   103   97   100   119   85   108   120   130   88

(a) What is the percentile rank of 96?
(b) What is the rank (from the top) of 96?
(c) What score corresponds to the 40th percentile?

For Exercises 17–22, find the values for Q_1, Q_2, and Q_3.

17. Number of drive-in theaters in nine selected states:

59   20   21   34   52   48   24   29   55

Source: National Association of Theater Owners

18. Average cost in cents per kilowatt hour of producing electricity using nuclear energy for the past 8 years:

1.83   2.18   2.36   2.04   2.10   2.25   2.48   2.57

Source: Nuclear Energy Institute

19. The costs of a 1-hour massage in 10 large cities are:

$75 $77 $78 $90 $87 $93 $89 $93 $95 $88

20. Number of passengers (in millions) at 10 selected airports in the United States:

32.6   28.9   15.5   16.6   19.4   15.9   31.6   15.4   29.1   15.7

Source: Aviation Statistics

21. The annual number of homicides in Milwaukee for a 10-year period is shown.

122   111   124   121   127   108   107   88   122   103

22. Below are the market caps in billions of dollars of nine of the largest companies that are 30 years old or younger.

Google	$140.6	Yahoo	$40.2
Home Depot	$85.2	EMC	$31.9
Apple	$73.0	Starbucks	$24.5
Dell	$53.4	Staples	$19.4
eBay	$45.8		

Source: *USA Today*

Critical Thinking

23. Is it possible to score 90% on a test and have a percentile rank less than 90th? Is it possible to score 90% and have a percentile rank of exactly 90?

24. What would you have to do in order to rank in the 100th percentile in your college graduating class?

Section 12-6 The Normal Distribution

LEARNING OBJECTIVES

☐ 1. Identify characteristics of a data set that is normally distributed.

☐ 2. Apply the empirical rule.

☐ 3. Compute *z* scores.

☐ 4. Use a table and *z* scores to find areas under the standard normal distribution.

If you grew up anywhere near maple trees, you're probably familiar with the seed pods they drop by the thousands in the spring. Like almost all living things, the individual pods vary in size—on any given tree, there's a typical size, with some pods bigger and some smaller.

On a beautiful spring day, I gathered 100 pods from the maple in my back yard, measured each, then grouped them according to their length. The smallest was 42 mm, the largest 59 mm, and in the photo they're grouped in classes 42–43, 44–45, 46–47, etc. An interesting thing happened—we see that the largest number of pods have lengths somewhere in the middle of the range, and the classes further away from the center have less pods.

A wide variety of quantities in the real world, like sizes of individuals in a population, IQ scores, life spans for batteries of a certain brand, and many others, tend to exhibit this same phenomenon. In fact, it's so common that frequency distributions of this type came to be known as *normal distributions*.

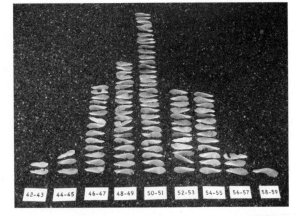

42-43   44-45   46-47   48-49   50-51   52-53   54-55   56-57   58-59

Suppose a researcher selects a random sample of 100 adult women, measures their heights, and constructs a histogram. The researcher would probably get a graph similar to the one shown in Figure 12-6a. If the researcher increases the sample size and decreases the width of the classes, the histograms will look like the ones shown in Figures 12-6b and 12-6c. Finally, if it were possible to measure the exact heights of all adult females in the United States and plot them, the histogram would approach what is called the *normal distribution,* shown in Figure 12-6d. This distribution is also known as a *bell curve* or a *Gaussian distribution,* named for the German mathematician Carl Friedrich Gauss (1777–1855) who derived its equation.

A normal distribution is defined formally as follows.

> A **normal distribution** is a continuous, symmetric, bell-shaped distribution.

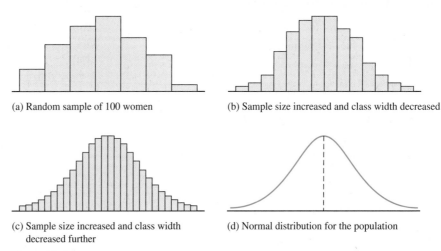

(a) Random sample of 100 women

(b) Sample size increased and class width decreased

(c) Sample size increased and class width decreased further

(d) Normal distribution for the population

Figure 12-6

Some properties of a normal distribution, including those mentioned in the definition, are explained next.

In a normal distribution, values cluster around a central value and fall off in both directions. Waiting times can be normally distributed.

☑ 1. Identify characteristics of a data set that is normally distributed.

Some Properties of a Normal Distribution

1. It is bell-shaped.

2. The mean, median, and mode are equal and located at the center of the distribution.

3. It is unimodal (i.e., it has only one mode).

4. It is symmetrical about the mean, which is equivalent to saying that its shape is the same on both sides of a vertical line passing through the center.

5. It is continuous—i.e., there are no gaps or holes.

6. The area under a portion of a normal curve is the percentage (in decimal form) of the data that falls between the data values that begin and end that region. (We will use this property extensively in Section 12-7.)

7. The total area under a normal curve is exactly 1. This makes sense based on property 6, since the area under the whole curve encompasses all data values.

The Empirical Rule

When data values are normally distributed, there is a rule that allows us to quickly determine a range in which most of the data values fall. It is known as the *empirical rule.*

> ### The Empirical Rule
>
> When data are normally distributed, approximately 68% of the values are within 1 standard deviation of the mean, approximately 95% are within 2 standard deviations of the mean, and approximately 99.7% are within 3 standard deviations of the mean (see Figure 12-7).

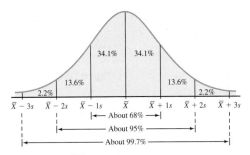

Figure 12-7 $\overline{X}$ = mean, s = standard deviation

EXAMPLE 1   Using the Empirical Rule

According to the website answerbag.com, the mean height for male humans is 5 feet 9.3 inches, with a standard deviation of 2.8 inches. If this is accurate, out of 1,000 randomly selected men, how many would you expect to be between 5 feet 6.5 inches and 6 feet 0.1 inch?

SOLUTION

The given range of heights corresponds to those within 1 standard deviation of the mean, so we would expect about 68% of men to fall in that range. In this case, we expect about 680 men to be between 5 feet 6.5 inches and 6 feet 0.1 inch.

☑ 2. Apply the empirical rule.

> ### ▼ Try This One 1
>
> A standard test of intelligence is scaled so that the mean IQ is 100, and the standard deviation is 15. If there are 40,000 people in a stadium, how many would you expect to have an IQ between 70 and 130?

The Standard Normal Distribution

Any set of data that is normally distributed has its own mean and standard deviation, so the exact shape and location of the associated normal curve varies accordingly. This presents a problem: to answer questions related to the number of data values that are likely to fall into a given range, we need a method for finding the area under the curve for each specific case. This is not an easy problem to solve. Instead, statisticians developed a way to standardize the normal curves for different data sets by using the *standard normal distribution.*

> The **standard normal distribution** is a normal distribution with mean 0 and standard deviation 1.

The standard normal distribution is shown in Figure 12-8. The values under the curve shown in Figure 12-8 indicate the proportion of area in each section. For example, the area between the mean and 1 standard deviation above or below the mean is about 0.341, or 34.1%.

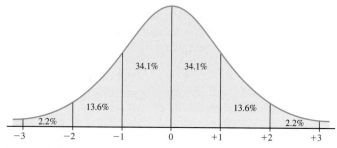

Figure 12-8

Tables have been compiled that help us to find the area under certain portions of a standard normal curve. In order to apply them to any data that are normally distributed, those data have to be altered to make the distribution have mean 0 and standard deviation 1. To accomplish that, we will use *z scores*.

> For a given data value from a data set that is normally distributed, we define that value's **z score** to be
>
> $$z = \frac{\text{Data value} - \text{mean}}{\text{Standard deviation}}$$
>
> The z score is a measure of position: it describes how many standard deviations a data value lies above (if positive) or below (if negative) the mean.

EXAMPLE 2   Computing a *z* Score

Based on the information in Example 1, find the *z* score for a man who is 6 feet 4 inches tall.

SOLUTION

Using the formula for *z* scores with mean 5 feet 9.3 inches and standard deviation 2.8 inches:

$$z = \frac{76 \text{ in.} - 69.3 \text{ in.}}{2.8 \text{ in.}} \approx 2.4$$

Math Note

Notice that the units divide out, so z scores have no units.

☑ 3. Compute *z* scores.

▼ Try This One 2

Using the information in Try This One 1, find the *z* score for a person with an IQ of 91.

The value of *z* scores is that they will allow us to find areas under a normal curve using only areas under a standard normal curve, which can be read from a table, like Table 12-3.

TABLE 12-3	Area Under a Normal Distribution Curve Between z = 0 and a Positive Value of z

Math Note

An area table with more values can be found in Appendix A. If you need the area for a z score between two values in Table 12-3, you can get an approximate area by choosing an area between areas in the table, or use the more extensive table in the appendix.

z	A	z	A	z	A
0.00	0.000	1.10	0.364	2.20	0.486
0.05	0.020	1.15	0.375	2.25	0.488
0.10	0.040	1.20	0.385	2.30	0.489
0.15	0.060	1.25	0.394	2.35	0.491
0.20	0.079	1.30	0.403	2.40	0.492
0.25	0.099	1.35	0.412	2.45	0.493
0.30	0.118	1.40	0.419	2.50	0.494
0.35	0.137	1.45	0.427	2.55	0.495
0.40	0.155	1.50	0.433	2.60	0.495
0.45	0.174	1.55	0.439	2.65	0.496
0.50	0.192	1.60	0.445	2.70	0.497
0.55	0.209	1.65	0.451	2.75	0.497
0.60	0.226	1.70	0.455	2.80	0.497
0.65	0.242	1.75	0.460	2.85	0.498
0.70	0.258	1.80	0.464	2.90	0.498
0.75	0.273	1.85	0.468	2.95	0.498
0.80	0.288	1.90	0.471	3.00	0.499
0.85	0.302	1.95	0.474	3.05	0.499
0.90	0.316	2.00	0.477	3.10	0.499
0.95	0.329	2.05	0.480	3.15	0.499
1.00	0.341	2.10	0.482	3.20	0.499
1.05	0.353	2.15	0.484	3.25*	0.499

*For z scores greater than 3.25, use $A = 0.500$

Finding Areas under the Standard Normal Distribution

Section 12-7 is entirely devoted to solving real-world problems that use areas under a normal distribution. In the remainder of this section, we will focus on simply finding those areas. We will find areas corresponding to z scores using Table 12-3 and the following key facts.

Two Important Facts about the Standard Normal Curve

1. The area under any normal curve is divided into two equal halves at the mean. Each of the halves has area 0.500.

2. The area between $z = 0$ and a positive z score is the same as the area between $z = 0$ and the negative of that z score.

Each of the facts in the colored box is a consequence of the fact that normal distributions are symmetric about the mean. Examples 3, 4, and 5 will illustrate how to find areas under a normal curve.

EXAMPLE 3 **Finding the Area between Two *z* Scores**

Find the area under the standard normal distribution

(a) Between $z = 1.55$ and $z = 2.25$.
(b) Between $z = -0.60$ and $z = -1.35$.
(c) Between $z = 1.50$ and $z = -1.75$.

SOLUTION

(a) Draw the picture, label *z* scores, and shade the requested area. See Figure 12-9.

Using Table 12-3, the area between $z = 0$ and $z = 2.25$ is 0.488, and the area between $z = 0$ and $z = 1.55$ is 0.439. The area we are looking for is the larger area minus the smaller:

$$0.488 - 0.439 = 0.049.$$

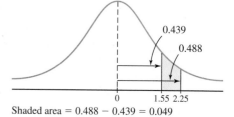

Shaded area $= 0.488 - 0.439 = 0.049$

Figure 12-9

The area between $z = 1.55$ and $z = 2.25$ is 0.049.

(b) Draw the picture, label *z* scores, and shade the requested area. See Figure 12-10.

Using key fact 2, we can find the area between $z = 0$ and the two given negative *z* scores by finding the corresponding positive *z* scores in the table. The areas are 0.226 for $z = -0.60$, and 0.412 for $z = -1.35$. Again, the area we're looking for is the larger area minus the smaller:

$$0.412 - 0.226 = 0.186$$

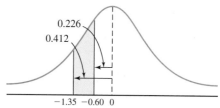

Shaded area $= 0.412 - 0.226 = 0.186$

Figure 12-10

The area between $z = -0.60$ and $z = -1.35$ is 0.186.

(c) Draw the picture, label the *z* scores, and shade the requested area. See Figure 12-11.

Since the *z* values are on opposite sides of the mean, the areas corresponding to the *z* values are added. The area corresponding to $z = -1.75$ is 0.460, and the area corresponding to $z = 1.50$ is 0.433.

$$0.460 + 0.433 = 0.893$$

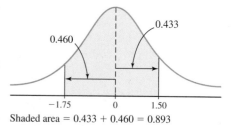

Shaded area $= 0.433 + 0.460 = 0.893$

Figure 12-11

The area between $z = 1.50$ and $z = -1.75$ is 0.893.

> **Math Note**
>
> Remember that the area under any portion of a normal distribution has to be non-negative and less than or equal to 1. If you don't get an area in that range, you must have made a mistake.

▼ Try This One 3

Find the area under the standard normal distribution

(a) Between $z = 2.05$ and $z = 2.40$.   (b) Between $z = -3.2$ and $z = -2.0$.
(c) Between $z = -0.55$ and $z = 1.6$.

When we want to find the area to the right or left of a single *z* score, we will use the fact that the area under half of the curve is exactly 0.500, as in Examples 4 and 5.

EXAMPLE 4   Finding the Area to the Right of a z Score

Find the area under the standard normal distribution

(a) To the right of $z = 1.70$.   (b) To the right of $z = -0.95$.

SOLUTION

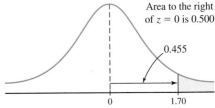

Area to the right
of $z = 0$ is 0.500

0.455

0

1.70

Shaded area = 0.500 − 0.455 = 0.045

Figure 12-12

(a) Draw the picture, label the z scores, and shade the area. See Figure 12-12.

The area of the entire portion to the right of $z = 0$ is 0.500. According to the table, the area of the portion between $z = 0$ and $z = 1.70$ is 0.455. So the shaded portion is the difference between 0.500 and 0.455:

$$0.500 - 0.455 = 0.045$$

The area to the right of $z = 1.70$ is 0.045.

(b) Draw the picture, label the z scores, and shade the area. See Figure 12-13.

This time, the area is the sum of 0.500 (the entire right half of the distribution) and the area between $z = 0$ and $= -0.95$, which we find to be 0.329 using Table 12-3.

$$0.500 + 0.329 = 0.829$$

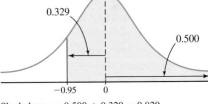

0.329

0.500

−0.95 0

Shaded area = 0.500 + 0.329 = 0.829

Figure 12-13

The area to the right of $z = -0.95$ is 0.829.

Math Note

Using a sketch and the two important facts on page 689 allows us to find areas without having to learn a variety of rules and formulas for the different possible situations.

▼ Try This One 4

Find the area under the standard normal distribution

(a) To the right of $z = -2.40$.   (b) To the right of $z = 0.25$.

EXAMPLE 5   Finding the Area to the Left of a z Score

Find the area under the standard normal distribution

(a) To the left of $z = -2.20$.   (b) To the left of $z = 1.95$.

SOLUTION

(a) Draw the picture, label the z scores, and shade the area. See Figure 12-14.

The shaded area is the entire left half (0.500) minus the area between $z = 0$ and $z = -2.2$, which is 0.486 according to Table 12-3.

$$0.500 - 0.486 = 0.014$$

The area to the left of $z = -2.2$ is 0.014.

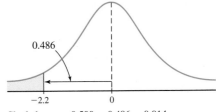

0.486

−2.2 0

Shaded area = 0.500 − 0.486 = 0.014

Figure 12-14

(b) Draw the picture, label the z scores, and shade the area. See Figure 12-15.

Table 12-3 gives us an area of 0.474 between $z = 0$ and $z = 1.95$. Adding to the area of the left half (0.500), we get

$$0.500 + 0.474 = 0.974$$

The area to the left of $z = 1.95$ is 0.974.

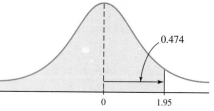

Shaded area = 0.500 + 0.474 = 0.974

Figure 12-15

CAUTION

Don't ignore your graph when writing your final answer! As long as you keep in mind that the total area under the distribution is 1, you can visually check if your answer is reasonable. In Example 5b, just from a quick glance at the graph you can see that most of the distribution is shaded, so your answer should be close to 1.

☑ 4. Use a table and z scores to find areas under the standard normal distribution.

▼ Try This One 5

Find the area under the standard normal distribution

(a) To the left of $z = -1.05$.

(b) To the left of $z = 0.1$.

To close the section, we should point out that no data set fits the normal distribution perfectly, since the normal curve is a theoretical distribution that would come from infinitely many data values. But there are many, many quantities that vary from a true normal distribution so slightly that the normal curve can be used to study those quantities very effectively.

Answers to Try This One

1 About 38,000

2 −0.6

3 (a) 0.012
   (b) 0.022
   (c) 0.654

4 (a) 0.992
   (b) 0.401

5 (a) 0.147
   (b) 0.540

EXERCISE SET 12-6

Writing Exercises

1. What is the distinguishing characteristic of a quantity that is normally distributed?
2. Write as many properties of a normal curve as you can think of.
3. What does the area under a portion of a normal curve tell you about the data in the associated distribution?
4. Explain what the empirical rule says.
5. What percentage of the area under a normal curve falls to the right of the mean? To the left? Explain.
6. Why does it make sense that the total area under a normal curve is 1?

Computational Exercises

For Exercises 7–10, assume that the data set described is normally distributed with the given mean and standard deviation, and with n total values. Find the approximate number of data values that will fall in the given range.

7. Mean = 12, standard deviation = 1.5, n = 50.
   Range: 10.5 to 13.5
8. Mean = 100, standard deviation = 8, n = 200.
   Range: 84 to 116
9. Mean = 400, standard deviation = 25, n = 500.
   Range: 325 to 475
10. Mean = −14.2, standard deviation = 1.6, n = 120.
    Range: −17.4 to −11

For Exercises 11–28, find the area under the standard normal distribution curve

11. Between $z = 0$ and $z = 1.95$.
12. Between $z = 0$ and $z = 0.55$.
13. Between $z = 0$ and $z = -0.5$.
14. Between $z = 0$ and $z = -2.05$.
15. To the right of $z = 1.0$.
16. To the right of $z = 0.25$.
17. To the left of $z = -0.40$.
18. To the left of $z = -1.45$.
19. Between $z = 1.25$ and $z = 1.90$.
20. Between $z = 0.8$ and $z = 1.3$.
21. Between $z = -0.85$ and $z = -0.20$.
22. Between $z = -1.55$ and $z = -1.85$.
23. Between $z = 0.25$ and $z = -1.10$.
24. Between $z = 2.45$ and $z = -1.05$.
25. To the left of $z = 1.20$.
26. To the left of $z = 2.15$.
27. To the right of $z = -1.90$.
28. To the right of $z = -0.20$.

Critical Thinking

29. Find a z value to the right of the mean so that 67.4% of the distribution lies to the left of it.
30. Find a z value to the left of the mean so that 98.6% of the area lies to the right of it.
31. Find two z values, one positive and one negative but having the same absolute value, so that the areas in the two tails (ends) total these values.
    (a) 4%
    (b) 8%
    (c) 1.6%

Section 12-7 Applications of the Normal Distribution

LEARNING OBJECTIVES

☐ 1. Use the normal distribution to find percentages.

☐ 2. Use the normal distribution to find probabilities.

☐ 3. Use the normal distribution to find percentile ranks.

Surely there must be someone out there who doesn't like Oreos, but I haven't met him or her. A standard package of America's favorite cookie contains 510 grams of sweet temptation. Of course, when you buy a package, you expect every one of those 510 grams. But there's variation in just about everything, so some packages will have more than the intended weight, and some will have less. The folks running Nabisco aren't dummies, though—they know that if someone decides to check the weight and finds it to be less than 510 grams, they won't be a very happy customer. So what to do?

This is exactly the sort of situation where weights tend to be normally distributed. The company would likely design its production and packaging process so that the mean is somewhat larger than 510 grams, with a standard deviation that assures that the vast majority of packages will weigh at least 510 grams.

In this section, we will see how the area calculations we practiced in Section 12-6 can be used to solve real-world problems for data that are normally distributed. Our general strategy will be to transform specific data into z scores, then use Table 12-3 to find areas. Finally, we'll interpret the area as it applies to the given data.

The reason this works is indicated by Figure 12-16. Suppose that the weight of Oreos in a package is normally distributed with mean 518 grams and standard deviation 4 grams. The distribution would look like Figure 12-16a. After using the z score formula to standardize, we get the graph in Figure 12-16b; now we can apply our area calculations.

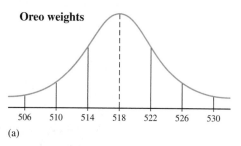

Oreo weights

506   510   514   518   522   526   530
(a)

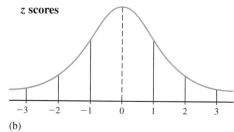

z scores

−3   −2   −1   0   1   2   3
(b)

Figure 12-16

EXAMPLE 1   Solving a Problem Using the Normal Distribution

If the weights of Oreos in a package are normally distributed with mean 518 grams and standard deviation 4 grams, find the percentage of packages that will weigh less than 510 grams.

SOLUTION

Math Note

It's typical for manufacturers to make sure that the listed weight for products packaged by weight is at least two standard deviations below the mean, ensuring that over 97% of the packages have the listed weight or more.

Step 1 Draw the figure and represent the area, as shown in Figure 12-17.

Step 2 Find the z score for data value 510.

$$z = \frac{\text{value} - \text{mean}}{\text{standard deviation}}$$

$$= \frac{510 - 518}{4} = -2$$

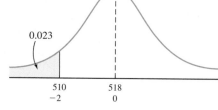

0.023

510   518
−2   0

Figure 12-17

This tells us that 510 grams is 2 standard deviations below the mean.

Step 3 Find the shaded area using Table 12-3. The shaded area is the area of the left half (0.5) minus the area between $z = 0$ and $z = -2$. The area between $z = 0$ and $z = -2$ is 0.477 (using $z = +2$ from the table).

$$\text{Area} = 0.5 - 0.477 = 0.023$$

Step 4 Interpret the area. In this case, an area of 0.023 tells us that only 2.3% of packages will have weights less than 510 grams.

☑ 1. Use the normal distribution to find percentages.

▼ Try This One 1

Based on data compiled by the World Health Organization, the mean systolic blood pressure in the United States is 120, the standard deviation is 16, and the pressures are normally distributed. Find each.

(a) The percent of individuals who have a blood pressure between 120 and 128
(b) The percent of individuals who have a blood pressure above 132
(c) The percent of individuals who have a blood pressure between 112 and 116
(d) The percent of individuals who have a blood pressure between 124 and 144
(e) The percent of individuals who have a blood pressure lower than 104

Our next interpretation for area under a normal distribution is tremendously important because it ties our study of statistics to the main topic of Chapter 11, probability.

Probability and Area under a Normal Distribution

The area under a normal distribution between two data values is the probability that a randomly selected data value is between those two values.

Example 2 illustrates the use of area to find probability.

EXAMPLE 2   Using Area under a Normal Distribution to Find Probabilities

Based on data in the 2009 *Statistical Abstract of the United States,* the average *American* generates 1,679 pounds of garbage per year. Let's assume that the number of pounds generated per person is approximately normally distributed with standard deviation 200 pounds. Find the probability that a randomly selected person generates

(a) Between 1,300 and 2,000 pounds of garbage per year.
(b) More than 2,000 pounds of garbage per year.

SOLUTION

(a) **Step 1** Draw the figure and represent the area. See Figure 12-18 below.

Step 2 Find the z scores for the two given weights.

$$1{,}300 \text{ pounds: } z = \frac{1{,}300 - 1{,}679}{200} \approx -1.9$$

$$2{,}000 \text{ pounds: } z = \frac{2{,}000 - 1{,}679}{200} \approx 1.6$$

Step 3 Find the shaded area. Using Table 12-3, the area between $z = 0$ and $z = 1.6$ is 0.445, and the area between $z = 0$ and $z = -1.9$ is 0.471. So the shaded area is

$$0.471 + 0.445 = 0.916$$

Step 4 Interpret the area. This tells us that if a person is selected at random, the probability that he or she generates between 1,300 and 2,000 pounds of garbage per year is 0.916, or 91.6%.

Figure 12-18

(b) Most of the work was already done in part a. We can adapt the graph a bit (Figure 12-19).

The shaded area is the area between $z = 0$ and $z = 1.6$ subtracted from the area of the entire right half (0.5).

$$0.5 - 0.445 = 0.055$$

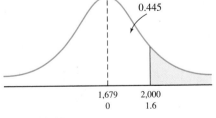

Figure 12-19

The probability that a randomly selected person generates more than 2,000 pounds of garbage per year is 0.055, or 5.5%.

Math Note

The probability that a randomly selected value from a normal distribution is less than some value is the area to the left of that value. The probability of a randomly selected value being greater than some value is the area to the right of that value.

2. Use the normal distribution to find probabilities.

▼ Try This One 2

The *Statistical Abstract* also indicates that of the 1,679 pounds of garbage generated by the average individual, 913 pounds will end up in a landfill. If these amounts are approximately normally distributed with standard deviation 160 pounds, find the probability that a randomly selected person generates

(a) Less than 600 pounds that end up in a landfill.
(b) Between 600 and 1,000 pounds that end up in a landfill.

Normal distributions can also be used to find percentiles, and answer questions of "how many?" Example 3 illustrates these types of questions.

EXAMPLE 3   Finding Number in a Sample and Percentile Rank

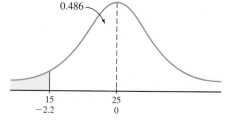

The American Automobile Association reports that the average time it takes to respond to an emergency call is 25 minutes. Assume the response time is approximately normally distributed and the standard deviation is 4.5 minutes.

(a) If 80 calls are randomly selected, approximately how many will have response times less than 15 minutes?
(b) In what percentile is a response time of 30 minutes?

SOLUTION

(a) **Step 1** Draw a figure and represent the area as shown in Figure 12-20.

Step 2 Find the z value for 15.

$$z = \frac{\text{Value} - \text{mean}}{\text{Standard deviation}}$$

$$= \frac{15 - 25}{4.5} \approx -2.2$$

0.486

15
−2.2

25
0

Figure 12-20

Step 3 Find the shaded area. Using Table 12-3, we find that the area between $z = 0$ and $z = -2.2$ is 0.486. The shaded area is the difference of the entire left half (0.5) and 0.486.

$$\text{Area} = 0.5 - 0.486 = 0.014.$$

Step 4 Interpret the area. An area of 0.014 tells us that 1.4% of calls will have a response time of less than 15 minutes. Multiply the percentage by the number of calls in our sample:

$$1.4\% \text{ of } 80 \text{ calls} = (0.014)(80) = 1.12$$

Approximately one call in 80 will have response time less than 15 minutes.

> **Math Note**
>
> Notice that in this case (number of calls), an answer of 1.12 doesn't make sense. We need to round to the nearest whole number.

(b) **Step 1** Draw a figure and represent the area as shown in Figure 12-21. Remember that to find the percentile, we are interested in the percentage of times that are less than 30 minutes.

0.364

25
0

30
1.1

Figure 12-21

Step 2 Find the z score for a response time of 30 minutes.

$$z = \frac{30 - 25}{4.5} \approx 1.1$$

Step 3 Find the shaded area. The area to the left of $z = 1.1$ is the area of the left half (0.5) plus the area between $z = 0$ and $z = 1.1$ (0.364 according to Table 12-3).

$$\text{Area} = 0.5 + 0.364 = 0.864$$

Step 4 Interpret the area. An area of 0.864 means that 86.4% of calls will get a response time of less than 30 minutes, so the time of 30 minutes is in the 86th percentile.

▼ Try This One 3

The mean for a reading test given nationwide is 80, and the standard deviation is 8. The variable is normally distributed. If 10,000 students take the test, find each.

☑ 3. Use the normal distribution to find percentile ranks.

(a) The number of students who will score above 90
(b) The number of students who will score between 78 and 88
(c) The percentile of a student who scores 94
(d) The number of students who will score below 76

Answers to Try This One

1 (a) 19.2%   (c) 9.3%   (e) 15.9%
(b) 22.7%   (d) 33.4%

2 (a) 0.026 or 2.6%
(b) 0.683 or 68.3%

3 (a) 1,060
(b) 4,400
(c) 96th percentile
(d) 3,080

EXERCISE SET 12-7

Writing Exercises

1. Explain why the normal distribution can be used to solve many real-life problems.

2. Given a data set, how could you decide if the distribution of the data was approximately normal?

Real-World Applications

3. The average hourly wage of production workers in manufacturing in 2007 was $17.41. Assume the variable is normally distributed. If the standard deviation of earning is $3.72, find these probabilities for a randomly selected production worker.

   (a) The production worker earns more than $18.55.
   (b) The production worker earns less than $14.00.

   Source: Statistical Abstract of the United States

4. The average cost for two people to go to a movie is $22. The standard deviation is $3. Assume the cost is normally distributed. Find the probability that at any given theater, the cost will be more than $26 for two people to go to a movie.

5. If the mean salary of public school teachers in the United States in 2007 was $49,294 and the standard deviation was $9,000, find these probabilities for a

randomly selected teacher. Assume the variable is normally distributed.

   (a) The teacher earns more than $55,000.
   (b) The teacher earns less than $45,000.

6. Average sales for an online textbook distributor were $71.12 per customer per purchase. Assume the sales are normally distributed. If the standard deviation of the amount spent on textbooks is $8.42, find these probabilities for a randomly selected customer of the online textbook distributor.

   (a) He or she spent more than $60 per purchase.
   (b) He or she spent less than $80 per purchase.

7. A survey found that people keep their television sets an average of 4.8 years. The standard deviation is 0.89 year. If a person decides to buy a new TV set,

find the probability that he or she has owned the old set for the given amount of time. Assume the variable is normally distributed.

(a) Less than 2.5 years   (b) Between 3 and 4 years
(c) More than 4.2 years

8. The average age of CEOs is 56 years. Assume the variable is normally distributed. If the standard deviation is 4 years, find the probability that the age of a randomly selected CEO will be in the given range.

(a) Between 53 and 59 years old
(b) Between 58 and 63 years old
(c) Between 50 and 55 years old

9. The average life of a brand of automobile tires is 30,000 miles, with a standard deviation of 2,000 miles. If a tire is selected and tested, find the probability that it will have the given lifetime. Assume the variable is normally distributed.

(a) Between 25,000 and 28,000 miles
(b) Between 27,000 and 32,000 miles
(c) Between 31,500 and 33,500 miles

10. The average time a person spends in each visit to an online social networking service is 62 minutes. The standard deviation is 12 minutes. If a visitor is selected at random, find the probability that he or she will spend the time shown on the networking service. Assume the times are normally distributed.

(a) At least 180 minutes   (b) At least 50 minutes

11. The average amount of snow per season in Trafford is 44 inches. The standard deviation is 6 inches. Find the probability that next year Trafford will receive the given amount of snowfall. Assume the variable is normally distributed.

(a) At most 50 inches of snow
(b) At least 53 inches of snow

12. The average waiting time for a drive-in window at a local bank is 9.2 minutes, with a standard deviation of 2.6 minutes. When a customer arrives at the bank, find the probability that the customer will have to wait the given time. Assume the variable is normally distributed.

(a) Between 5 and 10 minutes
(b) Less than 6 minutes or more than 9 minutes

13. The average time it takes college freshmen to complete the Mason Basic Reasoning Test is 24.6 minutes. The standard deviation is 5.8 minutes. Find these probabilities. Assume the variable is normally distributed.

(a) It will take a student between 15 and 30 minutes to complete the test.
(b) It will take a student less than 18 minutes or more than 28 minutes to complete the test.

14. A brisk walk at 4 miles per hour burns an average of 300 calories per hour. If the standard deviation of

the distribution is 8 calories, find the probability that a person who walks 1 hour at the rate of 4 miles per hour will burn the given number of calories. Assume the variable is normally distributed.

(a) More than 280 calories
(b) Less than 293 calories
(c) Between 285 and 320 calories

15. During September, the average temperature of Laurel Lake is 64.2° and the standard deviation is 3.2°. Assume the variable is normally distributed. For a randomly selected day in September, find the probability that the temperature will be

(a) Above 62°.   (c) Between 65° and 68°.
(b) Below 67°.

16. If the systolic blood pressure for a certain group of people has a mean of 132 and a standard deviation of 8, find the probability that a randomly selected person in the group will have the given systolic blood pressure. Assume the variable is normally distributed.

(a) Above 130   (c) Between 131 and 136
(b) Below 140

17. An IQ test has a mean of 100 and a standard deviation of 15. The test scores are normally distributed. If 2,000 people take the test, find the number of people who will score

(a) Below 93.   (c) Between 80 and 105.
(b) Above 120.   (d) Between 75 and 82.

18. The average size (in square feet) of homes built in the United States in the fourth quarter of 2008 was 2,343. Assume the variable is normally distributed and the standard deviation is 152 square feet. In a sample of 500 recently built homes, find the number of homes that will

(a) Have between 1,900 and 2,000 square feet.
(b) Have more than 3,000 square feet.
(c) Have less than 2,000 square feet.
(d) Have more than 1,600 square feet.

Source: National Association of Homebuilders

19. According to the National Association of Realtors, the mean sale price for existing homes in the United States in 2008 was $242,700. Assume that sale prices are normally distributed with a standard deviation of $41,000. If 800 home sales are selected at random, find the number of homes that cost

(a) More than $300,000.
(b) Between $200,000 and $300,000.
(c) Less than $150,000.

20. The average price of Stephen King paperbacks sold at bookstores across the country is $9.52, and the standard deviation is $1.02. Assume the price is normally distributed. If a national bookstore sells 1,000 Stephen King paperbacks during August,

find the number of Stephen King paperbacks that were sold

(a) For less than $8.00.
(b) For more than $10.00.
(c) Between $9.50 and $10.50.
(d) Between $9.80 and $10.05.

21. Refer to Exercise 3. If your buddy Earl gets a job as a manufacturing production worker making $15.20 per hour, what percentile is he in?

22. Refer to Exercise 7. If you buy a TV for your dorm and keep it for your 4 years of school then sell it, what percentile does that put you in?

23. Refer to Exercise 10. Suppose that your grades have been slipping, and you impose a new rule on yourself: no more than 20 minutes at a time on social networking sites. What percentile would that put you in?

24. Refer to Exercise 18. When the one-hit wonder band The Flaming Rogers falls off the charts, their singer is forced to downsize from the 5,000 square foot home he built earlier in the year to a more modest 2,000 square foot model. What was his change in percentile rank?

Critical Thinking

25. If a distribution of raw scores were plotted and then the scores were transformed into z scores, would the shape of the distribution change?

26. An instructor gives a 100-point examination in which the grades are normally distributed. The mean is 60 and the standard deviation is 10. If there are 5% A's and 5% F's, 15% B's and 15% D's, and 60% C's, find the scores that divide the distribution into those categories.

27. A researcher who is in charge of an educational study wants subjects to perform some special skill. Fearing that people who are unusually talented or unusually untalented could distort the results, he decides to use people who scored in the middle 50% on

a certain test. If the mean for the population is 100 and the standard deviation is 15, find the two limits (upper and lower) for the scores that would enable a volunteer to participate in the study. Assume the scores are normally distributed.

28. While preparing for their comeback tour, The Flaming Rogers find that the average time it takes their sound tech to set up for a show is 58.6 minutes, with a standard deviation of 4.3 minutes. If the band manager decides to include only the fastest 20% of sound techs on the tour, what should the cutoff time be for concert setup? Assume the times are normally distributed.

Section 12-8 Correlation and Regression Analysis

LEARNING OBJECTIVES

- ☐ 1. Construct scatter plots for two data sets.

- ☐ 2. Calculate correlation coefficients.

- ☐ 3. Determine if correlation coefficients are significant.

- ☐ 4. Find a regression line for two data sets.

- ☐ 5. Use regression lines to make predictions.

The Business Insider blog posted an article in November 2008 with the headline "Proof of a Correlation between MySpace Usage and Illiteracy." It certainly seems to imply that MySpace users tend to be illiterate. On what data were these claims based?

The key word in the claim is *correlation*. In statistics, that term describes an attempt to determine if a relationship exists between two sets of data, like literacy rates and MySpace usage.

In order to decide if a relationship exists between two data sets, we have to first gather data in such a way that values from each set can be paired together. In this case, the literacy rate for each state was recorded, as well as data from Google on how likely Internet users from each state were to search for the term "MySpace." We can then plot a graph designating one set of data as the *x variable* or **independent variable** and the other as the *y variable* or **dependent variable.** This graph is called a *scatter plot.*

> A **scatter plot** is a graph of the ordered pairs (x, y) consisting of data from two data sets.

After the scatter plot is drawn, we can analyze the graph to see if there is a pattern. If there is a noticeable pattern, such as the points falling in an approximately straight line, then a possible relationship between the two variables may exist.

If a strong relationship appears to exist between two data sets, we might further analyze the relationship by trying to find an equation relating the variables. This is known as *regression analysis,* which we will learn about later in the section. For now, we'll focus on scatter plots.

EXAMPLE 1   Constructing a Scatter Plot

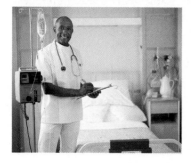

A medical researcher selects a sample of small hospitals in his state and hopes to discover if there is a relationship between the number of beds and the number of personnel employed by the hospital. Construct a scatter plot for the data shown.

No. of beds (x)	28	56	34	42	45	78	84	36	74	95
Personnel (y)	72	195	74	211	145	139	184	131	233	366

SOLUTION

Step 1 Draw and label the x and y axes, as shown.

Step 2 Plot the data pairs. See Figure 12-22.

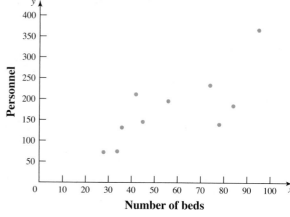

Figure 12-22

▼ Try This One 1

The data below represent the heights in feet and the number of stories of the tallest buildings in Pittsburgh. Draw a scatter plot for the data and describe the relationship.

Height (x)	485	511	520	535	582	615	616	635	728	841
No. of stories (y)	40	37	41	42	38	45	31	40	54	64

Source: *The World Almanac and Book of Facts*

Analyzing the Scatter Plot

There are several types of relationships that can exist between the x values and the y values in a scatter plot. These relationships can be identified by looking at the pattern of the points on the graphs. The types of patterns and corresponding relationships are:

1. *A positive linear relationship* exists when the points fall approximately in an ascending straight line from left to right, and both the x and y values increase at the same time. See Figure 12-23a on the next page.
2. *A negative linear relationship* exists when the points fall approximately in a descending straight line from left to right. See Figure 12-23b on the next page. The relationship then is as the x values are increasing, the y values are decreasing.

3. *A nonlinear relationship* exists when the points fall in a curved line. See Figure 12-23c. The relationship is described by the nature of the curve.
4. *No relationship* exists when there is no discernible pattern to the points. See Figure 12-23d.

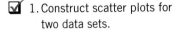

1. Construct scatter plots for two data sets.

The relationship between the variables in Example 1 might be a positive linear relationship. It looks like as the size of the hospital based on the number of beds increases, the number of personnel also increases.

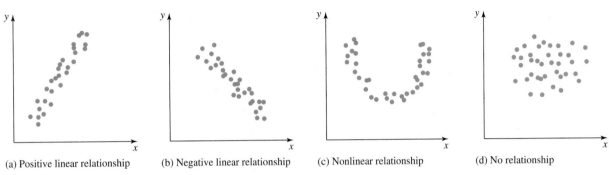

(a) Positive linear relationship   (b) Negative linear relationship   (c) Nonlinear relationship   (d) No relationship

Figure 12-23

The Correlation Coefficient

Deciding whether or not two data sets are related by simply looking at a scatter plot is a pretty subjective process, so it would be nice to have a way to quantify how strongly connected data sets are.

The **correlation coefficient** is a number that describes how close to a linear relationship there is between two data sets. Correlation coefficients range from -1 (perfect negative linear relationship) to $+1$ (perfect positive linear relationship). The closer this number is to one in absolute value, the more likely it is that the data sets are related. A correlation coefficient close to zero indicates that the data are most likely not related at all (see Figure 12-24). We use the letter r to represent the correlation coefficient. It doesn't depend on the units for the two data sets, and it also doesn't depend on which set you choose for the x variable.

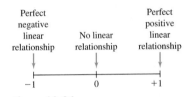

Figure 12-24

Calculating the Value of the Correlation Coefficient

In order to find the value of the correlation coefficient, we will use the following formula:

Math Note

The sign of r will indicate the nature of the relationship if one exists. That is, if r is positive, the linear relationship will be positive. If r is negative, the linear relationship will be negative. Looking at the scatter plots in Figure 12-23, for (a) r would be close to $+1$; for (b), r would be close to -1; for (c) and (d), r would be close to zero.

Formula for Finding the Value of r:

$$r = \frac{n(\Sigma xy) - (\Sigma x)(\Sigma y)}{\sqrt{[n(\Sigma x^2) - (\Sigma x)^2][n(\Sigma y^2) - (\Sigma y)^2]}}$$

where
n = the number of data pairs
Σx = the sum of the x values
Σy = the sum of the y values
Σxy = the sum of the products of the x and y values for each pair
Σx^2 = the sum of the squares of the x values
Σy^2 = the sum of the squares of the y values

When calculating the value of r, it is helpful to make a table, as shown in Example 2.

EXAMPLE 2   Calculating a Correlation Coefficient

Find the correlation coefficient for the data in Example 1.

SOLUTION

Step 1 Make a table as shown with the following headings: x, y, xy, x^2, and y^2.

Step 2 Find the values for the product xy, the values for x^2, the values for y^2, and place them in the columns as shown. Then find the sums of the columns.

x	y	xy	x^2	y^2
28	72	2,016	784	5,184
56	195	10,920	3,136	38,025
34	74	2,516	1,156	5,476
42	211	8,862	1,764	44,521
45	145	6,525	2,025	21,025
78	139	10,842	6,084	19,321
84	184	15,456	7,056	33,856
36	131	4,716	1,296	17,161
74	233	17,242	5,476	54,289
95	366	34,770	9,025	133,956
$\Sigma x = 572$	$\Sigma y = 1,750$	$\Sigma xy = 113,865$	$\Sigma x^2 = 37,802$	$\Sigma y^2 = 372,814$

Step 3 Substitute into the formula and evaluate (note that there are 10 data pairs):

$$r = \frac{n(\Sigma xy) - (\Sigma x)(\Sigma y)}{\sqrt{[n(\Sigma x^2) - (\Sigma x)^2][n(\Sigma y^2) - (\Sigma y)^2]}}$$

$$= \frac{10(113,865) - (572)(1,750)}{\sqrt{[10(37,802) - (572)^2][10(372,814) - (1,750)^2]}}$$

$$= \frac{137,650}{\sqrt{(50,836)(665,640)}}$$

$$\approx 0.748$$

The correlation coefficient for the two data sets is 0.748. This appears to confirm what our eyes tell us about the scatter plot in Example 1—it's certainly not a perfect linear relationship, but does tend to indicate that as bed space goes up, the number of personnel does as well.

▼ Try This One 2

2. Calculate correlation coefficients.

Find the correlation coefficient for the data in Try This One 1.

Next we will tackle the issue of how to interpret the correlation coefficient. In Example 2, the value of r was based on a sample of data. The population is all hospitals in a certain state with fewer than 100 beds, and a sample of such hospitals was chosen. When data from a sample is used, we can't be positive that it represents the entire population. So conclusions drawn, like the conclusion that there's a connection between numbers of beds and personnel, may not be correct.

Sidelight TECHNOLOGY AND THE CORRELATION COEFFICIENT

If there's just one thing you learned from Example 2, it's probably that finding a correlation coefficient is not exactly simple. Even for a reasonably small data set, the calculations involved are a little cumbersome. You can imagine how much worse it would be for larger data sets.

Fortunately, most graphing calculators and spreadsheets have built-in commands to compute correlation coefficients. In Microsoft Excel, enter the two data sets in two columns. Then choose another blank cell to enter the correlation coefficient. Next, choose Function . . . from the Insert menu: in the category dialog box choose Statistical, from the list of functions choose CORREL. You will then be prompted to choose the range of cells that make up each data set, and presto! The correlation coefficient appears in the chosen cell.

Using a standard graphing calculator, the data are entered on the list editing screen (STAT 1). This is shown in

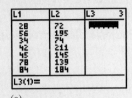
(a)

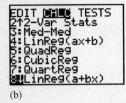
(b)

(c)

Figure 12-25

Figure 12-25a with the data from Example 1 entered. Next, push STAT right Arrow 8 as shown in Figure 12-25b, then ENTER. The resulting screen shows the correlation coefficient at the bottom, as well as the regression line for the data, which we will learn about shortly (see Figure 12-25c). If your calculator doesn't display *r*, push CATALOG, which is 2nd 0, then scroll down and choose DiagnosticOn.

Statisticians have traditionally agreed that when we conclude that two data sets have a relationship, we can be satisfied with that conclusion if there is either a 95% or 99% chance that we're correct. This corresponds to a 5% or 1% chance of being wrong. These percentages are called **significance levels.**

We know that the more data we have, the more likely that data are representative of the population. Not surprisingly, the value of *r* needed to be reasonably sure that two data sets are correlated is higher for small sample sizes, and lower for large sample sizes. In Table 12-4, we see the minimum *r* values needed to have a 5% and 1% chance of being wrong when we conclude that two data sets are related.

TABLE 12-4   Significant Values for the Correlation Coefficient

Sample Size	5%	1%	Sample Size	5%	1%
4	.950	.990	17	.482	.606
5	.878	.959	18	.468	.590
6	.811	.917	19	.456	.575
7	.754	.875	20	.444	.561
8	.707	.834	21	.433	.549
9	.666	.798	22	.423	.537
10	.632	.765	23	.412	.526
11	.602	.735	24	.403	.515
12	.576	.708	25	.396	.505
13	.553	.684	30	.361	.463
14	.532	.661	40	.312	.402
15	.514	.641	60	.254	.330
16	.497	.623	120	.179	.234

Using Significant Values for the Correlation Coefficient

If $|r|$ is greater than or equal to the value given in Table 12-4 for either the 5% or 1% significance level, then we can reasonably conclude that the two data sets are related.

The use of Table 12-4 is illustrated in Example 3.

EXAMPLE 3   Deciding if a Correlation Coefficient is Significant

Researchers could use correlation and regression analysis to find out if there is a correlation between the size of a family's home and the number of children in the family.

Determine if the correlation coefficient $r = 0.748$ found in Example 2 is significant at the 5% level.

SOLUTION

Since the sample size is $n = 10$ and the 5% significance level is used, the value of $|r|$ must be greater than or equal to the number found in Table 12-4 to be significant. In this case, $|r| = 0.748$, which is greater than or equal to 0.632 obtained from the table. We can conclude that there is a significant relationship between the data sets.

However, we can't conclude that there is a relationship between the data sets at the 1% significance level since r would need to be greater than or equal to 0.765. In this example, $r = 0.748$, which is less than 0.765.

▼ Try This One 3

Test the significance of the correlation coefficient obtained from Try This One 2. Use 5%, and then 1%.

CAUTION

Remember, the result of Example 3 doesn't guarantee that the data sets are actually related—there's still a 5% chance that they're not related at all.

Multi-symptom cold and cough relief without drowsiness

INDICATIONS: For the temporary relief of nasal congestion, minor aches, pains, headache, muscular aches, sore throat, and fever associated with the common cold. Temporarily relieves cough occurring with a cold. Helps loosen phlegm (mucus) and thin bronchial secretions to drain bronchial tubes and make coughs more productive.
DIRECTIONS: Adults and children 12 years of age and over, 2 liquid caps every 4 hours, while symptoms persist, not to exceed 8 liquid caps in 24 hours, or as directed by a doctor. Not recommended for children under 12 years of age.
WARNINGS: **Do not exceed recommended dosage.** If nervousness, dizziness, or sleeplessness occur, discontinue use and consult a doctor. Do not take this product for more than 10 days. A persistent cough may be a sign of a serious condition. If symptoms do not improve or if cough persists for more than 7 days, tends to recur, or is accompanied by rash, persistent headache, fever that lasts for more than 3 days, or if new symptoms occur, consult a doctor. Do not take this product for persistent or chronic cough such as occurs with smoking, asthma, chronic bronchitis, or emphysema, or where cough is accompanied by excessive phlegm (mucus) unless directed by a doctor. If sore throat is severe, persists for more than 2 days, is accompanied or followed by fever, headache, rash, nausea, or vomiting, consult a doctor promptly. Do not take this product if you have heart disease, high blood pressure, thyroid disease, diabetes, or difficulty in urination due to enlargement of the prostate gland unless directed by a doctor. As with any drug, if you are pregnant or nursing

Medication labels help users to become aware of the effects of taking medications.

☑ 3. Determine if correlation coefficients are significant.

How should we choose whether to use the 5% or 1% significance level in a given situation? It depends on the seriousness of the situation and the importance of drawing a correct conclusion. Suppose that researchers think that a new medication helps patients with asthma to breathe easier, but that some patients have experienced side effects. A correlation study would probably be done to decide if there is a relationship between the medication and these particular side effects. If the potential side effects are serious, like heart attacks or strokes, the 1% significance level would be used. If the side effects are mild, like headache or nausea, the 5% significance level would probably be considered sufficient, since the consequences of being wrong are not as dire as in the first case.

Regression

Once we have concluded that there is a significant relationship between the two variables, the next step is to find the *equation* of the **regression line** through the data points.

The regression line is a line that best fits the data. Broadly speaking, we say it is the line that passes through the points in such a way that the overall distance each point is from the line is at a minimum. The regression line is also called the *line of best fit.*

Recall from algebra that the equation of a line in the slope-intercept form is $y = mx + b$, where m is the slope and b is the y intercept. (See Section 7-1.) In statistics, the equation of the regression line is written as $y = a + bx$, where a is the y intercept and b is the slope. This is the equation that will be used here. In order to find the values for a and b, two formulas are used.

Formulas for Finding the Values of *a* and *b* for the Equation of the Regression Line

$$b = \frac{n(\Sigma xy) - (\Sigma x)(\Sigma y)}{n(\Sigma x^2) - (\Sigma x)^2} \quad \text{slope}$$

$$a = \frac{\Sigma y - b(\Sigma x)}{n} \quad y \text{ intercept}$$

EXAMPLE 4   Finding a Regression Line

Math Note

The procedure outlined in the Sidelight on page 703 is a great way to find regression lines using a graphing calculator. Because of potential rounding error, the answer may be a bit different than the one obtained using the procedure in Example 4. This procedure is very sensitive to rounding error, so using at least three decimal places is a good idea.

☑ 4. Find a regression line for two data sets.

Find the equation of the regression line for the data in Example 1.

SOLUTION

We already calculated the values needed for each formula in Example 2. Substitute into the first formula to find the value for the slope, *b*.

$$b = \frac{n(\Sigma xy) - (\Sigma x)\Sigma y}{n(\Sigma x^2) - (\Sigma x)^2} = \frac{10(113,865) - (572)(1,750)}{10(37,802) - (572)^2} = \frac{137,650}{50,836} \approx 2.7077$$

Substitute into the second formula to find the value for the *y* intercept, *a*, when *b* = 2.7077.

$$a = \frac{\Sigma y - b(\Sigma x)}{n} = \frac{(1,750) - 2.7077(572)}{10} = \frac{201.20}{10} = 20.120$$

The equation of the regression line is $y = 20.120 + 2.7077x$.

Try This One 4

Find the equation of the regression line for the data in Try This One 1.

After we find the equation of a regression line, we can see how it compares to the original data by graphing the line on the scatter plot. For the scatter plot in Example 1, we can graph the regression line by plotting two points using the equation we found in Example 4.

Choosing two *x* values between 0 and 100 (so that the points will appear on the scatter plot), if *x* = 30, then

$$y = 20.120 + 2.7077x$$
$$= 20.120 + 2.7077(30) \approx 101$$

If *x* = 70, then

$$y = 20.120 + 2.7077(70) \approx 210$$

So the points (30, 101) and (70, 210) are on the graph. We plot those two points and draw a line through them. See Figure 12-26.

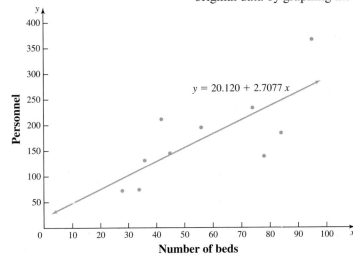

Figure 12-26

The Relationship between *r* and the Regression Line

Two things should be noted about the relationship between the value of *r* and the regression line. First, the value of *r* and the value of the slope, *b*, always have the same sign. Second, the closer the value of *r* is to +1 or −1, the better the points will fit the line. In other words, the stronger the relationship, the better the fit. Figure 12-27 shows the relationship between the correlation coefficient and the regression line.

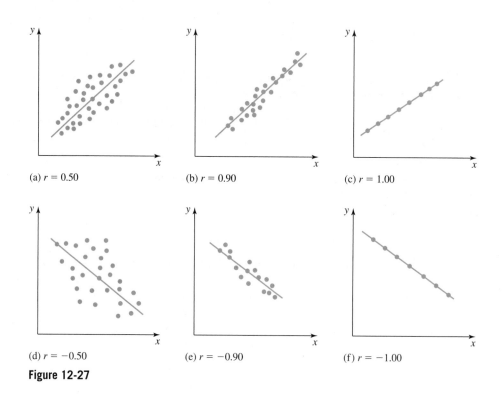

(a) *r* = 0.50   (b) *r* = 0.90   (c) *r* = 1.00

(d) *r* = −0.50   (e) *r* = −0.90   (f) *r* = −1.00

Figure 12-27

Once we have the equation of a regression line for two data sets, we can use it to predict a value for *y* given a particular value for *x*, as we will see in Example 5.

EXAMPLE 5   **Using a Regression Line to Make a Prediction**

Use the equation of the regression line found in Example 4 to predict the approximate number of personnel for a hospital with 65 beds.

SOLUTION

Substitute 65 for *x* into the equation $y = 20.120 + 2.7077x$ and find the value for *y*.

$$y = 20.120 + 2.7077(65) = 196.12 \text{ (which can be rounded to 196)}$$

We predict that a hospital with 65 beds will have approximately 196 personnel.

▼ **Try This One 5**

☑ 5. Use regression lines to make predictions.

Use the equation of the regression line found in Try This One 4 to predict the number of stories for a 670-foot building.

> **CAUTION** Never use a regression line to predict anything unless you've already checked that the correlation is significant! If it isn't significant, the regression line is meaningless.

Correlation and Causation

As you will see in the Sidelight below, there's more to the story of a relationship between two data sets than simply finding out that they're related. The nature of the relationship then needs to be further explored. The following is a list of possibilities to consider.

Possible Relationships between Data Sets

1. *There is a direct cause-and-effect relationship between two variables.* That is, x causes y. For example, water causes plants to grow, poison causes death, and heat causes ice to melt.

2. *There is a reverse cause-and-effect relationship between the variables.* That is, y causes x. Suppose that we find a correlation between excessive coffee consumption and nervousness. It would be tempting to conclude that drinking too much coffee causes nervousness. But it might actually be the case that nervous people drink a lot of coffee because they think it calms their nerves.

3. *The relationship between the variables may be caused by a third variable.* You could probably find a positive correlation between the amount of ice cream consumed per week and the number of drowning deaths for each week of the year. But this doesn't mean that eating ice cream causes you to drown. Both eating ice cream and swimming are more common during the summer months, and it stands to reason that more people will drown when more people are swimming. In this case, a third variable (seasonal weather) is affecting each of the original two variables.

Sidelight **DOES MYSPACE CAUSE ILLITERACY?**

At the beginning of this section, we looked at a claim that there's a correlation between using MySpace and illiteracy. How strong is that connection? And what does it mean?

A scatter plot of the data for all 50 states is shown in Figure 12-28. The x variable is the percent of the adult population that lacks basic literacy as measured by the National Assessment of Adult Literacy. The y variable is a scaled score that indicates how often Internet users from each state searched for the term MySpace on Google. The scatter plot looks like there is a positive linear correlation, and the correlation coefficient bears that out: it is almost exactly 0.6, which is well above the 1% significance level for a sample size of 50. So we can definitely conclude that the two data sets are related. (Note that $n = 50$ is not in Table 12-4, but we can see that 0.6 is within the 1% confidence interval for any sample size greater than 17.)

Then the most important question should be asked: what does it mean? This is the key point about correlation—there is a big difference between *correlation* and *causation*. When two data sets are related, that tells us nothing about *why* they are related. In this case, it would be inappropriate to conclude that being illiterate causes people to use MySpace, and it would be just plain silly to conclude that using MySpace

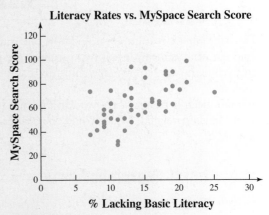

Literacy Rates vs. MySpace Search Score

Figure 12.28

causes people to be illiterate. There may be some other combination of factors that keep literacy rates low in certain states and make people more likely to search for the term MySpace. Or (and this is my best guess) it might just be one big, amazing coincidence. In any case, it's important to understand that correlation between data sets by itself never tells us anything about *how* or *why* two sets are related.

4. *There may be a complexity of interrelationships among many variables.* For example, a researcher may find a significant relationship between students' high school grades and college grades. But there probably are many other variables involved, such as IQ, hours of study, influence of parents, motivation, age, and instructors.

5. *The relationship might simply be coincidental.* For example, historians have noticed that there is a very strong correlation between the party that wins a presidential election and the result of the Washington Redskins' final game before the election. But common sense dictates that any such relationship has to be coincidental.

Answers to Try This One

1

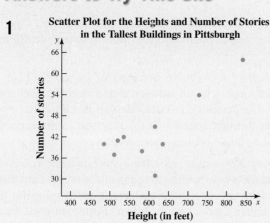

Scatter Plot for the Heights and Number of Stories in the Tallest Buildings in Pittsburgh

2 $r \approx 0.798$

3 Significant at both levels

4 $y = 1.634 + 0.0685x$

5 48 stories

EXERCISE SET 12-8

Writing Exercises

1. Describe what a scatter plot is and how one is used.
2. Explain what is meant when two variables are positively linearly related. What would the scatter plot look like?
3. Explain what is meant when two variables are negatively linearly related. What would the scatter plot look like?
4. Explain what the value of the correlation coefficient tells you about the relationship between two data sets.
5. What is a regression line for two data sets?
6. Describe how regression lines can be used to make predictions about situations.

Computational Exercises

For the data sets in Exercises 7–12,

(a) Draw a scatter plot.
(b) Find the value for r.
(c) Test the significance of r at the 5% level and at the 1% level.
(d) Find the equation of the regression line and draw the line on the scatter plot, but only if r is significant.
(e) Describe the nature of the relationship if one exists.

7.
x	1	4	6	2	3	5	7
y	8	15	20	10	11	16	25

8.
x	21	25	24	30	36	40
y	12	8	9	5	3	2

9.
x	75	80	85	90
y	10	5	11	4

10.
x	9	12	15	11	10	13
y	50	60	71	55	53	60

11.

x	27	35	48	43	32
y	19	13	8	10	15

12.

x	31	34	37	40	46
y	3	15	2	13	5

Real-World Applications

For the data sets in Exercises 13–18,

(a) Draw a scatter plot. (b) Find the value for r.
(c) Test the significance of r at the 5% level and at the 1% level.
(d) Find the equation of the regression line and draw the line on the scatter plot, but only if r is significant.
(e) Describe the nature of the relationship if one exists.
(f) Make the requested prediction using your regression line.

13. The data represent the heights in feet and the number of stories of the tallest buildings in Cleveland.

Height, x	947	708	658	529	450	446	430	420	419
Stories, y	57	52	46	40	31	28	24	26	32

Source: *The World Almanac and Book of Facts*

Predict the number of stories in a 500-foot building.

14. A researcher hopes to determine whether the number of hours a person jogs per week is related to the person's age.

Age, x	34	22	48	56	62
Hours, y	3.5	7	3.5	3	1

Predict the number of hours for a 35-year-old.

15. A study was conducted to determine if the amount a college student spends per month on recreation is related to the student's income.

Monthly income, x	Amount, y	Monthly income. x	Amount, y
$800	$160	$850	$145
$1,200	$300	$907	$190
$1,000	$260	$1,100	$250
$900	$235		

Predict the amount spent by a student with an income of $925.

16. A researcher hopes to determine if there is a relationship between the number of days an employee missed a year and the person's age.

Age, x	22	30	25	35	65	50	27	53	42	58
Days missed, y	0	4	1	2	14	7	3	8	6	4

Predict the number of days missed by a 56-year-old employee.

17. A statistics instructor plans to see it there's a relationship between the final exam score in Statistics 102 and the final exam scores of the same students who took Statistics 101.

Stat 101, x	87	92	68	72	95	78	83	98
Stat 102, y	83	88	70	74	90	74	83	99

Predict the stat 102 score for a student who got 90 on the stat 101 final.

18. The data shown indicate the number of wins and the number of goals scored for teams in the National Hockey League after the first month of the season.

No. of wins, x	No. of goals, y	No. of wins, x	No. of goals, y
10	23	7	21
9	22	5	16
6	15	9	12
5	15	8	19
4	10	6	16
12	26	6	16
11	26	4	11
8	26		

Source: *USA Today*

Predict the number of goals for a team with 8 wins.

Critical Thinking

19. Explain why when r is significant, you can't conclude that x causes y.

20. Find the value for r, then interchange the values for x and y and find the value of r. Explain the results.

x	1	2	3	4	5
y	3	5	7	9	11

21. Draw a scatter plot and determine if the variables are related. Explain the results. Then find the value for r for the data shown.

x	−3	−2	−1	0	1	2	3
y	9	4	1	0	1	4	9

22. Design your own correlation problem. Think of two quantities that you think might be correlated, then gather some data, and use the techniques of this section to decide if the data sets are correlated.

Section	Important Terms	Important Ideas

12-1	Data
	Statistics
	Population
	Sample
	Random sample
	Systematic sample
	Stratified sample
	Cluster sample
	Descriptive statistics
	Inferential statistics
	Raw data
	Categorical frequency
	  distribution
	Grouped frequency
	  distribution
	Stem and leaf plot
		Statistics is the branch of mathematics that involves the collection, organization, summarization, and presentation of data. In addition, researchers use statistics to make general conclusions from the data. When a study is conducted, the researcher defines a population, which consists of all subjects under study. Since populations are usually large, the researcher will select a representative subgroup of the population, called a sample, to study. There are four basic sampling methods. They are random, systematic, stratified, and cluster. Once the data are collected, they are organized into a frequency distribution. There are two types of frequency distributions. They are categorical and grouped. When the data set consists of a small number of values, a stem and leaf plot can be constructed. This plot shows the nature of the data while retaining the original data values.

12-2	Bar graph Pie chart Histogram Frequency polygon Time series graph	**In order** to represent data pictorially, graphs can be drawn. From a categorical frequency distribution, a bar graph and a pie chart can be drawn. From a grouped frequency distribution, a histogram and a frequency polygon can be drawn to represent the data. To show how data vary over time, a time series graph can be drawn.
12-3	Mean Data array Median Mode Midrange	**In addition** to collecting data, organizing data, and representing data using graphs, various summary statistics can be found to describe the data. There are four measures of average. They are the mean, median, mode, and midrange. The mean is found by adding all of the data values and dividing the sum by the number of data values. The median is the middle point of the data set. The mode is the most frequent data value. The midrange is found by adding the lowest and the highest data values and dividing by two.
12-4	Range Variance Standard deviation	**There are** three commonly used measures of variation. They are the range, variance, and standard deviation. The range is found by subtracting the lowest data value from the highest data value. The standard deviation measures the spread of the data values. When the standard deviation is small, most data values are close to the mean. When the standard deviation is large, the data values are spread out farther away from the mean.
12-5	Percentile Quartile	**The position** of a data value in a data set can be determined by its percentile rank. The percentile rank of a specific data value gives the percent of data values that fall below the specific value. Quartiles divide a distribution into quarters.

12-6	Normal distribution Empirical rule Standard normal distribution *z* score	**Many variables** have a distribution that is bell-shaped. These variables are said to be approximately normally distributed. Statisticians use the standard normal distribution to describe these variables. The standard normal distribution has a mean of zero and a standard deviation of 1. A variable can be transformed into a standard normal variable by finding its corresponding *z* score. A table showing the area under the standard normal distribution can be used to find areas for various *z* scores.
12-7		**Since many** real-world variables are approximately normally distributed, the standard normal distribution can be used to solve many real-world applications.
12-8	Correlation Independent variable Dependent variable Scatter plot Correlation coefficient Significance levels Regression line	**Statisticians** are also interested in determining whether or not two variables are related. In order to determine this, they draw and analyze a scatter plot. After the scatter plot is drawn, the value of the correlation coefficient is computed. If the correlation coefficient is significant, the equation of the regression line is found. Then a prediction for *y* can be obtained given a specific value of *x*.

MATH IN ▸ Sociology REVISITED

1. The scatter plot is shown below, with temperature as the *x* variable. While it's not at all clear whether there is a real correlation, it looks like there's at least a chance that the two data sets have a positive linear relationship.

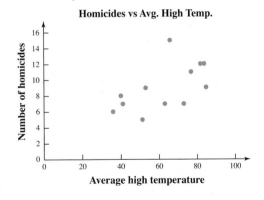

Homicides vs Avg. High Temp.

Number of homicides (y-axis, 0 to 16)
Average high temperature (x-axis, 0 to 100)

2. The correlation coefficient is about 0.584. According to the significance table, for a sample size of 12 this is significant at the 5% level (just barely), but not at the 1% level. So we can say with 95% confidence that the two data sets are related.

3. Absolutely not. In fact, no matter how strongly the data sets are related, we can't draw any conclusions about whether one causes the other. All we know is that for some reason, they appear to be related. There are a wide variety of theories trying to account for this phenomenon, but none have been proven or even widely accepted.

Review Exercises

Section 12-1

1. A sporting goods store kept a record of sales of five items for one randomly selected hour during a recent sale. Construct a frequency distribution for the data (B = baseballs, G = golf balls, T = tennis balls, S = soccer balls, F = footballs).

F	B	B	B	G	T	F
G	G	F	S	G	T	
F	T	T	T	S	T	
F	S	S	G	S	B	

2. The data set shown below represents the time in minutes spent using a computer at Kinko's Copy Center by 25 customers on a randomly selected day. Construct a stem and leaf plot for the data and analyze the results.

16	25	18	39	25	17	29	14	37
22	18	12	23	32	35	24	26	
20	19	25	26	38	38	33	29	

3. During June, a local theater company recorded the given number of patrons per day. Construct a grouped frequency distribution for the data. Use six classes.

102	116	113	132	128	117
156	182	183	171	168	179
170	160	163	187	185	158
163	167	168	186	117	108
171	173	161	163	168	182

Section 12-2

4. Construct a bar graph for the number of homicides reported for these cities.

City	Number
New Orleans	179
Washington, D.C.	186
Chicago	509
Baltimore	234
Atlanta	105

   Source: FBI

5. Draw a pie chart for the data in Exercise 4.

6. Draw a histogram and frequency polygon for the frequency distribution obtained from the data in Exercise 3.

7. The data set shown below indicates how much Janine earned each year from her part-time job at the Otherworld Internet Cafe during the 5 years that she attended college. Draw a time series graph for the data.

Year	Amount
2005	$8,973
2006	$9,388
2007	$11,271
2008	$13,877
2009	$19,203

Section 12-3

8. These data represent the number of deer killed by motor vehicles for eight counties in Southwestern Pennsylvania.

   2,343 1,240 1,088 600 497 1,925 1,480 458

   Source: *Pittsburgh Post-Gazette*

   Find each of these.

   (a) Mean   (c) Mode
   (b) Median   (d) Midrange

9. Twelve batteries were tested to see how many hours they would last. The frequency distribution is shown here.

Hours	Frequency
1–3	1
4–6	4
7–9	5
10–12	1
13–15	1

   Find the mean.

10. In your own words, explain the difference between mean, median, mode, and midrange. Include an explanation of why each is considered a measure of average.

Section 12-4

11. Find the range, variance, and standard deviation for the data in Exercise 8.

12. Which data set do you think would have a greater standard deviation: the ages of everyone currently working out in the gym on your campus, or the ages of everyone currently shopping at the nearest off-campus grocery store? Explain your answer.

Section 12-5

13. The number of previous jobs held by each of six applicants is shown here.

    2 4 5 6 8 9

    (a) Find the percentile for each value.
    (b) What value corresponds to the 30th percentile?

14. The data shown represent the number of days' inventory eight high-tech firms have on hand. Find the values for Q_1, Q_2, and Q_3.

    158 151 91 45 74 118 285 29

Section 12-6

15. Find the area under the standard normal distribution curve.

    (a) Between $z = 0$ and $z = 1.95$
    (b) Between $z = 0$ and $z = 0.40$
    (c) Between $z = 1.30$ and $z = 1.80$
    (d) Between $z = -1.05$ and $z = 2.05$
    (e) Between $z = -0.05$ and $z = 0.55$
    (f) Between $z = 1.10$ and $z = -1.80$
    (g) To the right of $z = 2.00$
    (h) To the right of $z = -1.35$
    (i) To the left of $z = -2.10$
    (j) To the left of $z = 1.70$

16. The weights of players on one college rugby team are normally distributed with mean 210 pounds and standard deviation 12 pounds. Use the empirical rule to estimate the number of players out of 35 that weigh between 186 and 234 pounds.

17. For a data set with 90 values that is normally distributed with mean 200 and standard deviation 25, approximately how many data values will fall in each range?

    (a) The range from 190 to 210.
    (b) The range of values greater than 240.

Section 12-7

18. The average number of years a person takes to complete a graduate degree program is 3. The standard deviation is 4 months or $\frac{1}{3}$ of a year. Assume the data are normally distributed. If an individual enrolls in the program, find the probability that it will take

    (a) More than 4 years to complete the program.
    (b) Less than 3 years to complete the program.
    (c) Between 3.8 and 4.5 years to complete the program.
    (d) Between 2.5 and 3.1 years to complete the program.

19. On the daily run of an express bus, the average number of passengers is 48. The standard deviation is 3. Assume the data are normally distributed. Find the probability that the bus will have

    (a) Between 36 and 40 passengers.
    (b) Fewer than 42 passengers.
    (c) More than 48 passengers.
    (d) Between 43 and 47 passengers.

20. The average weight of an airline passenger's suitcase is 45 pounds. The standard deviation is 2 pounds. Assume the weights are normally distributed. If an airline handles 2,000 suitcases in one day, find the number that will weigh less than 43.5 pounds.

21. The average cost of Cheetah brand running shoes is $83.00 per pair, with a standard deviation of $8.00. If 90 pairs of shoes are sold, how many will cost between $80.00 and $85.00? Assume the cost is normally distributed.

Section 12-8

22. A study is done to see whether there is a relationship between a student's grade point average and the number of hours the students watches television each week. The data are shown here.

Hours, x	10	6	8	15	5	6	12
GPA, y	2.4	4	3.2	1.6	3.7	3.7	3.0

Draw a scatter plot for the data and describe the relationship. Find the value for r and determine whether or not it is significant at the 5% significance level. If yes, find the equation of the regression line, and predict y when $x = 9$.

23. The table below displays the number of homicides committed in Chicago, and the number of wins by the Chicago Bears of the NFL for each year from 2000 to 2008.

Homicides	Wins	Homicides	Wins
628	5	449	11
666	13	452	13
647	4	442	7
598	7	509	9
448	4		

(a) Without doing any calculations, discuss whether or not you think the two data sets should be related.

(b) Find the correlation coefficient for the data sets, and then see if it is significant at the 5% level. Was your prediction from part (a) right or wrong?

Chapter Test

1. A questionnaire about the last 25 peripheral devices purchased at a computer store is shown below. Construct a frequency distribution (L = laser mouse, E = external hard drive, K = wireless keyboard, W = webcam)

   L L K E E K L E W K
   W W L K W E K W L W
   E K K L L

2. Draw a bar graph for the frequency distribution obtained in Exercise 1.
3. Draw a pie chart for the data found in Exercise 2.
4. The data (in millions of dollars) are the values of the 30 Major League baseball franchises. Construct a frequency distribution for the data using eight classes.

   1,500 912 320 700 356 277 347 722
   401 314 496 390 833 509 450 342
   373 486 400 353 319 288 405 445
   399 471 426 371 446 406

   Source: *Forbes Magazine*

5. Draw a histogram and frequency polygon using the frequency distribution for the data in Exercise 4.
6. A special aptitude test is given to job applicants. The data shown here represent the scores of 30 applicants. Construct a stem and leaf plot for the data and summarize the results.

   204 210 227 218 254
   256 238 242 253 227
   251 243 233 251 241
   237 247 211 222 231
   218 212 217 227 209
   260 230 228 242 200

7. The given data represent the federal minimum hourly wage in the years shown. Draw a time series graph to represent the data and analyze the results.

Year	Wage	Year	Wage
1960	$1.00	1990	3.80
1965	1.25	1995	4.25
1970	1.60	2000	5.15
1975	2.10	2005	5.15
1980	3.10	2009	7.25
1985	3.35		

8. These temperatures were recorded in Pasadena for a week in April.

   87 85 80 78 83 86 90

   Find each of these.
   (a) Mean   (c) Mode
   (b) Median   (d) Midrange

   (e) Range   (g) Standard deviation
   (f) Variance

9. The distribution of the number of errors 10 students made on a typing test is shown.

Errors	Frequency
0–2	1
3–5	3
6–8	4
9–11	1
12–14	1

   Find the mean.

10. The number of credits in business courses eight job applicants had is shown here.

    9 12 15 27 33 45 63 72

    (a) Find the percentile for each value.
    (b) What value corresponds to the 40th percentile?

11. Find the area under the standard normal distribution for each.

    (a) Between 0 and 1.50
    (b) Between 0 and -1.25
    (c) Between 1.56 and 1.96
    (d) Between -1.20 and -2.25
    (e) Between -0.06 and 0.73
    (f) Between 1.10 and -1.80
    (g) To the right of $z = 1.75$
    (h) To the right of $z = -1.28$
    (i) To the left of $z = -2.12$
    (j) To the left of $z = 1.36$

12. The mean time it takes for a certain pain reliever to begin to reduce symptoms is 30 minutes, with a standard deviation of 4 minutes. Assuming the time is normally distributed, find the probability that it will take the medication

    (a) Between 34 and 35 minutes to begin to work.
    (b) More than 35 minutes to begin to work.
    (c) Less than 25 minutes to begin to work.
    (d) Between 35 and 40 minutes to begin to work.

13. The average height of a certain age group of people is 53 inches. The standard deviation is 4 inches. If the heights are normally distributed, find the probability that a selected individual's height will be

    (a) Greater than 59 inches.
    (b) Less than 45 inches.
    (c) Between 50 and 55 inches.
    (d) Between 58 and 62 inches.

Age, x	No. of accidents, y
32	1
20	1
55	0
16	3
19	2
17	1
45	0
26	0
32	1
61	0

14. The average cost of a skateboard at Sk8 Gr8, a local skate shop, is $55.00, with a standard deviation of $8.00. The prices are normally distributed. If 200 skateboards are purchased, how many of them cost more than $60.00?

15. A study is conducted to determine the relationship between a driver's age at the beginning of the study and the number of accidents he or she has over a 1-year period. The data are shown here. Draw a scatter plot for the data and explain the nature of the relationship. Find the value for r and determine whether or not it is significant at the 5% significance level. If r is significant, find the equation of the regression line, and predict y when x is 61.

Projects

1. Survey at least 30 students on your campus to find out how many miles away from the campus they live. Construct a frequency distribution with at least five classes from the data. Draw a histogram and frequency polygon for your data, then compute the mean, median, mode, midrange, and standard deviation for the data. Write a report summarizing the results of your study, including a discussion of whether or not the data appear to be approximately normally distributed.

2. Survey at least 30 students on your campus to find out how many credit hours each is taking, and the estimated number of hours per week that they spend on schoolwork outside of class. Draw a scatter plot for the data. Then find the correlation coefficient and decide if it is significant at the 5% level and at the 1% level. Write a report summarizing your findings. Include a discussion of whether or not you were surprised by the results and why.

CHAPTER 13

Other Mathematical Systems

Outline

MATH IN ▶ Encryption

Cryptography is the study of hiding information by using some sort of code. There was a time when codes were of interest mostly to military officers, spies, and grade school kids passing notes they didn't want the teacher to read. But that time passed very quickly with the advent of the computer age. According to some reports, more than half of all Americans made at least one purchase online in 2008. When sensitive financial information and passwords are being transmitted, encryption becomes of supreme importance. Without proper encryption, you could find your identity lost in the endless depths of cyberspace.

In order to be sent via the Internet, information first has to be encoded, often into numeric form. If that information is sensitive, it then needs to be encrypted so that if it's intercepted by a third party, the information remains hidden. There are many methods for encrypting information, and many of them are based on the modular arithmetic we will study in this chapter.

For most of your life, you have worked with one numerical system: the real number system. Within that system, you're familiar with operations like addition and multiplication. In this chapter, we will learn about mathematical systems different than the one you're accustomed to. In most cases, the systems will use a set of numbers you're familiar with, but the operation of addition will be defined differently. This, in turn, will affect the other operations. In some cases, we will look at mathematical systems and operations that don't use numbers at all! An open mind will be key—without

one, you will probably have a hard time swallowing computations like $11 + 2 = 1$. But by the time you finish this chapter, computations of that nature will make perfect sense. In particular, after completing Section 13-3 on modular arithmetic, you will be able to answer the questions below.

Most encryption methods based on modular arithmetic are very complicated, by necessity—the simpler the encryption, the easier it is for a computer to break the code. Here's a simple example using some of the same ideas: the first string of numbers below is a verbal message encoded using a modular system. Each letter and space was given a number from 1 (A) to 27 (space) based on position in the alphabet. The numbers were added to 50 and the resulting numbers were replaced with their congruent number modulo 32. To decode the message, find the original numbers and translate back into letters.

The second string of numbers is the license number from a driver's license presented by a college student to a police officer doing spot checks for underage alcohol consumption. In this particular state, the last digit is a check digit: if you drop the last digit of the license number and find the number congruent to the result modulo 29, you should get the last digit. If you don't, the license number is fake. Is this number legitimate?

1. 27 22 23 0 6 27 6 11 13 6 26
   23 24 6 13 5 6 27 0 29 5
2. 0411039416

For answers, see Math in Encryption Revisited on page 738

Section 13-1 Mathematical Systems and Groups

LEARNING OBJECTIVES

❑ 1. Use an operation table to perform the operation in a mathematical system.

❑ 2. Determine which properties of mathematical systems are satisfied by a given system.

❑ 3. Decide if a mathematical system is a group.

When you're driving on city streets and come to a four-way intersection, you have four choices: right, left, straight, or U-turn. What you don't realize is that you've just landed in the middle of a *mathematical system*. A **mathematical system** consists of a finite or infinite set of symbols and at least one operation. In this case, the four symbols are R, L, S, and U, representing your four choices at the intersection.

What about the operation? Consider what happens if you make two of those choices consecutively. If you turn right and then left, you end up going in the same direction you started in, so this corresponds to going straight. (For this discussion, we're going to ignore what particular street you're on, and focus only on the direction.) If you make a U-turn, then turn left, you'll end up in the same direction as if you had turned right.

If we use the symbol + to represent combining consecutive turns, we can make a table describing the result of any two consecutive choices. The symbols down the left side of Table 13-1 represent the first choice, and the symbols along the top represent the second choice.

TABLE 13-1 An Operation Table for a Mathematical System

+	R	L	S	U	
R	U	Ⓢ	R	L	*Right + Left = Straight*
L	S	U	L	R	
S	R	L	S	U	
U	L	Ⓡ	U	S	*U-turn + Left = Right*

To find the result of two consecutive turns, look along the row corresponding to the first turn until you reach the column corresponding to the second turn. The symbols in color represent the combinations we already mentioned: R + L = S, and U + L = R. Table 13-1 represents a **finite mathematical system** because there are a finite number of symbols with an operation. The table is called an **operation table.** A system with infinitely many symbols and an operation is called an **infinite mathematical system.** The integers under addition are an example.

EXAMPLE 1 Using an Operation Table

Use Table 13-1 to find the result of each operation and describe what it means physically.

(a) L + S 　　(c) U + S
(b) R + R 　　(d) (S + U) + R

☑ 1. Use an operation table to perform the operation in a mathematical system.

SOLUTION

(a) The symbol in row L and column S is L, so L + S = L. If you turn left, then go straight, the direction is the same as just turning left.
(b) The symbol in row R and column R is U, so R + R = U. Turn right twice and your direction is the same as if you had made a U-turn.
(c) U + S = U; a U-turn followed by straight is the same direction as the U-turn itself.
(d) First, we find that S + U = U; then U + R = L. If you follow going straight and making a U-turn with a right turn, it's the same direction as just turning left.

▼ **Try This One 1**

Use Table 13-1 to find the result of each operation and describe what it means physically.

(a) R + U   (c) S + S
(b) U + U   (d) (U + R) + R

There are five important properties of mathematical systems that we will study: *closure, commutative, associative, identity, and inverse.*

Closure Property

For a system to be closed under an operation, when the operation is performed on any symbol, the result must be another symbol in the system. The system in Table 13-1 satisfies this property, and is called a **closed system** because any combination of two turns results in one of the four basic turns. The integers using operation division provide an example of a system that is not closed: sometimes when you divide two integers, the result (like $\frac{1}{2}$, for example) is not an integer.

Commutative Property

A system is commutative if the order in which you perform the operation doesn't matter. More formally, a system is commutative if for any two symbols a and b in a system with some operation $*$, $a * b = b * a$. The system in Table 13-1 is commutative because the result of any two consecutive turns is the same regardless of the order you perform them in. An example of a system that is not commutative is the integers under subtraction, because the order in which you subtract affects the result.

Associative Property

A system has the associative property if for any a, b, c in a system with operation $*$, $(a * b) * c = a * (b * c)$. There really isn't a quick way to show that a system is associative: you would have to try every possible combination of three symbols. (For a system with more than two symbols, the number of calculations required can be pretty large.) Typically, we'll check a few examples to try and get an idea of whether or not a system is associative. In Example 1 part d, we saw that (S + U) + R = L. Let's try S + (U + R): first, we find that U + R = L. Then S + L = L, so S + (U + R) and (S + U) + R both equal L. This doesn't prove that the system is associative—just that the property holds in this one case—but it turns out that the system is associative.

Identity Property

A system has the identity property if there is a symbol a in the system so that $a * b = b * a = b$ for any other symbol b. In short, if there's a symbol that leaves all the others unchanged when combined using the operation, that symbol is called the **identity element** for the system. For our system of turns, it's easy to see that S is the identity element: combining straight with any other turn results in the same direction as the turn itself.

Inverse Property

When a system has an identity element, the next question to consider is whether every symbol has another symbol that produces the identity element under the operation. That is, for any a in the system, is there always an **inverse element** b so that $a * b$ is the identity element? If there is, the system satisfies the inverse property. We can verify that the system of turns satisfies the inverse property by finding an inverse for each turn. For right, turning left results in straight (the identity element). For left, turning right results in straight. For straight, another straight results in straight, and for U-turns, another U-turn results in straight. We have displayed an inverse for each symbol, so the system satisfies the inverse property.

EXAMPLE 2 Identifying the Properties of a Finite Mathematical System

Which properties does the system defined by the given table exhibit?

&	0	1	2	3
0	2	3	0	1
1	1	2	1	0
2	0	1	2	3
3	1	0	3	2

SOLUTION

Closure property: Since every element in the body of the table is in the set the system is defined on, namely, $\{0, 1, 2, 3\}$, the system is closed.

Commutative property: Since the system is not symmetric with respect to the diagonal, it does not have the commutative property. For example, 0 & 1 = 3, but 1 & 0 = 1.

Associative property: Let's try some examples.

$$(1 \,\&\, 2) \,\&\, 3 = 1 \,\&\, 3 = 0 \qquad\qquad 1 \,\&\, (2 \,\&\, 3) = 1 \,\&\, 3 = 0$$
$$(1 \,\&\, 0) \,\&\, 3 = 1 \,\&\, 3 = 0 \qquad\qquad 1 \,\&\, (0 \,\&\, 3) = 1 \,\&\, 1 = 2$$

We found a counterexample, so the system is not associative.

Identity property: There is an identity element, 2, since 2 & x = x & 2 = x for all $x \in \{0, 1, 2, 3\}$

Inverse Property: 0 and 0 are inverses, 1 and 1 are inverses, 2 and 2 are inverses, and 3 and 3 are inverses. Since every element has an inverse, the system has the inverse property.

Therefore, the system exhibits *closure, identity,* and *inverse* properties.

> **CAUTION**
>
> It takes just one counterexample to prove that a system is *not* associative, but every possible combination must be verified to prove that a system *is* associative.

☑ 2. Determine which properties of mathematical systems are satisfied by a given system.

▼ Try This One 2

Which properties does the following system exhibit?

o	x	y	z
x	x	x	z
y	x	y	z
z	y	z	x

Sidelight MAGIC SQUARES

Have you ever heard of a magic square? These squares have fascinated and intrigued people ever since the first one was discovered more than 4,000 years ago.

The sum of the numbers in each row in the square below is equal to 15:

$$4 + 9 + 2 = 15$$
$$3 + 5 + 7 = 15$$
$$8 + 1 + 6 = 15$$

The sum of the numbers in each column is also 15:

$$4 + 3 + 8 = 15$$
$$9 + 5 + 1 = 15$$
$$2 + 7 + 6 = 15$$

And the sum of the two diagonals is also 15:

$$4 + 5 + 6 = 15$$
$$2 + 5 + 8 = 15$$

A magic square!

4	9	2
3	5	7
8	1	6

The first magic square appears in the Chinese classic *I-Ching* and is called *lo-shu*. It is said that the Emperor Yu saw the square engraved on the back of a divine tortoise on the bank of the Yellow River in 2200 BCE. The square was the same as the one shown in the above figure except that the numerals were indicated by black and white dots, the even numbers in black and the odd numbers in white.

Since some sort of magic was attributed to these squares, they were frequently used to decorate the abodes of gypsies and fortune tellers. They were very popular in India, and they were eventually brought to Europe by the Arabs.

Albrecht Dürer, a 16th-century artist from Germany, used the magic square below in his famous woodcut entitled "Melancholia." This square is indeed magic, for not only are the sums of the rows, columns, and diagonals all equal to 34, but also the sum of the four corners (16 + 13 + 4 + 1) is 34. Furthermore, the sum of the four center cells (10 + 11 + 6 + 7) is also 34, and the sum of the slanting squares (2 + 8 + 9 + 15 and 3 + 5 + 12 + 14) is 34. Finally, the year in which Dürer made the woodcut appears in the bottom center squares (1514).

16	3	2	13
5	10	11	8
9	6	7	12
4	15	14	1

A great mathematician, Leonhard Euler (1707–1783), constructed the magic square shown next. The sum of the rows and columns is 260. Stopping halfway on each row or column gives a sum of half of 260 or 130. Finally, a knight from a chess game can start on square 1 and proceed in L-shaped moves and come to rest on all squares in numerical order.

1	48	31	50	33	16	63	18
30	51	46	3	62	19	14	35
47	2	49	32	15	34	17	64
52	29	4	45	20	61	36	13
5	44	25	56	9	40	21	60
28	53	8	41	24	57	12	37
43	6	55	26	39	10	59	22
54	27	42	7	58	23	38	11

Magic squares have been a source of fascination for people throughout the ages. Interestingly, they're a lot easier to construct than you would think. An Internet search for *magic square* will identify several sources with methods for building them.

Groups and Abelian Groups

A mathematical system is said to be a **group** if it has closure, associative, identity, and inverse properties. A mathematical system is said to be an **Abelian group** if, in addition to closure, associative, identity, and inverse properties, it also has the commutative property.

EXAMPLE 3   Determining If a Mathematical System Is a Group

Do the natural numbers under the operation of addition form a group? An Abelian group?

SOLUTION

The natural numbers are given by the set $N = \{1, 2, 3, 4, \ldots\}$.

Closure: The natural numbers are closed under addition; that is, the sum of any two natural numbers is a natural number. Therefore the system is *closed*.

Associative: The associative property of addition holds for all real numbers, so it holds for the natural numbers as well. So the system is *associative*.

Identity: There is *no identity* element in the set of natural numbers (the identity element would be 0 under addition, but this element is not in N).

Inverse: Since there is no identity element, there can be *no inverse*. Therefore the inverse property does not hold.

Since the system does not have the four properties required to be a group, it is *not a group*. Since it is not a group, it is also not an Abelian group.

▼ Try This One 3

Do the whole numbers form a group under addition? An Abelian group?

EXAMPLE 4   **Determining if a Mathematical System is a Group**

Does the set $\{-1, 1\}$ form a group under the operation of multiplication? An Abelian group?

SOLUTION

Closure: The product of any two elements in the set is also an element of the set, therefore the system is *closed*.

Associative: The associative property holds for all elements in the set.

Identity: The identity element is 1.

Inverse: -1 and -1 are inverses as are 1 and 1. Therefore each element has an inverse, so the inverse property holds.

Since the system has *closure, associative, identity,* and *inverse* properties, *it is a group*. Furthermore, since the commutative property holds, *it is also an Abelian group*.

▼ Try This One 4

☑ 3. Decide if a mathematical system is a group.

Does the set $\{-1, 0, 1\}$ form a group under multiplication? An Abelian group?

Answers to Try This One

1 (a) $R + U = L$; a right turn followed by a U-turn results in the same direction as a left turn.

(b) $U + U = S$; two consecutive U-turns is the same direction as going straight.

(c) $S + S = S$; choosing to go straight twice leaves you in the same direction as going straight once.

(d) $(U + R) + R = S$; following a U-turn with a right turn, then going right again results in the same direction as going straight.

2 Closure, identity. Note that $(z \circ x) \circ x \neq z \circ (x \circ x)$.

3 Not a group; only zero has an inverse

4 No; 0 doesn't have an inverse

EXERCISE SET 13-1

Writing Exercises

1. What is a mathematical system?
2. What is an operation table for a mathematical system?
3. What does it mean for a system to be closed?
4. Explain why the positive integers are closed if the operation is addition, but not subtraction.

5. How can you quickly decide if a mathematical system is commutative by looking at the operation table for the system?
6. How can you tell if a mathematical system is a group?

Computational Exercises

For Exercises 7–21, use the elements C, D, E, and F, and the operation ? as defined by

?	C	D	E	F
C	D	F	C	E
D	F	E	D	C
E	C	D	E	F
F	E	C	F	D

7. $C\,?\,E$
8. $F\,?\,D$
9. $E\,?\,E$
10. $F\,?\,F$
11. $C\,?\,F$
12. $(D\,?\,E)\,?\,D$
13. $E\,?\,(C\,?\,C)$
14. $F\,?\,(D\,?\,C)$
15. $(E\,?\,D)\,?\,E$
16. $C\,?\,(D\,?\,E)$
17. Is the system closed under the operation?
18. Is there an identity for the operation?
19. Is the operation commutative?
20. What are the inverses for each element?
21. Find the value for x when $E\;?\;x = D$.

For Exercises 22–36, use the elements and the operation ∗ as defined by

∗	△	□	○
△	△	□	○
□	□	☆	△
○	○	△	□

22. $\triangle * \bigcirc$
23. $\square * \square$
24. $\square * \bigcirc$
25. $\bigcirc * \bigcirc$
26. $\triangle * \triangle$
27. $\triangle * (\square * \bigcirc)$
28. $\square * (\bigcirc * \triangle)$
29. $(\bigcirc * \bigcirc) * \square$
30. $(\square * \bigcirc) * \triangle$
31. $(\triangle * \triangle) * \square$
32. Is the system closed under ∗?
33. Is ∗ commutative?
34. Is there an identity for the system?
35. Is ∗ associative?
36. What is the inverse of $\bigcirc$?

For Exercises 37–46, determine which properties the given mathematical system exhibits. Identify any systems that are groups or Abelian groups.

37.

ℵ	A	B	C
A	A	A	A
B	B	B	B
C	C	C	C

38.

Ω	1	2	3	4
1	1	2	3	4
2	2	3	4	1
3	3	4	1	2
4	4	1	2	3

39.

•	α	β	γ	δ
α	δ	β	α	γ
β	β	α	β	α
γ	α	β	γ	δ
δ	γ	α	δ	β

40.

@	7	4	3
7	4	3	7
4	3	7	4
3	7	4	3

41.

⊕	q	r	s	t	u
q	q	r	s	t	u
r	s	t	u	r	q
s	r	s	t	u	q
t	u	q	r	s	t
u	t	u	s	r	s

42.

𝒫	1	2
1	1	2
2	2	1

43.

^	a	b	c
a	c	a	b
b	a	b	c
c	b	c	c

44.

#	0	1	2
0	0	0	0
1	0	0	0
2	0	0	0

45.

Π	1	2	3
1	1	2	3
2	2	3	1
3	3	1	2

46.

◊	P	Q
P	Q	P
Q	P	Q

For exercises 47–56, determine whether the given system forms (a) a group and (b) an Abelian group.

47. Integers under addition
48. Integers under multiplication
49. Whole numbers under multiplication
50. Natural numbers under multiplication
51. Rational numbers under multiplication
52. Rational numbers under addition
53. $\{-1, 1\}$ under addition
54. $\{\frac{1}{2}, 1, 2\}$ under multiplication
55. $\{-1, 0, 1\}$ under addition
56. $\{\ldots \frac{1}{256}, \frac{1}{16}, \frac{1}{4}, \frac{1}{2}, 1, 2, 4, 16, 256 \ldots\}$ under multiplication

Real-World Applications

Exercises 57–62 use the mathematical system described next. Many ceiling fans have a four-way switch on a pull chain, with positions off, high speed, medium speed, and low speed. We can build a mathematical system to describe the positions using 0 for off, 1 for high speed, 2 for medium speed, and 3 for low speed. For example, if the fan is off and you pull the chain once, it goes to high speed, so if we use + to represent the operation of combining positions by pulling the chain, $0 + 1 = 1$. If it's on medium speed and you pull the chain three times the result is also high speed (medium → low → off → high), so $2 + 3 = 1$.

57. Fill in the operational table we've started below for the mathematical system described by the ceiling fan pull chain.

*	0	1	2	3
0		1		
1			3	
2	2			1
3		0		

58. Is the mathematical system commutative?
59. Is the mathematical system associative?
60. Is the mathematical system closed?
61. Does the mathematical system satisfy the inverse property?
62. Is the mathematical system a group?

Exercises 63–68 use the mathematical system described next. Mixing paint using the three primary colors red (R), blue (B), and yellow (Y) can be thought of as a mathematical system with the operation being mixing of two primary colors.

M	R	B	Y
R			
B			
Y			

63. Using the symbol M to represent the mixing operator, fill in the operational table for this mathematical system. (Use the symbols P for purple, O for orange, and G for green.)
64. Is the mathematical system commutative?
65. Is the mathematical system associative?
66. Is the mathematical system closed?
67. Does the mathematical system satisfy the inverse property?
68. Is the mathematical system a group?

Critical Thinking

69. Prove that the mathematical system in Example 1 on page 718 is associative by testing the associative property on all possible choices of three symbols. (*Hint:* We already know that the system is commutative, so order doesn't matter.)

A truth table similar to one shown in Chapter 3 for the conjunction is shown in Figure 13-1(a). This can be converted to a mathematical system using T and F as the elements and ∧ as the operation. This is shown in Figure 13-1(b).

70. Construct a table for a mathematical system for $p \vee q$ using ∨ as the operation.
71. Construct a table for a mathematical system for $p \rightarrow q$. What properties are valid for this system?

p	q	$p \wedge q$
T	T	T
T	F	F
F	T	F
F	F	F

∧	T	F
T	T	F
F	F	F

(a)   (b)

Figure 13-1

72. Construct a table for a mathematical system for $p \leftrightarrow q$. What properties are valid for this system?

Section 13-2 Clock Arithmetic

LEARNING OBJECTIVES

☐ 1. Perform addition on the 12-hour clock.

☐ 2. Find the equivalent of any whole number on the 12-hour clock.

☐ 3. Perform multiplication on the 12-hour clock.

☐ 4. Perform subtraction on the 12-hour clock.

☐ 5. Perform operations in other clock systems.

☐ 6. Determine the properties of the 12-hour clock system.

Have you ever stopped to think about how much control the clock has over your life? You could make a pretty strong case that it has more influence over where you go and what you do than anything else. Strange, isn't it?

Because clocks are so familiar, most of us never really think about the unusual math involved in the simple act of telling time. Everywhere else in your life, 11 + 2 = 13. But when it comes to telling time, you accept as given that a 2-hour final exam beginning at the hour of 11 ends at 1, in which case 11 + 2 = 1.

In this section, we will study the math involved in working with clocks, and see how it applies to the mathematical systems we studied in Section 13-1. The math used in the 12-hour clock you learned as a child is an excellent example of a mathematical system: the elements are the whole numbers from 1 through 12, and the basic operation is addition. We will also take a look at the operations of multiplication and subtraction as they apply to clocks.

Addition on the 12-Hour Clock

The answers to addition problems on the 12-hour clock can be found by counting clockwise around the face of a clock. If it is 7 o'clock now, in 8 hours, it will be 3 o'clock, as shown in Figure 13-2. We can write this operation as 7 + 8 = 3.

Some other examples of addition on the 12-hour clock are:

$$7 + 6 = 1 \qquad 6 + 11 = 5$$
$$8 + 7 = 3 \qquad 4 + 3 \ = 7$$

Figure 13-2

EXAMPLE 1   **Adding on the 12-Hour Clock**

Using the 12-hour clock, find these sums.

(a) 9 + 12   (b) 6 + 5   (c) 8 + 8   (d) 3 + 11   (e) 5 + 7

SOLUTION

(a) 9. Start at 9 and count 12 hours clockwise, ending at 9.
(b) 11. Start at 6 and count 5 hours clockwise, ending at 11.
(c) 4. Start at 8 and count 8 hours clockwise, ending at 4.
(d) 2. Start at 3 and count 11 hours clockwise, ending at 2.
(e) 12. Start at 5 and count 7 hours, ending at 12.

☑ 1. Perform addition on the 12-hour clock.

▼ Try This One 1

Using the 12-hour clock, find these sums.

(a) 3 + 12   (b) 7 + 6   (c) 11 + 5   (d) 9 + 3

We can make the 12-hour clock look just like the mathematical systems we studied in Section 13-1 by making an operation table for addition.

+	1	2	3	4	5	6	7	8	9	10	11	12
1	2	3	4	5	6	7	8	9	10	11	12	1
2	3	4	5	6	7	8	9	10	11	12	1	2
3	4	5	6	7	8	9	10	11	12	1	2	3
4	5	6	7	8	9	10	11	12	1	2	3	4
5	6	7	8	9	10	11	12	1	2	3	4	5
6	7	8	9	10	11	12	1	2	3	4	5	6
7	8	9	10	11	12	1	2	3	4	5	6	7
8	9	10	11	12	1	2	3	4	5	6	7	8
9	10	11	12	1	2	3	4	5	6	7	8	9
10	11	12	1	2	3	4	5	6	7	8	9	10
11	12	1	2	3	4	5	6	7	8	9	10	11
12	1	2	3	4	5	6	7	8	9	10	11	12

Multiplication on the 12-Hour Clock

Multiplication in the real number system is defined in terms of repeated addition. We will use the same idea to define multiplication in our 12-hour clock system. Let's start with an example. In order to multiply 5×3, start at 12 o'clock and count around the clock in 3-hour portions 5 times. This is equivalent to adding $3 + 3 + 3 + 3 + 3$.

$$12 + 3 = 3 \qquad \textit{1 time}$$
$$3 + 3 = 6 \qquad \textit{2 times}$$
$$6 + 3 = 9 \qquad \textit{3 times}$$
$$9 + 3 = 12 \qquad \textit{4 times}$$
$$12 + 3 = 3 \qquad \textit{5 times}$$

We conclude that $5 \times 3 = 3$ on the 12-hour clock.

CAUTION | The biggest stumbling block that most students face in this kind of arithmetic is ignoring years of experience that wants you to write $5 \times 3 = 15$. You have to really concentrate!

Converting Whole Numbers to the 12-Hour Clock System

Next, we'll develop an approach that makes multiplication on the 12-hour clock quicker and easier. To convert any whole number to its equivalent on the 12-hour clock, we'll take advantage of the fact that any 12-unit rotation on the clock puts you back where you started. So 24 is equivalent to 12 because 24 represents two full turns, starting and ending at 12. For a number like 43, we can break it up into portions of 12, with some left over:

$$43 = \underbrace{12 + 12 + 12}_{\textit{3 full turns}} + 7$$

This shows that 43 is equivalent to 7 on the 12-hour clock.

A simple way to arrive at this answer is to divide the original number by 12 and find the remainder:

$$\begin{array}{r} 3 \\ 12\overline{)43} \\ -36 \\ \hline 7 \end{array}$$

The remainder is 7, so 43 is equivalent to 7 on the 12-hour clock.

Now we return to the multiplication problem 5×3. We can simply use regular real-number multiplication ($5 \times 3 = 15$) then convert the result to its equivalent number

Math Note

Since we have no zero on the 12-hour clock, but 12 plays the role of zero since it is our typical starting point, a remainder of zero corresponds to 12 on the 12-hour clock.

☑ 2. Find the equivalent of any whole number on the 12-hour clock.

on the 12 hour clock: $15 \div 12 = 1R3$ (1 remainder 3), so we conclude that $5 \times 3 = 3$ on the 12-hour clock. We can think of 1R3 as "one revolution, plus 3 more hours."

EXAMPLE 2   Multiplying on the 12-Hour Clock

Perform these multiplications on the 12-hour clock.

(a) 5×8 (d) 11×5
(b) 12×9 (e) $10(6 + 9)$
(c) 6×4

SOLUTION

(a) $5 \times 8 = 40$ and $40 \div 12 = 3$, remainder 4: $5 \times 8 = 4$.
(b) $12 \times 9 = 108$ and $108 \div 12 = 9$, remainder 0. Since 0 corresponds to 12 on the 12-hour clock, the answer is 12: $12 \times 9 = 12$.
(c) $6 \times 4 = 24$ and $24 \div 12 = 2$, remainder 0: $6 \times 4 = 12$.
(d) $11 \times 5 = 55$ and $55 \div 12 = 4$, remainder 7: $11 \times 5 = 7$.
(e) First do the addition inside parentheses: $6 + 9 = 3$. Now multiply: $10 \times 3 = 30$ and $30 \div 12 = 2$, remainder 6. So $10(6 + 9) = 6$.

Calculator Guide

To convert whole numbers to their equivalent on the 12-hour clock, for example, 40:

Standard Scientific Calculator

40 ÷ 12 = − 3 = ×

12 =

Standard Graphing Calculator

40 ÷ 12 ENTER − 3

Enter × 12 ENTER.

In each case, subtracting 3 leaves behind only the decimal part of the answer, and multiplying by 12 converts the decimal part back to a remainder.

▼ Try This One 2

Perform these multiplications on the 12-hour clock.

(a) 7×5 (b) 8×9 (c) 10×10 (d) $8(9 + 5)$

☑ 3. Perform multiplication on the 12-hour clock.

A table can be constructed for multiplication in the same manner as the addition table was constructed. The multiplication table is shown here.

×	1	2	3	4	5	6	7	8	9	10	11	12
1	1	2	3	4	5	6	7	8	9	10	11	12
2	2	4	6	8	10	12	2	4	6	8	10	12
3	3	6	9	12	3	6	9	12	3	6	9	12
4	4	8	12	4	8	12	4	8	12	4	8	12
5	5	10	3	8	1	6	11	4	9	2	7	12
6	6	12	6	12	6	12	6	12	6	12	6	12
7	7	2	9	4	11	6	1	8	3	10	5	12
8	8	4	12	8	4	12	8	4	12	8	4	12
9	9	6	3	12	9	6	3	12	9	6	3	12
10	10	8	6	4	2	12	10	8	6	4	2	12
11	11	10	9	8	7	6	5	4	3	2	1	12
12	12	12	12	12	12	12	12	12	12	12	12	12

Subtraction on the 12-Hour Clock

Subtraction can be performed on the 12-hour clock by counting counterclockwise (backward). For example, $8 - 10$ means that if it is 8 o'clock now, what time was it 10 hours ago? Figure 13-3 shows that if you start at 8 and count counterclockwise, you will end at 10 o'clock; so $8 - 10 = 10$.

Figure 13-3

| EXAMPLE 3 | **Subtracting on the 12-Hour Clock** |

Perform these subtraction operations on the 12-hour clock.

(a) $2 - 10$ (b) $12 - 7$ (c) $5 - 9$ (d) $6 - 12$ (e) $4 - 11$

SOLUTION

(a) Starting at 2 on the clock and counting backward 10 numbers, you will get 4.
(b) Starting at 12 and counting 7 numbers backward, you will get 5.
(c) Starting at 5 and counting 9 numbers backward, you will get 8.
(d) Starting at 6 and counting 12 numbers backward, you will get 6.
(e) Starting at 4 and counting 11 numbers backward, you will get 5.

☑ 4. Perform subtraction on the 12-hour clock.

▼ **Try This One 3**

Perform the following subtractions on the 12-hour clock.

(a) $7 - 2$
(b) $3 - 10$
(c) $9 - 12$

Clocks with Hours Different from 12

The military does not use a 12-hour clock, but a 24-hour clock. The hours on a military clock start at "zero hundred hours," then go to "one hundred hours" and so on up to "23 hundred hours." These are written 0000 hours, 0100 hours, etc., up to 2300 hours. A 24-hour clock is illustrated in Figure 13-4.

Arithmetic on the 24-hour clock can be performed just as on the 12-hour clock. If it is 0500 hours now, then 13 hours from now it will be $5 + 13$ or 18 (that is, 1800 hours). If it is 0400 hours now, then 10 hours ago it was $4 - 10 = 18$ (counting counterclockwise 10 units from 4 on the 24-hour clock).

In fact, the same arithmetic that can be performed on a 12-hour clock can be performed on a clock with any number of hours. Suppose, for example, it is 4 o'clock now; what time will it be 5 hours from now on a 6-hour clock? To figure this out we can draw a 6-hour clock, then starting at 4, count 5 hours, and end up at 3 (see Figure 13-5); so, on the 6-hour clock, $4 + 5 = 3$. Notice the same shortcut applies that applied to 12-hour clocks; that is, if 4 and 5 are added, the result is 9, and on a 6-hour clock this is 1 revolution plus 3, so $4 + 5 = 3$.

Figure 13-4

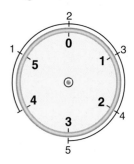

Figure 13-5

| EXAMPLE 4 | **Performing Arithmetic on Other Clocks** |

Perform the indicated operations:

(a) $7 - 5$ on an 8-hour clock
(b) $5 + 9$ on a 10-hour clock
(c) 2×6 on a 5-hour clock

SOLUTION

(a) $7 - 5 = 2$; on an 8-hour clock this is still 2.

(b) $5 + 9 = 14$; on a 10-hour clock 14 is one revolution plus 4, so $5 + 9 = 4$ on a 10-hour clock.

(c) $2 \times 6 = 12$; on a 5-hour clock 12 is two revolutions plus 2, so $2 \times 6 = 2$ on a 5-hour clock.

☑ 5. Perform operations in other clock systems.

▼ Try This One 4

Perform the indicated operations:

(a) $3 - 5$ on a 7-hour clock
(b) $5 + 7$ on a 4-hour clock
(c) 5×3 on an 11-hour clock

Properties of the 12-Hour Clock System

Next, we'll determine whether the 12-hour clock system satisfies any of the properties of mathematical systems we learned about in Section 13-1.

The closure property for addition and multiplication can be verified by looking at the two operation tables shown previously. The answers for every combination of addition problems and for every combination of multiplication problems are numbers on the clock.

The commutative properties for addition and multiplication can also be verified using the operation tables: both are symmetric about the main diagonal from upper left to lower right, so the system is commutative under both operations.

To verify the associative property, we would need to try every combination of 3 symbols chosen from the 12 in our system. This would require over 200 calculations. (If the system were not commutative, it would be even worse: 1,728 calculations!) In any case, we will just try one sample calculation, for addition: beyond that

---

Sidelight EVARISTE GALOIS

Evariste Galois (1811–1832) was a brilliant young mathematician who lived a short life with incredible bad luck. When he was 17 years old, he submitted a manuscript on the solvability of algebraic equations to the French Academy of Sciences. Augustin-Louis Cauchy, a famous mathematician of his time, was appointed as a referee to read it. However, Cauchy apparently lost the manuscript. A year later, Galois submitted a revised version to the academy. A new referee was appointed to read it but died before he could read it, and the manuscript was lost a second time.

A year later, Galois submitted the manuscript again for a third time. After a 6-month delay, the new referee, Siméon-Denis Poisson, rejected it, saying it was too vague and recommended that Galois rewrite it in more detail.

Galois at that time was considered a dangerous political radical, and he was provoked into a duel. (Some feel that the challenger was hired by local police to eliminate him.) Galois realized that he would probably die the next morning, so he spent the night trying to revise his manuscript as well as

some other papers he had written, but he did not have enough time to finish everything.

The next day, he was shot and killed. Eleven years after his death, Galois's writings were found by Joseph Liouville, who studied them, realized their importance, and published them. At last, Galois was given credit for his work, which made important advances in the study of groups. (We will see shortly that the 12-hour clock system is actually a group.)

you'll have to trust us that the system is in fact associative for both addition and multiplication.

$$\begin{array}{ll} (6 + 9) + 10 & 6 + (9 + 10) \\ = 3 + 10 & = 6 + 7 \\ = 1 & = 1 \end{array}$$

The identity element for addition is 12 since adding 12 hours to any number on the clock brings you back to the same number.

A quick look at the multiplication table shows that 1 is the identity element for multiplication: looking across the row and down the column beginning with 1 shows that all elements are unchanged when multiplied by 1.

Finally, we can use the addition and multiplication tables to check the inverse property. For addition, the identity element is 12, and 12 appears once in every row of the addition table. This shows that every number has exactly one other number that produces 12 when added to it. In other words, every number in the system has an additive inverse. But this is not the case for multiplication. The identity element is 1, but 1 appears only in the rows for 5, 7, and 11. That means the other numbers do not have multiplicative inverses, and the inverse property does not hold for multiplication.

☑ 6. Determine the properties of the 12-hour clock system.

In summary, addition on the 12-hour clock satisfies all of the closure, commutative, associative, identity, and inverse properties, so the 12-hour clock with operation addition forms an Abelian group. Multiplication satisfies the closure, commutative, associative, and identity properties, but not the inverse property, so the 12-hour clock with operation multiplication is not a group.

Answers to Try This One

1 (a) 3   (b) 1   (c) 4   (d) 12

2 (a) 11   (b) 12   (c) 4   (d) 4

3 (a) 5   (b) 5   (c) 9

4 (a) 5   (b) 0   (c) 4

EXERCISE SET 13-2

Writing Exercises

1. Explain why $10 + 5 = 3$ on a 12-hour clock.
2. Describe the procedure for finding 8×10 using remainders on a 12-hour clock.
3. Write out the 12 symbols used in 12-hour clock arithmetic and the 6 symbols used in 6-hour clock arithmetic. Why is zero used for one but not the other?
4. How do we define subtraction in the 12-hour clock system?

Computational Exercises

For Exercises 5–16, find the equivalent number on (a) the 12-hour clock, (b) a 6-hour clock, and (c) an 8-hour clock.

5. 27	9. 18	13. −5
6. 92	10. 42	14. −10
7. 155	11. 259	15. −3
8. 334	12. 3,230	16. −20

For Exercises 17–28, perform the additions on the 12-hour clock.

17. $5 + 9$	21. $12 + 3$	25. $(6 + 5) + 12$
18. $10 + 8$	22. $4 + 8$	26. $8 + (10 + 9)$
19. $11 + 11$	23. $10 + 20$	27. $3 + (11 + 8)$
20. $9 + 7$	24. $9 + 6$	28. $(5 + 7) + 2$

For Exercises 29–40, perform the subtractions on the 12-hour clock.

29. $8 - 6$
30. $12 - 10$
31. $9 - 11$
32. $10 - 12$
33. $0 - 6$
34. $6 - 10$
35. $3 - 12$
36. $0 - 8$
37. $4 - 5$
38. $12 - 8$
39. $3 - 11$
40. $2 - 7$

For Exercises 41–52, perform the multiplications on the 12-hour clock.

41. 3×2
42. 10×10
43. 8×6
44. 9×7
45. 2×5
46. 12×6
47. 3×7
48. 4×5
49. $5 \times (6 \times 9)$
50. $3 \times (2 \times 9)$
51. $(6 \times 4) \times 7$
52. $(8 \times 3) \times 5$

In Exercises 53–64, perform the indicated operation on the indicated clock.

53. $7 + 3$; 8-hour clock
54. $4 + 2$; 5-hour clock
55. $9 + 11$; 10-hour clock
56. $3 + 7$; 4-hour clock
57. $9 - 4$; 10-hour clock
58. $1 - 7$; 6-hour clock
59. $3 - 5$; 5-hour clock
60. $8 - 7$; 4-hour clock
61. 10×5; 3-hour clock
62. 7×4; 13-hour clock
63. 12×11; 6-hour clock
64. 6×6; 15-hour clock

For Exercises 65–74, find the additive inverse for each number on the 12-hour clock.

65. 12
66. 3
67. 5
68. 8
69. 2
70. 9
71. 7
72. 4
73. -5
74. -6

For Exercises 75–80, find the multiplicative inverse if it exists for each number on the 12-hour clock.

75. 4
76. 7
77. 12
78. 9
79. 1
80. 10

For Exercises 81–86, give on example of each using the 12-hour clock.

81. Associative property of addition
82. Commutative property of multiplication
83. Identity property of addition
84. Inverse property of multiplication
85. Distributive property
86. Commutative property of addition

For Exercises 87–96, find the value of y using the 12-hour clock.

87. $5 + y = 3$
88. $9 + y = 2$
89. $y - 5 = 8$
90. $y + 6 = 2$
91. $4 \times (2 + y) = 4$
92. $8 \times 2 = y$
93. $6 \times 9 = y$
94. $9 \times 4 = y$
95. $3 \times (4 + 10) = y$
96. $5 \times (6 - 11) = y$

Real-World Applications

97. A computer simulation takes 3 hours to run. If it is now 11 o'clock A.M., what time will it be when the simulation has run 10 times?

98. A sorority organizes a dance marathon to raise money for charity. It starts at 8 P.M. on Saturday evening. Participants dance for 2 hours, then switch partners. If the goal is for everyone to last through eight 2-hour sessions, at what time will the marathon end?

Time in the military is based on a 24-hour clock. From midnight to noon is designated as 0000 to 1200. From noon until 1 minute before midnight, time is designated as 1200 to 2359, where the first two digits indicate the hour and the last two digits represent the minutes. For example, 1824 means 6:24 P.M. For Exercises 99–105, translate military time into standard time.

99. 0948
100. 0311
101. 0500
102. 1542
103. 1938
104. 2218
105. 2000

For Exercises 106–114, change the standard times into military times.

106. 6:56 A.M.
107. 3:52 A.M.
108. 4:00 A.M.
109. 11:56 A.M.
110. 5:27 P.M.
111. 8:06 P.M.
112. 11:42 P.M.
113. 9:36 P.M.
114. 12:00 A.M.

For Exercises 115–118, find the standard time for each.

115. $0627 + 3$ hours and 42 minutes
116. $2342 + 5$ hours and 6 minutes
117. $1540 - 1$ hour and 4 minutes
118. $1242 - 2$ hours and 20 minutes

Critical Thinking

119. Does the distributive property of multiplication over addition hold in the 12-hour clock system? That is, is $a(b + c) = a \times b + a \times c$ for any a, b, and c in the system? Try several examples and draw a conclusion.

120. How could division be defined on the 12-hour clock? (*Hint:* $8 \div 4 = $ _____ can be rewritten as $4 \times $ _____ $= 8$.) Under what conditions will your division be defined within the system?

121. Calculate 4×4, 4×7, and 4×10 on a 12-hour clock. Explain why all of the answers are the same, then use your explanation to find three other numbers b on the 12-hour clock so that $3 \times b = 3 \times 3$.

Section 13-3 Modular Systems

LEARNING OBJECTIVES

☐ 1. Find congruent numbers in modular systems.

☐ 2. Perform addition, subtraction, and multiplication in modular systems.

☐ 3. Solve congruences in modular systems.

For most people, daylight savings time is not that big of a deal—you move all your clocks an hour twice a year, and get an extra hour of daylight for outdoor activities in the evening during the summer. But some people are strongly opposed to the idea for one reason or another, including some logically challenged farmers, who have argued that the extra hour of sun can cause their crops to wilt during the hottest part of the year.

Hopefully, you recognize the humor in that argument: the sun rises and sets at the same time regardless of what number human beings choose to attach to those points in time. In fact, our entire system of keeping time is basically arbitrary. If there were only six hours in a day, you wouldn't have any less time to get stuff done—each "hour" would just be four times as long.

In Section 13-2, we looked very briefly at arithmetic on clocks with numbers of hours other than 12. In this section, these clocks will become our main focus as we define the study of modular arithmetic. **A modular system** is a mathematical system with a specific number of elements in which the arithmetic is analogous to the clock arithmetic from Section 13-2. For example, a modular 5 system, denoted as *mod 5*, has as its five elements 0, 1, 2, 3, 4 and uses the clock shown in Figure 13-6a. A mod 3 system consists of elements 0, 1, 2 and uses the clock shown in Figure 13-6b. A mod 8 system consists of elements 0, 1, 2, 3, 4, 5, 6, 7 and uses the clock shown in

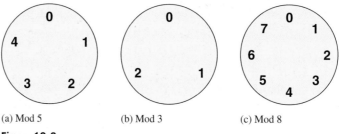

(a) Mod 5   (b) Mod 3   (c) Mod 8

Figure 13-6

Math Note

In modular systems, 0 is used in place of the modulus. For example, in mod 5, 0 is the starting number, not 5. When we work with mod 12 systems, we will also use 0 rather than 12, making it just a bit different from the 12-hour clock system.

Figure 13-6c. In general, a mod *m* system consists of *m* whole numbers starting at zero and ending at *m* − 1. The number *m* is called the **modulus** of the system.

The 12-hour clock system we studied in Section 13-2 is a system with modulus 12; the one difference is that we used the whole numbers from 1 through 12 rather than 0 through 11, but the idea is the same. One of the key things we learned how to do in Section 13-2 is convert any whole number to its equivalent in the 12-hour system. We will now focus on doing so for any modular system using the term *congruence*.

> *a* **is congruent to** *b* **modulo** *m* (written $a \equiv b$ mod *m*) if *a* and *b* have the same remainder when divided by *m*. Alternately, $a \equiv b$ mod *m* if *m* divides $b - a$.

To write a whole number in any given modulo system, we will divide that number by the modulus. The remainder tells us the congruent number in the modular system. This is illustrated in Example 1.

EXAMPLE 1   Finding Congruent Numbers in Modular Systems

Find the number congruent to each number in the given modular system.

(a) 19 mod 5   (b) 25 mod 3

SOLUTION

(a) Divide 19 by 5 and find the remainder, as shown.

$$
\begin{array}{r}
3\text{R}4 \\
5\overline{)19} \\
-15 \\
\hline
4
\end{array}
$$

So $19 \equiv 4 \bmod 5$. This answer can be verified by starting at 0 on the mod 5 clock and counting around 19 numbers.

(b) Divide 25 by 3 and find the remainder as shown.

$$
\begin{array}{r}
8\text{R}1 \\
3\overline{)25} \\
-24 \\
\hline
1
\end{array}
$$

So $25 \equiv 1 \bmod 3$.

▼ Try This One 1

Find the number congruent to each number in the given modular system.

(a) 27 mod 5   (b) 13 mod 3   (c) 50 mod 8

To write a negative number in modulo m, you can keep adding m to the negative number until you get a non-negative number. Another way to say this is that you add the smallest multiple of the modulus that yields a nonnegative number. This is illustrated in Example 2.

EXAMPLE 2   Finding a Negative Number in Modulo *m*

Find the number congruent to the given number in the given modular system.
(a) $-13 \bmod 7$ (b) $-1 \bmod 3$ (c) $-27 \bmod 10$ (d) 20 mod 5

SOLUTION

(a) Multiples of 7 are 7, 14, 21, etc. The smallest multiple of 7 that can be added to -13 that results in a non-negative number is 14. Therefore, -13 is congruent to $-13 + 14 \equiv 1 \bmod 7$.
(b) $-1 + 3 = 2$, so $-1 \equiv 2 \bmod 3$
(c) $-27 + 30 = 3$, so $-27 \equiv 3 \bmod 10$ *30 is 3 × the modulus*
(d) $-20 + 20 = 0$, so, $-20 \equiv 0 \bmod 5$ *20 is 4 × the modulus*

▼ Try This One 2

Find the number congruent to the given number in the given modular system.
(a) $-13 \bmod 6$ (c) $-42 \bmod 9$
(b) $-11 \bmod 4$ (d) $-36 \bmod 12$

Suppose that you need to take antibiotics three times a day for 10 days. Your first pill was a morning dose. You can't remember if you took your second pill today or not. To find out, count the remaining pills and convert to mod 3: if the answer is 1, you took your pill. (The one remaining pill is your evening dose.) If the answer is 2, you missed a dose. If the answer is 0, you missed two doses.

Adding, Subtracting, and Multiplying in Modular Systems

The operations of addition, subtraction, and multiplication in modular systems can be performed by adding, subtracting, or multiplying the numbers as usual, then

1. Find congruent numbers in modular systems.

converting the answers to equivalent numbers in the specified system like we did in Examples 1 and 2.

EXAMPLE 3   Adding and Multiplying in Modular Systems

Find the result of each operation in the given system

(a) 4×4 in mod 5   (c) 5×6 in mod 9
(b) $6 + 5$ in mod 7   (d) $9 + 7$ in mod 8

SOLUTION

(a) $4 \times 4 = 16$ and $16 \div 5 = 3$ remainder 1: $4 \times 4 \equiv 1$ mod 5.
(b) $6 + 5 = 11$ and $11 \div 7 = 1$ remainder 4: $6 + 5 \equiv 4$ mod 7.
(c) $5 \times 6 = 30$ and $30 \div 9 = 3$ remainder 3: $5 \times 6 \equiv 3$ mod 9.
(d) $9 + 7 = 16$ and $16 \div 8 = 2$ remainder 0: $9 + 7 \equiv 0$ mod 8.

▼ Try This One 3

Find the result of each operation in the given system

(a) $7 + 11$ in mod 12   (c) 5×5 in mod 6
(b) 3×7 in mod 8   (d) $15 + 12$ in mod 20

EXAMPLE 4   Subtracting in Modular Systems

Perform the following subtractions in the given modular system.
(a) $7 - 10$ mod 12   (b) $8 - 3$ mod 4   (c) $13 - 21$ mod 6

SOLUTION

(a) $7 - 10 = -3$; $-3 + 12 = 9$, so $-3 \equiv 9$ mod 12
(b) $8 - 3 = 5$; $5 \equiv 1$ mod 4
(c) $13 - 21 = -8$; $-8 + 12 = 4$, so $-8 \equiv 4$ mod 6

▼ Try This One 4

2. Perform addition, subtraction, and multiplication in modular systems.

Perform the following subtractions in the given modular system.

(a) $13 - 5$ mod 3   (b) $6 - 15$ mod 7   (c) $8 - 21$ mod 8

Solving Congruences in Modular Systems

An equation like $x + 2 = 5$ is simple to solve in the real number system because there's only one number that will result in 5 when added to 2, namely 3. But when we use congruence in modular systems rather than equality in the real number system, the picture is more complicated. In mod 6, for example, the congruence $x + 2 \equiv 5$ mod 6 has more than one solution. One is $x = 3$, but $x = 9$ is also a solution (because $9 + 2 = 5$ mod 6), as is $x = 15$. In fact, we can keep getting new solutions by adding 6 to the previous one. We can use this idea to solve congruences, as we will see in Examples 5 and 6.

EXAMPLE 5 Solving a Congruence in a Modular System

Find all natural number solutions to $3x - 5 \equiv 1 \bmod 6$.

SOLUTION

The first whole number that is congruent to 1 mod 6 is 1, so we begin by solving $3x - 5 = 1$.

$$3x - 5 = 1$$
$$3x = 6$$
$$x = 2$$

The next number that is congruent to 1 mod 6 is 7:

$$3x - 5 = 7$$
$$3x = 12$$
$$x = 4$$

The next number that is congruent to 1 mod 6 is 13:

$$3x - 5 = 13$$
$$3x = 18$$
$$x = 6$$

The pattern emerging is that each new solution is found by adding 2 to the previous solution. So the set of solutions is $\{2, 4, 6, 8, 10, \dots\}$.

A lamp with a four-way switch (off, low, medium, and high) can be represented by addition in the mod 4 system (0, 1, 2, 3). Turning the knob is like doing addition—two turns moves you up two notches, and so on. What is the inverse of 1 in the system? (That is, if the lamp is on low, how many turns does it take to turn it off?)

▼ **Try This One 5**

Find all natural number solutions to $2x - 7 \equiv 3 \bmod 8$.

EXAMPLE 6 Solving a Congruence in a Modular System

Find all natural number solutions to $6x \equiv 12 \bmod 3$.

SOLUTION

First, notice that 12 mod 3 is the same as 0 mod 3, so we can rewrite the congruence as $6x \equiv 0 \bmod 3$. Next, note that any multiple of 6 will have remainder 0 when dividing by 3; this means that any natural number is a solution, so the solution is $\{1, 2, 3, 4, 5, \dots\}$.

▼ **Try This One 6**

Find all natural number solutions to $4x \equiv 24 \bmod 8$.

☑ 3. Solve congruences in modular systems.

In Section 13-1, we saw that a mathematical system can be defined using any symbols you like as long as you define an operation on those symbols. In Sections 13-2 and 13-3, we learned that it's possible to define new mathematical systems using the numbers you're familiar with by revising the standard operations of addition and multiplication.

Sidelight CHECK DIGITS AND MODULAR ARITHMETIC

One important application of modular arithmetic is the check digit, which is a method that allows computers to recognize whether a code number for some purpose is valid. One example is the nine-digit routing number on the bottom left of all checks. The number's purpose is to identify the financial institution, but only the first eight digits accomplish that. The last is a check digit, with a purpose of making sure that none of the previous eight digits was read incorrectly or transposed. Here's how it works.

If we use the symbol d_1 for the first digit, d_2 for the second, and so on, the nine digits are plugged into the formula

$$7d_1 + 3d_2 + 9d_3 + 7d_4 + 3d_5 + 9d_6 + 7d_7 + 3d_8 + 9d_9$$

If the result is not congruent to 0 mod 10, the computer reading the number knows there was an error. This particular formula allows computers to detect a single-digit error, as well as a switch of two consecutive digits, and most switches

of two digits that are one space apart from each other. It can also detect a counterfeit routing number.

A similar formula is used for the check digit on UPC codes (see "Math in Retail Sales" in Chapter 4), and another is used by most states to make sure that drivers' license numbers are not fake. In most states, the last digit of the driver's license number is the remainder when the number without that digit is divided by some modulus, but the modulus varies from state to state, making it hard to counterfeit licenses.

Answers to Try This One

1   (a) 2   (b) 1   (c) 2

2   (a) 5   (b) 1   (c) 3   (d) 0

3   (a) 6   (b) 5   (c) 1   (d) 7

4   (a) 2   (b) 5   (c) 3

5   {5, 9, 13, 17, 21, ... }

6   {2, 4, 6, 8, 10, ... }

EXERCISE SET 13-3

Writing Exercises

1. Explain how modular systems apply to clock arithmetic.
2. Describe the process for finding the number congruent to 25 in the mod 7 system.
3. Describe the process for finding the number congruent to −11 in the mod 3 system.
4. Explain how the process you described in Exercise 2 is used to define addition, multiplication, and subtraction in modular systems.

Computational Exercises

For Exercises 5–14, find the values of each number in the given modular system.

5. $32 \equiv \text{mod } 6$
6. $51 \equiv \text{mod } 4$
7. $135 \equiv \text{mod } 7$
8. $48 \equiv \text{mod } 5$
9. $16 \equiv \text{mod } 9$
10. $92 \equiv \text{mod } 10$
11. $326 \equiv \text{mod } 3$
12. $451 \equiv \text{mod } 5$
13. $987 \equiv \text{mod } 8$
14. $1{,}656 \equiv \text{mod } 11$

For Exercises 15–44, perform the following operations in the specified modular system.

15. $4 + 3 \equiv \text{mod } 5$
16. $8 + 6 \equiv \text{mod } 9$
17. $3 + 3 \equiv \text{mod } 4$
18. $5 + 6 \equiv \text{mod } 7$
19. $5 \times 8 \equiv \text{mod } 9$
20. $3 \times 7 \equiv \text{mod } 8$
21. $3 \times 3 \equiv \text{mod } 4$
22. $4 \times 6 \equiv \text{mod } 7$
23. $3 - 8 \equiv \text{mod } 9$
24. $5 - 7 \equiv \text{mod } 10$

25. $2 - 3 \equiv \text{mod } 4$

26. $1 - 9 \equiv \text{mod } 11$

27. $(3 + 5) + 2 \equiv \text{mod } 7$

28. $(4 + 4) + 4 \equiv \text{mod } 6$

29. $2 + (3 + 5) \equiv \text{mod } 8$

30. $2 + (3 + 4) \equiv \text{mod } 5$

31. $4 \times (2 \times 3) \equiv \text{mod } 6$

32. $(2 \times 2) \times 2 \equiv \text{mod } 3$

33. $7 \times (3 \times 5) \equiv \text{mod } 9$

34. $(2 \times 6) + 4 \equiv \text{mod } 7$

35. $6 \times (2 - 5) \equiv \text{mod } 8$

36. $5 \times (8 + 3) \equiv \text{mod } 9$

37. $7 \times (3 - 5) \equiv \text{mod } 10$

38. $4 \times (1 - 7) \equiv \text{mod } 8$

39. $2 - (3 - 5) \equiv \text{mod } 6$

40. $3 - (1 - 4) \equiv \text{mod } 5$

41. $(4 - 7) - 3 \equiv \text{mod } 9$

42. $(2 - 10) - 1 \equiv \text{mod } 11$

43. $8 - (2 - 5) \equiv \text{mod } 12$

44. $(1 - 1) - 1 \equiv \text{mod } 2$

For Exercises 45–54, find all natural number solutions for each congruence.

45. $3 + y \equiv 1 \text{ mod } 6$

46. $y + 3 \equiv 2 \text{ mod } 4$

47. $1 - y \equiv 6 \text{ mod } 8$

48. $3 - y \equiv 5 \text{ mod } 9$

49. $7 \times y \equiv 6 \text{ mod } 8$

50. $9 + y \equiv 8 \text{ mod } 10$

51. $y + 4 \equiv 1 \text{ mod } 5$

52. $y - (-1) \equiv 7 \text{ mod } 8$

53. $4 \times y \equiv 6 \text{ mod } 7$

54. $1 \times y \equiv 6 \text{ mod } 7$

Real-World Applications

The days of the week can be thought of as a modular system using 0 = Sunday, 1 = Monday, 2 = Tuesday, etc. Using this system, find the answer to each and give it as the day of the week.

55. Sunday + 30 days

56. Monday + 5 days

57. Tuesday + 45 days

58. Friday + 120 days

59. Saturday + 360 days

60. Wednesday + 20 days

For Exercises 61–64, decide if the given nine-digit number is a legitimate bank routing number. (See Sidelight on page 736.)

61. 274070413

62. 741302058

63. 513939274

64. 042000314

65. Jamaal has 34 boxes of soda with 111 cans each, and he wants to break them up into 12-packs to sell. How many will be left over when he makes the 12-packs? Use modular multiplication with modulus 12 to find your answer.

66. Lenore has 44 boxes containing 89 eggs, each delivered fresh from the farm, and she wants to break them up into 6-egg cartons to sell. How many will be left over when she makes the 6-egg cartons? Use modular multiplication with modulus 6 to find your answer.

67. Business days are generally considered to be Monday through Friday of any given week, and can be thought of as the modular system 0 = Monday, 1 = Tuesday, 2 = Wednesday, 3 = Thursday, 4 = Friday. If a transaction will take 32 business days and starts on a Wednesday, on what day will the transaction be completed?

68. It is currently 11 A.M. and the concert you've been waiting to see is just 83 hours from now. At what time does the concert start?

69. Janice has been 21 for exactly 430 hours. If she turned 21 at midnight on April 5, what is today's date, and what time is it?

70. This coming Friday, Macy's will be holding a 100-hour sale that starts at 6 A.M. On what day and time will the sale end?

71. Sven is sailing west when a storm hits and his boat is rotated 1,890 degrees counterclockwise. In which direction does he face after the rotation? (Recall that 360 degrees is one full rotation.)

72. On a game board, there is a spinner that has spaces marked with the numbers 0 through 8 in order. The pointer is on the 3 and Shira spins it so that it moves 60 spaces and lands exactly on a number. What number does the spinner land on?

73. A truck delivers 50 laptops to be set up at a job fair for the employers to use. Each table can accommodate three employers with laptops. How many tables are needed and how many empty spaces will there be?

74. A shipment of 1,345 textbooks of the same size were delivered and a shelf can only hold 60 books. How many books will be on the shelf that is not fully stacked?

75. A machine that dispenses lemonade can hold up to 1,200 fluid ounces. Each cup that the campus café uses can hold 14 fluid ounces of lemonade. How many fluid ounces of lemonade will the last customer get?

76. A fortune teller told Mary that she would be married in 59 months, and she visited the fortune teller in March of 2009. For what month and year should she book a reception hall?

Critical Thinking

77. Look back at the mathematical system of possible turns at an intersection on page 718. Can you turn the system into a modular system by assigning numbers to the turns? Explain why you can or cannot.

78. Consider the congruence $x^2 \equiv 4 \text{ mod } 5$.

    (a) Check that $x = 2$ and $x = -2$ are solutions.

    (b) Find the next number greater than 2 that is congruent to 4 mod 5 and find two more natural number solutions.

    (c) Make a conjecture about how many other integer solutions there are, and find the next two pairs of solutions.

79. Fighting a nasty upper respiratory infection, you are supposed to take an antibiotic capsule four times a day until the bottle is empty, starting on Wednesday morning. As you might expect, the doctor prescribed a number of pills that is a multiple of 4. The following Monday afternoon, you can't remember if you took your second dose or not. You empty the bottle and find the number of pills is congruent to 3 modulo 4. Did you remember your pill?

Section	Important Terms	Important Ideas
13-1	Mathematical system Infinite system Finite system Operation table Closed system Identity element Inverse element Group Abelian group	**A mathematical system** consists of a nonempty set of elements and at least one operaton. A finite mathematical system has a specific number of elements, whereas an infinite mathematical system has an unlimited number of elements. A mathematical system is called a group if it is closed under the operation, has an identity element, satisfies the associative property for the operation, and every element has an inverse. If the operation is commutative, then the group is called an Abelian group. It is possible to create mathematical systems using elements other than numbers. Some of these systems are shown in this section.
13-2	Clock arithmetic	**We can define** a finite mathematical system with 12 elements using the numbers on a 12-hour clock, and defining addition to correspond to adding times on the clock. For example, $11 + 3 = 2$ on a 12-hour clock. We can then define multiplication and subtraction on the 12-hour clock. The 12-hour clock system using addition is an Abelian group, but the system with multiplication is not a group. We can also define similar systems using clocks with numbers of hours other than 12.
13-3	Modular system Modulus Congruent modulo m	**A modular system** with modulus m is a system consisting of m numbers in which arithmetic is defined analogously to the clock arithmetic studied in Section 13-2. In any modular system, we can find a number congruent to any other integer with the given modulus. For example, 5 is congruent to 2 modulo 3 because starting at zero and counting 5 units on a 3-hour clock will result in an ending position of 2. Congruence statements containing variables can be solved in a manner similar to solving equations in the real number system.

MATH IN ▶ Encryption REVISITED

1. The tricky part is that "undoing" congruence produces many possible answers. For example, the first number in the string (27) is a congruence modulo 32. It could be 27, 59, 91, 123, etc. The key is that the original numbers were all between 1 and 27, so when 50 was added, they ended up between 51 and 77. Of all the numbers congruent to 27 modulo 32, only one of them, 59, is between 51 and 77. Using this idea, the other numbers can be translated to the string

59 54 55 64 70 59 70 75 77 70 58
55 56 70 77 69 70 59 64 61 69

It's then easy to subtract 50 from each number and translate back into letters, giving us the message "Identity theft stinks."

2. Our friend is going to have some explaining to do. When you drop the last digit, the resulting number is 041103941; divide by 29 and subtract off the part to the left of the decimal place. The result is 0.2758621. Multiply by 29 to convert to the remainder: with a slight rounding error, the result is 8, which should be the check digit of the license number. Uh oh!

Review Exercises

Section 13-1

For Exercises 1–11, use the elements A, B, C and operation @ defined by

@	A	B	C
A	C	A	B
B	A	B	C
C	B	C	A

1. $C@B =$
2. $A@C =$
3. $B@B =$
4. $A@(B@C) =$
5. $(C@B)@B =$
6. $B@(C@C) =$
7. Is the system closed under operation @?
8. Is the system commutative?
9. Is the system associative?
10. Is there an identity element? If so what is it?
11. Does the system have the inverse property? If so, name the inverses of A, B, and C.

*For Exercises 12–16, use the elements %, *, &, and # and the operation / defined by*

/	%	*	&	#
%	&	*	%	%
*	%	*	&	#
&	#	&	*	%
#	*	#	#	&

12. Is the system closed under operation /?
13. Is the system commutative?
14. Is the system associative?
15. Is there an identity element? If so what is it?
16. Does every element have an inverse? If so what are the inverses?

For Exercises 17–20, determine if the given system forms (a) a group and (b) an Abelian group.

17. Integers under addition.
18. Rational numbers under multiplication.
19. $\{\frac{1}{2}, 2\}$ under multiplication.
20. $\{-1, 0, 1\}$ under multiplication.

Section 13-2

For Exercises 21–26, perform the indicated operation in the 12-hour clock system.

21. $4 + 11$
22. $4 - 11$
23. 3×8
24. 2×6
25. $5(8 + 10)$
26. $3(2 - 5)$

For Exercises 27–32, perform the indicated operation on the specified clock.

27. $3 - 6$; 5-hour clock

28. $8 + 10$; 11-hour clock
29. 3×7; 15-hour clock
30. $12 + 3$; 10-hour clock
31. $19 - 26$; 24-hour clock
32. $12 + 15$; 16-hour clock
33. At Miami University, final exam week for Monday through Friday classes begins at 8:00 A.M. the Monday after classes end, and lasts for 103 hours. When does the last exam end?
34. The U.S. military uses a 24-hour clock; the period from midnight to noon is 0000 to 1200, and the period from noon to 1 minute before midnight is 1200 to 2359, where the first two digits are the hour and the second two are the minutes. If a military exercise begins at 0720 and lasts for 21 hours, when does it end? If a flight is scheduled to leave Guantanamo Bay, Cuba at 2320 and land in Washington, D.C., at 0240, how long does it last?

Section 13-3

For Exercises 35–54, find the equivalent number for the given modular system.

35. $67 \equiv$ mod 5
36. $41 \equiv$ mod 3
37. $532 \equiv$ mod 8
38. $861 \equiv$ mod 6
39. $22 \equiv$ mod 4
40. $10 \equiv$ mod 2
41. $37 \equiv$ mod 10
42. $999 \equiv$ mod 7
43. $56 \equiv$ mod 9
44. $80 \equiv$ mod 5
45. $173 \equiv$ mod 9
46. $45 \equiv$ mod 7
47. $250 \equiv$ mod 10
48. $64 \equiv$ mod 3
49. $18 \equiv$ mod 3
50. $1,235 \equiv$ mod 6
51. $4,721 \equiv$ mod 8
52. $856 \equiv$ mod 11
53. $1,000 \equiv$ mod 12
54. $25 \equiv$ mod 4

For Exercises 55–74, perform the indicated operation for the given modular system.

55. $5 + 9 \equiv$ mod 11
56. $2 - 10 \equiv$ mod 12
57. $6 \times 6 \equiv$ mod 7
58. $7 + 8 \equiv$ mod 9
59. $3 - 7 \equiv$ mod 8
60. $4 \times 5 \equiv$ mod 6
61. $3 + 2 \equiv$ mod 4
62. $5 - 12 \equiv$ mod 13
63. $6 \times 7 \equiv$ mod 10
64. $10 \times 10 \equiv$ mod 12
65. $3 - 4 \equiv$ mod 5
66. $5 \times 5 \equiv$ mod 6
67. $5 \times (3 + 7) \equiv$ mod 8
68. $2 \times (2 + 9) \equiv$ mod 12
69. $3 - (3 - 5) \equiv$ mod 6
70. $(10 - 6) - 9 \equiv$ mod 11
71. $5 \times (7 - 9) \equiv$ mod 12
72. $8 + 8 + 8 \equiv$ mod 10
73. $4 \times 3 \times 5 \equiv$ mod 9
74. $3 \times (4 + 5) \equiv$ mod 7

For Exercises 75–84, find all natural number solutions.

75. $6 + y \equiv 2$ mod 8
76. $y + 7 \equiv 1$ mod 10
77. $y + 7 \equiv 1$ mod 9
78. $3 - y \equiv 6$ mod 8
79. $y - 2 \equiv 5$ mod 6
80. $3 \times y \equiv 6$ mod 8
81. $y + 2 \equiv 1$ mod 12
82. $5 - y \equiv 6$ mod 9
83. $3 \times 5 \equiv y$ mod 7
84. $5 \times (2 + y) \equiv 1$ mod 12

85. A bakery has 220 cookies left over from a street fair, and the owners decide to give them away in packs of six to customers until they run out. How many cookies will be in the last package?

86. The owner of an eBay store gets a great deal on 100 cans of tennis balls with three balls in each can, and plans to repackage them for resale, with five balls in each package. Will there be any tennis balls left over? If so, how many?

87. Suppose that one state uses a 10-digit driver's license number, but the 10th digit is a check digit. The number formed by the first nine digits should be congruent to the tenth digit modulo 23. A college student presents a license with the number 0245601183 on it to a bouncer. Is the number legitimate?

Chapter Test

For Exercises 1–8, use the system shown.

*	x	y	z
x	x	y	z
y	y	x	z
z	z	z	s

1. Find $x * z$.
2. Find $(y * x) * z$.
3. Find $z * z$.
4. Find $x * (z * y)$.
5. Find $(z * x) * x$.
6. What is the inverse of y?
7. Is the operation $*$ commutative?
8. Is the system closed?

For Exercises 9–24, use this system:

·	a	−1	−a	1
a	−1	−a	1	a
−1	−a	1	a	−1
−a	1	a	−1	−a
1	a	−1	−a	1

9. Find $a \cdot a$.
10. Find $-1 \cdot a$.
11. Find $a \cdot 1$.
12. Find $a \cdot (a \cdot a)$.
13. Find $(-a \cdot a) \cdot (-1)$.
14. Find $(1 \cdot 1) \cdot (-a)$.
15. Find $(-a)^3$.
16. Find the value of y when $a \cdot y = 1$.
17. Find the value of y when $a \cdot (y \cdot a) = 1$.
18. Is $(-a \cdot 1) \cdot a = -a \cdot (1 \cdot a)$?
19. Is $a^3 = a^7$?
20. Is the system closed under $\cdot$?
21. Is the system commutative?
22. What is the identity for the system?
23. What is the inverse of a?
24. What is the inverse of -1?

For Exercises 25–27, perform the indicated operation on the 12-hour clock.

25. $6 + 10$
26. 8×5
27. $7(4 - 12)$

For Exercises 28–30, perform the indicated operation on the given clock.

28. $2 + 5$ on a 4-hour clock
29. 8×9 on a 10-hour clock
30. $7(2 - 5)$ on an 8-hour clock

For Exercises 31–34, find the equivalent number for the given modular system.

31. $43 \equiv \text{mod } 6$
32. $518 \equiv \text{mod } 3$
33. $-6 \equiv \text{mod } 4$
34. $-15 \equiv \text{mod } 5$

For Exercises 35–40, perform the indicated operation for the given modular system.

35. $8 + 6 \equiv \text{mod } 10$
36. $3 + 7 \equiv \text{mod } 9$
37. $4 - 6 \equiv \text{mod } 7$
38. $8 - 10 \equiv \text{mod } 12$
39. $5 \times 9 \equiv \text{mod } 11$
40. $4 \times 7 \equiv \text{mod } 10$

For Exercises 41–44, find all natural number solutions for each congruence.

41. $2 + y \equiv 4 \text{ mod } 6$
42. $y + 8 \equiv 6 \text{ mod } 10$
43. $3 \times y \equiv 0 \text{ mod } 12$
44. $3 \times y \equiv 0 \text{ mod } 5$

45. In March 2009, Philips Electric announced a new LED light bulb that lasts for 46,000 hours of use. If that claim is exactly accurate, and you turn one on at noon and leave it on until it burns out, what time of day will that happen?

46. An entire baseball league is signed up for an out-of-town tournament. If there are eight teams with 16 players plus two coaches each, and the league rents buses that will hold 38 people, how many people will be on the bus that isn't full?

47. When a drill sergeant catches Private Pyle sending text messages to his girlfriend during a training exercise, he decides that it would be a good idea for the private to spend 30 straight hours peeling potatoes. If he starts peeling at 2 P.M., at what time can he stop?

48. According to the information in the sidelight on page 736, is 121144612 a legitimate bank routing number?

Projects

1. In the Sidelight on page 736, we learned about a formula that is used to find the check digit for bank routing numbers. Two very common coding systems that also use check digits are UPC numbers on the products we buy and the ISBN number that identifies all books published. (ISBNs can be found on the publisher information page at the beginning of books.) Use the Internet as a resource to find the formulas that are used for the check digits in both UPC and ISBN numbers. Write a brief paper on your findings, then write down the UPC from five products you have in your house/apartment/dorm room and use the formula to verify the check digit. Then do the same for the ISBN on all of the textbooks you currently own or use.

2. A mathematical system can be defined using geometry by rotating a five-pointed star about its center point (as in Figure 13-7). A clockwise rotation of 72° will move one of the points labeled with letters to the next one. We will define an operation on the symbols *A*, *B*, *C*, *D* and *E* using the symbol Ⓡ as follows: to find *B* Ⓡ *C*, start at position *B*, then rotate the number of degrees that correspond to position *C*. In Figure 13-7, we see that this is 144°. The rotation will move *B* two positions, to position *D*, so *B* Ⓡ *C* = *D*. To find *C* Ⓡ *E*, start at position *C* and rotate the star 288°, which is the rotation corresponding to position *E*. This moves *C* four spots to position *B*, so *C* Ⓡ *E* = *B*.

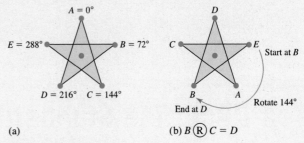

(a) (b) *B* Ⓡ *C* = *D*

Figure 13-7

Answer these questions:
(a) Perform each operation.
  (i) *B* Ⓡ *B*
  (ii) *C* Ⓡ *A*
  (iii) *D* Ⓡ *E*
  (iv) *E* Ⓡ *C*
  (v) *A* Ⓡ *B*
  (vi) *C* Ⓡ *B*
(b) Construct a table for the operation.
(c) Is the system commutative?
(d) Is there an identity? If so, what is it?
(e) What is the inverse of *B*?
(f) What is the inverse of *C*?
(g) Is the system closed?
(h) The modular system with modulus 5 has the same number of symbols as this system. Are the two systems really the same system with different labeling? Explain.

APPENDIX A

Area Under the Standard Normal Distribution

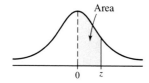

The area in the A column is the area under the normal distribution between $z = 0$ and the positive value of z found in the z column.

z	A	z	A	z	A	z	A	z	A	z	A	z	A
.00	.000	.25	.099	.50	.192	.75	.273	1.00	.341	1.25	.394	1.50	.433
.01	.004	.26	.103	.51	.195	.76	.276	1.01	.344	1.26	.396	1.51	.435
.02	.008	.27	.106	.52	.199	.77	.279	1.02	.346	1.27	.398	1.52	.436
.03	.012	.28	.110	.53	.202	.78	.282	1.03	.349	1.28	.400	1.53	.437
.04	.016	.29	.114	.54	.205	.79	.285	1.04	.351	1.29	.402	1.54	.438
.05	.020	.30	.118	.55	.209	.80	.288	1.05	.353	1.30	.403	1.55	.439
.06	.024	.31	.122	.56	.212	.81	.291	1.06	.355	1.31	.405	1.56	.441
.07	.028	.32	.126	.57	.216	.82	.294	1.07	.358	1.32	.407	1.57	.442
.08	.032	.33	.129	.58	.219	.83	.297	1.08	.360	1.33	.408	1.58	.443
.09	.036	.34	.133	.59	.222	.84	.300	1.09	.362	1.34	.410	1.59	.444
.10	.040	.35	.137	.60	.226	.85	.302	1.10	.364	1.35	.412	1.60	.445
.11	.044	.36	.141	.61	.229	.86	.305	1.11	.367	1.36	.413	1.61	.446
.12	.048	.37	.144	.62	.232	.87	.308	1.12	.369	1.37	.415	1.62	.447
.13	.052	.38	.148	.63	.236	.88	.311	1.13	.371	1.38	.416	1.63	.449
.14	.056	.39	.152	.64	.239	.89	.313	1.14	.373	1.39	.418	1.64	.450
.15	.060	.40	.155	.65	.242	.90	.316	1.15	.375	1.40	.419	1.65	.451
.16	.064	.41	.159	.66	.245	.91	.319	1.16	.377	1.41	.421	1.66	.452
.17	.068	.42	.163	.67	.249	.92	.321	1.17	.379	1.42	.422	1.67	.453
.18	.071	.43	.166	.68	.252	.93	.324	1.18	.381	1.43	.424	1.68	.454
.19	.075	.44	.170	.69	.255	.94	.326	1.19	.383	1.44	.425	1.69	.455
.20	.079	.45	.174	.70	.258	.95	.329	1.20	.385	1.45	.427	1.70	.455
.21	.083	.46	.177	.71	.261	.96	.332	1.21	.387	1.46	.428	1.71	.456
.22	.087	.47	.181	.72	.264	.97	.334	1.22	.389	1.47	.429	1.72	.457
.23	.091	.48	.184	.73	.267	.98	.337	1.23	.391	1.48	.431	1.73	.458
.24	.095	.49	.188	.74	.270	.99	.339	1.24	.393	1.49	.432	1.74	.459

Continued

z	A	z	A	z	A	z	A	z	A	z	A	z	A
1.75	.460	1.97	.476	2.19	.486	2.41	.492	2.63	.496	2.85	.498	3.07	.499
1.76	.461	1.98	.476	2.20	.486	2.42	.492	2.64	.496	2.86	.498	3.08	.499
1.77	.462	1.99	.477	2.21	.487	2.43	.493	2.65	.496	2.87	.498	3.09	.499
1.78	.463	2.00	.477	2.22	.487	2.44	.493	2.66	.496	2.88	.498	3.10	.499
1.79	.463	2.01	.478	2.23	.487	2.45	.493	2.67	.496	2.89	.498	3.11	.499
1.80	.464	2.02	.478	2.24	.488	2.46	.493	2.68	.496	2.90	.498	3.12	.499
1.81	.465	2.03	.479	2.25	.488	2.47	.493	2.69	.496	2.91	.498	3.13	.499
1.82	.466	2.04	.479	2.26	.488	2.48	.493	2.70	.497	2.92	.498	3.14	.499
1.83	.466	2.05	.480	2.27	.488	2.49	.494	2.71	.497	2.93	.498	3.15	.499
1.84	.467	2.06	.480	2.28	.489	2.50	.494	2.72	.497	2.94	.498	3.16	.499
1.85	.468	2.07	.481	2.29	.489	2.51	.494	2.73	.497	2.95	.498	3.17	.499
1.86	.469	2.08	.481	2.30	.489	2.52	.494	2.74	.497	2.96	.499	3.18	.499
1.87	.469	2.09	.482	2.31	.490	2.53	.494	2.75	.497	2.97	.499	3.19	.499
1.88	.470	2.10	.482	2.32	.490	2.54	.495	2.76	.497	2.98	.499	3.20	.499
1.89	.471	2.11	.483	2.33	.490	2.55	.495	2.77	.497	2.99	.499	3.21	.499
1.90	.471	2.12	.483	2.34	.490	2.56	.495	2.78	.497	3.00	.499	3.22	.499
1.91	.472	2.13	.483	2.35	.491	2.57	.495	2.79	.497	3.01	.499	3.23	.499
1.92	.473	2.14	.484	2.36	.491	2.58	.495	2.80	.497	3.02	.499	3.24	.499
1.93	.473	2.15	.484	2.37	.491	2.59	.495	2.81	.498	3.03	.499	3.25	.499
1.94	.474	2.16	.485	2.38	.491	2.60	.495	2.82	.498	3.04	.499		*
1.95	.474	2.17	.485	2.39	.492	2.61	.496	2.83	.498	3.05	.499		
1.96	.475	2.18	.485	2.40	.492	2.62	.496	2.84	.498	3.06	.499		

*For z values beyond 3.25 use $A = 0.500$.

SELECTED ANSWERS

CHAPTER 2: SETS

Exercise Set 2-1

7. $S = \{s, t, r, e\}$ **9.** $P = \{51, 52, 53, 54, 55, 56, 57, 58, 59\}$

11. $Q = \{1, 3, 5, 7, 9, 11, 13\}$ **13.** $G = \{11, 12, 13, \ldots\}$

15. $Y = \{2{,}001, 2{,}002, 2{,}003, \ldots, 2{,}999\}$

17. $W = \{$Sunday, Monday, Tuesday, Wednesday, Thursday, Friday, Saturday$\}$

19. $D = \{$hearts, diamonds, spades, clubs$\}$

21. The set of even natural numbers

23. The set of the first four multiples of 9

25. The set of letters in Mary

27. The set of natural numbers from 100 to 199

29. $\{x \mid x$ is a multiple of $10\}$ **31.** $X = \{x \mid x \in N$ and $x > 20\}$

33. $\{x \mid x$ is an odd natural number less than $10\}$

35. There are no natural numbers less than zero so $H = \varnothing$.

37. $\{7, 14, 21, 28, 35, 42, 49, 56, 63\}$

39. $\{102, 104, 106, 108, 110, 112, 114, 116, 118\}$

41. Well-defined   **43.** Not well-defined   **45.** Well-defined

47. Not well-defined   **49.** True   **51.** True   **53.** True

55. Infinite   **57.** Finite   **59.** Infinite   **61.** Finite

63. Equal and equivalent   **65.** Neither   **67.** Equivalent   **69.** Neither

71. $\{10, 20, 30, 40\}$ **73.** $\{1, 2, 3, \ldots, 25, 26\}$
$\updownarrow \ \updownarrow \ \updownarrow \ \updownarrow$ $\updownarrow \ \updownarrow \ \updownarrow \quad \updownarrow \ \updownarrow$
$\{40, 10, 20, 30\}$ $\{a, b, c, \ldots, y, \ z\}$

75. $n(A) = 5$ **77.** $n(C) = 7$ **79.** $n(E) = 1$ **81.** $n(G) = 0$ **83.** True

85. True   **87.** False   **89.** False

91. (a) $\{$California, New York, Florida$\}$
(b) $\{$Virginia, Massachusetts, Georgia, Maryland$\}$
(c) $\{$California, New York, Florida, Texas, New Jersey$\}$
(d) $\{$Texas, New Jersey, Illinois$\}$

93. (a) $\{$Drunk driving, Injury, Assault$\}$
(b) $\{$Injury, Health problems, Unsafe sex$\}$
(c) $\{$Injury, Assault, Drunk driving$\}$
(d) $\{97{,}000, 1{,}700, 150{,}000\}$
(e) Answers vary

95. (a) $\{$Employment fraud, Bank fraud$\}$
(b) $\{18$–$29, 30$–$39, 40$–$49\}$
(c) $\{$Utilities/phone fraud, Credit card fraud, Other$\}$
(d) $\{20, 13, 9\}$
(e) $\{$Employment fraud, Bank fraud, Utilities/phone fraud$\}$

97. (a) $\{2000, 2001, 2002\}$
(b) $\{2002, 2003, 2004, 2005\}$
(c) $\{2002, 2003, 2004, 2005, 2006\}$
(d) $\{2004, 2005, 2006\}$

99. Yes   **101.** Answers vary   **103.** Answers vary

Exercise Set 2-2

11. $A' = \{2, 3, 17, 19\}$ **13.** $C' = \{2, 3, 5, 7, 11\}$

15. $\varnothing; \{r\}; \{s\}; \{t\}; \{r, s\}; \{r, t\}; \{s, t\}; \{r, s, t\}$

17. $\varnothing; \{1\}; \{3\}; \{1, 3\}$ **19.** $\{\ \}$ or $\varnothing$

21. $\varnothing; \{5\}; \{12\}; \{13\}; \{14\}; \{5, 12\}; \{5, 13\}; \{5, 14\}; \{12, 13\};$
$\{12, 14\}; \{13, 14\}; \{5, 12, 13\}; \{5, 12, 14\}; \{5, 13, 14\}; \{12, 13, 14\};$
$\{5, 12, 13, 14\}$

23. $\varnothing; \{1\}; \{10\}; \{20\}; \{1, 10\}; \{1, 20\}; \{10, 20\}$ **25.** $\varnothing$ **27.** None

29. True   **31.** False   **33.** False   **35.** False   **37.** True

39. 8 subsets, 7 proper subsets   **41.** 1 subset, no proper subsets

43. 4 subsets, 3 proper subsets   **45.** $U = \{1, 2, 3, 4, 5, 6, 7, 8, 9\}$

47. $B = \{5, 6, 7, 8, 9\}$ **49.** $A \cup B = \{2, 3, 5, 6, 7, 8, 9\}$

51. $B' = \{1, 2, 3, 4\}$ **53.** $(A \cap B)' = \{1, 2, 3, 4, 6, 7, 8\}$

55. $A \cup C = \{10, 30, 40, 50, 60, 70, 90\}$

57. $A' = \{20, 40, 60, 80, 100\}$ **59.** $A' \cap (B \cup C) = \{20, 40, 60, 80, 100\}$

61. $(A \cup B)' \cap C = \varnothing$ **63.** $(B \cup C) \cap A' = \{20, 40, 60, 80, 100\}$

65. $P \cap Q = \{b, d\}$ **67.** $P' = \{a, c, e, h\}$ **69.** $R' \cap P' = \{a, c, h\}$

71. $(Q \cup P)' \cap R = \{e\}$ **73.** $(P \cup Q) \cap (P \cup R) = \{b, d, f, g\}$

75. $W \cap Y = \{2, 4, 6\}$ **77.** $W \cup X = $ the universal set

79. $W \cap X = \varnothing$ **81.** $(X \cup Y) \cap Z = \{2, 5, 6, 11\}$ **83.** $W' \cap X' = \varnothing$

85. $A \cap B = B$

87. $A \cap (B \cup C') = \{x \mid x$ is an odd multiple of 3 or an even multiple of 9$\}$
$= \{3, 9, 15, 18, 21, 27, 33, 36, 39, \ldots\}$

89. $A - B = \{20, 110\}$ **91.** $B - C = \{60\}$ **93.** $C \cap B' = \{110\}$

95. $C - B = \{p\}$ **97.** $B - C = \{s, u\}$ **99.** $B \cap C' = \{s, u\}$

101. $A \times B = \{(9, 1), (9, 2), (9, 3), (12, 1), (12, 2), (12, 3), (18, 1), (18, 2), (18, 3)\}$

103. $A \times A = \{(9, 9), (9, 12), (9, 18), (12, 9), (12, 12), (12, 18), (18, 9), (18, 12), (18, 18)\}$

105. $A \times B = \{(1, 1), (1, 3), (2, 1), (2, 3), (4, 1), (4, 3), (8, 1), (8, 3)\}$

107. $B \times B = \{(1, 1), (1, 3), (3, 1), (3, 3)\}$

109. $\{$cell phone, laptop, iPod$\}, \{$cell phone, laptop$\}, \{$cell phone, iPod$\}$, $\{$laptop, iPod$\}, \{$cell phone$\}, \{$laptop$\}, \{$iPod$\}, \varnothing$

111. $2^7 = 128$ **113.** $2^4 = 16$ **115.** Answers vary

117. Answers vary

Exercise Set 2-3

5.

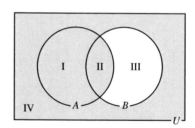

7.

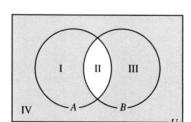

9.

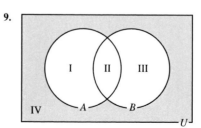

11.

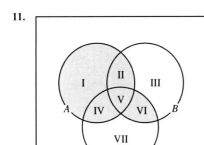

13.

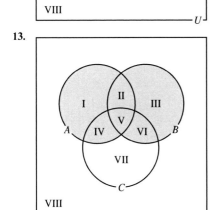

15.

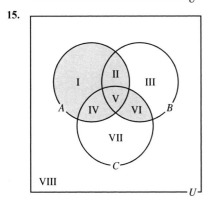

17.

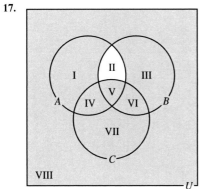

19.

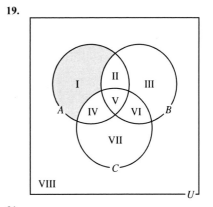

21.

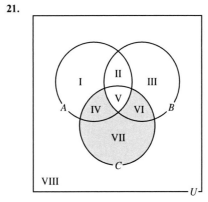

23.

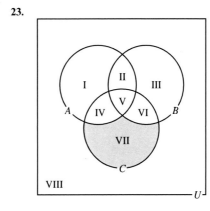

25.

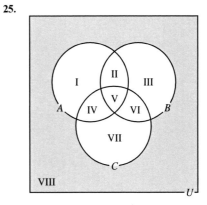

27.

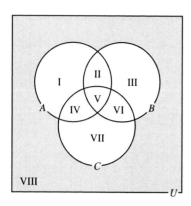

29. equal **31.** equal **33.** not equal **35.** not equal **37.** $n(A) = 6$
39. $n(A \cap B) = 2$ **41.** $n(A') = 6$ **43.** $n(A' \cap B') = 3$
45. $n(A - B) = 4$ **47.** $n(A) = 6$ **49.** $n(A \cap B) = 4$
51. $n(A \cap B') = 2$ **53.** $n(A') = 6$ **55.** $n(A - B) = 2$
57. People who drive an SUV or a hybrid vehicle

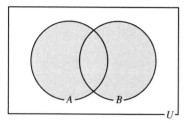

59. People who do not drive an SUV

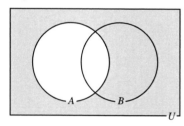

61. Students in online courses and blended or traditional courses

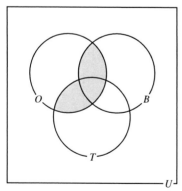

63. Students who are in blended, online, and traditional courses

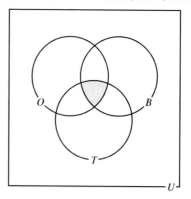

65. Students not voting democrat or voting republican

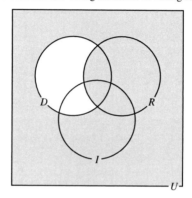

67. Students voting democrat or republican but not independent

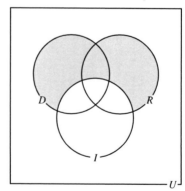

69. People who regularly use Google but not Yahoo!

71. People who do not regularly use Google, Yahoo!, or MSN Live

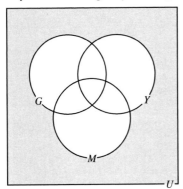

73. Region IV   **75.** Region VII   **77.** Region V   **79.** No; Answers vary

Exercise Set 2-4

  1. (a) 13   (b) 18   (c) 2
  3. (a) 8   (b) 5   (c) 0
  5. (a) 2   (b) 9   (c) 35
  7. (a) 16   (b) 7   (c) 14   (d) 3
  9. (a) 67   (b) 2   (c) 37
11. (a) 22   (b) 3   (c) 15
13. (a) 32   (b) 37   (c) 58
15. 6   **17.** The total of the eight regions is 39 but the researcher surveyed 40 people.

Exercise Set 2-5

  5. $7n$ **7.** 4^n **9.** $-3n$ **11.** $\dfrac{1}{n+1}$ **13.** $4n-2$ **15.** $\dfrac{n+1}{n+2}$
17. $100n$ **19.** $-3n-1$

For 21 through 30 we will show each set is infinite by putting it into a one-to-one correspondence with a proper subset of itself.

21. $\{3,\ 6,\ 9,\ 12,\ 15,\ \dots,\ 3n,\ \dots\}$
$\quad\quad\updownarrow\ \ \updownarrow\ \ \updownarrow\ \ \updownarrow\ \ \updownarrow\quad\quad\quad\updownarrow$
$\quad\{6,\ 12,\ 18,\ 24,\ 30,\ \dots,\ 6n,\ \dots\}$
23. $\{9,\ 18,\ 27,\ 36,\ 45,\ \dots,\ 9n,\ \dots\}$
$\quad\quad\updownarrow\ \ \updownarrow\ \ \updownarrow\ \ \updownarrow\ \ \updownarrow\quad\quad\quad\updownarrow$
$\quad\{18,\ 36,\ 54,\ 72,\ 90,\ \dots,\ 18n,\ \dots\}$
25. $\{2,\ 5,\ 8,\ 11,\ \dots,\ 3n-1,\ \dots\}$
$\quad\quad\updownarrow\ \ \updownarrow\ \ \updownarrow\ \ \updownarrow\quad\quad\quad\updownarrow$
$\quad\{5,\ 11,\ 17,\ 23,\ \dots,\ 6n-1,\ \dots\}$
27. $\{10,\ \ 100,\ \dots,\ \ 10^n,\ \dots\}$
$\quad\quad\updownarrow\quad\ \updownarrow\quad\quad\ \updownarrow$
$\quad\{100,\ 10{,}000,\ \dots,\ 10^{2n},\ \dots\}$
29. $\left\{\dfrac{5}{1},\dfrac{5}{2},\dfrac{5}{3},\ \dots,\ \dfrac{5}{n},\ \dots\right\}$
$\quad\quad\updownarrow\ \updownarrow\ \updownarrow\quad\quad\ \updownarrow$
$\quad\left\{\dfrac{5}{2},\dfrac{5}{3},\dfrac{5}{4},\ \dots,\ \dfrac{5}{n+1},\ \dots\right\}$
31. $\aleph_0+1=\aleph_0$ and $\aleph_0+\aleph_0=\aleph_0$
33. The rational numbers can be put into a one-to-one correspondence with the natural numbers.

Review Exercises

  1. $D=\{52,54,56,58\}$ **3.** $L=\{l,e,t,r\}$
  5. $B=\{501,502,503,\dots\}$ **7.** $M=\varnothing$
  9. $\{x\,|\,x$ is even and $16<x<26\}$
11. $\{x\,|\,x$ is an odd natural number greater than $100\}$
13. Infinite   **15.** Finite   **17.** Finite   **19.** False   **21.** False
23. $\varnothing; \{r\}; \{s\}; \{t\}; \{r,s\}; \{r,t\}; \{s,t\}; \{r,s,t\}$
25. $2^5=32$ subsets; 31 proper subsets
27. $A\cap B=\{t,u,v\}$ **29.** $(A\cap B)\cap C=\varnothing$ **31.** $A-B=\{p,r\}$
33. $(A\cup B)'\cap C=\{s,w,z\}$ **35.** $(B\cup C)\cap A'=\{s,w,x,y,z\}$
37. $(B'\cap C')\cup A'=\{p,q,r,s,w,x,y,z\}$
39. $M\times N=\{(s,v),(s,w),(s,x),(t,v),(t,w),(t,x),(u,v),(u,w),(u,x)\}$
41. $M\times M=\{(s,s),(s,t),(s,u),(t,s),(t,t),(t,u),(u,s),(u,t),(u,u)\}$
43. $A-B$ **45.** $B-A$ **47.** $(A\cup B)-(A\cap B)$

49.

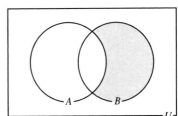

51.

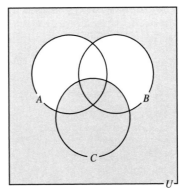

53. 20   **55.** Region V   **57.** Region II   **59.** (a) 12   (b) 3
61. (a) 3   (b) 5   (c) 6   **63.** $-3-2n$

Chapter 2 Test

  1. $P=\{92,94,96,98\}$ **3.** $K=\{e,n,v,l,o,p\}$
  5. $X=\{1,2,3,4,\dots,79\}$ **7.** $J=\{\text{January, June, July}\}$
  9. $\{x\,|\,x\in E$ and $10<x<20\}$
11. $\{x\,|\,x$ is an odd natural number greater than $200\}$
13. Infinite   **15.** Finite   **17.** Finite
19. $\varnothing; \{p\}; \{q\}; \{r\}; \{p,q\}; \{p,r\}; \{q,r\}; \{p,q,r\}$
21. $A\cap B=\{a\}$ **23.** $B'=\{b,c,d,e,f,h\}$
25. $(A\cap B)'\cup C'=\{a,b,c,d,e,f,g,h,i,j,k\}$
27. $B-C=\{a,g,i,k\}$ **29.** $A-C=\{a,b,d,f\}$
31. $A\times B=\{(@,\pi),(@,\#),(!,\pi),(!,\#),(\alpha,\pi),(\alpha,\#)\}$
33. $B\times B=\{(\pi,\pi),(\pi,\#),(\#,\pi),(\#,\#)\}$
35.

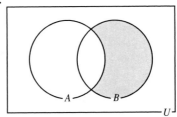

37.

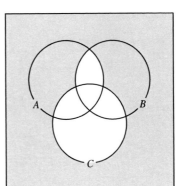

39. (a) 11   (b) 4
41. $\{1,\ -1,\ 2,\ -2,\ 3,\ -3,\ \dots,\ n,\ \ -n,\ \dots\}$
$\quad\ \updownarrow\ \ \updownarrow\ \updownarrow\ \ \updownarrow\ \updownarrow\ \ \updownarrow\quad\quad\updownarrow\quad\ \ \updownarrow$
$\quad\{1,\ \ 2,3,\ \ 4,5,\ \ 6,\ \dots,\ 2n-1,2n,\ \dots\}$
43. True   **45.** True   **47.** True   **49.** False   **51.** False   **53.** True

CHAPTER 3: LOGIC

Exercise Set 3-1

5. Not a statement **7.** Statement **9.** Not a statement
11. Not a statement **13.** Not a statement **15.** Compound statement
17. Compound statement **19.** Simple statement
21. Compound statement **23.** Simple statement **25.** Conjunction
27. Biconditional **29.** Disjunction **31.** Biconditional
33. The sky is not blue. **35.** The dorm room is large.
37. You will fail this class. **39.** Universal **41.** Existential
43. Universal **45.** Existential **47.** Universal **49.** Existential
51. Not all fish swim in water; Some fish do not swim in water.
53. No people who live in glass houses throw stones.
55. Not every happy dog wags its tail; Some happy dog does not wag its tail. **57.** There is no four-leaf clover.
59. Someone with green eyes wears glasses.
61. None of my friends have an iPhone.
63. $p \wedge q$ **65.** $\sim q \rightarrow p$ **67.** $\sim q$ **69.** $q \vee \sim p$ **71.** $q \leftrightarrow p$
73. $\sim q$ **75.** $q \rightarrow p$ **77.** $\sim q \vee p$ **79.** $q \leftrightarrow p$ **81.** $\sim q \rightarrow p$
83. The plane is on time and the sky is clear.
85. If the sky is clear, then the plane is on time.
87. The plane is not on time and the sky is not clear.
89. The plane is on time or the sky is not clear.
91. If the sky is clear, then the plane is or is not on time.
93. Trudy does not live off campus.
95. Mark lives on campus or Trudy does not live off campus.
97. If Mark does not live on campus, then Trudy does not live off campus. **99.** Mark lives on campus or Trudy lives off campus.
101. Trudy lives off campus or Mark lives on campus.
103. It cannot be classified as true or false.

Exercise Set 3-2

5. FFFT **7.** FFTF **9.** FTTF **11.** TTFF **13.** TFTT **15.** TTFF
17. TTFF **19.** TTFFTFFF **21.** TTTTTTTT **23.** TFFFTFTF
25. TTTFFFTF **27.** FTFTFTTT **29.** FFFTTTTT
31. FFFFTFFF **33.** TFTFFFFF **35.** False **37.** True **39.** True
41. Let p be "if you take their daily product," q be "you cut your calorie intake by 10%, and r be "you lose at least 10 pounds in the next 4 months." **43.** TFTTTTTT **45.** True
47. Let p be "the attendance for the following season is over 2 million," q be "he will add 20 million dollars to the payroll," and r be "the team will make the playoffs the following year." **49.** TFFFTTTT
51. True **53.** The statements are equivalent. **55.** False

Exercise Set 3-3

7. Tautology **9.** Self-contradiction **11.** Tautology **13.** Neither
15. Neither **17.** Equivalent **19.** Neither **21.** Neither
23. Negations **25.** Neither **27.** $q \rightarrow p$; $\sim p \rightarrow \sim q$; $\sim q \rightarrow \sim p$
29. $p \rightarrow \sim q$; $q \rightarrow \sim p$; $\sim p \rightarrow q$ **31.** $\sim q \rightarrow p$; $\sim p \rightarrow q$; $q \rightarrow \sim p$
33. The concert is not long and it is not fun.
35. It is cold or I am not soaked.
37. I will not go to the beach or I will get sunburned.
39. The student is not a girl and the professor is a man.
41. It is not right and it is not wrong. **43.** $p \rightarrow q$ **45.** $p \rightarrow q$
47. $p \rightarrow q$ **49.** $\sim p \rightarrow \sim q$
51. *Converse*: If he did get a good job, then he graduated with a Bachelor's degree in Management Information Systems.
Inverse: If he did not graduate with a Bachelor's degree in Management Information Systems, then he will not get a good job.
Contrapositive: If he did not get a good job, he did not graduate with a Bachelor's degree in Management Information Systems.

53. *Converse*: If I host a party in my dorm room, then the *American Idol* finale is today.
Inverse: If the *American Idol* finale is not today, then I will not host a party in my dorm room.
Contrapositive: If I do not host a party in my dorm room, then the *American Idol* finale is not today.
55. *Converse*: If I go to Nassau for spring break then I will lose 10 pounds by March 1.
Inverse: If I do not lose 10 pounds by March 1 then I will not go to Nassau for spring break.
Contrapositive: If I do not go to Nassau for spring break then I did not lose 10 pounds by March 1.
57. $\sim(p \rightarrow q) \equiv p \wedge \sim q$ **59.** Answers vary **61.** Equivalent

Exercise Set 3-4

7. Valid **9.** Invalid **11.** Invalid **13.** Valid **15.** Invalid
17. Valid **19.** Valid **21.** Invalid **23.** Valid **25.** Invalid
27. Valid **29.** Valid **31.** Invalid **33.** Invalid **35.** Invalid
37. Valid **39.** Invalid **41.** Invalid **43.** Invalid **45.** Valid
47. Invalid **49.** Valid **51.** Valid **53.** Answers vary
55. Answers vary

Exercise Set 3-5

5.

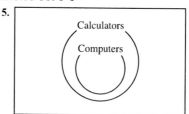

7.

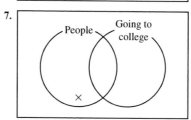

9.

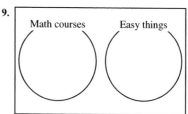

11.

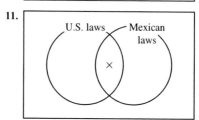

13.

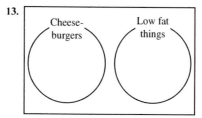

15. Invalid **17.** Valid **19.** Invalid **21.** Valid **23.** Invalid
25. Invalid **27.** Invalid **29.** Valid **31.** Invalid **33.** Invalid
35. Valid **37.** Invalid **39.** All *A* is *C*.
41. No calculators can make breakfast.

Review Exercises

1. Not a statement **3.** Not a statement **5.** Not a Statement
7. Simple **9.** Compound **11.** It is not scary.
13. The Popsicle is not green.
15. No failing students can learn new study methods.
17. All printers have ink.
19. None of the contestants will be voted off the island.
21. Conjunction **23.** Disjunction **25.** Conditional
27. $q \to p$ **29.** $q \land \sim p$ **31.** $\sim(q \land p)$ **33.** $\sim q \leftrightarrow \sim p$
35. $\sim p \land \sim q$ **37.** If it is cloudy, then it is cool.
39. If it is cool or cloudy, then it is cool. **41.** FTTF
43. FFFT **45.** FFFT **47.** TFTFFFTF **49.** False **51.** True
53. Tautology **55.** Neither **57.** Neither **59.** Not equivalent
61. The Internet connection is not dial-up and it's not DSL.
63. The signature is authentic or the check is valid.
65. Let *p* be the statement "I will be happy" and *q* be the statement "I get rich." The compound statement is $p \to q$.
67. *Converse:* If I start riding my bike to work, gas prices will go higher.
Inverse: If gas prices do not go any higher, I will not start riding my bike to work.
Contrapositive: If I do not start riding my bike to work, then gas prices will not go any higher.
69. *Converse:* If it rains, the festival will move inside the student center.
Inverse: If the festival did not move inside the student center, then it did not rain.
Contrapositive: If it does not rain, then the festival will not move inside the student center.
71. Invalid **73.** Invalid **75.** Invalid **77.** Invalid **79.** Invalid
81. Valid **83.** Invalid **85.** Invalid

Chapter 3 Test

1. Statement **3.** Not a statement
5. The image is not uploading to my online bio.
7. No students ride a bike to school. **9.** $p \land q$ **11.** $p \leftrightarrow q$
13. $\sim(\sim p \land q)$ **15.** It is sunny or not warm.
17. It is sunny if and only if it is warm.
19. It is not the case that it is not sunny or it is warm.
21. FFTFTFTF **23.** TTFF **25.** Self-contradiction
27. Neither **29.** Tautology **31.** Equivalent
33. It is cold or it is not snowing. **35.** Invalid **37.** Valid
39. Invalid **41.** Valid **43.** Invalid **45.** Valid

CHAPTER 4: NUMERATION SYSTEMS

Exercise Set 4-1

7. 35 **9.** 20,225 **11.** 30,163 **13.** 20,314 **15.** 1,112,010

17. |||||| **19.** ∩∩∩||||||

21. ⌒∩∩∩∩∩||||||||

23. ⌒⌒⌒⌒⌒⌒⌒⌒⌒|

25. ⌒⌒⌒∩∩∩|||||

27. ⌒∩||||||

29. ⌒⌒⌒⌒⌒⌒⌒⌒∩∩∩|||||

31. ⌒⌒⌒⌒⌒⌒⌒⌒⌒⌒⌒⌒⌒⌒⌒⌒⌒⌒⌒⌒⌒
∩∩∩∩∩∩∩∩||||||

33. 189 **35.** 52 **37.** 713

39. 八十九 **41.** 二百八十四 **43.** 二千三百五十六

45. hundreds **47.** ten thousands **49.** ones **51.** $8 \times 10^1 + 6$
53. $1 \times 10^3 + 8 \times 10^2 + 1 \times 10^1 + 2$ **55.** $6 \times 10^3 + 2$
57. $1 \times 10^5 + 6 \times 10^4 + 2 \times 10^3 + 8 \times 10^2 + 7 \times 10^1 + 3$
59. $1 \times 10^7 + 7 \times 10^6 + 5 \times 10^5 + 3 \times 10^4 + 1 \times 10^3 + 8 \times 10^2 + 1$
61. 12 **63.** 51 **65.** 40,871 **67.** 109,284 **69.** 792

71. ⧫⧫⧫⟨⟨ **73.** ⟨ ⟨⟨⟨⟨⟨⟨⟨⟨⟨

75. ⟨⟨⟨⟨ ⟨⟨⟨⟨⟨⟨⟨⟨ **77.** ⟨⟨⟨⟨⟨⟨⟨ ⟨⟨⟨

79. ⟨ ⟨⟨⟨⟨⟨⟨⟨⟨ ⟨⟨⟨⟨⟨⟨⟨⟨⟨⟨

81. 17 **83.** 43 **85.** 86 **87.** 418 **89.** 490 **91.** XXXIX
93. DLXVII **95.** MCCLVIII **97.** MCDLXII **99.** MMM
101. 1939 **103.** 1978 **105.** 2005 **107.** Answers vary
109. Because the Babylonian system is an ancient number system which is not in use today.

Exercise Set 4-2

3. 252 **5.** 391 **7.** 3,740 **9.** 448 **11.** 216 **13.** 253 **15.** 368
17. 374 **19.** 392 **21.** 270 **23.** 10,488 **25.** 166,786 **27.** 791,028
29. 58,625 **31.** 203,912 **33.** 4,707 **35.** 1,035 **37.** 5,781
39. 36,344 **41.** Answers vary **43.** Answers vary

Exercise Set 4-3

3. 11 **5.** 33 **7.** 108 **9.** 106 **11.** 311 **13.** 69 **15.** 359 **17.** 184
19. 37,406 **21.** 1,166 **23.** 11111_{two} **25.** 1333_{six} **27.** 22_{seven}
29. 1017_{nine} **31.** 10110_{two} **33.** 33_{five} **35.** $939_{sixteen}$ **37.** 1042212_{five}
39. 44_{seven} **41.** 100000000_{two} **43.** 111010_{two} **45.** 81_{twelve}
47. 310_{four} **49.** $1B6_{twelve}$ **51.** 3665_{seven}
53. (a) 3272_{eight} **57.** (a) 2731_{eight} **61.** (a) 6553_{eight}
   (b) $6BA_{sixteen}$ (b) $5D9_{sixteen}$ (b) $D6B_{sixteen}$
55. (a) 637_{eight} **59.** (a) 3775_{eight}
   (b) $19F_{sixteen}$ (b) $7FD_{sixteen}$
63. 1101111000_{two} **65.** 110101000100_{two} **67.** 110010000_{two}
69. 110001_{two} **71.** 110100011010101_{two} **73.** 110101000101011_{two}
75. 10101011_{two} **77.** 1101100010_{two} **79.** 101001011101_{two}
81. 110010101001011_{two} **83.** 5 lb 7 oz **85.** 34 yd 2 ft 8 in.
87. STOP **89.** CLASSISOVER **91.** ITISRAINING
93. 13256 **95.** 67138 **97.** 44501

99. ||ı|ı|ı||ıııı||||ıı||ı||ı|| **101.** ıı|||ıı|ı|ıı|ıı|ı|ı|ıı|

103. ||ı|ıı||ı||ı|ıı|ııı|ıı|ı|

105. one symbol; same as tally system **107.** 6; manufacturer's
109. 0; product

Exercise Set 4-4

3.

+	0	1	2
0	0	1	2
1	1	2	10
2	2	10	11

5.

×	0	1	2	3
0	0	0	0	0
1	0	1	2	3
2	0	2	10	12
3	0	3	12	21

7. 32_{five} **9.** 11212_{four} **11.** 2020_{six} **13.** 6657_{nine} **15.** 31_{five} **17.** 101_{seven}
19. 40040_{nine} **21.** 571_{twelve} **23.** 332_{six} **25.** 56067_{nine} **27.** $3976A_{\text{twelve}}$
29. 482_{nine} remainder 2_{nine} **31.** 230_{five} remainder 3_{five} **33.** 10000_{two}
35. 403_{sixteen} **37.** 1001_{two} **39.** $4DCA_{\text{sixteen}}$ **41.** 110010_{two}
43. 2894_{sixteen} **45.** 11_{two} remainder 10_{two}
47. $B23_{\text{sixteen}}$ remainder 2_{sixteen} **49.** base 8 **51.** L
53. G **55.** 01000100 01001111 01010010 01001101
57. 01010101 01001110 01001001 01001111 01001110

Review Exercises

1. 1,000,221 **3.** 681 **5.** 419 **7.** 2,604

9. **11.**

13. DIII **15.**

17.

19. 276 **21.** 147 **23.** 330 **25.** 156 **27.** 1,955 **29.** 365,687
31. 2,542 **33.** 13,965 **35.** 119 **37.** 17,327 **39.** 1,246
41. 2,058 **43.** 215 **45.** 52_{six} **47.** 2663_{nine} **49.** 101011_{two}
51. 103_{four} **53.** 1000_{seven} **55.** (a) 733_{eight} (b) $1DB_{\text{sixteen}}$
57. (a) 1547_{eight} (b) 367_{sixteen} **59.** $111011010100_{\text{two}}$
61. $1010010110110011_{\text{two}}$ **63.** 251_{nine} **65.** 111011_{two}
67. $15AB6_{\text{twelve}}$ **69.** 101100_{two} **71.** 331_{four} **73.** 21331_{nine}
75. 1011011_{two} **77.** 230_{five} remainder 2_{five} **79.** 342_{eight} remainder 6_{eight}

Chapter 4 Test

1. 2,000,312 **3.** 1,271 **5.** 426

7.

9. **11.** DCV **13.** 221 **15.** 267,904
17. 96 **19.** 17,375 **21.** 1,231 **23.** 500 **25.** 241 **27.** 133_{five}
29. 6362_{nine} **31.** 10001_{two} **33.** 1123_{four} **35.** 1160_{seven}
37. (a) 731_{eight} (b) $1D9_{\text{sixteen}}$ **39.** $111011010100_{\text{two}}$ **41.** 282_{nine}
43. 1000111_{two} **45.** $14B25_{\text{twelve}}$ **47.** 10010111_{two} **49.** 1030_{four}
51. 1250_{six} **53.** 151_{eight} remainder 3_{eight}

CHAPTER 8: CONSUMER MATHEMATICS

Exercise Set 8-1

7. 63% **9.** 2.5% **11.** 156% **13.** 20% **15.** $66.\overline{6}\%$ **17.** 125%
19. 0.18 **21.** 0.06 **23.** 0.625 **25.** 3.2 **27.** $\frac{6}{25}$ **29.** $\frac{9}{100}$ **31.** $2\frac{9}{25}$
33. $\frac{1}{200}$ **35.** $\frac{1}{6}$ **37.** $15; $314.99 **39.** $9.00; $158.99 **41.** 60%
43. 24% **45.** $95.99 **47.** $149.99 **49.** $1,256 **51.** About 2,446
53. 8.5% **55.** 60% **57.** 52.8% **59.** No; the total discount is 44%.
61. Total discount will be 75%, not 100%

Exercise Set 8-2

7. $1,440 **9.** 2 years **11.** 5% **13.** $985 **15.** 3.2% **17.** $128.25
19. 6.5 years **21.** 10% **23.** 6% **25.** 3 years **27.** $960
29. $1,120 **31.** $490.44 **33.** $1.65 **35.** $35 **37.** $26.47
39. (a) $720 (b) $2,280 (c) 10.5% **41.** (a) $4,400 (b) $17,600
(c) 6.25% **43.** (a) $421.20 (b) $358.80 (c) 13% **45.** 8.43%
47. $141,509.43 **49.** 3 years **51.** 4.25 years or 51 months
53. $2,096.25 **55.** $7,316 **57.** $6 **59.** (a) $5,400 (b) $12,600
(c) 7.1% **61.** The personal loan **63.** The repair loan
65. They are the same regardless of principal.

Exercise Set 8-3

5. $I = 396.20 and $A = $1,221.20$ **7.** $I = 14.67 and $A = 89.67
9. $I = 991.92 and $A = $1,616.92$ **11.** $I = 688.05 and $A = $2,683.05$
13. $I = 70.62 and $A = 820.62 **15.** $2,604.21 **17.** $8,167.15
19. $58,541.39 **21.** $18,072.57 **23.** $7,710.98 **25.** 6.14%
27. 6.66% **29.** 4.5% compounded semiannually
31. 3.1% compounded quarterly **33.** $12,175.94 **35.** $335,095.61
37. $20,548.25 **39.** $27,223.76 **41.** $24,664.64 **43.** $59,556.16
45. $2,095.18 **47.** $114,717.32 **49.** $8,347.30 **51.** $1,235.34

Exercise Set 8-4

7. $480
9. Down payment: $56.25; Installment Price: $383.25
11. $43.17 **13.** 8.5% **15.** 12% **17.** 9.5%
19. $u = 709.50; payoff amount: $10,956.50
21. $u = 14.54; payoff amount: $482.81
23. $u = 14.66; payoff amount: $615.34
25. $180.13 **27.** $8.22 **29.** $5.18 **31.** $16.65; $1,124.15
33. $39.49; $3,368.60 **35.** $13.32; $411.35
37. (a) $602.14 (b) $7.23 (c) $669.15
39. (a) $370.55 (b) $5.19 (c) $350.76
41. (a) $370.92 (b) $4.08 (c) $533.30 **43.** $3,636.36

Exercise Set 8-5

5. (a) $21,750 (b) $123,250 (c) $871.38 (d) $138,164
7. (a) $80,000 (b) $120,000 (c) $720.00 (d) $139,200
9. (a) $32,500 (b) $292,500 (c) $1,924.65 (d) $631,332
11. (a) $360,000 (b) $840,000 (c) $5,779.20 (d) $547,008
13. $1,499.44 **15.** $1,148.90 **17.** $4,215.22 **19.** $3,746.38

21.

Payment number	Interest	Payment on Principal	Balance of Loan
1	$718.96	$152.42	$123,097.58
2	$718.07	$153.31	$122,944.27
3	$717.17	$154.21	$122,790.06

23.

Payment number	Interest	Payment on Principal	Balance of Loan
1	$3,850	$1,929.20	$838,070.80
2	$3,841.16	$1,938.04	$836,132.76
3	$3,832.28	$1,946.92	$834,185.84

25. If you can afford the higher payment of the 20-year mortgage at 9% after making the 25% down payment, then that is the better option since the total interest paid is less. However, if you can only manage a 10% down payment, or need lower monthly payments, the 25-year mortgage at 7% wold be the better choice.

Exercise Set 8-6

7. $97.25 per share **9.** $1.23 per share **11.** 4,626,000 shares
13. $8.87 per share **15.** $766.29 **17.** $40.08 per share **19.** $0.04
21. 345,000 shares **23.** $1.49 per share **25.** $156.20
27. $50.87 per share **29.** $0.67 **31.** 9,662,000 shares
33. $2.53 per share **35.** $820.75 **37.** 24.91
39. 15.02 **41.** $0.34 per share **43.** $1.98 per share
45. lost $432.48 **47.** lost $2,022.63
49. The second investment would be the better choice.

Review Exercises

1. 0.875; 87.5% **3.** $\frac{4}{5}$; 0.8 **5.** $\frac{37}{20}$; 1.85 **7.** 5.75; 575%
9. $\frac{91}{200}$; 0.445 **11.** 69.12 **13.** 1,100 **15.** $60 **17.** 73.5%
19. $2,322 **21.** 2.5 years **23.** 7% **25.** $1,375
27. $I = $1,800$ and $A = $7,800$ **29.** 1.4% **31.** $25.56
33. Discount: $1,080; David received $4,920
35. $I = 603.67 and $A = $2,378.67$ **37.** $I = 12.07 and $A = 57.07
39. 12.55% **41.** $8,129.93
43. Total installment price: $788.25
Monthly payment: $84.47
45. 10.5% **47.** $u = 156.44; payoff amount $= $3,873.56
49. $15.24 **51.** $124.13; $7,424.53 **53.** $1,827.94
55. $342 **57.** $33.04 **59.** She earned $203.94

Chapter 8 Test

1. 31.25% **3.** $\frac{7}{25}$ **5.** 80% **7.** 300 **9.** $2,568 **11.** $486
13. $I = 8.16, $A = 443.16. The monthly payment is $73.86.
15. $I = 216, $A = $2,016$. The monthly payment is $168.
17. Discount: $5,692.50; Latoya received $6,957.50
19. $I = $7,885.08$ and $A = $17,635.08$ **21.** 8.16%
23. Total installment price: $967.73; Monthly payment: $114.54
25. The unearned interest is $438.36 and the payoff amount is $7,186.64.
27. The finance charge is $20.
The new balance is $1,030.
29. 11% **31.** $2,834.66 **33.** $60 **35.** $26.65

CHAPTER 11: PROBABILITY AND COUNTING TECHNIQUES

Exercise Set 11-1

5. 3,628,800 **7.** 362,880 **9.** 1 **11.** 12 **13.** 336 **15.** 420
17. 22,350 **19.** 56 **21.** 479,001,600 **23.** 720 **25.** 1 **27.** 990
29. 840 **31.** 151,200 **33.** 5,527,200 **35.** 300 **37.** 210 **39.** 720
41. 57,120 **43.** 120 **45.** 210 **47.** 210 **49.** 2,520 **51.** 43,680
53. $\approx 5.1988 \times 10^{35}$ **55.** 362,880; 40,320

Exercise Set 11-2

5. 10 **7.** 35 **9.** 15 **11.** 1 **13.** 66
15. $_8C_5 = 56$ **17.** $_6C_2 = 15$ **19.** $_9C_9 = 1$
$_8P_5 = 6,720$ $\quad\quad$ $_6P_2 = 30$ $\quad\quad$ $_9P_9 = 362,880$
21. Combination **23.** Permutation **25.** Permutation
27. Combination **29.** 2,598,960 **31.** 126; 35 **33.** 120
35. 462 **37.** 166,320 **39.** 14,400 **41.** 67,200 **43.** 53,130
45. 126 **47.** 30,045,015

Exercise Set 11-3

9. Yes **11.** No **13.** No **15.** Yes **17.** Empirical **19.** Classical
21. (a) $\frac{1}{6}$ (b) $\frac{1}{2}$ (c) $\frac{1}{3}$ (d) 1 (e) 1 (f) $\frac{5}{6}$ (g) $\frac{1}{6}$
23. (a) $\frac{1}{7}$ (b) $\frac{3}{7}$ (c) $\frac{3}{7}$ (d) 1 (e) 0 **25.** $\frac{4}{9}$ **27.** $\frac{9}{16}$
29. 0.91 **31.** 0.84 **33.** $\frac{3}{13}$ **35.** $\frac{5}{11}$ **37.** $\frac{17}{25}$ **39.** $\frac{13}{35}$ **41.** 0
43. (a) ≈ 0.26 (b) ≈ 0.96 **45.** (a) 0.42 (b) 0.90
47. It is likely that the penny is unbalanced.
49. (a) $\frac{6}{25}$ (b) $\frac{2}{5}$ (c) $\frac{9}{25}$ (d) $\frac{12}{25}$ (e) $\frac{1}{5}$

Exercise Set 11-4

3. (a) $\frac{3}{8}$ (b) $\frac{1}{8}$ (c) $\frac{7}{8}$ **5.** (a) $\frac{5}{12}$ (b) $\frac{1}{4}$ (c) $\frac{1}{6}$
7. (a) $\frac{1}{3}$ (b) $\frac{1}{3}$ (c) $\frac{1}{9}$ (d) $\frac{4}{9}$ (e) $\frac{1}{3}$
9. (a) $\frac{1}{4}$ (b) $\frac{3}{4}$ (c) $\frac{1}{4}$ (d) $\frac{1}{8}$ **11.** (a) $\frac{3}{5}$ (b) $\frac{1}{2}$ (c) $\frac{4}{5}$
13. (a) $\frac{1}{2}$ (b) $\frac{1}{6}$ (c) $\frac{1}{4}$
15. (a) $\frac{1}{13}$ (b) $\frac{1}{4}$ (c) $\frac{5}{52}$ (d) $\frac{2}{13}$ (e) $\frac{4}{13}$ (f) $\frac{4}{13}$ (g) $\frac{1}{2}$ (h) $\frac{1}{26}$
(i) $\frac{7}{13}$ (j) $\frac{1}{26}$
17. (a) $\frac{1}{9}$ (b) $\frac{2}{9}$ (c) $\frac{1}{6}$ (d) $\frac{5}{18}$ (e) $\frac{11}{36}$ (f) $\frac{1}{2}$ (g) $\frac{3}{4}$ (h) 1
19. The outcomes are not equally likely because there is a $\frac{1}{4}$ probability of getting WW; each of the other six outcomes has a probability of $\frac{1}{8}$
21. 216 **23.** $\frac{5}{108}$

Exercise Set 11-5

3. (a) 0.0004 (b) 0.15 (c) 0.383 (d) 0.45
5. (a) 0.033 (b) 0.0083 (c) 0.3 (d) 0.075 (e) 0.15
7. (a) 0 (b) 0.51 (c) 0.018
9. (a) 0.07 (b) 0.42 (c) 0.015 (d) 0.16 (e) 0.336
11. 0.01 **13.** 0.42 **15.** 0.0012 **17.** 0.00144 **19.** 0.0211
21. 0.0000015 **23.** 0.0000628

Exercise Set 11-6

7. (a) 1:11 (b) 1:35 (c) 5:1 (d) 17:1 (e) 1:5
9. (a) 1:12 (b) 3:10 (c) 3:1 (d) 1:12 (e) 1:1
11. (a) $\frac{7}{11}$ (b) $\frac{5}{7}$ (c) $\frac{3}{4}$ (d) $\frac{4}{5}$ **13.** $\frac{5}{14}$ **15.** $-\$3.00$
17. \$0.83 **19.** $-\$1.00$ **21.** $-\$0.50$; $-\$0.52$

Exercise Set 11-7

3. No **5.** No **7.** Yes **9.** $\frac{1}{6}$ **11.** $\frac{11}{19}$ **13.** (a) $\frac{17}{20}$ (b) $\frac{11}{20}$ (c) $\frac{3}{5}$
15. (a) $\frac{8}{17}$ (b) $\frac{6}{17}$ (c) $\frac{9}{17}$ (d) $\frac{12}{17}$ **17.** (a) $\frac{6}{7}$ (b) $\frac{4}{7}$ (c) 1
19. (a) $\frac{67}{118}$ (b) $\frac{81}{118}$ (c) $\frac{44}{59}$ **21.** (a) $\frac{38}{45}$ (b) $\frac{22}{45}$ (c) $\frac{2}{3}$
23. (a) $\frac{14}{31}$ (b) $\frac{23}{31}$ (c) $\frac{19}{31}$ **25.** (a) $\frac{467}{1,392}$ (b) $\frac{25}{32}$ (c) $\frac{1,955}{2,784}$
27. $\frac{7}{10}$ **29.** 0.06 **31.** 0.30

Exercise Set 11-8

5. Independent **7.** Dependent **9.** Independent **11.** Dependent
13. 0.0058 **15.** 0.4746 **17.** 0.0625 **19.** $\frac{1}{12}$ **21.** $\frac{1}{8}$ **23.** $\frac{1}{15}$
25. 0.1311 **27.** (a) 0.00018 (b) 0.0129 (c) 0.1176
29. 0.0179 **31.** $\frac{1}{6}$ **33.** $\frac{2}{11}$ **35.** $\frac{1}{4}$ **37.** $\frac{2}{3}$ **39.** 1 **41.** 0.61
43. $\frac{1}{2}$ **45.** $\frac{25}{216}$ **47.** $\frac{1}{133,225}$

Exercise Set 11-9

5. 0.288 **7.** 0.0616 **9.** 0.0000304 **11.** 0.0994 **13.** 0.00615
15. 0.00463 **17.** 0.0750 **19.** 0.1546 **21.** 0.2461 **23.** 0.2340
25. 0.1906 **27.** 0.1585 **29.** 0.1593 **31.** 0.1541 **33.** 0.6870
35. Answers vary

Review Exercises

1. 2,184 **3.** 175,760,000; 88,583,040 **5.** 120 **7.** 84
9. In a permutation order matters, in a combination order does not matter. **11.** 78 **13.** 729 **15.** b, c, and e
17. (a) $\frac{1}{4}$ (b) $\frac{1}{52}$ (c) $\frac{4}{13}$ (d) $\frac{1}{13}$ (e) $\frac{1}{2}$
19. (a) 0 (b) $\frac{1}{2}$ (c) $\frac{1}{3}$ **21.** (a) $\frac{9}{35}$ (b) $\frac{23}{35}$ (c) $\frac{19}{35}$ (d) $\frac{19}{35}$
23. (a) $\frac{1}{4}$ (b) $\frac{1}{6}$ (c) $\frac{1}{4}$ (d) $\frac{1}{4}$ (e) 0 (f) 1
25. $S = \{$1H, 1T, 2H, 2T, 3H, 3T, 4H, 4T, 5H, 5T, 6H, 6T, 7H, 7T, 8H, 8T$\}$
27. $\frac{2}{25}$ **29.** $\frac{12}{55}$ **31.** $\frac{33}{182}$ **33.** 1:5
35. 10.5 **37.** \$7.23
39. Mutually exclusive
41. (a) $\frac{17}{50}$ (b) $\frac{4}{25}$ **43.** Dependent
45. Dependent **47.** $\frac{1}{7}$ **49.** 0.016
51. (a) $\frac{1}{26}$ (b) $\frac{1}{4}$ (c) $\frac{1}{8}$
53. 0.0165 **55.** 0.1684

Chapter 11 Test

1. 380 **3.** 95,040
5. Probability is a number that represents the likelihood of an event.
7. 1,188,137,600; 710,424,000 **9.** 35 **11.** 40,320
13. (a) 64 (b) 24 **15.** (a) $\frac{1}{13}$ (b) $\frac{1}{13}$ (c) $\frac{4}{13}$
17. (a) $\frac{12}{31}$ (b) $\frac{12}{31}$ (c) $\frac{27}{31}$ (d) $\frac{24}{31}$ **19.** $S = \{$H1, H3, H5, T2, T4, T6$\}$
21. (a) 0.025 (b) 0.000495 (c) 0 **23.** $\frac{1}{2}$ **25.** $\frac{1}{2}$
27. 8; $S = \{$M,CH; M,IN; SF,CH; SF,IN; P,CH; P,IN; H,CH; H,IN$\}$
29. 5:4 **31.** $5\frac{1}{6}$ **33.** $\frac{8}{33}$ **35.** 0.1144

CHAPTER 12: STATISTICS

Exercise Set 12-1

9. Cluster **11.** Random **13.** Stratified

15.

Rank	Frequency
Fr	18
So	12
Jr	6
Se	4

17.

Show	Frequency
S	6
P	5
B	7
A	7

19.

Class	Frequency
27–33	7
34–40	14
41–47	14
48–54	12
55–61	3
62–68	3
69–75	2

21.

Class	Frequency
0–39	8
40–79	10
80–119	10
120–159	7
160–199	3
200–239	8
240–279	4

23.

Class	Frequency
150–1,276	2
1,277–2,403	2
2,404–3,530	5
3,531–4,657	8
4,658–5,784	7
5,785–6,911	3
6,912–8,038	7
8,039–9,165	3
9,166–10,292	3
10,293–11,419	2

25.

Class	Frequency
839–949	12
950–1,060	9
1,061–1,171	7
1,172–1,282	1
1,283–1,393	1
1,394–1,504	0
1,505–1,615	2

27. Most registered vehicles per car stolen are in the range of 80–89, while the least are in the 0–49 range. The most common are 84 and 89.

Stems	Leaves
3	8
4	1
5	0 0 2 3 3 6 8 9
6	6 8 9 9
7	0 0 3 4 5 8
8	0 1 3 3 4 4 4 5 7 9 9 9
9	0 2 4

29.

Stems	Leaves
0	3
1	5 9
2	2
3	1 1
4	1 4 6 6
5	2 6 6 6 9
6	0 0 6 6
7	7
8	7 8
9	6 8

31. Descriptive   **33.** Descriptive   **35.** Answers vary

Exercise Set 12-2

5.

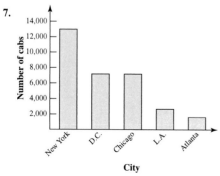

7.

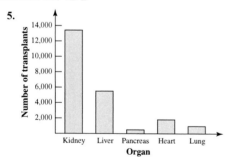

9.

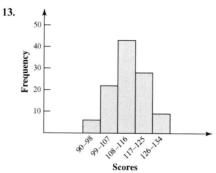

11.

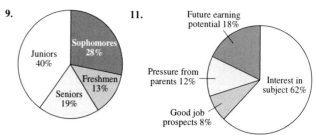

13.

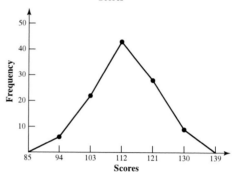

15.

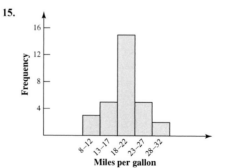

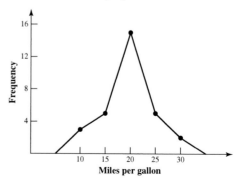

17.

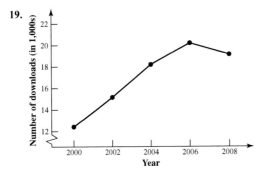

19.

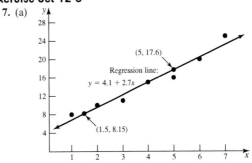

21. Pie chart   **23.** Time series graph   **25.** Pie chart
27. The scale makes the increase look greater.

Exercise Set 12-3
7. mean ≈ 15.11, median = 7, mode = 3, midrange = 31
9. mean = 612.6, median = 475, no mode, midrange = 820
11. mean = 2,907.7, median = 2,723.5, no mode, midrange = 3,353.5
13. mean = 189.6, median = 151, no mode, midrange = 207.5
15. mean = 8.25, median = 8.5, mode = 9, midrange = 9
17. mean $\approx 17,163.9$, median = 16,740, no mode, midrange = 18,566
19. mean = 21.76   **21.** mean ≈ 4.4 seconds
23. mean ≈ 42.87 or $42.87 million   **25.** mean = \$180.28
27. Answers vary   **29.** Median   **31.** Mode   **33.** Mode

Exercise Set 12-4
7. $s_1 < s_2$ **9.** $s_1 > s_2$
11. $R = 60$, variance = 406.75, $s \approx 20.17$
13. $R = 1,799$, variance = 438,113.6, $s \approx 661.90$
15. $R = 99$, variance $\approx 1,288.19$, $s \approx 35.89$
17. $R = 10$, variance = 9, $s = 3$
19. $R = \$3.83$, variance ≈ 2.79, $s \approx 1.67$
21. $R = \$39.50$, variance ≈ 242.59, $s \approx 15.58$
23. $R = 738$, variance $\approx 57,844.95$, $s \approx 240.5$
25. $R = 432$, variance $\approx 29,141.36$, $s \approx 170.7$
27. The variation is not the same.

Exercise Set 12-5
5. (a) 20th percentile   (b) 75th percentile   (c) 35th percentile
   (d) 5th percentile   (e) 90th percentile
7. 75th percentile   **9.** 79th percentile
11. 10   **13.** Maurice is ranked higher.
15. (a) 60th percentile   (b) 8   (c) 23 years
17. $Q_1 = 22.5$, $Q_2 = 34$, $Q_3 = 53.5$ **19.** $Q_1 = 78$, $Q_2 = 88.5$, $Q_3 = 93$
21. $Q_1 = 107$, $Q_2 = 116$, $Q_3 = 122$ **23.** yes; yes

Exercise Set 12-6
7. 34   **9.** 499   **11.** 0.474   **13.** 0.192   **15.** 0.159   **17.** 0.345
19. 0.077   **21.** 0.223   **23.** 0.463   **25.** 0.885   **27.** 0.971
29. $z = +0.45$ **31.** (a) $z = \pm2.05$ (b) $z = \pm1.75$ (c) $z = \pm2.40$

Exercise Set 12-7
Probabilities were found using the table in Appendix A.
3. (a) 0.378   (b) 0.179   **5.** (a) 0.264   (b) 0.316
7. (a) 0.005   (b) 0.162   (c) 0.749
9. (a) 0.153   (b) 0.774   (c) 0.187
11. (a) 0.841   (b) 0.067   **13.** (a) 0.776   (b) 0.405
15. (a) 0.755   (b) 0.811   (c) 0.284
17. (a) 638   (b) 184   (c) 1,074   (d) 136
19. (a) 65   (b) 616   (c) 10   **21.** 28th percentile   **23.** 0th percentile
25. No   **27.** 90, 110

Exercise Set 12-8
7. (a)

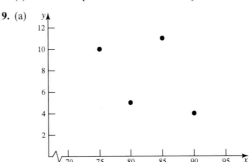

   (b) $r \approx 0.977$
   (c) r is significant at the 5% and the 1% level
   (d) $y = 4.1 + 2.7x$
   (e)   There is a positive linear relationship.

9. (a)

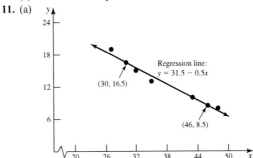

   (b) $r \approx -0.441$
   (c) r is not significant at 5% nor at 1% level.
   (d)   no regression line
   (e)   No relationship exists.
11. (a)

   (b) $r \approx -0.983$
   (c) r is significant at the 5% and 1% level.
   (d) $y = 31.5 - 0.5x$
   (e)   There is a negative linear relationship.

13. (a)

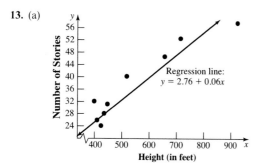

(b) $r \approx 0.942$
(c) r is significant at the 5% and 1% level.
(d) $y = 2.76 + 0.06x$
(e)   There is a positive linear relationship.   (f) 33 Stories

15. (a)

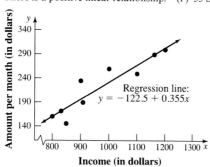

(b) $r \approx 0.896$
(c) r is significant at the 5% and 1% level.
(d) $y = -122.5 + 0.355x$
(e)   There is a positive linear relationship.   (f) $205.88

17. (a)

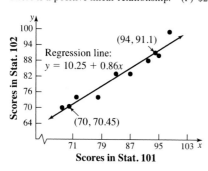

(b) $r \approx 0.963$ (c) r is significant at the 5% and 1% level.
(d) $y = 10.25 + 0.86x$
(e) There is a positive linear relationship.   (f) 88

19. Answers vary
21. Non-linear relationship; $r = 0$

Review Exercises

1.

Item	Frequency
B	4
F	5
G	5
S	5
T	6

3.

Rank	Frequency
102–116	4
117–131	3
132–146	1
147–161	4
162–176	11
177–191	7

5.

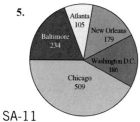

7.

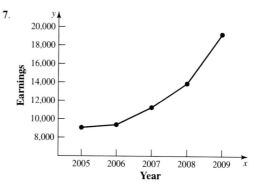

9. mean $= 7.25$ **11.** $R = 1,885$, variance $\approx 475,610.1$, $s \approx 689.6$

13. (a)

Value	Percentile
2	0th
4	17th
5	33rd
6	50th
8	67th
9	83rd

(b) 5

15. (a) 0.474   (f) 0.828
(b) 0.155   (g) 0.023
(c) 0.061   (h) 0.912
(d) 0.833   (i) 0.018
(e) 0.229   (j) 0.955

17. (a) 28   (b) 5   **19.** (a) 0.004   (b) 0.023   (c) 0.5   (d) 0.324
21. 22
23. (a) Answers vary
(b) $r \approx -0.144$; answers vary

Chapter 12 Test

1.

Source	Frequency
W	6
L	7
K	7
E	5

3.

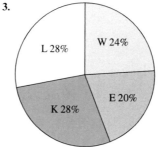

5.

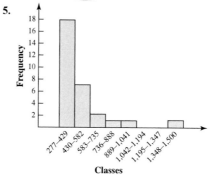

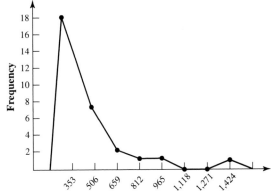

7.

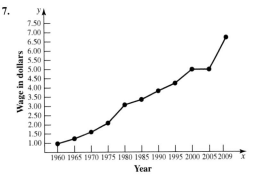

9. mean = 6.4

11. (a) 0.433   (f) 0.828
    (b) 0.394   (g) 0.040
    (c) 0.034   (h) 0.900
    (d) 0.103   (i) 0.017
    (e) 0.291   (j) 0.913

13. (a) 0.067   (b) 0.023
    (c) 0.465   (d) 0.094

15.

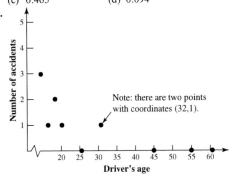

Note: there are two points with coordinates (32,1).

$r \approx -0.714$, r is significant at the 5% level.
$y = 2.31 - 0.04x$
$y \approx 0$ when $x = 61$

CHAPTER 13: OTHER MATHEMATICAL SYSTEMS

Exercise Set 13-1
7. C **9.** E **11.** E **13.** D **15.** D
17. Yes   **19.** Yes   **21.** D **23.** ☆   **25.** □
27. △   **29.** ☆   **31.** □   **33.** Yes   **35.** No
37. closure, associative
39. closure, commutative, identity
41. closure
43. closure, commutative, identity, inverse
45. closure, commutative, identity, inverse, associative; Abelian group
47. Abelian group   **49.** not a group   **51.** not a group
53. not a group   **55.** not a group

57.

*	0	1	2	3
0	0	1	2	3
1	1	2	3	0
2	2	3	0	1
3	3	0	1	2

59. yes
61. yes, 0 is its own inverse, 2 is its own inverse, and 1 and 3 are inverses.

63.

Ⓜ	R	B	Y
R	R	P	O
B	P	B	G
Y	O	G	Y

65. no   **67.** no

71.

→	T	F	Closure
T	T	F	
F	T	T	

Exercise Set 13-2
5. (a) 3   (b) 3   (c) 3   **7.** (a) 11   (b) 5   (c) 3
9. (a) 6   (b) 0   (c) 2   **11.** (a) 7   (b) 1   (c) 3
13. (a) 7   (b) 1   (c) 3   **15.** (a) 9   (b) 3   (c) 5
17. 2   **19.** 10   **21.** 3   **23.** 6   **25.** 11   **27.** 10   **29.** 2   **31.** 10
33. 6   **35.** 3   **37.** 11   **39.** 4   **41.** 6   **43.** 12   **45.** 10   **47.** 9
49. 6   **51.** 12   **53.** 2   **55.** 0   **57.** 5   **59.** 3   **61.** 2   **63.** 0
65. 12   **67.** 7   **69.** 10   **71.** 5   **73.** 5   **75.** None   **77.** None
79. 1   **81.** Answers vary   **83.** Answers vary   **85.** Answers vary
87. $y = 10$ **89.** $y = 1$ **91.** $y = 11, 2, 5$ and 8   **93.** $y = 6$
95. $y = 6$ **97.** 5:00 P.M.   **99.** 9:48 A.M.   **101.** 5:00 A.M.
103. 7:38 P.M.   **105.** 8:00 P.M.   **107.** 0352   **109.** 1156   **111.** 2006
113. 2136   **115.** 10:09 A.M.   **117.** 2:36 P.M.   **119.** The property holds.

Exercise Set 13-3
5. 2   **7.** 2   **9.** 7   **11.** 2   **13.** 3   **15.** 2   **17.** 2   **19.** 4   **21.** 1
23. 4   **25.** 3   **27.** 3   **29.** 2   **31.** 0   **33.** 6   **35.** 6   **37.** 6   **39.** 4
41. 3   **43.** 11   **45.** {4, 10, 16, 22, 28, … }
47. {3, 11, 19, 27, 35, … }   **49.** {2, 10, 18, 26, 34, … }
51. {2, 7, 12, 17, 22, … }   **53.** {5, 12, 19, 26, 33, … }
55. Tuesday   **57.** Friday   **59.** Tuesday   **61.** Valid   **63.** Invalid
65. 6 cans   **67.** Friday   **69.** It's April 22nd, 10 P.M.   **71.** south
73. 17 tables; one empty space   **75.** 10 oz   **77.** Answers vary
79. You did not take your second dose.

Review Exercises
1. C **3.** B **5.** C **7.** yes   **9.** yes
11. yes; A and C are inverses, B is its own inverse.
13. no   **15.** no   **17.** Abelian group   **19.** not a group   **21.** 3
23. 12   **25.** 6   **27.** 2   **29.** 6   **31.** 17   **33.** Friday at 3 P.M.
35. 2   **37.** 4   **39.** 2   **41.** 7   **43.** 2   **45.** 2   **47.** 0   **49.** 0
51. 1   **53.** 4   **55.** 3   **57.** 1   **59.** 4   **61.** 1   **63.** 2   **65.** 4
67. 2   **69.** 5   **71.** 2   **73.** 6   **75.** {4, 12, 20, 28, 36, … }
77. {3, 12, 21, 30, 39, … }   **79.** {1, 7, 13, 19, 25, … }
81. {11, 23, 35, 47, 59, … }   **83.** $y = 1$ **85.** 4 cookies   **87.** no

Chapter 13 Test
1. z **3.** s **5.** z **7.** Yes   **9.** -1 **11.** a **13.** -1 **15.** a
17. $y = -1$ **19.** Yes   **21.** Yes   **23.** $-a$ is the inverse of a
25. 4   **27.** 4   **29.** 2   **31.** 1   **33.** 2   **35.** 4   **37.** 5   **39.** 1
41. {2, 8, 14, 20, 26, … }   **43.** {0, 4, 8, 12, 16, … }   **45.** 4 A.M.
47. 8 P.M. the following day

ADDITIONAL EXERCISES

CHAPTER 2 SECTION 2-1

Critical Thinking

1. Write two sets that are equivalent but not equal. Why is it not possible to write two sets that are equal but not equivalent?
2. We know that two sets are equivalent if we can match up their elements in a one-to-one correspondence.
   (a) Which set has more elements: $A = \{1, 2, 3, 4, 5, 6, \ldots\}$ or $B = \{2, 4, 6, 8, 10, \ldots\}$?
   (b) Write out a correspondence between A and B where every element in A gets matched with its double in B. Does this change your mind about your answer to part (a)? (If you find this problem interesting, you'll like Section 2-5 very much.)
3. Explain why each of the following sets is *not* well-defined.
   (a) The set of all Americans.
   (b) The set of luxury cars in the 2011 model year.
   (c) The set of all colleges with a legitimate chance to win the NCAA basketball tournament. (There are at least two reasons!)
   (d) The set of all jobs that pay over $50,000 per year.
   (e) The set of mothers.
4. (a) List all of the different sets you can form using only the elements in the set $\{2, 4, 6\}$.
   (b) There are eight sets that can be formed in part (a). Did you find seven of them? If so, can you figure out why you missed one?

CHAPTER 2 SECTION 2-2

Real-World Applications

Exercises 1 through 4 use the following sets:
U = the set of all people who have been charged with a felony.
A = the set of people who are on trial or awaiting trial on felony charges.
B = the set of people who have been convicted of a felony.
C = the set of people who have been convicted of a felony and have been released from prison.
D = the set of people who were charged with a felony and found not guilty.
E = the set of people who were charged with a felony and had charges dropped before standing trial.
Write a verbal description of each set.

1. (a) $B \cup C$ (b) $C \cup D$ (c) $D \cup E$
2. (a) A' (b) C' (c) E'
3. (a) $B \cap C$ (b) $A \cap B$ (c) $C \cap B'$
4. (a) $(A \cup B)'$ (b) $(B \cup D)'$ (c) $A - (B \cap C)$

Critical Thinking

5. (a) Make up two sets A and B with somewhere between 4 and 8 elements in each so that $A \cap B$ is nonempty. Find each of $n(A)$, $n(B)$, $n(A \cup B)$, and $n(A \cap B)$.
   (b) Repeat part (a) with two completely different sets A and B.
   (c) Use the results of part (a) and (b) to make a conjecture about a formula for finding the cardinality of a union of two sets.
6. (a) Write two sets A and B for which $n(A \cup B) > n(A \cap B)$.
   (b) Write two sets A and B for which $n(A \cup B) = n(A \cap B)$.
   (c) Can you write two sets A and B for which $n(A \cup B) < n(A \cap B)$? Use a Venn diagram to illustrate why you can or cannot.

CHAPTER 2 SECTION 2-3

Critical Thinking

In Exercises 1 through 6, (a) use a Venn diagram to show that the two sets are not equal in general; (b) try to find specific sets A, B (and C if necessary) for which the two sets are equal; and (c) try to find a general condition under which the two sets are always equal. Recall that U represents the universal set.

1. $A \cap B$ and B
2. $A - B$ and A
3. $(A \cap B)'$ and U
4. $(A \cap B)'$ and A'
5. $(A - C) \cap B$ and $B \cap A$
6. $(A - C) \cup (B - A)$ and $B - C$

CHAPTER 2 SECTION 2-4

Real-World Applications

1. A court record search of 250 incoming freshmen at a state university shows that 26 had been arrested at some point for underage drinking, but not drug possession, and 12 had been arrested for possession but not underage drinking. There were 202 who had been arrested for neither.
   (a) How many of the students had been arrested for drug possession?
   (b) How many had been arrested for underage drinking?
2. In a study of 400 meals served at 75 campus cafeterias, 70 had less than 10 grams of fat but not less than 350 calories; 48 had less than 350 calories but not less than 10 grams of fat; 140 had over 350 calories and over 10 grams of fat.
   (a) What percentage of meals had less than 10 grams of fat?
   (b) What percentage of meals had less than 350 calories?
3. Of the 50 largest cities in the United States, 11 have a team in the National Basketball Association but not a major league baseball team; 9 have a major league baseball team but not a team in the NBA; 12 have neither.
   (a) How many cities have both a major league baseball team and a team in the NBA?
   (b) Chicago, New York, and Los Angeles have two baseball teams, but Los Angeles is the only city with two basketball teams. Each of those cities has teams in both leagues. How many teams are there in each league?
4. One hundred new books are released nationally over a busy three-day stretch in December. Eight had an ebook version available only on Amazon, 5 were available only on Google books, and 18 were available only on iTunes. There were 26 total available on Google, 7 that could be found on both Amazon and Google but not iTunes, and 4 that could be found on both iTunes and Google but not Amazon. Draw a Venn diagram representing this information and use it to answer the following questions:

(a) How many books were available on all three services?

(b) Explain why you can't find the number of books that were not available on any of the three services.

(c) If every book released was available as an ebook on at least one of Amazon, Google, or iTunes, how many were available on Amazon and iTunes, but not Google?

(d) In that case, how many were available on exactly two of those three services?

5. Give the students in your class a three-question survey. Find out how many are left-handed, how many work in addition to going to school, and how many were born in the state your college is in. Then tabulate the results and summarize with a Venn diagram.

Critical Thinking

6. A TV network considering new contracts to televise pro sports hires a marketing consultant to conduct a survey of randomly selected TV viewers asking them which of football, baseball, and basketball they go out of their way to watch on TV. Of those surveyed, 35 watch baseball, 235 watch basketball, 295 watch football, 90 watch basketball and football, and 560 watch none of the three.

(a) Explain why this is not enough information to find the total number of people surveyed.

(b) Upon looking at the results more carefully, a member of the consultant team discovers that every single person who watches baseball also watches basketball, and none of those people watch football. Now can you find the number of people surveyed?

(c) How many people watch only football? How many watch only basketball?

CHAPTER 2 SECTION 2-5

Critical Thinking

Exercises 1 and 2 use the fact that the cardinality of the set of natural numbers $\{1, 2, 3, 4, \ldots\}$ is $\aleph_0$.

1. (a) Define a one-to-one correspondence between the set of natural numbers and the set $\{0, 1, 2, 3, 4, \ldots\}$.

(b) Write an arithmetic problem involving $\aleph_0$ that is illustrated by part (a). (Hint: How many more elements than the natural numbers does the set $\{0, 1, 2, 3, 4, \ldots\}$ have?

2. (a) Define a one-to-one correspondence between the set of natural numbers and the set of all integers excluding zero. (b) Write an arithmetic problem involving $\aleph_0$ that is illustrated by part (a).

In Exercises 3 through 8, find the cardinality of the given set. You may find the ideas in Exercises 1 and 2 helpful.

3. $\{10, 11, 12, 13, 14, \ldots\}$
4. $\{-1, -2, -3, -4, -5, \ldots\}$
5. $\{1, 3, 5, 7, 9, \ldots, 29\}$
6. $\{2, 4, 6, 8, 10, \ldots, 24\}$
7. The set of odd natural numbers.
8. The set of even negative integers.

CHAPTER 3 SECTION 3-1

Critical Thinking

1. (a) Write a verbal translation of the statement $a < 20$.
(b) Write the negation of the statement you wrote in (a).
(c) Write your statement from (b) in inequality form.
2. (a) Write a verbal translation of the statement $b > 10$.
(b) Write the negation of the statement you wrote in (a).
(c) Write your statement from (b) in inequality form.

Statements involving negations and quantifiers can be confusing—sometimes intentionally. Evaluate each statement in Exercises 3 through 6 and try to write exactly what it actually says in simpler language.

3. All of our fans will not be attending all of our games.
4. You can't fool some of the people all of the time.
5. I wouldn't say that everybody doesn't like my history professor.
6. Everyone in this class doesn't have time to do their homework.

CHAPTER 3 SECTION 3-2

Computational Exercises

If p and r are false statements, and q is a true statement, find the truth value of each compound statement.

1. $q \vee (p \wedge \sim r)$
2. $(p \wedge q) \vee (q \wedge r)$
3. $r \rightarrow \sim (p \vee q)$
4. $\sim (p \wedge q) \vee \sim r$
5. $\sim (p \wedge \sim (r \vee \sim q)$
6. $(p \rightarrow r) \rightarrow (\sim q \rightarrow p)$

CHAPTER 3 SECTION 3-3

Critical Thinking

Decide if the given compound statement is true or false. Be careful, and explain your reasoning.

1. The moon is made of green cheese if and only if Justin Bieber is the king of Siam.
2. The average student takes less than 6 years to complete an undergraduate degree if the University of Southern California is in Tahiti.
3. Drinking and driving increases the risk of an accident if and only if driving on the left side of the road is standard in the United States.
4. If my parents were born in outer space, then Venus orbits around the Earth every 28 days.
5. The current year is before 1970 if there are more than a million people in the United States.
6. Fewer than 20 people watched the finale of *American Idol* last year if and only if the winner was 14 inches tall.

CHAPTER 3 SECTION 3-4

Real-World Applications

In Exercises 1 through 4, decide if each argument is valid or invalid.

1. John Moneybags will get elected if and only if he spends the most money on his campaign. An inside source told me last week that either John will spend the most money or his opponent will hire thugs to intimidate potential voters. Just today I found out that John's opponent decided not to hire thugs for intimidation purposes, so I conclude that John won't win the election.
2. If Allie is a fine arts major, then she lives on campus. Allie's Facebook page says that she lives on campus and her best friend's name is Moose. So if Allie's best friend's name isn't Moose, she's majoring in something other than fine arts.
3. My company will get a huge contract if and only if I convince the client that our company will best represent its interests. If I manage to convince the client of this, I'll get a big bonus this year. So if I don't get a big bonus this year, you'll know that my company didn't get the huge contract.
4. Defendants who are convicted of manslaughter always serve time in prison. The defendant in the case Elena tried was represented by a public defender and was convicted of manslaughter. So if the defendant was represented by a public defender, he will not serve time in prison.

Critical Thinking

5. Make up your own example for each of the four common valid argument forms discussed in Section 3-4. Try to use topics that have some relevance to your life.
6. Make up your own example for each of the four common fallacies discussed in Section 3-4 (including the one in the Sidelight on page 130). Try to use topics that have some relevance to your life.

CHAPTER 3 SECTION 3-5
Critical Thinking

1. Write a valid argument that would correspond to the Euler circle diagram if x represents a guy named Bob.

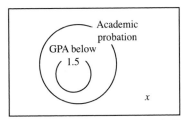

2. Write an argument that would correspond to the Euler circle diagram if x represents your dog Scruffy. Is the argument valid?

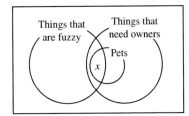

Real-World Applications

In Exercises 3 through 6, use Euler circles to decide if the argument is valid.

3. Every police officer carries a gun, and some people who carry guns cannot be trusted. So it's clear to me that some police officers can't be trusted.

4. I've seen bosses who don't treat their employees well. Everyone I know has a boss, so some of them don't get treated well.

5. All of the teams in the NCAA tournament won more games than they lost this year, and some of them won at least two-thirds of their games. So all of the teams that won more than two-thirds of their games are playing in the NCAA tournament.

6. Some of the people who got flu shots this year got the flu anyhow. Nobody in my family got a flu shot this year, so I'm sure that none of us will get the flu.

CHAPTER 4 SECTION 4-1
Computational Exercises

In Exercises 1 and 2, convert each number from the multiplicative grouping system in Example 6 on page 152 to the Hindu-Arabic system. In Exercises 3 and 4, convert each number from the Hindu-Arabic system to the system in Example 6.

1. (a) ιφ ηα   (b) δφ θα   (c) φφ φα
2. (a) αφ χα   (b) φφ αα   (c) βφ εα
3. (a) 85   (b) 39   (c) 107
4. (a) 44   (b) 21   (c) 6

In Exercises 5 through 8, perform the operation using the multiplicative grouping system in Example 6 on page 152. First, try to perform the operations without changing to Hindu-Arabic numerals, then check your answers by converting to Hindu-Arabic numerals, performing the operation, and converting back.

5. θφ γα + χφ χα
6. εφ ια + δφ βα
7. βα (φ + χφ ηα)
8. δφ α (χφ − βφ η)

Critical Thinking

9. Neither the Egyptian nor Babylonian systems provide symbols for zero or negative numbers. Why do you think that is? Discuss possible reasons.

10. In the Hindu-Arabic system, if two numbers are positive and have a different number of digits, the one with the smaller amount of numerals is always the smaller number. For each of the other systems discussed in this section, decide whether or not a number can be larger than a different number with fewer numerals. Include examples.

CHAPTER 4 SECTION 4-2
Computational Exercises

In Exercises 1 through 4, use the method in the Sidelight on page 164 to perform each division.

1. 372 ÷ 12
2. 624 ÷ 16
3. 1,387 ÷ 19
4. 2,200 ÷ 25

Critical Thinking

Now we'll modify the method from Exercises 1 through 4 to work for divisions where there is a fractional part to the quotient.

5. (a) Perform the division 230 ÷ 18 using regular long division.
   (b) To divide 230 ÷ 18 using a modified Egyptian algorithm, set up the division as in Exercises 1 through 4. After you finish doubling the two columns, stopping when the next row would have a number greater than 230, find the combination of numbers in the right column whose sum is closest to 230 without going over. Then add the corresponding numbers in the left column, and find the difference between the sum of numbers in the right column and 230. How do these results compare with numbers you came up with in the long division? Use the result to develop a method for division using the Egyptian algorithm.

6. Refer to Exercise 5. Use the method developed in part (b) to perform the following divisions:
   (a) 427 ÷ 30   (b) 900 ÷ 21   (c) 1,324 ÷ 18.

CHAPTER 4 SECTION 4-3
Critical Thinking

1. (a) Fill in the following table with binary equivalents for base 10 numbers.

Base 10	1	2	3	4	5	6	7	8	9
Binary									

Base 10	10	11	12	13	14	15	16	17	18
Binary									

   (b) Which base 10 numbers have two digits in their binary form? Three digits? Four digits?
   (c) Make a conjecture as to which base 10 numbers have five digits in their binary form. How can you check your answer by finding the binary form of just one base 10 number?

2. Based on the results of Exercise 1, find a formula for the number of nonzero base 10 numbers that have n digits in their binary form. Use your formula and the results of Exercise 1 to find the base 10 number that has binary form 1000000 without directly converting that binary number to base 10, then check your answer by converting directly.

3. (a) Build a table similar to the one in Exercise 1, but for base 3 rather than binary forms. Continue the table until you reach the first base 10 number that has four digits in its base 3 form.
   (b) How many nonzero base 10 numbers have one digit in their base 3 form? Two digits? Three digits?
   (c) Make a conjecture as to which base 10 numbers have four digits in their base 3 form, then write a formula for the number of nonzero base 10 numbers that have n digits in their base 3 form.

4. (a) Let's change our approach from Exercises 1 through 3. We have seen that for any base *n*, the first two-digit number is 10, the first three-digit number is 100, and so on. Find the base 10 equivalent of 10_{four}, 100_{four}, 1000_{four}, and 10000_{four}. How many numbers in base 4 have one digit? Two digits? Three digits? Four digits?

(b) Make a conjecture as to how many base 4 numbers have five digits.

(c) (This one is challenging! Demand extra credit.) Based on all of the information in Exercises 1 through 3, write a general formula that tells you how many nonzero numbers have *n* digits in their base *b* expansion.

CHAPTER 4 SECTION 4-4
Critical Thinking

1. Each of the symbols ♥, ♠, and ♦ represents one of the numerals in a base 3 system. Use the following addition problem to figure out which numerals correspond to each symbol.

2. Refer to Exercise 1. Use the following subtraction problem to figure out which numerals correspond to each symbol. The answer may or may not be the same as Exercise 1.

3. Each of the symbols ♣, ♥, ♠, and ♦ represents one of the numerals in a base 4 system. Use the following addition problem to figure out which numerals correspond to each symbol.

4. Each of the symbols A, E, I, O, and U represents one of the numerals in a base 5 system. Use the following addition problem to figure out which numerals correspond to each symbol.

$$\begin{array}{r} \text{E O I U}_{\text{five}} \\ + \quad \text{E U A U}_{\text{five}} \\ \hline \text{O O E A A}_{\text{five}} \end{array}$$

CHAPTER 8 SECTION 8-1
Real-World Applications

1. The Hawaii Department of Labor issued a press release at the beginning of 2011 projecting that "green jobs" (jobs related to renewable energy and energy efficiency) would increase by 26% between 2010 and 2012. Green jobs in the private sector in Hawaii were estimated at 11,145 in 2010, accounting for 2.4% of total private employment.

(a) How many total jobs were there in the private sector in Hawaii in 2010?

(b) How many green jobs in the private sector were expected by 2012?

(c) If the overall job market was projected to increase by 4.3%, what percentage of total private-sector jobs were projected to be green by 2012?

2. In early 2011, the U.S. Department of Housing and Urban Development reported some grim numbers on the housing industry. There were 523,000 building permits issued for single-family home construction in 2010, but that number was projected to decrease by 27.0% in 2011. Construction was expected to start on 375,000 new homes in 2011, which would represent a 28.8% decrease from 2010. Also, in the 12-month period through January 2011, 298,000 new homes were sold, but this represented just 66.0% of new homes completed.

(a) How many fewer permits were expected to be issued for single-family homes in 2011 as compared to 2010?

(b) How many fewer new homes were started in 2011 compared to 2010?

(c) How many new homes were completed in the 12-month period through January 2011, and how did that compare to the number of new homes started in 2010?

The following graph, based on information from Zillow.com, displays the estimated value of my house (orange) and the average for all houses in my town (green) for the period from mid-2006 to April 1, 2011. The marks on the graph occur on April 1 of each year. Use the graph to answer Exercises 3 through 6.

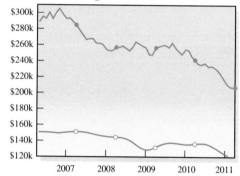

3. Find the percent decrease in the value of my house from April 1, 2007 to April 1, 2011. Then find the percent decrease in the average price of all houses in my town over the same period. Use $120,000 as the average for April 1, 2011.

4. Find the percent change for both my home and the average home in my town for each one-year period starting on April 1, 2007.

5. If the market turned around and my house started gaining value at 6% each year, how many years would it take to get back to the highest value on the chart? Repeat for the town average.

6. Find the sum of the yearly changes for both my home and all homes in my town. How do the results compare to the answers for Exercise 3? What can you conclude?

CHAPTER 8 SECTION 8-2
Real-World Applications

1. Suppose that you borrow $10,000 for school expenses at 6% interest for 5 years.

(a) How much simple interest would you pay?

(b) Suppose the bank splits the 5-year loan into five 1-year loans, so that the future value of the loan would be recalculated at the end of each one-year period, with interest charged on the new amount for the next year. Fill in the following table, which will show the future value of the loan at the end of each one-year period. Round to the nearest dollar.

End of year	1	2	3	4	5
Future value					

(c) How much more interest would you end up paying with the loan being split this way?

(d) Repeat parts (b) and (c) for the situation where the loan is split into two loans, each with length 2½ years.

2. A local bank offers two choices for a certificate of deposit with a term of 4 years. In option 1, you get 4% simple interest for the entire term. In option 2, you get just 3.5% simple interest per year, but the CD is split into four separate one-year CDs, similar to the loan in Exercise 1.
   (a) If you plan to invest $5,000, which CD is the better option? How much more will the better option be worth?
   (b) Would your answers to part (a) change if the amount you invest is $50,000? Why or why not?

CHAPTER 8 SECTION 8-3

Critical Thinking

In these exercises, we'll examine what happens to the compound interest formula when we keep compounding more and more often.

1. The compound interest formula is $A = P\left(1 + \frac{r}{n}\right)^{nt}$, where n is the number of times per year that interest is compounded.
   (a) If we perform the algebraic substitution $u = \frac{n}{r}$, show that the compound interest formula becomes $A = P\left(1 + \frac{1}{u}\right)^{urt}$, and it then can be rewritten as $A = P\left[\left(1 + \frac{1}{u}\right)^{u}\right]^{rt}$.
   (b) When the number of times per year that interest is compounded grows larger and larger, what happens to the expression we called u? (In this case, we say that n is *tending to infinity*.)
   (c) Using a calculator, fill in the following table. Round to three decimal places.

u	50	100	500	1,000	1,500	2,000	2,500
$\left(1 + \frac{1}{u}\right)^{u}$							

   What can you conclude about the value of $\left(1 + \frac{1}{u}\right)^{u}$ as the number of times interest is compounded gets very large?

2. The number that you should have found in Exercise 1(c) is about 2.718, and is denoted e. (Actually, e is irrational, so its decimal equivalent neither terminates nor repeats: $e = 2.718\ldots$) What is the result of the compound interest formula from Exercise 1(a) when the number of times interest is compounded tends to infinity? (In this case, we say that interest is *compounded continuously*. You can think of this as the interest being compounded every instant of every day.)

3. Use the formula $A = Pe^{rt}$ to find the future value after 20 years of a $5,000 account that earns 4% interest compounded continuously, then compare that to the future value of the same account if interest is compounded annually.

4. Now let's compare interest compounded continuously to simple interest. Suppose that $50,000 is invested in two accounts: one earns 6% simple interest (see Section 8-2), the other earns 6% compounded continuously. Fill in the following table with the future value of each account after each term.

Years	5	10	15	20	25	30
6% simple interest						
6% compounded continuously						

CHAPTER 8 SECTION 8-4

Real-World Applications

1. When the engine falls out of Rhonda's old car, it's time to shop for something newer. She is hoping to keep her monthly payment at $150, and the loan will be 6.2% simple interest.
   (a) If Rhonda plans to make a down payment of $2,000 and finance her car for 48 months, what's the price of the most expensive car she can afford? (Hint: Let x = the price of the car and use the formulas on p. 446 and the simple interest formula to set up an equation.)
   (b) How much does the highest price she can afford go up if she puts down $4,000?

2. Refer to Exercise 1. A salesman tries to convince Rhonda that she would be able to get a much better car if she raises the payment by just $30 per month.
   (a) With her down payment of $2,000, how much higher is the maximum price she can shop for if she adds $30 to the monthly payment?
   (b) How much more will Rhonda end up paying total if she goes with the $180 payment?

Critical Thinking

3. (a) For the credit cards in Exercises 37, 39, and 41 of Section 8-4, find the new balance on the first of the month following the given purchases if the credit card company uses the unpaid balance method, rather than the average daily balance method. Assume that the monthly interest rate remains the same.
   (b) Calculate the difference in the amount each customer would owe with the two methods.
   (c) Under what circumstances does the unpaid balance method work out better for the consumer?

4. Repeat Exercise 3 parts (a) and (b) for the accounts in Exercises 38, 40, and 42 of Section 8-4. Does this help you draw any conclusions about when each method is better for the consumer?

Real-World Applications

5. In most cases, payments on student loans are deferred until the borrower graduates, although interest does get added to the principal while the student is in school. If Jaime takes out a student loan for $40,000 in 2012 at 4.5% simple interest and graduates in four years, find the monthly payment that would be required when he graduates if he plans to pay off the loan in 8 years after graduation.

6. Refer to Exercise 5. Rather than borrowing a lump sum at the beginning of college, Cheryl decides to borrow $10,000 each year at the beginning of the school year. If these are treated as four individual loans at 4.5% simple interest, how much more or less would Cheryl owe at the end of four years compared to Jaime?

CHAPTER 8 SECTION 8-5

Real-World Applications

A young couple has saved up $14,000 for a down payment on a home. They are currently paying $1,300 per month to rent a condo. Use this information in these exercises.

1. The couple is pre-approved for a 30-year mortgage at 4.9%, and their realtor estimates that they will need to set aside $3,000 for taxes and other costs at the time of sale. What is the price of the most expensive home they can buy without raising their monthly housing payment?

2. If the couple instead opts for a 15-year mortgage at 4.2%, how much is the most expensive home they can buy?

3. If the couple were to borrow the maximum amount you found in Exercises 1 and 2, how much more do you think they would pay in interest with the 30-year mortgage? Make a guess, then calculate the exact amount.

4. If the couple decides that they can afford to go up to $1,500 per month, how much more can they afford to spend on a home for each loan option?

CHAPTER 8 SECTION 8-6

Real-World Applications

1. Some companies pay an annual dividend to stockholders, while others choose to instead invest that money back into the company. Suppose that you buy 500 shares of stock at $22 in a company that pays an annual dividend of $1.70 per share, then sell all of your shares at $38 three years later. Your best friend buys 500 shares of stock at $20 in a company that doesn't pay dividends, and sells it at $38 three years later. Which of you will make more money? (You can ignore commissions on the sales.)

2. Suppose that the investor in Examples 5 and 6 of Section 8-6 had used an online brokerage that charges a flat fee of $39.95 for all trades, rather than a percentage of the sale. How much greater would her profit have been?

3. Shares of stock in the Ford Motor Company reached a low of $1.43 on November 10, 2008. One year later, the stock closed at $8.41. If you had invested $20,000 in Ford stock on 11/10/08, buying as many shares as possible while paying an online brokerage fee of $19.99 for the purchase, then sold the stock a year later with the same fee, how much profit would you have made? How much money would you have made per day for holding the stock for a year?

4. Refer to Exercise 3.
(a) If you'd been wise and patient enough to wait until January 10, 2011 to sell the stock at $18.65, how much greater would your profit have been?
(b) Using the Internet as a resource, investigate why Ford stock was so low in November 2008, and why it went up so much, then write a short essay summarizing your findings.

CHAPTER 11 SECTION 11-1

Real-World Applications

While making up his schedule for spring semester, Tom complains that he doesn't have very many choices of schedule because of the general education requirements he has to meet. His advisor tells Tom that he has to take one course from each of English (3 choices), History (5 choices), Math/Stats (5 choices), Computer Science (4 choices) and general Science (6 choices). Does Tom have a legitimate gripe?

1. If every possible course is available at the time he's registering, how many possible schedules can he choose from (disregarding when the classes meet)?

2. If Tom hasn't met the prerequisites for two of the Math/Stat courses and three of the science courses, by how much does this reduce his number of possible schedules?

3. When trying to schedule, Tom finds that all but one of the English courses is closed, as are two history courses and one science course. How many schedules does he have to choose from now?

4. In an unprecedented effort to make the general education requirements more accessible, the dean of Tom's college decides to double the number of acceptable courses in each of those five areas. What effect does this have on the number of possible schedules?

CHAPTER 11 SECTION 11-2

Critical Thinking

1. In a class of 30 people, the professor decides that everyone should get to know each other, so she insists that everyone have at least a 2-minute conversation with everyone else in the class. What's the least amount of total time that will be spent on these conversations?

2. (a) Refer to Exercise 1. Find the least amount of time needed if the class has 10 students, 20 students, and 40 students.
(b) Based on the amount of time calculated for 10, 20, 30, and 40 students, try to make a conjecture as to the time needed if there are 50 students, then check your answer.

3. (a) The 2011 baseball team at the Ohio State University consisted of 10 freshmen, 9 sophomores, 7 juniors, and 7 seniors. The coaches want to choose two players from each class to represent the team at a booster club banquet. How many different ways can they choose?
(b) The coaches also need to choose four players overall to visit elementary schools in the community, with each player going to a different school. How many different ways can they make this choice?

4. A state lottery offers two games in which you choose six numbers. In the first, there are 25 numbers to choose from and you need to match the numbers in the order in which they are drawn. In the second, there are 50 numbers to choose from, and you need to match all six regardless of the order. Which one is easier to win?

CHAPTER 11 SECTION 11-3

Critical Thinking

1. (a) Compute the empirical probability of a randomly selected person in your math class being left-handed. (You'll need to find out which hand everyone writes with.)
(b) Do some research on the Internet to compare that probability to the probability that a person in the general population is left-handed. How do they compare?
(c) The website mlb.com lists rosters for all 30 Major League Baseball teams, along with which hand each player throws with. Look up your favorite team (or the one closest to your campus if you don't have one) and see how the empirical probability of a player being left-handed compares to your class and the general population. Try to explain any apparent discrepancies.

2. (a) Compute the empirical probability of a randomly selected person in your math class having blue eyes.
(b) Do some research on the Internet to compare that probability to the analogous probability for the general public in the United States. If the results for (a) and (b) are significantly different, do some more research to make up a list of possible reasons.

3. (a) Find the classical probability of rolling a number less than 3 with one roll of a single die.
(b) Roll a die each of the number of times in the following table, record the results, and fill in the empirical probabilities. Describe any trends or anomalies that you observe, with possible explanations. (If you don't have any dice, do a Google search for "roll dice online.")

Number of rolls	10	20	30	40	50
Probability of rolling less than 3					

4. (a) Find the classical probability of rolling either 6, 7, or 8 with two dice.
(b) Roll two dice each of the number of times in the following table, record the results, and fill in the empirical probabilities. Describe any trends or anomalies that you observe, with possible explanations. (If you don't have any dice, do a Google search for "virtual dice.")

Number of rolls	10	20	30	40	50
Probability of rolling 6, 7, or 8					

CHAPTER 11 SECTION 11-4

Critical Thinking

1. (a) We know that when flipping a coin, the probability of getting tails is $\frac{1}{2}$. Use a tree diagram to find the probability of getting tails twice in a row.
(b) We also know that the probability of rolling a 5 with one die is $\frac{1}{6}$. Use tree diagrams to find the probability of getting tails and then rolling a 5 when you flip a coin and then roll a single die.
(c) Based on the results of parts (a) and (b), how do you think you find the probability of two unconnected events occurring consecutively when you know the probability of each occurring individually? (Answer successfully, and you've discovered an important rule we'll study in Section 11-8.)

2. In the finals of an Angry Birds tournament, Bob is the number one seed, and he will win the championship if he wins one game in the finals. The other two finalists are Fran and Julio, and they each need to win two games to claim the title.
(a) Draw a tree diagram and find the sample space for each possible result of the finals.
(b) Assuming that all three players have an equal likelihood of winning any individual game, find the probability of each outcome in the sample space. (Hint: Use the rule you discovered in 1[c].) Make sure that all of your probabilities add to 1!
(c) Use the results of (b) to find the probability of each contestant winning the championship.

3. Disappointed in her failure to gain the top seed for the tournament in Exercise 2, Fran resorts to using a banned substance that improves her reflexes and makes her twice as likely to win any individual game as Bob or Julio. Find the probability of each winning the championship.

4. If Fran's cheating (see Exercise 3) had made her three times as likely to win any individual match as Bob or Julio, would this have been enough to make her the most likely winner?

CHAPTER 11 SECTION 11-5

Critical Thinking

1. Many lottery games are based on choosing some numbers from a larger group. Devise a lottery game with at least three different ways of winning, compute the probability of winning for each way, and assign payouts for each winning combination that you think are fair.

2. (a) Suppose that we choose 3 letters at random from the first 10 letters of the alphabet without repeats. Find the probability of choosing ABC in that order, then find the probability of choosing ABC in any order.
(b) If we change the scenario in part (a) to include repeats, recompute the probabilities.

3. (a) What is the arithmetic relationship between the two probabilities in Exercise 2(a)?
(b) Suppose the scenario in Exercise 2 is repeated, this time choosing four letters rather than three. Without actually computing either probability, what do you think the relationship between the two probabilities will be? Explain how you got your answer. (Hint: Think about part [a] and the effect of order mattering.)

4. Think of a real-life scenario for which it would be reasonable to compute probabilities using combinations, and one in which it would be reasonable to use permutations. (No stealing any of the scenarios from the section!)

CHAPTER 11 SECTION 11-6

Critical Thinking

In many respects, investing in the stock market is just another form of gambling: you pay money for stocks, and when you sell them at some point, you can gain money, lose money, or break even. Use what you learned about expected value to answer the questions in Exercises 1 and 2 about buying and selling stock.

1. The Bui family decides to invest their $4,000 tax refund in the stock market for one year. An analyst suggests that they choose between two stocks. A computer analysis of past performance predicts that if they invest in RZ Electronics, there's a 40% chance they'll make a profit of $1,600, a 40% change they'll make $200, and a 20% chance they'll lose $2,000. For Jackson Builders, there's a 75% chance they'll make $800, and a 25% chance that they'll lose $300.
(a) Without doing any calculations, which sounds like the better investment to you? Why?
(b) Find the expected value of each investment.

2. You're given the option of investing $10,000 in one of three mutual funds. A prominent market analyst posts the following estimates of performance for the three funds. The Hetrick Fund: 40% chance of a 35% gain; 40% chance of a 30% loss; 20% chance of breaking even. The Abercrombie Fund: 80% chance of breaking even; 12% chance of an 18% gain; 8% chance of a 9% loss. The Goldberg Fund: 25% chance of a 90% gain; 25% chance of a 5% gain; 40% chance of breaking even; 10% chance of losing everything. Answer parts (a) and (b) without doing any calculations.
(a) If your primary objective is to shoot for the largest possible return without regard to risk, which would you be likely to choose?
(b) If your primary objective is the least risk of losing big, which would you be likely to choose?
(c) Find the expected value for each fund. With these choices, who would be most likely to be successful: a timid investor, or an aggressive one?

Real-World Applications

In sports betting, odds are often given in terms of the profit on a $100 bet if your team wins. For example, if a team is listed as +130, that means if you bet $100 and win, you'll get back $230: your original $100 plus a profit of $130. If the odds against a team winning are 5:1, it means that a $1 bet would return a total of $6, making a profit of $5.

3. At the beginning of the 2011 NBA playoffs, the four Las Vegas favorites to win were the L.A. Lakers at +160, the Miami Heat and Chicago Bulls, both at +300, and the Boston Celtics at +550. According to the oddsmakers, what was the probability of each team winning the title?

4. At the beginning of the 2011 Major League Baseball season, the four Las Vegas favorites to win the world series were Philadelphia (3:1 odds against), Boston (9:2 odds against), New York Yankees (5:1 odds against), and San Francisco (15:1 odds against). According to the oddsmakers, (a) what was the probability of each team winning the World Series, and (b) how would the odds have been listed in terms of profit on a $100 bet?

CHAPTER 11 SECTION 11-7

Critical Thinking

Exercises 1 through 4 require some careful thought (and maybe some research), and may be open to interpretation. Analyze the situation and decide if the two events are or are not mutually exclusive, then write an explanation of your answer.

1. Being acquitted of a crime and spending time in jail after the trial

2. Being born outside the boundaries of the United States and being elected president of the United States

3. Being a freshman, being a sophomore, and being a junior

4. Getting fewer votes than your opponent when running for the presidency and winning the election

5. Use a Venn diagram to illustrate the probability calculation in Try This One 5 on page 619.

6. Use a Venn diagram to illustrate the probability calculation in Try This One 6 on page 619.

CHAPTER 11 SECTION 11-8

Critical Thinking

1. In many lotto games, the player chooses six numbers from a pool of 40 or more, and if he or she matches all six numbers drawn, they win the jackpot. If there is more than one winner, the jackpot is split evenly among all winners.
(a) First instinct, if you were playing a lotto game, would you choose the numbers 1, 2, 3, 4, 5, and 6? Why or why not?
(b) After the first winning number is drawn, does it have any effect on what number is drawn next? Think carefully, then use your answer and the idea of independence of events and probability to explain why there's nothing wrong with choosing 1, 2, 3, 4, 5, and 6.
(c) In fact, something in the statement that begins this exercise indicates that 1, 2, 3, 4, 5, and 6 might be a desirable choice. What is it?

2. Classify each statement as sensible or silly, and briefly explain your answer.
(a) I flipped a coin five times in a row and got heads, so I'm willing to bet $100 that it will be tails on the next flip.
(b) There's a 30% chance of rain tomorrow and there's a 50–50 chance of my only class getting cancelled, so there's a 35% chance I'll be able to go golfing without missing class. (By the way, I'm not going to go golfing if it rains.)
(c) According to duilawblog.com, the probability of being convicted when charged with DUI in California is 0.794. If 50% of those convicted get at least 48 hours in jail, the probability of spending at least 48 hours in jail if charged with DUI in California is 1.294.
(d) If I buy one ticket to a multistate lottery, I have a better chance of being struck by lightning than I do of winning the grand prize.

Real-World Applications

The following table shows the number of active-duty personnel in each branch of the military in 2008, as well as the percentage that were women. (Source: The World Almanac and Book of Facts 2010.*) Find each probability.*

Branch	Army	Navy	Marines	Air Force	Coast Guard
Total	539,170	331,785	193,040	328,771	42,424
% Women	13.6%	15.0%	6.1%	19.6%	12.2%

3. An individual on active duty was a woman given that he or she was in either the Air Force, Marines, or Coast Guard.
4. An individual was in the Army given that it was a man.
5. An individual was a man given that he or she was not in the Navy.
6. An individual was not a Marine given that it was a woman.

CHAPTER 11 SECTION 11-9

Critical Thinking

We know that to qualify as a binomial experiment, individual trials have to be independent and the probability of success has to remain the same for each trial. But when sampling from a large population without replacement, as in Example 4 in Section 11-9, we assume that these conditions are very close to being met.

1. Decide if it would be reasonable to apply the binomial probability formula to each question. You don't need to find the probability.
(a) According to the U.S. Department of Health and Human Services, just 3.9% of men in America are taller than 6′2″. What is the probability that 3 out of 5 people chosen in your class are 6′3″ or taller?
(b) The Bureau of Labor Statistics reported that 13.7% of work-eligible residents in the Las Vegas metro area were unemployed in February 2011. If 30 people from that area were chosen at random, what was the probability that 5 were unemployed?
(c) There are 27 people in my Calc 2 class right now, and 22 of them are passing. If I pick 6 at random, what is the probability that all six are passing?
2. (a) Write an example of a binomial experiment in real life in which the conditions are all met, and lack of replacement is not an issue.
(b) Write an example of a binomial experiment in real life without replacement, in which case we would need a large sample to use the binomial probability formula.

CHAPTER 12 SECTION 12-1

Real-World Applications

For these exercises, all the students in your class will need to fill out the following survey. Then use the results to answer questions 1 through 4.

Birthday (Day of Month)	Year in School	Credit Hours This Semester	Pick a Number Between 0 and 100

1. Draw a stem-and-leaf plot for the results of the birthday question.
2. Draw a frequency distribution for the year in school data.
3. Draw a grouped frequency distribution for the "number between 0 and 100" data.
4. Of the three methods for organizing data in this section, choose the one you think would be most appropriate for the credit hours data, describe why you chose that method, then use the method to organize the data.

CHAPTER 12 SECTION 12-2

Real-World Applications

1. Using the Internet as a resource, find the number of games won by your school's men's basketball team over the last 10 seasons and draw a table to organize the data. (If your school doesn't have a basketball team, choose a nearby school that does.) Draw a time series graph for your data and use the graph to analyze the team's performance.
2. Using the Internet as a resource, find the number of games won by the closest professional football team to your campus over the last 20 years. (If the closest team hasn't existed for 20 years, pick another team that has.) Divide the wins into classes and draw a frequency distribution for the data.

Critical Thinking

3. Make up your own pie chart problem: using the Internet, a newspaper, or a library as a resource, find some data that you find interesting that would lend itself to being described by a pie chart, then draw the chart.
4. Make up your own frequency polygon problem: using the Internet, a newspaper, or a library as a resource, find some data that you find interesting that would lend itself to being divided into classes and described by a frequency polygon, then organize the data and draw the polygon.

CHAPTER 12 SECTION 12-3

Critical Thinking

1. For the data in Exercises 17 and 18 in Section 12-3, analyze the data set and the measures of average. Which of the measures of average do you think best describes what you think of as a meaningful average for the data? Explain your decision.
2. Describe a data set for which you think the mode would be the most meaningful measure of average.
3. Describe a data set for which you think the midrange would be the most meaningful measure of average.
4. Under what circumstances would the median for a data set be likely to be close to the mean? When would those two measures of average be very different?

CHAPTER 12 SECTION 12-4

Critical Thinking

1. When playing golf, in most cases the player will want to get the ball as close as possible to the hole when hitting a shot approaching the green. Suppose that two players hit 10 approach shots to a green, and their results are as shown in the two figures. The black dot is the hole, and the white dots are where each shot ended up.

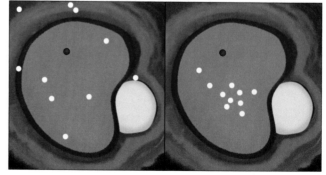

Pat's shots   Ron's shots

(a) If you were to "average" the locations of all of the results for each player, where would you estimate the average shot would be for each?
(b) How would you describe the measures of variation for each of the players?
(c) Which is a better player in your opinion? What does that say about the importance of measures of average compared to measures of variation in some situations?

2. The table shows the number of class periods missed over the last 10 courses by two students.

Helena	3	4	3	2	2	4	3	2	2	3
Juanita	0	9	2	1	0	6	0	4	0	8

(a) Find the mean number of classes missed for each student.
(b) Without doing the calculations, how do you think the measures of variation compare for the two students?
(c) Which is a better student in your opinion? What does that say about the importance of measures of average compared to measures of variation in some situations?

3. Think of a real-world quantity that would be likely to have a fairly small standard deviation if you compiled some data on that quantity.

4. Think of a real-world quantity that would be likely to have a fairly large standard deviation if you compiled some data on that quantity.

CHAPTER 12 SECTION 12-5

Critical Thinking

The box plot is a graphical way to evaluate the spread of a data set. In particular, it makes it easy to identify data points that are "outliers"—those that appear to be aberrational. Follow these steps to complete a box plot for the data in Exercises 1 through 4. (The sample that follows is a box plot for the data in Exercise 21 in chapter 12.)

(a) Find the values for Q_1, Q_2, and Q_3.
(b) Draw a number line ranging from the least to greatest values in the data set, and label Q_1, Q_2, and Q_3 on it.
(c) Draw a rectangular box over the number line, beginning it at Q_1 and ending it at Q_3. (See sample.) Then draw a vertical line through the box at Q_2.
(d) Find the distance from Q_1 to Q_3, and multiply it by 1.5. Any data point that is more than this distance away from the box is considered to be an outlier.

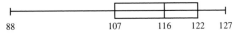

88   107   116   122   127

1. The following data are the number of Internet users, in millions, in the top 15 countries for Internet usage. (Source: *Computer Industry Almanac*)

235   234   108   99   57   45   41   39
37   37   36   33   26   25   23

(a) Draw a box plot for the data.
(b) What does the position of the box tell you about the data set?
(c) Are there any outliers in the data set? What are they?
(d) What about the data set do the values inside the box represent?

2. The table shows the median price (in thousands) of all existing homes sold in the United States for the years from 1998 to 2010. (Source: National Association of Realtors)

Year	98	99	00	01	02	03	04
Median Price	128.4	133.3	139.0	147.8	158.1	180.2	195.2

Year	05	06	07	08	09	10
Median Price	219.0	221.9	217.9	198.1	172.5	172.9

(a) Draw a box plot for the data.
(b) What does the position of the box tell you about the data set?
(c) Are there any outliers in the data set? What are they?

3. Draw a box plot for the data in Exercise 22 of Section 12-5, then write an analysis of the data using your box plot. What can you learn from the box plot that was not apparent from just finding the quartiles?

4. Draw a box plot of a data set that you gathered, then write an analysis of the data using your box plot. The data set should have at least 10 values.

CHAPTER 12 SECTION 12-6

Real-World Applications

Use the empirical rule to answer the following questions.

1. The College Board reported that SAT scores in the early 2000s were normally distributed with mean 1026 and standard deviation 210.
(a) What percent of students scored over 606?
(b) Out of every 500 students, how many scored between 816 and 1236?

2. According to 9monthsafter.com, the durations of human pregnancies are normally distributed with mean 268 days and standard deviation 15 days.
(a) What is the probability that you were born more than 298 days after you were conceived?
(b) If a child is conceived on April 19, what is the probability that it will be born before January 27?

3. According to the label, a bag of Kettle brand Tias tortilla chips contains 8 ounces of chips. Suppose that the bagging process is normally distributed with a standard deviation of 0.14 ounces. If the manager wants there to be greater than a 97% chance that any given bag has at least 8 ounces, and the weight they set their filling machine for provides the mean weight, at what value should they set the machine?

4. The final scores for students in my Math 102 classes over the last 10 years are approximately normally distributed with mean 74 and standard deviation 10.7. If I decide to assign one student's grade this semester by randomly choosing a score of some student in the last 10 years, what's the approximate probability that the student will get a score that is (a) between 63 and 85, and (b) over 53?

CHAPTER 12 SECTION 12-7

Critical Thinking

1. The number of incoming students at two campuses of a midwestern university have historically been normally distributed. The main campus incoming class has a mean of 3,402 and a standard deviation of 425, and the regional campus incoming class has a mean of 730 and a standard deviation of 102. If there were 3,740 incoming students on the main campus and 822 on the regional campus, which had the more successful year in student recruitment based on z scores?

2. Discuss whether or not you think each of the given quantities is likely to be normally distributed.
(a) Gas prices over a two-year period
(b) The number of M&Ms in a two-pound bag
(c) The heights of players on professional basketball teams
(d) The daily number of hits for Facebook
(e) The ages of all active-duty military personnel

CHAPTER 12 SECTION 12-8

Critical Thinking

For each pair of quantities, decide if they are likely to be positively correlated, negatively correlated, or uncorrelated.

1. Total number of years of school completed and average annual salary.
2. Speed limit on a stretch of road and the probability of surviving an accident on that road.
3. Number of primary schools in a town and average SAT scores of
4. Number of class meetings missed by college students and their average score in the course.
5. Most people assume that there's a very strong connection between the price of crude oil and gasoline prices. But how strong is it? Do an Internet search for "oil prices historical" and "gas prices historical" and find prices for each on at least 10 dates over a span of at least two years. Then draw a scatter plot and calculate the correlation coefficient. Discuss how strong the connection appears to be.

6. You would think that there would be a strong correlation between a person's height and their shoe size. Is that really the case? Find the heights and shoe sizes of 10 different people, calculate the correlation coefficient, and see if it's significant at the 5% and 1% levels.

CHAPTER 13 SECTION 13-1

Computational Exercises

In Exercises 1 through 4, we'll build a finite mathematical system using the numbers 1, 2, 3, and 4. To perform the operation, multiply the numbers, then subtract their sum.

1. Build an operation table for this system.

Critical Thinking

2. Based on your knowledge of arithmetic operations, (or maybe algebra—that's a hint) should this system be commutative? Explain. Then check your answer using the operation table.

3. Repeat Exercise 2 for the associative property.

4. If we change the operation to be the sum minus the product, how could you quickly build the operation table based on your answer to Exercise 1?

Exercises 5 through 8 are based on the classic game of Rock, Paper, Scissors. (If you're not familiar with the game, ask someone for the rules, or look it up on Wikipedia.) Use the rules of the game to build a mathematical system. The elements are rock, paper, and scissors, and the result of the operation is which of the two elements wins the game.

5. Without building a table, how can you tell that the system will not be closed?

6. Will the system be commutative? Why or why not?

Computational Exercises

7. Build the operation table for this system.

Critical Thinking

8. Which, if any, of the remaining properties we studied in this section are satisfied by this system?

CHAPTER 13 SECTION 13-2

Computational Exercises

In Exercises 1 through 4, we'll deal with a clock system that will require some mental flexibility: a negative six-hour clock system, where the hours are 0, −1, −2, −3, −4, and −5 (arranged in clockwise fashion as listed), and the clock runs counterclockwise (represented by +). Perform each operation.

1. (a) $-3 + -2$ (b) $-4 + -5$
2. (a) $0 + -3$ (b) $-2 + -4$
3. (a) $-2 + -4 + -3$ (b) $-5 + -3 + -1$
4. (a) $2(-4)$ (b) $3(-5)$

Critical Thinking

5. Find the multiplicative inverse, if there is one, for 2 in a 4-hour clock system. Then repeat for a 5-hour clock, then 6-hour, and continue all the way up to the 12-hour clock.

6. Find the multiplicative inverse, if there is one, for 3 in a 4-hour clock system. Then repeat for a 5-hour clock, then 6-hour, and continue all the way up to the 12-hour clock.

7. Refer to Exercises 5 and 6. Can you draw a general conclusion as to which clock systems the number 2 will have a multiplicative inverse in? What about 3?

8. Based on the results of Exercise 7, find a general condition that describes when a number n will and will not have a multiplicative inverse in an m-hour clock system.

CHAPTER 13 SECTION 13-3

Critical Thinking

1. Suppose that there's a large lecture class with 124 students in it, and the instructor wants to divide the class into groups with the same number of students in each group.
(a) Describe how finding the possible number of people per group is a modular arithmetic problem.
(b) How many different group sizes are possible?

2. The admissions office at Toga Tech U. received 154 scholarship applications this spring, and they want to divide them into packets to be distributed to graders, with the same number of applications in each packet. Assume that every packet will have more than one application.
(a) Describe how finding the possible number of applications in each packet is a modular arithmetic problem.
(b) How many different packet sizes are possible?
(c) How many different packet sizes are possible if the head of admissions decides to hold back 8 applications to grade herself?

3. As I write this problem, the date is Thursday, April 21, 2011. It's 11:00 A.M., but that's irrelevant. What day of the week will it be exactly one year and 3 days from now? Explain how this is a modular arithmetic problem, and solve it. (*Hint*: The year is important!)

4. Refer to Exercise 3. What day of the week will be exactly two years and 3 days from now?

Real-World Applications

5. Write a congruence that solves each problem, then find the answer.
(a) If a log is 212 inches long and will be cut into foot-long sections, how long will the leftover piece be?
(b) If a job that normally takes 586 minutes is divided into hour-long portions, how many minutes long will the leftover portion be?

6. Write a congruence that solves each problem, then find the answer.
(a) After graduation from college, Jed decides to backpack the Appalachian Trail, and he plans a trip of 53 days, leaving on a Wednesday. On what day of the week will he return?
(b) If 84 players show up and divide into teams for pickup basketball games, how many leftover players won't get on a team? (There are five players per team.)

7. Let's try an experiment based on bank routing numbers, as described in the Sidelight on p. 736. Make up 10 nine-digit numbers off the top of your head. Then test each and see how many would work as legitimate bank routing numbers. What do you conclude?

8. Refer to Exercise 7. If you have some expertise in Excel or calculator programming, write a program that can quickly check any nine-digit number to see if it's a legitimate bank routing number, then run the test in Exercise 7 on 100 different randomly selected nine-digit numbers. (You can find a wide variety of websites that will generate a list of random numbers.) With this bigger sample, how is your conclusion from Exercise 7 changed?

ADDITIONAL EXERCISES ANSWERS

CHAPTER 2: SETS

Additional Exercise Set 2-1
1. Answers vary. If two sets are equal, they have the exact same elements, so they must have the same number of elements.
3. (a) It's not clearly defined who qualifies as "an American."
   (b) Who decides what a "luxury car" is?
   (c) "Legitimate chance" is subjective. Also, which tournament? Men's? Women's? Division II?
   (d) What exactly defines pay? Salary? Salary and benefits? Is overtime included?
   (e) Biological mothers? Adopted mothers? Foster mothers?

Additional Exercise Set 2-2
1. (a) The set of people who have been convicted of a felony.
   (b) The set of people who have been convicted of a felony and have been released, or charged with a felony and found not guilty.
   (c) The set of people who were charged with a felony and either found not guilty or had charges dropped before standing trial.
3. (a) The set of people who have been convicted of a felony and have been released from prison.
   (b) The set of people who have previously been convicted of a felony, and are currently awaiting trial on another felony charge.
   (c) There's nobody in this set.
5. (a), (b): Answers vary.
   (c) $n(A \cup B) = n(A) + n(B) - n(A \cap B)$

Additional Exercise Set 2-3
1. (a)

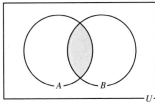

   (b) Answers vary.   (c) $B \subseteq A$
3. (a)

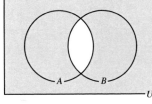

   (b) Answers vary.   (c) A and B are disjoint.
5. (a)

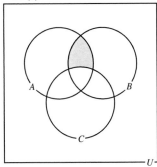

   (b) Answers vary. (c) B and C are disjoint.

Additional Exercise Set 2-4
1. (a) 22   (b) 36
3. (a) 18   (b) 30 in each league
5. Answers vary.

Additional Exercise Set 2-5
1. (a) Correspond every number to the number that is one less.
   (b) $\aleph_0 + 1 = \aleph_0$
3. $\aleph_0$
5. 15
7. $\aleph_0$

CHAPTER 3: LOGIC

Additional Exercise Set 3-1
1. (a) a is less than 20.
   (b) a is not less than 20.
   (c) $a \geq 20$ (This is if we assume that a is a real number. Otherwise, the statement would be $a \geq 20$ or a is not a real number.)
3. There will not be any fans at any of the games.
5. There is at least one person who likes my history professor.

Additional Exercise Set 3-2
1. True
3. True
5. True

Additional Exercise Set 3-3
1. Both statements are false, and a biconditional is true when both individual statements have the same truth value.
3. The first statement is true and the second false, and a biconditional is false when the two statements have opposite truth values.
5. This statement can be written as T $\rightarrow$ F, so it is false.

Additional Exercise Set 3-4
1. Invalid
3. Valid
5. Answers vary.

Additional Exercise Set 3-5
1. One possibility: All students with GPAs less than 1.5 are on academic probation. Bob is not on academic probation, so his GPA is not less than 1.5.
3. Invalid
5. Invalid

CHAPTER 4: NUMERATION SYSTEMS

Additional Exercise Set 4-1
1. (a) 98   (b) 46   (c) 110
3. (a) ηφ εα   (b) χφ ια   (c) φφ γα
5. φφ
7. ιφ θα
9. Answers vary.

Additional Exercise Set 4-2
1. 31
3. 73
5. (a) $12\frac{7}{9}$
   (b) After finding the appropriate combination in the right column, the sum of the associated numbers in the left column is the whole number part of the quotient; the difference between the sum in the right column and the divisor is the remainder, which you then write over the dividend to form the fractional part of the quotient.

Additional Exercise Set 4-3

Note that all binary numbers in Exercises 1 and 2 are written without the 2 subscript.

1. (a)

Base 10	1	2	3	4	5	6	7	8	9
Binary	1	10	11	100	101	110	111	1000	1001

Base 10	10	11	12	13	14	15	16	17	18
Binary	1010	1011	1100	1101	1110	1111	10000	10001	10010

(b) Two digits: 2 and 3; three digits: 4 through 8; four digits: 9 through 15

(c) Conjecture: 16 through 31. The binary form of 32 is 100000, making it the first one with six digits.

3. Note that base 3 numbers in this problem are written without the 3 subscript.

(a)

Base 10	1	2	3	4	5	6	7	8	9
Base 3	1	2	10	11	12	20	21	22	100

Base 10	10	11	12	13	14	15	16	17	18
Base 3	101	102	110	111	112	120	121	122	200

Base 10	19	20	21	22	23	24	25	26	27
Base 3	201	202	210	211	212	220	221	222	1000

(b) One digit: 2; two digits: 6; three digits: 18

(c) Conjecture: 27 through 80; formula: $2 \cdot 3^{n-1}$

Additional Exercise Set 4-4

1. ♠ = 0, ♦ = 1, ♥ = 2

3. ♣ = 0, ♠ = 1, ♥ = 2, ♦ = 3

CHAPTER 8: CONSUMER MATHEMATICS

Additional Exercise Set 8-1

1. (a) 464,375   (b) 14,043   (c) 2.9%

Note: The answers for 3 through 6 can vary some depending on how you read the values from the graph.

3. (a) 27.4%; 20%

5. Almost 7 years; almost 4 years

Additional Exercise Set 8-2

1. (a) $3,000

(b)

End of year	1	2	3	4	5
Future value ($)	10,600	11,236	11,910	12,625	13,383

(c) $383

(d)

End of year	$2\frac{1}{2}$	5
Future value ($)	11,500	13,225

You'd pay $225 more.

Additional Exercise Set 8-3

1. (a) If $u = \frac{n}{r}$, then $\frac{r}{n} = \frac{1}{u}$ and $n = ur$, so $P\left(1 + \frac{r}{n}\right)^{nt} = P\left(1 + \frac{1}{u}\right)^{urt}$.

Then use a property of exponents to write it as $A = P\left[\left(1 + \frac{1}{u}\right)^{u}\right]^{rt}$.

(b) When n tends to infinity, n/r does as well.

(c)

u	50	100	500	1,000	1,500	2,000	2,500
$\left(1 + \frac{1}{u}\right)^{u}$	2.692	2.705	2.716	2.717	2.717	2.718	2.718

The formula gets closer and closer to 2.718.

3. Continuously: $11,127.70; Annually: $10,955.62

Additional Exercise Set 8-4

1. (a) $7,769.23   (b) $2,000 more. The change in down payment doesn't affect the amount financed.

3. (a) Ex. 37: $669.45; Ex. 39: $347.78; Ex. 41: $529.94

(b) Ex. 37: Unpaid balance method is $0.30 higher.

Ex. 39: Unpaid balance method is $2.98 lower.

Ex. 41: Unpaid balance method is $3.36 lower.

(c) When purchases total a lot more than payments, unpaid balance is the better method, especially if payments are made late in the month.

5. $641.67

Additional Exercise Set 8-5

1. $255,947

3. $162,444

Additional Exercise Set 8-6

1. You make a profit of $10,550, your friend makes $9,000.

3. $97,484.58, or $267.08 per day

CHAPTER 11: PROBABILITY AND COUNTING TECHNIQUES

Additional Exercise Set 11-1

1. 1,800

3. 300

Additional Exercise Set 11-2

1. 870 minutes, or 14.5 hours

3. (a) 714,420   (b) 982,080

Additional Exercise Set 11-3

1. Answers vary.

3. (a) $\frac{1}{3}$ (b) Answers vary.

Additional Exercise Set 11-4

1. (a) $\frac{1}{4}$ (b) $\frac{1}{12}$

(c) Multiply the individual probabilities.

3. Bob: $\frac{1}{2}$; Fran: $\frac{3}{8}$; Julio: $\frac{1}{8}$

Additional Exercise Set 11-5

1. Answers vary.

3. (a) The probability of any order is six times as great as the probability of in order.

(b) The probability of any order should be 24 times as great. The difference between the number of possibilities is the number of permutations of the letters chosen. When it was 3 letters, any order was 3! = 6 times more likely. For 4 letters, it should be 4! = 24 times more likely.

Additional Exercise Set 11-6

1. (a) Answers vary.

(b) RZ Electronics: +$320; Jackson Builders: +$525

3. L.A.: 0.38; Miami and Chicago: 0.25; Boston: 0.15

Additional Exercise Set 11-7

These answers are my interpretation, which may or may not be the only one.

1. Not mutually exclusive. You could be acquitted of a crime and convicted of a different one at the same time, leading to jail time after being acquitted. Or you could have been in the middle of a sentence for a different crime when tried.

3. Not mutually exclusive. There are different ways of being categorized: you could be a chronological junior (in your third year) but only have enough credits to be considered a sophomore academically.

5.

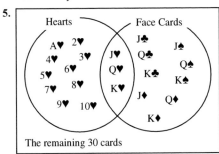

Additional Exercise Set 11-8
1. (a) Answers vary.
   (b) Every number drawn is independent of the previous numbers chosen, so the probability of 1, 2, 3, 4, 5, 6 is no different than the probability of any other six numbers.
   (c) That combination might be desirable because it's likely nobody else will choose it and you won't have to split the prize if it wins.
3. 0.14
5. 0.86

Additional Exercise Set 11-9
1. (a) Yes   (b) Yes   (c) No

CHAPTER 12: STATISTICS
Additional Exercise Set 12-1
1–4. Answers vary.

Additional Exercise Set 12-2
1–4. Answers vary.

Additional Exercise Set 12-3
1–4. Answers vary.

Additional Exercise Set 12-4
1. (a) Average would be close to the hole for Pat, close to the center of the green for Ron.
   (b) Pat has a large variation, Ron has a very small variation.
   (c) Answers vary, but this example shows that variation can sometimes be more meaningful than average.
3–4. Answers vary.

Additional Exercise Set 12-5
1. (a)

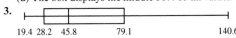

   (b) The majority of values are on the low end of the distribution.
   (c) Both 234 and 235 are outliers.
   (d) The box displays the middle 50% of all values.
3.

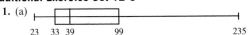

   Google is a huge outlier in this data set, but even if Google is ignored, the box is still on the lower end, and the median is on the lower end of the box. So overall we can see that the majority of the values are near the bottom end of the distribution.

Additional Exercise Set 12-6
1. (a) About 97.65%
   (b) 340
3. 8.28 ounces

Additional Exercise Set 12-7
1. The regional campus with a z score of 0.902, compared to 0.795

Additional Exercise Set 12-8
1. Positive
3. None (but you could make a case that small-town students might get a better education than those in large urban districts, in which case it would be negative.)
5–6. Answers vary.

CHAPTER 13: OTHER MATHEMATICAL SYSTEMS
Additional Exercise Set 13-1
1.

	1	2	3	4
1	−1	−1	−1	−1
2	−1	0	1	2
3	−1	1	3	5
4	−1	2	5	8

3. It should not. If we use @ to represent the operation in this system:
$(a @ b) @ c = (ab − (a + b)) @ c = (ab − (a + b)) c − ((ab − (a + b)) + c)$
$= abc − ac − bc − ab + a + b − c$
$a @ (b @ c) = a @ (bc − (b + c)) = a (bc − (b + c)) − (a + (bc − (b + c)))$
$= abc − ab − ac − a − bc + b + c$
These two expressions are not equal.
5. The result of combining two identical elements results in a tie; there is no element that represents the winner. (In fact, we would have to define "tie" as the outcome in that case for the system to be well-defined.)
7.

	Rock	Paper	Scissors
Rock	Tie	Paper	Rock
Paper	Paper	Tie	Scissors
Scissors	Rock	Scissors	Tie

Additional Exercise Set 13-2
1. (a) −1   (b) −5
3. (a) −1   (b) −1
5.

Hours	4	5	6	7	8	9	10	11	12
Mult. Inverse	None	3	None	4	None	5	None	6	None

7. For 2, only the odd numbers have a multiplicative inverse. For 3, any number not divisible by 3 has a multiplicative inverse.

Additional Exercise Set 13-3
1. (a) We would need to find group sizes g for which $124 \equiv 0 \bmod g$.
   (b) There are only 4: 2, 4, 31, and 62 (and the last two are pretty ridiculous group sizes).
3. There are 366 days in the next year (2012 is a leap year), plus 3 more, so we need to find 369 mod 7; this will tell us how many days of the week after Thursday that day is. The answer is Tuesday.
5. (a) $212 \equiv x \bmod 12$; 8"
   (b) $586 \equiv x \bmod 60$; 46 minutes
7–8. Answers vary.

Design Elements

(Pizza, Silver pan, Calculator: (c) iStockphoto.

Chapter 1

Opener: © Robert Voets/CBS Photo Archive via Getty Images; p. 4: © The McGraw-Hill Companies, Inc./C.P. Hammond, photographer; p. 5: © Photodisc RF; p. 8: © Mark Burnett/ Stock, Boston/PictureQuest; p. 16: © Photodisc/Alamy RF; p. 19: © Jupiterimages RF; p. 28(top): © ETH-Bibliothek Zurich, Image Archive; p. 28(bottom): © Alinari Archives/ Corbis; p. 30: © Thinkstock Images/Jupiterimages RF; p. 31(top): © De Agostini/Getty Images; p. 31(bottom): © Bruce Laurance/Getty Images; p. 35: © Robert Voets/CBS Photo Archive via Getty Images.

Chapter 2

Opener: © Marc Serota/Getty Images; p. 42: © PhotoLink/ Getty RF; p. 43: © Phil Walter/Getty Images; p. 48: © Corbis RF; p. 55: © The McGraw-Hill Companies, Inc./Barry Barker, photographer; p. 61: © Alamy RF; p. 71: © Getty/Digital Vision RF; p. 74: © Digital Vision Ltd./SuperStock RF; p. 76: © Digital Vision RF; p. 77: © BananaStock Ltd. RF; p. 82: © Corbis RF; p. 84: © IMS Communications Ltd./Capstone Design/FlatEarth Images RF; p. 87: © Marc Serota/Getty Images.

Chapter 3

Opener(left): © Muskopf Photography, LLC/Alamy; Opener(right): © Gino's Premium Images/Alamy; p. 92: © The McGraw-Hill Companies, Inc./Jill Braaten, photographer; p. 94: National Library of Medicine, #81192; p. 97: © Life File/Getty RF; p. 98: © Cat Sobecki; p. 101: © The McGraw-Hill Companies, Inc./John Flournoy, photographer; p. 104: © Comstock Images/Alamy RF; p. 105: © Photodisc/Getty RF; p. 106: © Creatas/PictureQuest RF; p. 107: © Getty RF; p. 111: © Robert Landau/Corbis; p. 115: © The McGraw-Hill Companies, Inc./Jill Braaten, photographer; pp. 116–119: © Cat Sobecki; p. 121: © Getty RF; p. 124: © Christina Lane; p. 126: © Corbis RF; p. 128: © StockTrek/Getty RF; p. 129: © liquidlibrary/PictureQuest RF; p. 134: Library of Congress, Prints and Photographs Division [LC-USZ62-13016]; p. 135: © Corbis RF; p. 141(left): © Muskopf Photography, LLC/ Alamy; p. 141(right): © Gino's Premium Images/Alamy.

Chapter 4

Opener: © Spencer Platt/Getty Images; p. 148: © The Studio Dog/Getty RF; p. 157: © Scala/Art Resource, NY; p. 159(top): © ThinkStock/Jupiterimages RF; p. 159(bottom): © Getty/ Digital Vision RF; p. 163: © Digital Vision/Getty RF; p. 167: © SSPL/The Image Works; p. 169: © Hulton Archive/Getty Images; p. 172: National Radio Astronomy Observatory; p. 176: © Kevin Winter/Getty Images; p. 178: © Getty RF; p. 180: © The McGraw-Hill Companies, Inc./Jill Braaten, photographer; p. 190: Courtesy, Naval Historical Center; p. 193: © Spencer Platt/Getty Images.

Chapter 5

Opener: © Brand X Pictures/PunchStock RF; p. 198: © Photodisc RF; p. 206: © The Granger Collection, New York; p. 210: © Steve Bronstein/Getty Images; p. 211: © Christina Lane; p. 216: © Creatas/PunchStock RF; p. 218: © C Squared Studios/Getty RF; p. 221(top): © Jamie Squire/Getty Images; p. 221(bottom): © David Young-Wolff/PhotoEdit; p. 228(top): © Cat Sobecki; p. 228(bottom): © Corbis RF; p. 236: © Hulton Archive/Getty Images; p. 244: © Stockdisc/Getty RF; p. 247: © Duncan Smith/Getty RF; p. 251: © Nick Laham/Getty Images; p. 258(top): © Getty Images/Digital Vision RF; p. 258(bottom), p. 261: © Getty RF; p. 263: © Thinkstock Images/Jupiterimages RF; p. 264: © Getty RF; p. 272: © Brand X Pictures/PunchStock RF.

Chapter 6

Opener: © Scott Olson/Getty Images; p. 278: © Getty RF; p. 282: © The Trustees of the British Museum; p. 283: © Blend Images/Getty RF; p. 296(top): © Digital Vision/Getty RF; p. 296(bottom): © The McGraw-Hill Companies, Inc./Ken Cavanagh, photographer; p. 304: © Corbis RF; p. 305(top): © Getty RF; p. 305(bottom): © Corbis RF; p. 311: © 1999 Copyright IMS Communications Ltd./Capstone Design. All Rights Reserved RF; p. 312: © PhotoLink/Getty RF; p. 313(top): USDA; p. 313(bottom): © Life File/Getty RF; p. 314: © Getty RF; p. 315: © Photodisc/PunchStock RF; p. 319: © Stockbyte/ Getty RF; p. 324: © Getty RF; p. 325: © The McGraw-Hill Companies, Inc./Christopher Kerrigan, photographer; p. 326: © Getty RF; p. 328: © Brand X Pictures/Jupiterimages RF; p. 341: © Scott Olson/Getty Images.

Chapter 7

Page 349: © Lowell Georgia/Corbis; p. 350: © C Squared Studios/Getty RF; p. 353, p. 356(top): © Getty RF; p. 356(bottom): © liquidlibrary/Jupiterimages RF; p. 363: © PhotoLink/Getty RF; p. 370: © Getty RF; p. 374: © StockTrek/Getty RF; p. 380: © Digital Vision/Getty RF; p. 389: © Corbis RF; p. 390: © Susan Van Etten/PhotoEdit; p. 391: © PhotoLink/Getty RF; p. 394: © Corbis RF; p. 401: © Getty RF; p. 402: © Joel Gordon; p. 404: © Comstock RF; p. 405: © Comstock Images/Alamy RF; p. 408(top, bottom): © Getty RF; p. 409: © James L. Amos/Photo Researchers, Inc.

Chapter 8

Opener: © Corbis RF; p. 420: © PhotoLink/Getty RF; p. 423: © Photodisc/Getty RF; p. 424: © Corbis RF; p. 425: © Getty RF; p. 429: © Stockbyte/PunchStock RF; pp. 430–431: © PhotoLink/Getty RF; p. 432: © Corbis RF; p. 435: © Corbis RF; p. 439: © Jeff Greenberg/PhotoEdit; p. 446: © Getty RF; p. 447(top): © Cat Sobecki; p. 447(bottom): © Getty RF; p. 453(top): © Corbis RF; p. 453(bottom): © Getty RF; p. 458: © Brand X Pictures RF; p. 460: © PhotoLink/Getty RF; p. 461: © Getty RF; p. 462: © Photodisc/Getty RF; p. 465: © Comstock RF; p. 467: © Corbis RF; p. 470: © The McGraw-Hill Companies, Inc./Jill Braaten, photographer; p. 475: © Corbis RF.

Chapter 9

Opener: © Panoramic Images/Getty Images; p. 482: © Stockbyte/PunchStock RF; p. 483: © Pixtal/SuperStock RF; p. 484: © PhotoLink/Getty RF; p. 485: © Brand X Pictures/PunchStock RF; p. 486: © Brand X Pictures RF; p. 487: © Cat Sobecki; p. 490, p. 491: © Corbis RF; p. 492: © Getty RF; p. 494: © Erica S. Leeds; p. 499(top): © AFP/Getty Images; p. 499(bottom): © Creatas/PictureQuest RF; pp. 500–501: © Corbis RF; p. 502(top): © Creatas/PunchStock RF; p. 502(bottom): © The McGraw-Hill Companies, Inc./Ken Cavanagh, photographer; p. 506: © Panoramic Images/Getty Images.

Chapter 10

Opener(all), p. 512(top): © Cat Sobecki; p. 512(bottom): © Getty RF; p. 516: © Hulton Archive/Getty Images; p. 521: © Life File/Getty RF; p. 524: © Corbis RF; p. 525: © Brand X Pictures RF; p. 527: © Brand X Pictures/PunchStock RF; p. 531: © Digital Vision/Getty RF; p. 532(left): © Ingram Publishing/Alamy RF; p. 532(middle): © Image Club RF; p. 532(right): © Stockbyte/Getty RF; p. 534: © Digital Vision RF; p. 536: © Comstock Images/PunchStock RF; p. 539(top): © Getty RF; p. 539(bottom): © Getty RF; p. 541: NASA; p. 544: © Comstock Images/Jupiterimages/Alamy RF; p. 548: © Cat Sobecki; p. 549(left): © The McGraw-Hill Companies, Inc./Ken Cavanagh, photographer; p. 549(right): © Getty RF; p. 552: © Brand X Pictures RF; p. 556: © Purestock/Alamy RF; p. 557: © Corbis RF; p. 559: © Photodisc/Getty RF; p. 563: M.C. Escher's "Symmetry Drawing E110" © 2009 The M.C. Escher Company-Holland. All rights reserved. www.mcescher.com; p. 566(all): © Cat Sobecki.

Chapter 11

Opener(top left): © Corbis RF; Opener(top right): © Amanita Pictures RF; Opener(bottom left): © Getty RF; Opener(bottom middle): © Stockbyte/PunchStock RF; Opener(bottom right): © Corbis RF; p. 574: © Corbis/agefotostock RF; p. 575(top): © C Squared Studios/Getty RF; p. 577: © MedioImages RF; p. 580: © PhotoLink/Getty RF; p. 582–584: © Christina Lane; p. 587: © Corbis RF; p. 588: © Photodisc/Getty RF; p. 589: © Getty RF; p. 590: © Stockbyte/Alamy RF; p. 591, p.592: Getty RF; p. 593: © The McGraw-Hill Companies, Inc./C.P. Hammond, photographer; p. 597: © MedioImages RF; p. 599: © Bettmann/Corbis; p. 600: © Corbis RF; p. 601: © The McGraw-Hill Companies, Inc./C.P. Hammond, photographer; p. 605(top): © Stockbyte/PunchStock RF; p. 605(bottom): © BananaStock/Jupiterimages RF; p. 606: © PhotoLink/Getty RF; p. 609: © Rob Carr/AP Photo; p. 613: © PhotoLink/Getty RF; p. 614: © STAN HONDA/AFP/Getty Images; p. 616: Courtesy of the Office of the Historian, U.S. House of Representatives; p. 620: © Getty RF; p. 623: © The McGraw-Hill Companies, Inc./Barry Barker, photographer; p. 624: © moodboard/agefotostock RF; p. 627: © Digital Vision/SuperStock RF; p. 628: © Corbis RF; p. 632: © Veer RF; p. 635: © BananaStock/agefotostock RF; p. 640(top left): © Corbis RF; p. 640(top right): © Amanita Pictures RF; p. 640(bottom left): © Getty RF; p. 640(bottom middle): © Stockbyte/PunchStock RF; p. 640(bottom right): © Corbis RF.

Chapter 12

Opener: © Julie Dermansky/Photo Researchers, Inc.; p. 648: © Corbis RF; p. 649: U.S. Fish & Wildlife Service/Mike Lockhart; p. 650: © Brand X Pictures RF; p. 65, p. 653, p. 658, p. 660, p. 661, p. 665, p. 666: © Getty RF; p. 667: © Purestock/PunchStock RF; p. 668(top): © /Getty RF; p. 668(bottom): NASA; p. 670: © Image Source/PunchStock RF; p. 671: © Marc Serota/Getty Images; p. 672: © Corbis RF; p. 675(top): © Tim Davis/Corbis; p. 675(bottom): © Chris Collins/Corbis; p. 681(top): © Comstock Images/Jupiterimages RF; p. 681(bottom): © Getty RF; p. 682(top): United States Navy; p. 682(bottom): © Comstock Images/Jupiterimages RF; p. 685: © Cat Sobecki; p. 686: © Getty RF; p. 693: © The McGraw-Hill Companies, Inc./John Flournoy, photographer; p. 694, p. 695: © Getty RF; p. 696: © Life File/Getty RF; p. 699: © The McGraw-Hill Companies, Inc./John Flournoy, photographer; p. 700(top): © Digital/SuperStock RF; p. 700(bottom): © Corbis RF; p. 704(top): © Getty RF; p. 704(bottom): © The McGraw-Hill Companies, Inc./C.P. Hammond, photographer; p. 707: © The McGraw-Hill Companies, Inc./John Flournoy, photographer; p. 711: © Julie Dermansky/Photo Researchers, Inc.

Chapter 13

Opener: © Getty RF; p. 725: © Corbis RF; p. 729: http://commons.wikimedia.org/wiki/File:Evariste_galois.jpg#filelinks; p. 732: © Corbis RF; p. 733, p 735, p 738: © Getty RF.

Chapter 14

Opener: © Nick Laham/Getty Images; p. 744: © Comstock Images/PunchStock RF; p. 745: © Digital Vision Ltd./SuperStock RF; p. 747: © The McGraw-Hill Companies, Inc./Jill Braaten, photographer; p. 751: © Doug Benc/Getty Images; p. 755: © The McGraw-Hill Companies, Inc./Lars A. Niki, photographer; p. 759: © The McGraw-Hill Companies, Inc./John Flournoy, photographer; p. 761: © Corbis RF; p. 763: © Kenneth J. Arrow; p. 764: © Corbis RF; p. 767(top): © Getty RF; p. 767(bottom): © Corbis RF; p. 770: © BananaStock Ltd. RF; p. 774: © Comstock Images/Alamy RF; p. 778: Library of Congress, Prints and Photographs Division [LC-USZC4-422]; p. 779: © Creatas/PunchStock RF; p. 782: © IT Stock/Alamy RF; p. 785: © Nick Laham/Getty Images.

Chapter 15

Opener: © Digital Vision RF; p. 792: © Stockdisc/Digital Vision RF; p. 800: © Design Pics Inc./Alamy RF; 806: © Getty RF; p. 807: © Digital Vision RF; p. 814: © Comstock Images/Alamy RF; p. 817: © PhotoLink/Getty RF; p. 823: © Digital Vision RF.